W9-DGI-027

Reading and Visual Fatigue

LEONARD CARMICHAEL, Ph.D.
PRESIDENT, TUFTS COLLEGE, AND DIRECTOR,
TUFTS RESEARCH LABORATORY OF SENSORY
PSYCHOLOGY AND PHYSIOLOGY

WALTER F. DEARBORN, M.D., Ph.D.
DIRECTOR, PSYCHO-EDUCATIONAL
CLINIC, AND PROFESSOR OF EDUCATION
HARVARD UNIVERSITY

Houghton Mifflin Company
BOSTON · NEW YORK · CHICAGO · DALLAS · ATLANTA · SAN FRANCISCO
The Riverside Press Cambridge

The Riverside Press
CAMBRIDGE • MASSACHUSETTS

PRINTED IN THE U.S.A.

Contents

List of Figures

List of Tables in Text

Preface

THE EXPERIMENTS AND OTHER WORK that have made this book possible were largely financed by the Committee on Scientific Aids to Learning. This committee consisted of Dr. James B. Conant, Chairman, Dr. Irvin Stewart, Director, Dr. Vannevar Bush, Dr. Ross G. Harrison, Dr. Frank B. Jewett, Dr. Bethuel M. Webster, and Dr. Ben D. Wood. In evaluating the special projects of which the studies here reported were a part, a subcommittee consisting of the following scientists was formed to consider the matter: Dr. Adelbert Ames, Jr., Chairman, Dr. Conrad Berens, Dr. Wallace O. Fenn, Dr. Walter R. Miles, and Dr. Brian O'Brien.

In September, 1940, a financial grant was made to Harvard University and Tufts College to make these studies. An additional grant was made in June, 1942. Harvard University and Tufts College have also made contributions to this work by the provision of equipment and in other ways.

The authors jointly assumed responsibility for the investigations and have worked in close co-operation. They are responsible for the initial planning of this project and for the supervision of the experiments here described. One or the other and sometimes both were present in the laboratory during most of the experimental periods. They also jointly participated in the other aspects of the work.

In the conduct of the total investigation, they affiliated with themselves a number of full- and part-time research associates. In the experimental design of the present investigations, in the development of the apparatus used, in the detailed selection of subjects, in the conduct of the experiments, in the study and summarizing of the relevant literature, in the reading of records, in the statistical analysis of results, and in the writing of the book these associates made significant contributions at every step.

Especially basic work on almost every part of the whole project, including the preparation of the first draft of the complete report of the experiments and the direction of the detailed statistical work of the project, was done by Dr. Arthur C. Hoffman. Dr. Hoffman began his work in the experimental study of the reading process by performing experiments in collaboration with Carmichael. Some of these studies were used by Hoffman as the basis of his Master's thesis at the University of Rochester. These experiments, which are reviewed in this volume, were concerned with a quantitative comparison of the corneal-reflection photographic technique of recording eye movements, and one form of the electrical recording of such movements. Later, Hoffman served as an assistant of Dearborn's at the Psycho-Educational Clinic of the Harvard Graduate School of Education. During this period he wrote his doctoral dissertation on a study of prolonged reading behavior. This study was conducted in the Research Laboratory of Sensory Psychology and Physiology at Tufts College because the necessary electronic apparatus was available there. Both Dearborn and Carmichael participated to some extent in the conduct of these experiments. The thesis which was based upon this work was by prior arrangement presented at the University of Rochester, where Hoffman received his Ph.D. degree. Hoffman later joined the faculty of Tufts College and was employed, during the period of active experimentation on the problems reported here, through funds provided by the Committee on Scientific Aids to Learning.

The special form of the electrical recording apparatus which made the experiments here reported possible, while to some extent assembled from commercially available units, was the product of the engineering skill of Mr. Bertram Wellman, who served as a full-time research associate of Carmichael's at the University of Rochester and in the Tufts laboratory. Mr. Wellman is an electronics engineer of unusual inventive skill, and it is interesting to note that, in spite of the complexity of the electronic apparatus used, no single experimental period had to be canceled or postponed during the whole period of the experiments recorded here because of apparatus difficulty. Wellman also contributed to the planning and execution of the experiments themselves.

The important work of selecting and arranging for the presence of subjects at the experiments and conducting the actual reading periods was the joint responsibility of all the individuals concerned in the investigation. This part of the work, however, was primarily under the direction of Mrs. Clifford T. Morgan. Mrs. Morgan also contributed to the experiments in many other ways, especially as one of the principal workers who assisted in the editing and reading of the miles of records that have been studied. The success of the experiments is due in no small measure to her accuracy and persistence and to her tact with subjects. Mrs. John L. Kennedy and Mrs. Bertram Wellman also gave expert assistance in the management of the subjects and in other aspects of the experiments.

Dr. Leonard C. Mead of the Psychology Department of Tufts College contributed some suggestions concerning the development, conduct, and reporting of the experiments and read the final draft of the manuscript and made valuable suggestions for its improvement. He also made, in collaboration with other members of the research staff, a motion picture, which is referred to in the book. This film shows in detail the recording techniques used in the experiments. Dr. John L. Kennedy of the Psychology Department of Tufts College made important suggestions concerning the plan of the experiments.

Miss Miriam Nash, now Mrs. Arthur C. Hoffman, assisted in the laborious task of record reading, and she also typed the first draft of the report which forms the basis of the book. The final typing of the manuscript, the detailed checking of the bibliography and references, and the preparation of the index are the work of Miss Ellen Peck of Tufts College.

As the study was originally planned, it was to have been done in part in co-operation with Dr. Ross A. McFarland of Harvard University. This arrangement was carried out in that certain subjects were employed in common in both experimental programs and some conferences concerning the planning of the experiments were held. It did not prove feasible, however, to carry on the two experimental programs in close co-operation. Dr. McFarland and his collaborators have published the report of their investigations separately.

Special mention should be made of the fact that the Spencer microfilm reader in the form used in these experiments was prepared by the Committee on Scientific Aids to Learning under the supervision of the Director of the Committee, Dr. Irvin Stewart, now president of West Virginia University.

Gratitude is here expressed to the many authors and publishers who have granted us permission to reproduce material from their works. In this connection we wish to mention especially the American Psychological Association. Specific credit is given in each case by means of bibliographical references.

LEONARD CARMICHAEL, *Tufts College*
WALTER F. DEARBORN, *Harvard University*

Reading and Visual Fatigue

Chapter I

What Is Visual Fatigue?

THERE IS probably no single way in which the demands made by modern industrialized civilization upon the human organism differ more from those of earlier times than in the requirements now made upon the eyes. Present-day American educational methods make more individuals in each generation use their eyes for close and detailed study than ever before. The everyday demands for visual work made upon the comparatively small fraction of the population which, until recently, attended secondary schools are now extended to an ever-increasing percentage of all young Americans. Some writers assert that the frequency with which ocular difficulties are today observed in men examined in schools or colleges or on induction into the Army or Navy is directly traceable to the prolonged activity imposed on the eyes by the educational and vocational demands of present-day life. Some physicians even go so far as to attribute what they characterize as the neurotic tendency of our times in part to the fact that continued eye fatigue imposes a cumulative strain upon modern man.

In view of these observations, eye fatigue in reading, in studying, and in industrial and military tasks requiring close visual work deserves full scientific study. The ultimate purpose of knowledge gained by such study is the control of ocular behavior in such a way as to avoid undue eyestrain and the effects of excessive use of the visual mechanism. It is the purpose of the present book to summarize and discuss some of the relevant scientific literature on this subject and then to describe a new or rather a newly modified method for the quantitative study of visual work. In the latter part of the book, experiments using this method conducted by the authors and their co-workers are described and discussed in detail as they bear upon the central question of visual fatigue. As a special application of this method, these experiments were designed to determine the presence or absence of fatigue after the reading — for long periods of time — of books printed in the ordinary way on paper and books reproduced as microfilm projections.

In the performance of these experiments, changes in what may be characterized as the work output of the eyes while reading continuously have been given detailed analysis. On the basis of a consideration of the previous scientific work in this field and of the findings of these new investigations, certain recommendations regarding the use of the eyes during long periods of work are presented.

It is hoped that the present volume will be useful to those interested in the general hygiene of the eyes. This, of course, includes every reader so far as his own eyes are concerned and also those charged with the care of the eyes of workers in industry and of students in schools, colleges, and the home.

There have been a number of investigations of visual performance calculated to measure the "fatigue" of the eyes. In studying these reports it becomes clear that the basic problems of visual fatigue have not always been explicitly faced even by those who have worked scientifically in some part of this general field. Therefore, at the outset of this book, even at the risk of repeating what may seem to certain readers to be familiar material, a summary is given of some of the current views concerning the nature of fatigue and also of the structure and function of the eyes and related visual mechanisms. In the concluding chapters of the book, the contributions of the new experiments are presented.

The Nature of Fatigue

Fatigue is one of those common concepts familiar to all mankind which turn out on close inspection to be far from clear or simple. In popular speech the word "fatigue" or "tiredness" seems explicit enough. When a child who has been playing, an athlete who has been practicing, or a laborer who has been working says that he "feels tired," the meaning is generally quite clear. In this sense fatigue means that the individual is experiencing an unpleasant feeling-tone as an aftermath of preceding activity. Such an individual will ordinarily report that in a fatigued state he feels that he cannot perform whatever he has been doing so well as he could in a fresh or unfatigued state. The first great difficulty in the study of fatigue becomes apparent at this point. If the individual is induced to continue the activity which he believes has fatigued him, he may often be able to continue the work in question with as few errors and just as quickly as he could before he felt tired. Thus it seems clear at the outset that the subjective feeling of fatigue and the ability of the organism to continue effective work are not necessarily the same phenomenon.

But what happens to this popular concept of fatigue when it is taken into the laboratory? Here, if fatigue is to be studied, it should be clearly defined. It is important in scientific work not to use fatigue in one place as a *description* of what the organism does and then without explanation to use the same word as a *cause.* If fatigue is used as a descriptive term, it may be recognized as what is called a "linguistic construct" characterizing certain changes in organisms or parts of organisms following activity. In this sense, the word fatigue may be applied to the same or to different patterns of psychological, physiological, biochemical, or even physical alterations, provided only that these patterns develop under certain conditions. In this sense of the word, fatigue may apply to all or some of the following phenomena: subjective feeling-tone; alteration of behavior, motivation, or physiological activity; biochemical change in active tissues; even the molecular or other physical changes in a living tissue; and, in analogy at least, the alterations seen in the so-called fatigue of metals and other nonliving structures or systems. In this sense, fatigue is not "discovered." It is rather a word used to describe or summarize in a general way changes, and, it may be, quite dissimilar changes, that follow activity.

If fatigue is viewed in this way, it will be seen that it is a most convenient *descriptive* concept. The changes basic to the phenomena summarized by this concept may then be given other and more fundamental scientific study. If the word fatigue is used in this descriptive sense, it is clear that decreased activity is only in a loose sense "caused" by fatigue. To say that fatigue, defined as a descriptive term, *causes* decreased activity would be equivalent in certain instances to saying that decreased activity causes decreased activity.

Besides the use of fatigue in a purely descriptive way, there are other current uses of the word (see 18[1]). Some writers have said that fatigue is a more or less unitary and specific psychological, physiological, biochemical, or physical state or entity. If such an entity could be discovered, it would of course be appropriate to use the simple idea of fatigue as a cause or as a simple quantitative functional variable. In this sense fatigue could, if isolated and rigidly described, be considered a reason for changes in activity. Unfortunately for those who advocate this view, the study of all changes called fatigue shows them to be very dissimilar. For example, muscle activity and other processes basic to organic activity disclose complex and by no means always identical biochemical changes following exercise. Thus, the idea that all characteristics called fatigue in common speech can be reduced to a single chemical reaction or a definite toxin of known chemical composition which is the same in all muscles, nerves, and other tissue, or to a special state of the blood stream, is not acceptable.

For the reasons given above, the word fatigue will be used in this book as far as possible as a descriptive term. Where causation is sought, we will attempt to present the current scientific knowledge concerning the specific chemical and physical changes which take place in living systems during and following activity.

In recent years much progress has been made in understanding the metabolism of living tissues. At the present time more is known than was known even quite recently concerning the physical and chemical alterations which take place in active living cells and in the fluids which surround them. Much has also been learned about the time required and the chemical and other reactions necessary for the restoration of specific types of cells to the condition in which they were before activity. The ultimate basis of those changes which take place when fatigue may be present will be found in the biochemistry and biophysics of living matter in action. It is important to point out that these basic changes may sometimes be in the physiological mechanisms fundamental to motivation and in "the desire to continue work," rather than in the localized muscle cells, for example, of a finger that has been exercised in repeated work. This fact must not be lost sight of in considering the fatigue of any special muscular complex or other living system of the total organism. Unfortunately, in spite of the fact that probably most psychologists would

[1] For references see the numbered bibliography at the end of the book.

agree that these complex states are directly grounded in physiological conditions, there is no unanimity in describing exactly what these physiological states are. Further research alone can make this clear. It may be that the local muscle *can* continue to respond when the organism has ceased to react. In such a situation, it is the physiological basis of what we call the "desire to work," as well as the local neuromuscular system that has been altered by previous action, that causes a "work decrement" to appear.

Actually, more than twenty-five years ago, B. Muscio (255), after making a critical examination of various definitions of fatigue then in common use, recommended that the word itself be banished from scientific discussions. In its stead, he suggested simply measuring and recording the effect of different amounts of work directly upon specific functions of the living organism. J. B. Watson (388) expresses a similar point of view in recommending that all those factors which are not touched or approached by the problem at hand should be left out of discussion. He held that the observed and, if possible, quantified loss of efficiency, as it may occur in prolonged activity of a particular function under observation, is sufficient description and explanation. These proposals are, of course, in line with other modern "operational" scientific thinking. In not a few experiments, this objective approach to fatigue has been carefully followed. Some of these investigations have been conducted without making preliminary assumptions as to the nature of fatigue. In such studies the scientist has been content to gather data on the physical, chemical, histological, behavioral, or subjective changes that take place in living organisms, or subsystems of organisms, as a function of time or of time of activity. These experiments are in general the ones which have been of greatest value in making the modern state of the present-day empirical science of human work possible.

Fatigue studies of this objective sort, if not initiated, were at any rate given impetus by the work of A. Mosso (251) and his colleagues and followers. This is especially true of his so-called ergographic approach to the problem. Mosso described changes in the work done by specific muscle groups in lifting a given mass through a measured distance at a given frequency for a specific number of times. A recording stylus attached to the moving weight or to the working muscle group offered a convenient method of recording and later measuring the characteristics of the work done by muscles under these conditions. Such an ergographic record is sometimes translated into a "work curve." Sample curves are shown in Figure 1. Analysis of these work curves established the fact of the *work decrement,* which may be defined in terms of the actual characteristics of the work curve. The work decrement is really a typical alteration in the work done by a muscle group showing a loss in efficiency and is typically associated with prolonged and continuous performance of a particular, simple task.

The term "work decrement" has sometimes been taken as an objective substitute for the word fatigue. A definition of fatigue in terms of work decrement has corrected much of the earlier loose thinking about fatigue, but even this conception has tended to limit the use of fatigue as a descriptive concept in such a way as to exclude from consideration certain psychological or behavioral factors or processes such as motivation. Those who have studied work decrements by the ergographic method have often tried to hold the motivation or attitude of their human subjects as constant as possible. This is perfectly justifiable in any given experiment, but one must not consider that a variable does not exist in real life because it has been held constant in certain experiments. Thus, when what would now be called a classical work decrement has been secured in an ergographic experiment, it is often possible by offering a strong financial or other incentive to the human subject in the experiment to have a new spurt of activity appear in the record which looks quite like that of a relatively unfatigued muscle system. In such a case, it is important to realize that the work curve has not necessarily shown only the cumulative and definite biochemical change in the localized active muscle group which had gradually made further action impossible. Rather, such a result may show the progressive alteration in the physiological processes underlying what may be termed the psychological state of motivation or "readiness to disregard feelings of local pain and unpleasantness." Certainly the record may show this modification as well as evidence of specific changes in the local muscles of the overexercised arm and finger.

In view of these observations, it may be well to consider some of the formal definitions of fatigue that have been presented. According to R. A. Spaeth (322),

> Fatigue is the decreased capacity for doing work as a direct result of having worked; the amount of decrement varies with the duration, rate, and intensity of the work, and with the initial strength or capacity of the organic mechanism involved.

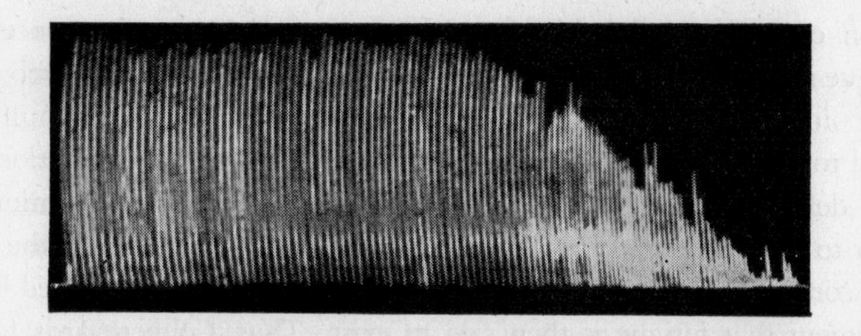

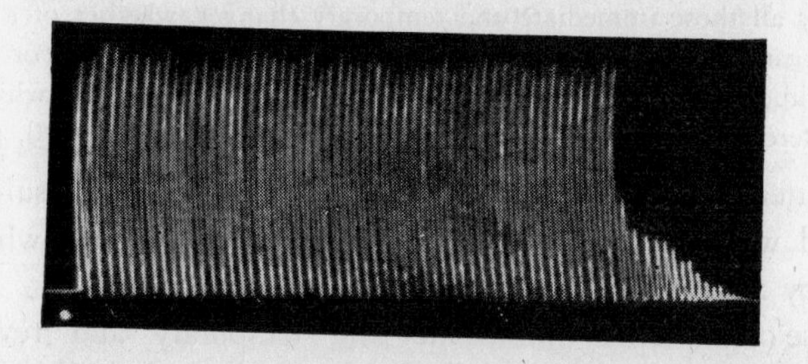

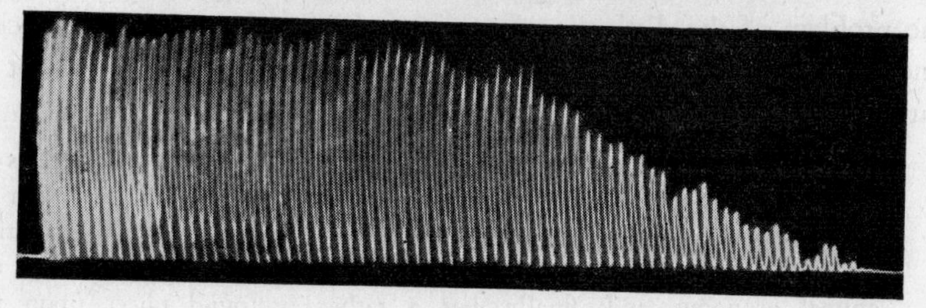

Figure 1

ERGOGRAPHIC RECORDS OF WORK CURVES

(After S. Yochelson, 408)

An example of definitions which attempt to orient the concept of fatigue in the realm of psychological functions is that of P. W. Cobb (64). He points out that the animal organism adjusts to energy (stimuli) applied to it in certain specific ways by making some sort of reaction. He then defines fatigue as the general tendency of a response to diminish or even to disappear upon repeated or continuous application of the stimulus condition which called out the act. This definition is followed by the statement that fatigue is then said to exist. Thus, Cobb regards fatigue as a descriptive term or construct.

Some definitions stress the point that fatigue may be a "general, organismic factor" rather than a specifically localized phenomenon. These definitions also imply an awareness of the scientific pitfalls possible when the attempt is made to disentangle psychological and physiological fatigue processes and to consider one set of factors to the exclusion of the other. The following statement by I. E. Ash may be taken as representative:

> Fatigue is a comprehensive term which in its widest application embraces all those immediate and temporary changes, whether of a functional or organic character, which take place within an organism or any of its constituent parts as a direct result of its own exertions, and which tend to interfere with or inhibit the organism's further activities. (10, p. 1.)

M. E. Bitterman (37) offers a definition of fatigue as resulting from continued work and marked by a reduction of efficiency which is reversible by rest.

The use of the terms "immediate" and "temporary" and "reversible by rest" in connection with changes in the efficiency of performance raises the problem of the distinction between fatigue and the organic process known as adaptation. P. A. Snell, who accepts a physiological concept of fatigue, states that fatigue

> is a metabolic state resulting from the inability of anabolic processes to proceed as rapidly as catabolic ones during the activity of an organ or part. Fatigue . . . is delayed in its occurrence following the presentation of an adequate stimulus, is slow to develop, brings about harm to the animal economy, and, finally, has a rather profound effect upon the organism. (320, p. 368.)

and that adaptation

> is a reaction which occurs immediately following the presentation of the situation calling for it, takes place rapidly, brings about a benefit to the organism, and, finally, has a slight, if any, subjective effect upon the organism. (320, p. 368.)

This distinction is primarily a logical one. It is conceivable that in some instances fatigue, even as Snell has defined it, could be as immediate, rapid, quickly recoverable, and protective to the organism as adaptation is defined to be. It must not be forgotten that fatiguing exercise is used as a means of making the athlete stronger. These considerations indicate that fatigue and adaptation cannot yet be logically or, what is more important, quantitatively differentiated in an easy way in any given set of experimental conditions depending upon the passage of known time. C. S. Myers (257) would distinguish both fatigue and adaptation by considering each as due to different "sets" or physical attitudes in the organism. His discussion of these sets suggests that adaptation is a change in the readiness of a mechanism to react. Fatigue, on the one hand, even though it may appear as the same process at first sight, is defined as an active interference or inhibition seen when incompatible acts or processes are set against each other. It is important for the present discussion to note that these statements by Myers are instances of definitions in which fatigue is regarded primarily as a psychological phenomenon.

Until more evidence is available, it would seem, as suggested above, that the concept of fatigue may best be used simply as a generic term to refer to many types of observed changes in the organism resulting from previous action which may be quantitatively or at least objectively recorded. Such a definition would have the advantage of allowing for the future elaboration of the concept of fatigue as new data are found. If desired, "adaptation" and mechanical or other effects following eating, locomotion, and so forth, may be by explicit definition excluded from the general definition just presented.

The definition of fatigue offered by A. G. Bills (35) has, with slight modification, the requisites just described. His definition uses fatigue as a term to include three types of phenomena: The first type included may be called subjective: feelings of weariness or of exhaustion, and the like, on the part of the worker as he gives evidence of them in language, change of attitude, and so forth. In attitude change, an increase in conflict is often noted. That is, a task which at first in the unfatigued state is done with zest and interest later is done with difficulty and with constant interference so that the subject is aware of his desire to stop the task and rest or turn to other activity. The second set of phenomena is organic, referring to changes in the chemical and physical condition of the organ systems or cells in the parts of the body undergoing excessive or prolonged activity. It should be noted that the organ system or mechanism involved need not be physically incapable of further activity or regarded as exhausted. Often activity decreases or stops when it could go on if really necessary. At such times, there may be demonstrated in the system certain chemical substances which are not present when the system is in a resting or rested state. The third objectively defined group of phenomena includes the changes in the quantity or quality of output which result from the continued work or operation of the system. There are two aspects to be recognized as characteristic of such changes in output: work decrement or diminished output, and changes in the "qualitative" pattern of the way work is done (even though its "amount" in certain respects may not have diminished).

The descriptive term fatigue includes all three of these classes of phenomena. In a definition of fatigue, therefore, one should include reference to changes in subjective state, demonstrated changes in bodily condition, such as those shown by a chemical study of the blood, and also changes in the output of work, when in each case the observed change or changes can be referred back to previous work performed by the organism or some organ system of the organism. In general, as previously noted, we shall use the word fatigue in this book in this inclusive and essentially descriptive sense.

The definition just offered means that the word fatigue may be employed to describe any or all of the phenomena summarized under the headings given above. For example, a reliable subject's own report of his feelings of fatigue is a fact. It is a verbal report. It does not necessarily mean that the subject's blood has changed in a special way at that time. Also, if motivation is held constant, there may be little doubt about the characteristics in time of any demonstrated change in the work done by the individual or by an isolated muscle or other cellular system of the individual as a function of continued work. It is often difficult, however, to show satisfactorily correlations between the biochemical and biophysical changes and other fatigue phenomena on which these verbal reports or other behavioral characteristics are sometimes assumed to depend. An example may make this more clear. On a very hot day, a golfer may know that he is fatigued after nine holes. He also is very likely to complete the remaining nine holes and to *want* to do this very earnestly. In this case there are no doubt some physicochemical changes present in the golfer's organism, but he may or may not feel fatigued while on the course. His performance on the last nine holes may or may not show a work decrement. E. E. Foltz, F. T. Jung, and L. E. Cisler (107) in a recent study of human work in relation to internal factors show a low correlation between "feeling-tone" and work output.

Thus, in the study of work changes in the organism, as in so many other situations in physiological psychology, the external stimulus conditions calling out the behavior in question can be measured, the response can be measured, and the subjective experience can be quantified on a rating scale, but the so-called *causative* physiological conditions may remain obscure. This fact has led many writers of basic discussions of fatigue to study all that is positively known about the physiology, chemistry, and physics of muscle and nerve action. At any time after reviewing the current state of this knowledge, the scientist may formulate hypotheses to extend this physiological knowledge as a means of predicting or "explaining" measured changes in behavior or in subjective feelings of fatigue. When this has been done, the hypotheses thus formulated can, at least in certain cases, be tested by the physiologist to discover whether or not the observed state is a valid "guess as to causation."

In theorizing of this limited sort, it is important that all that is really known at any given date about the chemistry and physics of the activity of living tissues be fully considered. There is no greater error possible in the study of fatigue than to theorize about the explanation of observed work decrements in terms of some unknown and hypothetical "toxin" of fatigue, when such toxin or blood state is said to have properties which are already known *not* to be present in the blood or in living cells during or after work. This difficulty of describing the results of previous action in precise terms has led to the use of quite general physiological terms in discussing the results of work. Thus J. I. Kurtz says:

> Fatigue, from a physiological standpoint, may be due to the exhaustion of substances used for cell nourishment and the increased production of the waste products. . . . From a psychological standpoint, fatigue may be caused by abnormal mental states in general and poor emotional adjustments in particular. (177, p. 211.)

This particular distinction between psychological and physiological viewpoints offers a dichotomy which has been attractive to many writers but is not fundamental. The dangerous use of the word "caused" in this excerpt should be noted. In almost all instances, it is recognized that this double classification of physiological and psychological fatigue may be used as a convenience in speech rather than as a fundamental characteristic of the work of the organism.

The basic physiological viewpoint just noted deals with those aspects of fatigue that can be described in purely biochemical and biophysical terms. For example, fatigue in this sense has been regarded (322) as essentially an imbalance in the physiological equilibrium between catabolism and anabolism — the former being predominant. This is, of course, merely a summarizing statement describing much more complex processes. The very words "catabolism," the tearing down of living matter, and "anabolism," the building up of living matter, are themselves being abandoned in physiology. Essentially they add nothing to previous descriptions of actual states as given in chemical and physical terms. A statement of the changes in the amounts of sugar, oxygen, carbon dioxide, lactic acid, phosphates, and other products present in muscles and in the blood stream after exercise is a surer way of describing the results of work than is the use of a blanket term such as catabolism.

The physiological processes underlying fatigue are related to the transformation of substances necessary for activity into decomposition products and the release of energy in some form. The waste products are often referred to in very general terms as "metabolites" or "fatigue toxins." This biochemical view of fatigue has often been spoken of as the "toxin theory." A typical example of this way of considering fatigue is the statement by J. T. Goorley

> that the blood stream must continually supply dextrose and oxygen and remove excess carbon dioxide and lactic acid formed during exercise or else a chemical state of fatigue arises. (122, p. 95.)

D. H. Dolley (94) describes a "fatigue of excitation" as being peculiar to the using up of the dextrose, oxygen, and so forth, and a "fatigue of depression" as due to the progressive chemical changes resulting in the accumulation of the carbon dioxide, lactic acid, and so forth.

Because nerve cells and muscle cells actually undergo definite structural changes as a result of prolonged activity, a histological view of fatigue changes also has been presented. The observed histological changes are perhaps corollaries of the chemical changes mentioned above. That is, the histological change in living cells may be the result of the chemical reactions involved in metabolism. For example, in some instances of prolonged activity, there are reported an actual decrease in the size of the nerve cell, a loss of stainable material, and a loss of other protoplasmic substance causing a vacuolated condition of the cell and a ragged, more sharply defined contour. What relation this change bears to other characteristics, such as alterations in behavior or in feelings of fatigue, is not known.

There are some students who tend to reject the notion that fatigue toxins are the primary factors in a fatigue condition. J. C. Bose (42) has demonstrated the similarity of what may be called fatigue and recuperation in metals, plants, and animals. These phenomena are explained as due to a molecular change and recovery. G. C. Nuttall (261) suggests that some change in the function or arrangement of molecules in living protoplasm may, in general, explain the nature of physiological fatigue. F. S. Lee and B. Aronovitch (188) cite experiments in which injecting chemical material from the fatigued muscles of cats and guinea pigs into rested cats and guinea pigs produced results identical with those following injection of material from unfatigued muscle. If fatigue toxins were crucial to the fatigue condition, different results might have been expected. These negative experiments do not seem to be conclusive, but they do indicate that the "toxin views" of fatigue should be subjected to further study. It seems impossible to believe that the depletion of energy-producing substances in muscles and the consequent accumulation of waste products, such as lactic and carbonic acids in the blood stream, are unrelated to complete or partial exhaustion. Certainly in extreme cases this relationship must hold. It is not correct, however, to suppose that an exact and final quantitative chemical theory of fatigue has yet been developed. No perfect correlation has been found between a recorded quantitative change in the functional efficiency of some small muscle of a total living organism and a measured change in the chemical makeup of the total blood stream of that organism.

There are a number of places in the nervous and the muscular systems where fatigue changes may be primarily localized. Histological anomalies, fatigue toxins, or other changes following activity could produce their first and primary effects in such loci as (1) the muscle mechanism, (2) the peripheral nerve fibers, afferent or efferent, (3) the nerve cell bodies, (4) the junctions of the neurons with the muscle fibers at the motor end-plate, (5) the synapses between the nerve cells in the central nervous system, and (6) the sensory receptor cells themselves or the auxiliary mechanism of the sense organs.

The importance of current knowledge concerning the chemical mediation of the nerve impulse through the liberation of acetylcholine or adrenin should not be forgotten in reviewing much of the early literature in this field. E. Jackson (155) regards the motor end-plate as the most likely place for fatigue to appear. The synapses in the central nervous system are next in importance, since another set of nerve paths can then be brought into play when one has ceased functioning. S. Cobb and A. Forbes (67) report that muscular work is associated with an increase in the action current potential from nerve and muscle, but with a decrease in the frequency of the discharge. This they suggest is due either to a block in the neuromuscular junction or to a decrease in the irritability of the muscle. This work will no doubt receive further elaboration. C. Reid (296) drew a similar conclusion from his experiments on the fatigue of skeletal muscles. He holds that central factors are involved in such fatigue but that there may be an overlapping effect in the failure of the muscle itself to contract. Local conditions arising in the muscle seem to have an inhibiting influence on the activity of the muscle, an effect mediated, it may be, by impulses from the proprioceptors or sensory endings in the muscles, tendons, or joints. This effect seems to follow whether or not the afferent impulses lead to activity that is accompanied by sensation. H. Cason has used evidence of this sort in describing what might be called a "fatigue arc" or "fatigue stimulus-response pattern."

> In the total organic pattern, the activity of striped muscles modifies the afferent impulses from these muscles to the central nervous system, these afferent impulses change the functions of the central nervous system, the central nervous system influences the efferent impulses to the muscles, and these impulses alter the conditions and activities of the muscles. (57, pp. 341-342.)

In a discussion of his own and related research, Cason concludes that the more highly differentiated nerve centers are apparently more susceptible to fatigue than the lower reflex centers:

> It has been found that in the circle of nerves and other structures connected with striped muscles, the largest amount of fatigue occurs in the central nervous system, the least amount in nerve trunks, and an intermediate amount in sense organs, muscles, and motor endplates. It is gen-

erally thought that the synapse is more susceptible to fatigue, to anesthetics, and to nicotine than other parts of the nervous system. The extreme claim that the central nervous system hardly fatigues at all (Thorndike), or that practically all fatigue occurs in the central nervous system (Mosso) has been contradicted by experimental data. (57, pp. 340-341.)

It would be well to recall these statements when psychological theories postulating breakdown of central control and co-ordination as basic to fatigue phenomena are discussed.

In this connection it is interesting to point out that not all decrements in performance are necessarily to be regarded as fatigue or the result of fatigue. R. Dodge has stated:

> However long a mental process may be continued and however insignificant the decrement in returns, there comes a moment when it stops. . . . In any case, the work decrement of the consequent break can never be fully understood if we regard it as a direct product of fatigue, but only in connection with the intercurrent, competing tendencies. Fatigue may be a contributing factor, but the apparent decrement of the break will bear no regular relation to the degree of absolute fatigue in the tissues which performed the discontinued work. (86, pp. 110-111.)

Further, Dodge doubts whether

> . . . any of the mental work decrements, so commonly treated as mental fatigue, are ever simply conditioned by true fatigue processes in nervous tissue. Conversely, real fatigue may not appear as a decrement at all. (86, p. 94.)

It is here assumed that the term "true fatigue" is used to mean exhaustion or an organic inability to respond. Dodge cites as evidence for his position the resistance to fatigue of nervous tissue *in situ;* for example, no absolute refractory phase was found for the eye-wink reflex. On the basis of evidence of this type, Dodge concludes that there are no grounds for assuming a complete mental inability to repeat an act. He notes, however, the tendency on the part of experimenters and theorists to overlook in discussions of fatigue the possible effects of normal psychophysical rhythms and their mechanisms, of which sleep is the most significant example. There is the ever present possibility that these rhythms and other psychological processes, such as learning or associational rivalry, are indications of what may be termed pseudo-fatigue effects. Dodge also notes the important role of cortical inhibition in mental life which might also operate to produce a pseudo-fatigue work decrement.

Myers presents an interesting point of view on fatigue:

> Throughout mental and muscular activity, the exercise of *direction* and the elaboration of material for the production of *acts* concur—attitude and posture being the setting or matrix in which acts take place. In everyday life, fatigue of direction is of far greater importance than fatigue of act. On it depend the acquisition, preservation, and manifestation of skill, attitudes of attention, etc.; but of its nature we know nothing. (257, p. 16.)
>
> Prolonged exercise may affect both the controlling and directing activities and the activities which they control or direct. (258, p. 306.)

These statements may be compared with the following:

> Being engaged in mental work, all conflicting nervous impulses must be inhibited. Such inhibition involves effort, and fatigue, it seems, lessens the ability to preserve the proper attitude toward work. (392, p. 247.)
>
> Fatigue itself does not lessen ability, but serves to affect those factors of motivation, interest, initiative, attention, and concentration which are necessary to the learning process. (392, p. 266.)
>
> Work without rest . . . becomes less satisfying (1) by losing the zest of novelty, (2) by producing ennui, a certain intellectual nausea, sensory pains, and headache, and (3) by imposing certain deprivations—for instance, from physical exercise, social intercourse, and sleep. (339, p. 122.)
>
> These facts support the general doctrine that the effect of lack of rests is far greater upon whatever is the physiological basis of interest, willingness, or tolerability, than upon the physiological basis of quantity and quality of product produced. Or, in other words, the mechanisms determining the mind's achievement are left able to do their customary work, but in such a condition that their customary action is less satisfying, so that (except for extrinsic motives) the individual can relax, intermit or abandon the action in question. (338, p. 266.)

From the above statements, it may be inferred that, psychologically, the character or quality of certain prolonged activities may be affected by a decrement in the efficiency of those mechanisms which co-ordinate, control, motivate, or direct behavior. It seems probable of course that these changes are determined by the physiological factors discussed previously. There is certainly much evidence cited by the authors quoted above to support as one part of the concept of fatigue a decline in the efficiency of control or "regulation" of behavior.

Contemporary studies of "mental work" show that the amount of decrement varies with many factors, such as the nature and the difficulty of the task. Not only do there seem to be differences among individuals, but also differences in the "fatigue potential" of various behavior patterns within one individual.

The statement appears frequently that established habit systems show less fatigue decrement than those of new habits or the so-called higher mental processes. Conversely, fatigue effects appear more rapidly or more prominently in those processes demanding the complex functioning of the higher levels of the nervous system and a more involved system of facilitation and control. There is fairly general agreement that acts requiring great skill are the first to show qualitative changes when action is prolonged; particularly is this true of those skills requiring delicately co-ordinated action of many muscles (164).

F. C. Bartlett (15) has pointed out that highly skilled work cannot be adequately studied by the methods which proved valuable in the study of muscular fatigue, simply because skilled work is such a complex of co-ordinated and accurately timed activities. When the experimental procedure is such that these characteristics *can* be observed, fatigue manifests itself not as a decrement in total activity but as an increment in errors. Fatigue in this sense shows itself in the likelihood of performing the right reactions at the wrong time or the wrong reactions at the right time. The ignoring of marginal stimuli, a restriction of the effective range of stimuli, changes in the effect of distracting stimuli, and changes in subjective feeling-tone and personal reactions (such as irritability and the desire to stop) must all be considered in this connection.

It is helpful here also to consider what is involved in the maintenance of proper control or co-ordination in relation to the activity required by a homogeneous or even monotonous task, as contrasted to the reactions required in a more varied task. There is much casual evidence to support the assumption that it may be more difficult, or more "fatiguing," for some individuals to continue a task, or a series of tasks very much alike in their general nature, than it is to persist in working at tasks which are diverse in the demands which they make on the working individual.

E. S. Robinson and A. G. Bills (300) assigned to subjects tasks which had been ranked, in a fairly objective order, according to degree of homogeneity. The amount of general decrement shown during continued activity was found to be directly related to the degree of homogeneity of the task prolonged; that is, more decrement was found in the more homogeneous task. In an experiment by M. Newburger (259) fatigue was measured by the number of problems solved and errors made during the intervals of a working period. He concluded that there is less decrement in the performance of varied tasks than in homogeneous mental work. The least fatigue was noted when the task was judged to be both difficult and heterogeneous. His subjects were individuals of normal or superior intelligence.

H. Winkler (402) suggests that homogeneity is not independently effective but is related to the susceptibility of a given individual to the monotony of the task assigned him. He concludes, in the specific case of his experiment, that the decrement is influenced by the degree to which the subject is able to "escape" from the homogeneity of the task by turning his attention elsewhere. Work with the feebleminded suggests that homogeneity as a fatiguing factor is dependent upon the intellectual capacity of the individual subject. A task that is homogeneous and hence fatiguing to a very intelligent individual may not be so to one of lesser intelligence. If, as these several studies show, homogeneity or monotony of the task, intellectual capacity, readiness to respond, and similar factors are correlated with the degree of decrement in performance, it is at least an easy assumption to make that changes in the processes of motivation, control, or co-ordination are in part responsible for the observed decrement.

This so-called fatigue of direction, control, or co-ordination manifests itself in certain instances as increasing variability of response during continuous activity. It has been frequently reported that while the mean or average level of performance may remain fairly steady during prolonged periods of activity, the statistical indices of variability of response increase in magnitude as the experiment progresses.

The supposition has been made, in accounting for increased variability of response during long periods of time, that fatigue of control or co-ordination is essentially a breaking down of the psychophysiological mechanisms of so-called higher inhibition. This breakdown results in a lack of "concentration," or what is commonly called the inability to fixate attention. Sometimes, it is the speed rather than the accuracy of performance that is most impaired. Also there is the finding that abnormally high "persistence of attention" sometimes characterizes the behavior of an individual who reports himself to be in a "fatigued state." In some cases this persistence is achieved at the expense of a diminished field or span of attention. It almost seems as if the fatigued man had "funneled" his experience. That is, he still responds effectively to stimuli which in descriptive terms may be said to be in the center of his attention, but increasingly he disregards stimuli that are outside this funneled stream and thus are located in the periphery of attention.

> It must not be forgotten that this improvement in performance may itself be a sign of bodily impairment; it comes from a more effective distribution of available energy with respect to a particular task, not from an increase in energy available for general expenditure. (164, p. 191.)

Another idea considered often in psychological discussions of fatigue is the distinction between fatigue and exhaustion. The word fatigue has often been applied to phenomena which might more exactly have been called exhaustion. This is especially true in the instances where one type of fatigue has been distinguished from another, for example, fatigue of "set," "control," or "conflict" as opposed to the inability of organic tissue to continue functioning or reacting. Fatigue, almost paradoxically, according to H. F. Whiting and H. B. English, may be regarded as essentially a psychological phenomenon which, unlike exhaustion, is *not* symptomatic of inability to do work.

> Its strong emotional coloring, the unanalyzable complex of visceral and organic sensations, the internal stimulus, and especially the direct and obvious relation to motor activity all suggest classification as an emotional appetite. . . . Thus, where exhaustion affects primarily the mechanism by which work is accomplished, fatigue tends to withdraw or reduce the motive power or drive. Or rather, the effect of fatigue is to raise the threshold at which a work motive may be effective, but does not lower the efficiency of the work, granted the adequacy of the positive motive. (396, p. 48.)

It is an easy step from this conclusion to a hypothesis which regards fatigue as a process in the bodily economy that may be assigned, by one who wishes to think teleologically, the function of preserving or protecting the organism from exhaustion.

> Relative fatigue, then, is not a mere limitation of human efficiency. It is not exhaustion, but prevents it. It is a conservator of organic equilibrium, as well as a condition of organic development. (86, p. 112.)

> The feelings of fatigue and other affective processes appear to exercise a protective influence in preventing excessive use of volitional activity. (258, p. 306.)

These statements would suggest, for example, that the desire to go to sleep, to quit work, or to do something else when activity is prolonged is really an equilibratory mechanism functioning to forestall the ill effects on the organism of exhaustion.

From the above, it may be seen why it has been held that the compensating or protective nature of fatigue is "responsible" for the pauses of brief duration which have been observed to occur at fairly regular intervals during certain types of prolonged activity. It is, however, at just this point that we must remind ourselves that in this book we plan to use fatigue as a descriptive and not as a causal concept. These pauses have well been called "blocks" by Bills (31) for the reason that activity is stopped as if actively blocked by some antagonistic process. For experimental purposes, Bills (31) defines a block or momentary cessation of activity as a pause equivalent to the time of two or more average responses. He concludes from his experiments that:

> Mental performance is not perfectly continuous, but is interspersed with short pauses or blocks which may have a recuperative function because they increase in length and frequency in proportion to the length and difficulty of the task. (35, p. 450.)

The term "mental" in this and similar statements is used simply to distinguish tasks such as doing arithmetic, discriminating colors, and reading from tasks involving the activity of gross muscles, or the larger movements of the body. Such prolonged mental tasks might tend to be homogeneous — essentially the same process or procedure would be repeated over and over again, though the actual materials of the work would, of course, change.

In this connection, it may be significant to note the finding of N. M. Mailloux and M. Newberger (218) that psychotics — those who have largely escaped from the normal motivations of real life — block more frequently and respond less frequently than do normal individuals. N. Warren and B. Clark (387) have noted the phenomena of blocking in otherwise normal individuals required to maintain a 65-hour vigil. They found that the number of pauses in continuous activity, such as alternate addition and subtraction, color naming, and tapping with the index finger of the right hand increased, with the most noticeable increase appearing after the vigil had been maintained for 40 hours. This increase was evident in spite of the fact that the time required to make the average response did not appreciably change. These blocks could be interpreted as periods of momentary exhaustion. But the facts that the temporal characteristics of the average response do not change and that the blocks may occur at fairly regular intervals make it equally likely that these pauses are such as to allow recuperation in the mechanisms which make response possible.

From the points of view just considered, "fatigue" is seen as a name for the operation of processes in the organism which tend to limit activity, so that, in the long run, the normal functioning of the processes under consideration shall *not* be permanently impaired. T. R. Murroughs and L. Manas (254) point out that sensations of fatigue serve to warn the organism of possible impairment as the threshold of neuromuscular irritability increases. In this connection, it must be remembered that some of the changes induced in cells by oxygen deprivation, for example, are within limits reversible, but beyond these limits the damage once done is not subject to later reparation. It may be that "fatigue" phenomena "ring a bell" or "flash a light" to say that really disadvantageous bodily changes are ahead if the organism persists. A related idea is suggested by Cobb:

> With the continued output of energy, a certain impairment takes place—or rather it would, if it were not for the fact that by increased effort it is possible for the working organism to offset the deficiency and go on as well as before, or maybe better. (64, p. 428.)

D. E. Smith (318) points out the necessity of investigating the interrelationships between practice and fatigue in continuous work. He required of his subjects one hundred trials of an eye-hand co-ordination test. Rather than a decrement, an improvement was found in the time required per trial, even though the subjects reported feelings of fatigue. In an experiment by J. A. Glaze (121), three subjects performed the monotonous task of writing "ababa," and so forth, as rapidly as possible for 20 minutes each day for from 23 to 36 days. The average work decrement in terms of speed of writing was much more pronounced during the first five days than it was later. These findings were corroborated by E. S. Robinson and F. R. Robinson (301) using ten subjects working five days of the week for three weeks. Glaze concluded

> . . . that the effects of repeated performance of such a task as ours tend to mask the manifestations of fatigue. Adaptation and the attainment of a fairly high degree of efficiency proceed regularly, eliminating the result that is manifest in the early practice-period. (121, p. 630.)

H. M. Johnson has discussed the possibility that compensatory mechanisms, or even the protective aspect of fatigue itself, will often effect an improvement in performance. This improvement effect may not always be overcome; as far as output is concerned or measured, no fatigue will be demonstrated. However,

> The earliest effects, though expressed in immediate improvement of performance, may not be beneficial if the future demands are considered; for the same agents which are improving performance at the moment may be operating to reduce the individual's fitness for work to be performed a little later. The duration of the fatiguing process, therefore, becomes a matter of first importance . . . (164, p. 189.)

If fatigue is intrinsically a process in the adjustment or total equilibrium of the organism, the practice of isolating one organ and attempting to identify and measure fatigue in it may easily result in erroneous or incomplete conclusions. J. Romano and his coworkers (305) in a study of fatigue in relation to experiences in simulated altitudes of 35,000 feet in a decompression chamber point out that fatigue seems to be determined by such factors as emotional flexibility, "psychologic defenses," anxiety, suddenness of given experiences, identification with the group, and motivation in general. See also J. M. Brozek (47).

In view of the above discussion, it is clear that the investigator who plans to study fatigue must decide in advance exactly what he is about to measure. If his definition is satisfactory and if his measures are valid, his results should be clear-cut. He will or will not find evidence of "fatigue." If his measurements do not show a consistent change of the sort he has defined, it is safe to assume that in the conditions of his experiment there is no such change. If he has defined fatigue as a work decrement of some sort and if no decrement appears after work, he must then assume that there has been no fatigue as shown by the functions which he measures in his experiment. He must not assume that there has been no change in functions that he has not studied. These statements may sound like truisms, but there are those who challenge them in the interpretation of their own or others' results in experiments on fatigue. For example, some writers say that if no fatigue is found where they had expected it, there must be some sort of "hidden cost" to the organism. To allege that all work is done at a hidden cost to the organism is to forget that some muscle mechanisms of the living body grow strong and improve in performance under well-directed exercise.

It is also easy to forget that the heart muscle "rests" between beats. The student of fatigue must be on his guard against a too simple analogy between any organic system, such as the visual mechanism, and a simple mechanical system of moving gears and bearings. In the ordinary moving machine, each operation does indeed progressively "wear out" the parts that are active. Exercise of the living organism, on the contrary, strengthens many functions. Learning which results from action improves many acts of skill. From one standpoint fatigue may be taken as an incompletely defined clinical syndrome, that is, a pattern of symptoms sufficiently well organized to be generally recognizable but not always presenting exactly the same picture or showing the same components. This may be summarized in another way by saying that fatigue studies should deal where possible with facts of measurement and be quite conservative in passing by analogy from one measured change to the conclusion that some other, at the time unmeasured, change has also taken place. T. A. Ryan (307) has recently presented a case for classifying the varieties of fatigue reported with corresponding tasks or working conditions.

On the basis of the review of the meaning of the word fatigue given so far, we may now turn more explicitly to a consideration of the question of the changes that take place in the visual mechanism when this mechanism is required to function during specific periods of time and under varying conditions. It is believed that the facts discussed above will make it clear that in attempting to study visual fatigue in an objective way, it is not possible to describe some unitary and simple process called "eye fatigue." Rather, in setting up our experiments, a comprehensive quantitative study of the changes resulting from prolonged visual work had to be planned.

Besides "fatigue," the other technical word of our title is "visual." It may now be asked to what part, if any, of the total visual mechanism the term fatigue can be made to apply. It is important to recognize at the outset that the concept of visual fatigue as used in this book refers to changes not in the intrinsic and extrinsic structures of the eyeball alone but in the total sensory, neural, and motor mechanism involved in any and all human acts of seeing, especially as such seeing involves reading.

The Visual Mechanism

From ancient times it has been recognized that the functioning of the eyes cannot be satisfactorily thought of as unrelated to the functioning of the total living body. The state of the organism of which the eyes are a part affects the organism's ability to see. It is clear, however, that the eyes themselves have evolved in the animal series as organs to make possible the more effective reception, by the living individual, of stimuli with particular characteristics. The evolution of the eyes and their associated neural mechanisms has made it possible for the living animal to respond in a more adaptive way to certain forms of physical energy in its environment. In thinking about the visual mechanism and the fatigue of that mechanism, it is important first of all to consider the fundamental nature of the environmental energies which stimulate the eye and initiate the act of seeing.

Only a very narrow band of the total known energy spectrum adequately stimulates any of the sense receptors which have evolved in the living organism. The band of radiant energy which adequately stimulates the retina of the eye and initiates sight is still more restricted. Reference to Figure 2 may make this well-known fact clear. The effective, or, as it is technically called, "adequate," stimulus for the eye is described by the physicist as a narrow band of radiant energy which has certain special characteristics.

It is now essentially agreed that radiant energy is an electromagnetic disturbance capable of traveling through empty space with tremendous velocity. Radiant energy is treated as an undulation. One characteristic of this oscillation, its wave length, may be used to describe a particular sample of radiant energy. The period or wave length of an oscillation is usually measured in terms of millimicra (a millimicron is a millionth of a millimeter). Radiant oscillations having wave lengths between approximately 350 and approximately 750 millimicra are the stimuli, or the band of radiant energies, which activate the visual mechanism. These wave lengths are often referred to for convenience as "light" and collectively make up the visual spectrum. Radiation from some energy source, such as the sun or an incandescent lamp filament, which produces radiation in the visible spectrum is always an antecedent of seeing. Energy of this type activates the eye when it comes to the sensitive retina. Usually, this energy comes directly from a surface which differentially absorbs and reflects it.

After such direct or reflected radiation reaches the front surface of the living eye, it passes through the various optical media of the eye. In

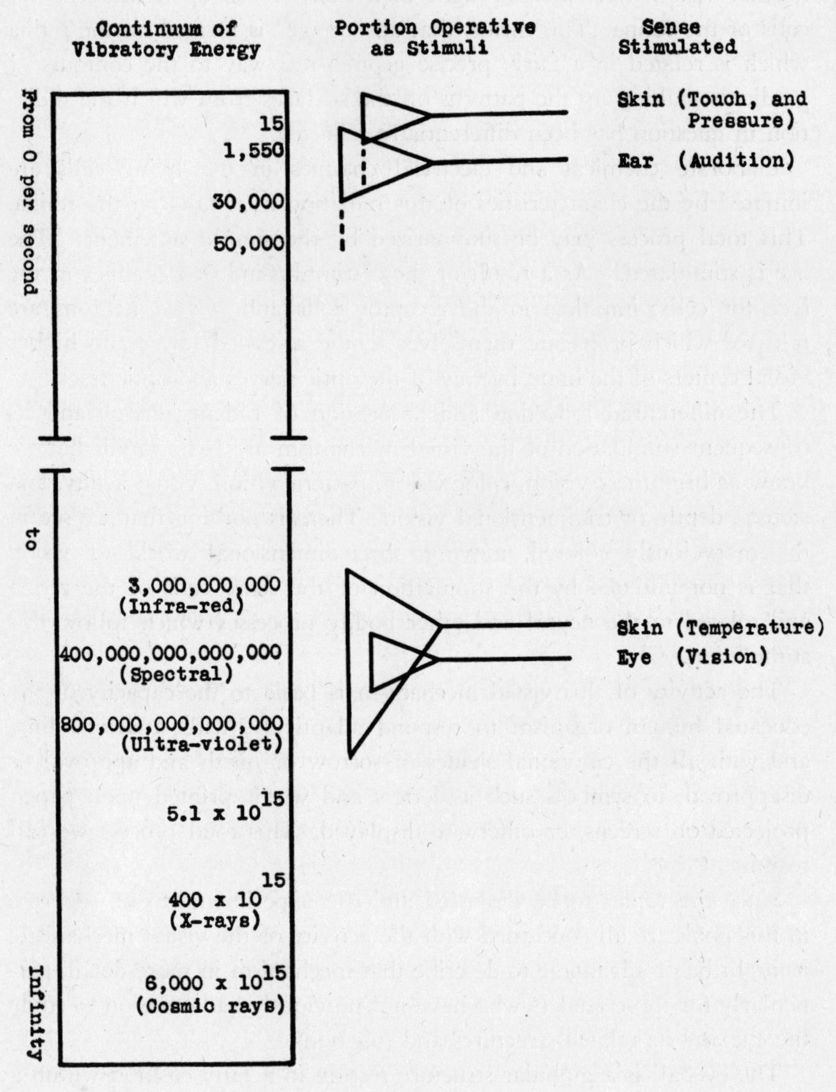

Figure 2

REPRESENTATION OF THE RELATION BETWEEN SENSE ORGANS AND THE PHYSICAL ENERGIES OF THE ENVIRONMENT

(After G. L. Freeman, 110)

normal vision, it is then brought to a sharp focus upon the sensitive cells of the retina. This means that an "image" is formed on the retina which is related in a fairly precise geometrical way to the contours or gradients making up the patterns on the surfaces from which the radiation in question has been differentially reflected.

Elaborate chemical and electrical changes in the living cells are initiated by the characteristics of this radiation as it falls on the retina. This total process may be summarized by the simple statement: "The eye is stimulated." As a result of these stimulus-induced changes in the receptor cells, impulses in the receptor cells and related neurons are released which propagate themselves to the so-called lower and higher visual centers of the brain by way of the optic nerves and optic tracts.

The differential reflection and absorption of radiant energy and its consequent stimulation of the visual mechanism are basic to all that we know as brightness vision, color vision, pattern vision, visual acuity, and stereo-, depth, or tridimensional vision. There is nothing that we see in the marvelously colored, moving, three-dimensional world of vision that is not initiated by the stimulation of the sense cells of the retina and related to the neural and other bodily processes which follow this stimulation.

The activity of this visual mechanism is basic to the capacity of the educated human organism to respond adaptively, with understanding, and with all the emotional shades of sorrow or mirth and approval or disapproval, to symbols such as letters and words printed upon paper, projected on screens, or otherwise displayed. This total process we call reading.

Since the topics to be discussed and the experiments to be reported in this book are all concerned with the activity of the visual mechanism, it might be of advantage to describe that mechanism in more detail, particularly for those readers who have not previously had occasion to study the eye and its related structures and functions.

The eyeball is a globular structure resting in a fatty cushion within a bony socket in the head. When freshly excised from this socket, it looks like a dark globe covered with a white and glistening coat. Description of the eyeball may conveniently be made with reference to the accompanying diagrams (Figures 3 and 4). The first figure represents a cut down the center of the eye; the second is of the fundus of the eye (the back or the internal surface of the eyeball).

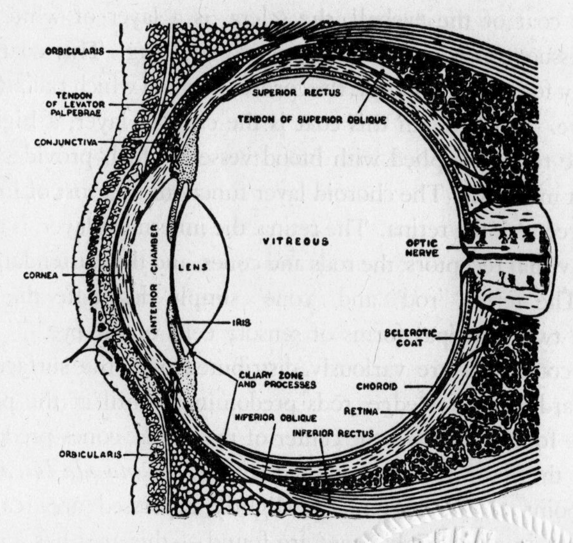

Figure 3

THE INTERNAL STRUCTURE OF THE EYEBALL

Vertical Section of the Eyeball

(After H. Parent, 269)

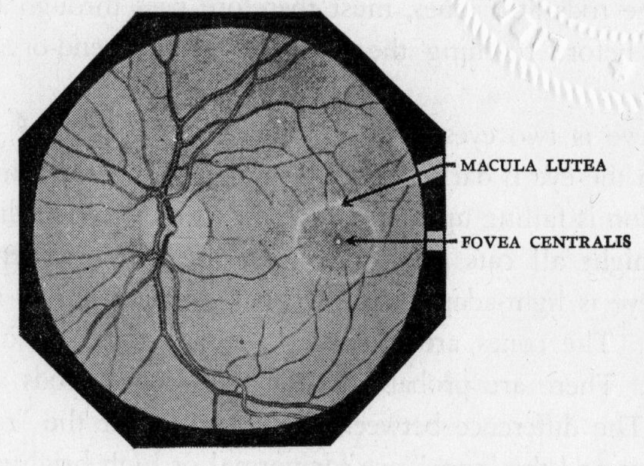

Figure 4

THE FUNDUS OF THE EYE

(After M. Salzmann, 308)

The outer coat of the eyeball, the sclera, is a layer of white, tough, connective tissue which acts as a protective covering. This coat is continuous except for a front window, the cornea, through which radiant energy enters the eye. Just beneath this coat is the choroid layer, a highly pigmented tissue richly supplied with blood vessels, which provides the eye with nutrient materials. The choroid layer functions as a sort of incidental absorbing screen for the retina. The retina, the innermost layer, is made up of the actual visual receptors, the rods and cones, and their attendant neural structures. The terms "rod" and "cone" simply designate the general shape of the two principal forms of sensory cells of the eye.

Rod and cone cells are variously distributed over the surface of the retina. Toward the outer edge, rods predominate until at the periphery only rods are found. Toward the center of the retina, cones predominate, especially in the central, yellow-colored region, the *macula lutea.* About at the midpoint of the retina is a slightly depressed area called the *fovea centralis,* in which only cones are found — this area has a diameter of about 1 to 1.5 millimeters. Stimulation of the fovea in optimal conditions of light gives rise to the most acute and detailed vision (most efficient resolution, as it is called) of which the human eye is capable.

Because of the embryological sequence of development of the retinal layer, the visual receptors, the rods and cones, are inverted and located in the layer of the retina furthest from the front of the eye. Light, in order to stimulate the rods and cones, must therefore pass through the other retinal layers before reaching the sensitive receptor end-organs themselves.

Essentially, each eye is two eyes. The rod-like receptor cells of the retina function when the eye is dark-adapted — that is, when a minimal amount of illumination is falling upon the eye. The rods do not mediate color vision — "at night all cats are gray." The cones of the retina function when the eye is light-adapted and when light is bright or not below that of dusk. The cones are the receptors which are basic to normal color vision. There are probably about 137,000,000 rods and cones in each eye. The difference between the sensitivity of the "rod" eye for low brightness and the "cone" eye for normal or high brightness is remarkable. It has been calculated that the illumination of white paper in direct sunlight reflects about 7,000,000,000 times as much light as is necessary under ideal conditions to be seen by a dark-adapted (rod) eye.

The retinal layer does not extend completely around the globe of the inner eye but forms a jagged edge, the *ora serrata,* a little ahead of the midline circumference of the sphere. The sclerotic coat, however, at the front of the eyeball merges with the transparent cornea, the window of the eye. The choroid layer behind the retina terminates, in a sense, as the iris, the structure which determines the so-called color of a person's eye. The variably round aperture in the iris is, of course, the pupil. Separating the cornea and the iris is a watery fluid called the aqueous humor. Stretched just behind the iris by means of suspensory ligaments is the lens. This living lens is a lamellated structure, layered like an onion, which corresponds to the ground and polished glass lens of a camera. Between the lens and the retinal layer is another fluid, the vitreous humor, more viscous than the aqueous humor.

An analogy, older than the photographic camera itself, compares the function of the human eye to that of the old-fashioned pinhole camera long used as a sketching device by artists. The analogy even more aptly applies to the modern photographic camera with its sensitive plate at the back. Light entering the eye must, as in such a camera, be properly focused and introduced to the sensitive receptors in order to initiate the first steps of the act of "seeing." The cornea, the pupil, the lens, and the humors of the eye constitute the refractive media or image-forming mechanism of the eye. The degree of refraction or bending is related to the curvature of the surface and the media through which the light passes. Most of the necessary refraction of the radiant energy that is to stimulate the retina takes place as it passes through the front surface and outer fixed media of the eye. The further necessary refraction is accomplished by appropriately changing the curvature of the lens — the so-called accommodatory reflex. This change is controlled by the action of small muscles (the ciliary bodies). The contraction of these muscles allows the suspensory ligaments to relax, and the elastic lens thus becomes thicker so that near objects are brought to focus on the retina. When these muscles relax, the lens becomes less curved, and the eye is again accommodated for far vision.

The iris is essentially a group of muscle fibers, some of which are circularly arranged and others radially. When the circular fibers are activated, the pupil is caused to constrict; when the radial fibers are innervated, the pupil dilates. The iris muscles thus adjust the size of the pupils. This is called the pupillary light reflex. The amount of light affects the retina and the central nervous system, which in turn controls within limits the amount of light which enters the eye by changing the pupillary opening.

In a very real sense, the image-forming mechanisms that have just been discussed may be regarded as accessory mechanisms which make effective stimulation of the eye possible and, with such stimulation, the initiation of those adaptive responses which the higher animal makes to the so-called visual world.

The rods and cones are the actual visual sense organs, for it is they that are stimulated by light. The accessory apparatus, when normal, simply transmits and brings to a clear focus upon the rods and cones the light rays originating in sources of radiation or reflected by objects at various distances from the eye.

It is known that when light falls upon the rods and cones, chemical activity is induced. Some of these chemical changes have been studied in detail. In the rods has been isolated a photosensitive substance known as rhodopsin; in the cones, a similar photosensitive substance called iodopsin. This latter substance was not discovered until quite recently (59, 384) and as yet little is known about its properties. Rhodopsin, or visual purple, when acted upon by light, is bleached to what has been called visual yellow or retinene; upon further exposure to light, visual yellow is bleached to a substance referred to as visual white. In the intact eye, however, rhodopsin can be reconstituted or resynthesized. S. Hecht (137) and others have developed photochemical theories to describe and explain the sequence of events which follows the action of light upon the rods. These theories postulate the presence and production of substances and energies which well account for the known temporal and other characteristics of vision.

The end result of rod and cone activity, however, is the initiation of nerve impulses in the adjacent neural structures. A nerve impulse is a disturbance, electrochemical in nature, propagated along a neuron as a result of progressive release of the energy self-contained within the neuron fiber itself. The series of nerve impulses initiated in the retina are propagated along various neurons making up neural tracts. These impulses finally activate other neurons in the visual portion of the central nervous system.

The neural paths of vision are complex (294). Something of their relationships may be seen in the accompanying chart and diagram

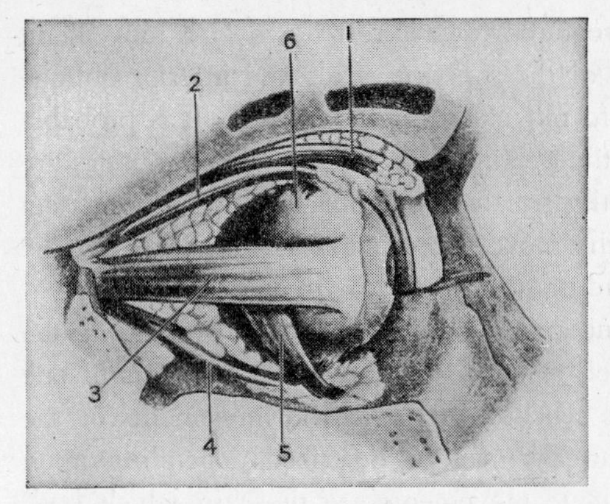

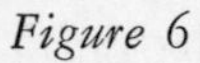
Figure 6

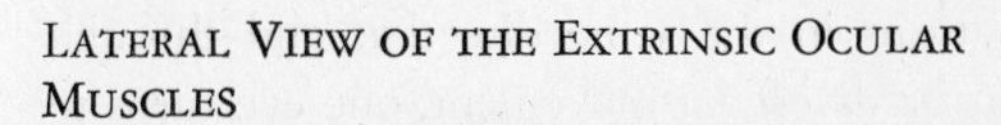
LATERAL VIEW OF THE EXTRINSIC OCULAR MUSCLES

1. Levator palpebrae superioris
2. Superior rectus
3. External rectus
4. Inferior rectus
5. Inferior oblique
6. Superior oblique

(After W. S. Duke-Elder, 95)

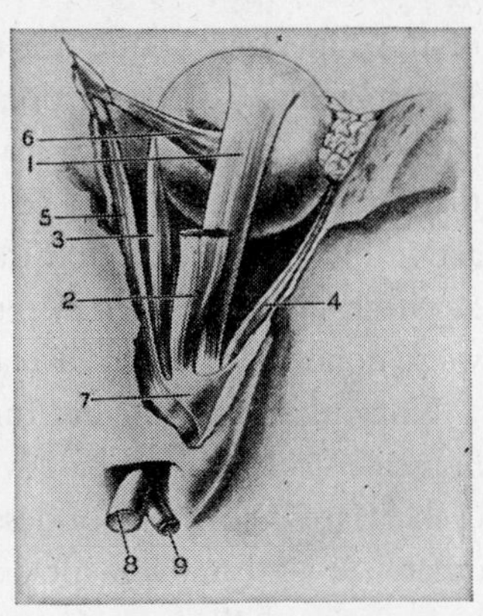

Figure 7

THE EXTRINSIC OCULAR MUSCLES VIEWED FROM ABOVE THE EYEBALL

1. Superior rectus
2. Levator palpebrae superioris
3. Internal rectus
4. External rectus
5. Superior oblique
6. Reflected tendon of superior oblique
7. Annulus of Zinn
8. Optic nerve
9. Ophthalmic artery

(After W. S. Duke-Elder, 95)

is raised by the *levator palpebrae superioris* muscle. This muscle is innervated by the third cranial nerve — as are also certain of the extrinsic ocular muscles. The lids are voluntarily or reflexly closed by the action of a sphincter muscle, *obicularis palpebrarum,* which is innervated by the seventh or *facial* cranial nerve.

The origin and insertion of the six external eye muscles are such that contraction of the superior rectus rotates the eyeball upward and inward. The inferior rectus rotates it downward and inward. The external rectus rotates the eyeball outward; the internal rectus, inward. Contraction of the superior oblique rotates the eyeball in a downward and outward direction; of the inferior oblique, upward and also outward.

The contraction of the inferior rectus and the compensating action of the superior oblique are required for a direct downward movement. The co-ordinated contraction of the superior rectus and inferior oblique is required for a direct upward movement of the eyeball. It is probable that for every movement of the eyes not only the dominant muscles are active but also the anatomically situated antagonistic muscles which act as check elements to make the movement accurate. In considering the work done by the eyes in reading, this should be remembered.

Not only is the normal functioning of the six muscles controlling the movement of each eyeball well co-ordinated, but the movements of one eyeball are also more or less synchronized with the movements of the other. Several movement patterns may be described depending upon how the eyeballs act. Conjugate movements are those in which both eyes move in the same direction; for example, one eye turns to the right, and the other eye also turns in the same direction and through the same distance. In the case of a divergent movement, one eye turns to the right and the other eye turns through about the same distance but in the opposite direction, to the left. When the two eyeballs turn toward each other, they converge. The term vergence, however, is used to include both types of movements. Torsion movements of the eyeballs may be thought of as a special instance of conjugate movement: in addition to moving through a particular distance in a certain direction, each eyeball may rotate slightly on its longitudinal axis.

Mention may also be made here of several other types of eye movements. Pursuit movements are co-ordinated responses of the eyes made in following a moving stimulus. The direction and rate of such movements are related to those of the stimulus. Compensatory eye movements are reactions which tend to restore the eye to such a position that a line of regard which has been disturbed by head or other movement is regained. That is, if the head is rotated to the left, the eyes tend to make compensatory movements to the right. Nystagmus movements are reactions of the eyes composed of alternate slow and quick phases in opposite directions or rapid oscillations. Nystagmus may be caused by many ways of stimulating the internal ear: by electricity, by temperature, or by rotation. So-called visual nystagmus, sometimes called "railroad nystagmus," results from retinal stimulation produced by observing the moving striation of a rotating drum or watching objects move continuously by.

It might be expected that activity in the extrinsic ocular muscles—contraction, tonus—would give rise to kinesthetic neural impulses by which the central nervous system might be "aware" of what is going on at the periphery. The exact course, however, of these impulses from the muscles to the central nervous system and the exact receptor systems involved are not fully understood. It is presumed that fibers originating in the receptors of the extrinsic muscles join the tracts transmitting deep sensibility and eventually reach the centers controlling ocular movements. The immediate motor control of the extrinsic muscles, however, is known to take place in the nuclei variously located in the brain stem. The cell bodies of these nuclei give origin to efferent fibers which terminate in the extrinsic muscles of the eye. Evidence as to the actual nerve tracts involved in bringing these nuclei under the control of higher centers is not yet complete (297). The actual cortical control of the ocular movements, however, has been fairly well determined to reside principally in the lower extremity of the second and third convolutions of the frontal lobe of the cortex. It has been assumed that from this area the chief so-called volitional control of ocular movements takes its origin.

Mention should be made at this point of a theory developed by S. T. Orton (267) that the adequacy of cortical control over the visual system depends upon the nature of the functional organization in the visual components of the two cerebral hemispheres. It is suggested by this writer and by others that the activity of one hemisphere must be dominant over that of the other to insure the proper co-ordination of nervous impulses to and from the cortex. In the large majority of people, the left hemisphere is dominant. Interferences or anomalies in the reading habit, in the use of the eyes in general, and in writing, spelling, speech, and so forth, are regarded by Orton and some others as due to a failure to establish the physiological dominance of the activity of one cortical hemisphere over the functioning of the other, nondominant cortex.

Alexia, or the neurally based inability to read, congenital or acquired, is attributed by some authors to a defect in specific subcortical or cortical regions. A reading center in the posterior occipital lobe and a visual speech center in the lower left parietal lobe have been described. For further discussion of this and related topics see E. E. Lord, L. Carmichael, and W. F. Dearborn (195). The exact cortical and subcortical neural mechanism of normal reading, including "comprehension," is still as obscure and as much a function of speculation as is the specific "seat" of the mechanism of "thought" in the brain.

The detailed eye movements measured in the present experiments depend primarily on the activity of the extrinsic ocular muscles. It is interesting to note that these muscles are much more favorably situated in regard to mechanical advantage than are most other muscles of the body. The general skeletal muscles of the body are so inserted that they pull on the short arm of the lever arrangement whose movement they control. But the eye muscles are so attached to the eyesphere that they always pull at the end of a diameter of the eyeball. This is a decided mechanical advantage, since by this arrangement more of the action of the muscle is directly engaged in moving the eyeball than in overcoming the physical resistance of a lever system.

W. B. Lancaster (185) has calculated that the amount of force required to move the eyeball through an arc of 10 degrees in 0.04 second is equal to 1.73 grams. But the power of the muscle to overcome this load is equivalent to from 750 to 1000 grams. An allowance for friction and resistance or the counteraction of antagonistic muscles has been made in these calculations. This working power of the ocular muscles is calculated from the physiologist's estimate that the contractile power of striated muscle is around 62.5 grams per square millimeter — the six ocular muscles are about 36 millimeters long and from 7 to 12 square millimeters in cross-section. Considering the difference between the load and the working power of the extrinsic muscles, there is thus a large latitude between reserve force and actual demand in the muscle movements required to reorient the eyeballs in their orbits. It is difficult to impair the efficiency of any specific neuromuscular unit unless it is made to work against a near maximum load. These facts, which may be recalled when in later chapters we discuss the resistance to fatigue of the visual mechanism in reading, are of great significance in understanding the results of the present experiments.

In addition, there is excellent evidence that the extrinsic muscles, like most other skeletal muscles, maintain their activity by a mechanism which protects them from exhaustion. Under normal conditions, the various fibers in a muscle support the load by turns, so that each individual fiber works for a small fraction of the time. It would seem that the eye muscles as total structures can "rest as they work," a recuperative rest period which is adequate for restorative purposes occurring between bursts of activity. Thus, it is possible that in long periods of continuous work, the total activity of the receptor-neuromotor mechanism of the eyes (such as that required in reading) in reality establishes a new "steady state" in much the same way as does the heart, which seemingly shows little or no work decrement during a lifetime of normal but fluctuating activity.

It must be emphasized, however, that this absence of "fatigue," if it can be experimentally demonstrated in some eye-muscle movements which are visually initiated and controlled, must apply to the whole visual mechanism, including retina and nervous system, as well as eye muscles. No part of the visual mechanism exists for itself. The whole sensory and muscular mechanisms of the eyes have evolved in order to make the adjustment of the organism which maintains the eyes as effective as possible to certain forms of radiant energy in its environment. Visual activity does not end in the eye or the thalamus or the visual cortex of the brain. Rather, it must be remembered that, as a result of the central nervous system activity following stimulation of the eye, additional neural activities are in turn initiated. These brain activities lead to the adjustment of the behavior and the posture of the whole organism appropriate to the present visual stimuli. As we have just seen, activity of the eyes is neurally determined, for impulses coming out from the central nervous system to the eyes determine all, or virtually all, ocular behavior that is dependent on muscular contractions. In a sense the eyes are little *independent mobile organisms* which are related to but are surprisingly independent of the great total organism of the body in which they are located. By the very nature of that relationship, ocular behavior is an integral part of the activity of the whole individual, but a part of that behavior which at times has a surprising autonomy. In this connection it may be remembered that the posture of the body and the rotation and turning of the body or the head affect the eye muscles through reflex activities which are initiated in the internal ear and in certain receptors associated with the muscles of the body. The regular slow and fast phases of this "vestibular nystagmus" of the eyes, brought on by rotation of the body and head, are examples of such eye behavior determined by stimulation other than that of the retina.

What has just been said may make it clear that when the terms "visual fatigue," "eye fatigue," or "reading fatigue" are used, it does not mean that in some peculiar way the fatigue is necessarily localized in the sensory cells or in the muscles of the eyeball itself. Rather, a change in the efficiency of performance in any part of the entire visual mechanism is implied by such phrases. Strangely, this fact has not always been emphasized by investigators of visual fatigue. Some students have assumed that even tiredness of the eyes must be essentially a simple, retinal alteration. Others have attributed decrements to the changes resulting from the work of some special brain center or of the central nervous system as a whole. Still others impute eye fatigue to one or more of the muscular or motor mechanisms of the eye.

It seems best, however, to the present authors to deal with the total mechanism involved in vision, at least in an investigation of the visual work decrement and other phenomena related to fatigue in reading. The motor performance of the eye required in reading or similar visual tasks must be regarded as a function of the total visual mechanism and even, as noted above, of the body as a whole. The end stage of this activity may be measured in a most accurate way. Thus, any changes that take place during the activity of the total mechanism involved in sight are measured and may be analyzed as a function of experimentally varied conditions. The basic fact that the eyes move in their orbits as a result of the neural activation of the extrinsic eye muscles presents an admirable condition for quantitative study. It is, therefore, this eye behavior itself that has been chosen as the direct object of study in the present investigation of fatigue in reading. It is understood, of course, that an evaluation of the above point of view in relation to the problem of fatigue will depend, as our discussion has already shown, upon the way in which the concept of fatigue is used.

In the light of this previous discussion, it would seem that quantitative study of the behavior of the visual mechanism might reveal any of several possible changes as activity is prolonged. Any changes of muscular function attributed to general fatigue will affect visual behavior. If such changes take place, the visual mechanism, like the rest of the body, may correctly enough be said not to be working in an optimal way and may be "fatigued." Kurtz has suggested a relationship between general and ocular fatigue in the statement:

> . . . when general fatigue is present for fifteen minutes it begins to affect efficiency of ocular activity, and ocular fatigue begins to set in. The reverse may be equally true, that is, when ocular fatigue sets in first, it may gradually affect other parts of the body and thus become general. (178, p. 308.)

This may be a true statement, but it is hard to find experimental results which can validate it. If fatigue is regarded as a name for a complex of phenomena, it is reasonable to assume that visual fatigue may be an instance of general fatigue, or that prolonged activity of even the relatively small ocular mechanism may have some reverberations throughout the total organism. It should be remembered, however, that the very small mass of the eye muscles as related to the great mass of the body muscles as a whole might make the direct influence of fatigue in the eye muscles upon the general system very insignificant chemically. If any change in the eyes takes place which makes the adaptation of the total organism to its environment less effective, there may well be indirect effects of a general sort upon the total organism following alteration in the effectiveness of the visual system.

M. Luckiesh and F. K. Moss (203) have drawn the conclusion that the visual mechanism will temporarily compensate for poor conditions of seeing by an increased expenditure of energy. This suggests that the eyes may perform as well under adverse circumstances as they do under more favorable conditions. This activity, it is suggested, is maintained at an increased expenditure of energy and "costs" the organism more than ordinary action. An ultimate depletion of the available energy would be expected, according to this view. As noted above in connection with a related concept, it is very hard to formulate this opinion in such a way as to evaluate it by quantitative experiments.

There is also the possibility that as the activity of a visual behavior pattern is prolonged, changes occur in the systems which direct, control, or co-ordinate the ocular mechanisms. Kurtz points out

> that coordination of each of the six muscles of the eye with each other is of prime importance in the proper functioning of the visual system, and the lack of this coordination is largely responsible for the major part of ocular fatigue. (177, p. 213.)

Since, at best, the balance of the eye muscles is rather imperfect, it is not surprising that the so-called fatigue of co-ordination is a conspicuous symptom in patients seeking ophthalmological advice. H. Hartridge (136) describes a special instance in which fatigue of control or direction may occur in the visual mechanism as a result of dysfunction of one or more of the ocular mechanisms. In normal vision there is a close association between the nerve centers controlling the shape of the lens in the eye and the vergence movements of the eyeballs when adjusting for the distance of a seen object. If, however, an individual is far-sighted, accommodation of the lens must be effected without convergence; or if the individual is near-sighted, convergence adjustments must be made without apparently changing the shape of the lens. Hartridge suggests that eyestrain or visual fatigue may be due to the effort required to dissociate these normally co-ordinated functions. If anomalies in co-ordination are associated with feelings of eyestrain, the further assumption is that fatigue may bear some relation to the efficiency of control or co-ordination. W. F. Dearborn and I. H. Anderson have suggested a similar consideration in the case of aniseikonia, a condition of the eyes in which the ocular images are unequal either in size or in shape:

> First, because of the interference with the ability to fuse, the aniseikonia may produce either ocular or general fatigue, or both, and thereby raise the threshold of effective motivation and decrease the length of the periods of concentration. This inability to persevere, especially while reading for the purposes of study, is a common complaint of aniseikonic patients. After relatively brief periods of reading, many of these cases find themselves perusing pages mechanically without any recollection of the material covered. Second, aniseikonia may interfere directly with the visual processes during reading. Its effect in this connection, however, may begin only when the reader tries to increase his perceptual span, that is, when he attempts to read in larger units than single words or syllables. Reading, like efficient driving of an automobile in traffic, demands a very skillful use of peripheral vision. It is with this peripheral view of the line of print, which is so requisite for the proper spacing of the fixation pauses, that aniseikonia may interfere. This follows because the incongruent images falling on the periphery of each eye would present different space cues for the movements of the eyes as they are shifted from one point within the line to the next. Furthermore, since the paper or book may appear tilted because of the aniseikonia, slight readjustments of the accommodation and convergence may be necessary. (79, p. 562.)

It must be emphasized that, if there are such localized fatigue changes, they should show themselves in the continued performance of work by the eyes in reading, and, further, that if such changes are *not* observed, the only remaining question would seem to be as to whether or not the measures employed are appropriate and sufficiently sensitive to record the purported changes.

There is also evidence to suggest that fatigue changes in visual performance may be the effects of attitudinal or motivational factors. For example, K. Winkler (403) is of the opinion that individual differences in visual work decrements are due not so much to anatomical and physiological differences as to differences in effort or attitude toward the task. If such motivational factors can influence decrement, is it unreasonable to suppose that these same factors may in part be responsible for any decrement that is measured? O. Löwenstein and E. D. Friedman (192) prolonged the pupillary light reflex until a state of pupillary immobility was reached. This immobility gave the appearance of a state of exhaustion, but, when it was merely suggested to the subjects that pain would be induced with subsequent stimulation of the eye, the pupillary response reappeared. The pupillary response evidently was not exhausted. It may be, then, that the original "immobility" was also the result of or due to psychological factors of an attitudinal nature.

The summary of relevant scientific literature on the nature of fatigue given in this chapter shows that the word fatigue is not always used in the same way by different writers. At the present time, there is evidence that the basis of fatigue is a change in substances necessary to maintain activity and, concomitantly, the accumulation of waste products which further reduce the supply of energy, hamper the activity of the organs doing the work, and interfere with the resynthesis or reaccumulation of the necessary energy substances. This viewpoint is concerned with the specific locus of the "fatigue" conditions, especially as they may be found either in the peripheral organs or in the central nervous system. But it is clear that these biochemical changes are not the only ones required for a full view of the alterations of the organism during work which are called fatigue. The attitude of the individual and the mechanisms basic to changes in activity due to inhibition, compensation, and coordination must also be considered in understanding the temporal and other characteristics of fatigue. The student of behavior who would give a complete picture of the changes induced by previous work must deal with full and also all degrees of partial exhaustion as an organic state and also with functional changes which are noted as "fatigue phenomena," such as feelings of unpleasantness, of blocking, and of conflict.

It seems clear, therefore, that the growth of knowledge concerning the causes and prevention of fatigue will require the use of many techniques that are biochemical, physiological, and psychological. As Cason has said:

> . . . it is unwise for a person to postulate "physical" and "mental" fatigue and then assume that he has disentangled what cannot be disentangled in the body. (57, p. 338.)

A full study of human fatigue will require the study of *changes* in the functions of the body or its parts following activity. These changes may show themselves as what have been called work decrements, changes in output, or changes of attitude. They may be related to variations in structure, biochemistry, or electrical activity of the active organ system. Changes in function also show themselves in the breakdown of patterns of response and changes in the variability measures of performance. Similarly, the differential performance of various individuals and, above all, the motivational, attitudinal, and feeling aspects of prolonged activity must be considered in the study of certain aspects of the changes which result from completely or partially exhausting activity.

Only by the use of many different approaches can an increasingly useful and explicit knowledge be secured of the varied phenomena of human work called by the single name *fatigue.* This statement is especially true of what has been termed visual fatigue.

The studies reported in later chapters of this book were not undertaken with the idea that they would give a complete and final answer to the problems of visual fatigue in reading. Such is not the way of science. Rather, it is intended here to summarize previous scientific work and describe new experiments which seem to make a contribution to the understanding of this problem. It is hoped that this approach will advance to some extent in both a theoretical and a practical way what is known about the favorable or unfavorable effect of prolonged reading upon the eyes and upon the whole organism.

Chapter 2

The Visual Task of Reading

MOST previous experimental studies of visual fatigue have singled out for analysis some relatively simple function of what may be called the ocular repertory. Examples of such studies are those of pupillary size, convergence movements, and flicker fusion. Experiments which measure changes in performance as a function of time have especially tended to deal with such specific and simple responses. These observations of the prolonged activity of discrete functions of the eye offer many data and some especially valuable clues as to the nature of the changes which may take place when the visual mechanism is "fatigued." However, in the practical problem of studying the presence or absence of fatigue of the eyes as they are used in the adaptive life of the organism, attention to the more typical and usual function of the eyes seems to be desirable if not requisite.

For a study of this sort, the investigation of the eye movements involved in prolonged reading has peculiar advantages. Reading is a pattern involving many ocular functions, but in spite of its complex character, it is a pattern of ocular behavior that is now quite well understood. The characteristic eye movements in reading have been analyzed with success in much previous experimentation.

Reading involves discrete physiological functions as well as the behavioral integration of those functions to mediate what are really whole series of effective adjustments of the human organism. It involves patterned movements of the eyes and adjustments of the eyes themselves to bring into appropriate view, in a suitable temporal order, symbols which are to be perceived as words or phrases. These words and the processes which are related to them then evoke images, ideas, and action and lead to states called by such names as comprehension and enjoyment. Should certain aspects of fatigue be a matter of interference or blocking, it may be likely that these effects would be more manifest in reading than in more discrete functions of the eye. Should fatigue be considered as akin to exhaustion, the depletion of energy supplies, or the curtailment of activity by toxic substances, the responses of the organism involved in reading behavior would presumably be affected.

The fact that reading is at once seen to consist of a pattern of eye movements emphasizes not only the types of movement that the eyes make, but also the fact that these movements bear some relation to each other. Together these movements form a recognizable pattern. This pattern differs in detail from individual to individual, but it has certain general characteristics which are now well known. Should fatigue, as has been suggested, be manifested at least in part as a breakdown in the control or integration of behavior, that is, in the co-ordination that must be achieved for effective response, then the experimenter investigating the component movements of prolonged reading is observing a pattern which might well be expected to show such alterations. It is possible that a particular function of the eye may manifest certain changes when active alone but may behave quite differently when involved in a co-ordinated pattern. Unfortunately, it is seldom possible in the living organism to deduce the characteristics of complex functions by merely adding together the known properties of isolated component functions. In this respect the analyses and syntheses of common mechanical systems as studied in the science of physics cannot be applied to organic processes.

The study of the fatigue of the reading pattern also has the advantage of many practical considerations. Reading is a task sooner or later required of nearly all normal adults, at least in modern western civilized society. One of the purposes of research in visual fatigue is to improve the efficiency of this all-important intellectual tool. The more directly this behavior may be observed in the experimental situation, the more likely it is that the recommendations resulting from scientific study will be both valid and of practical use. The demands made upon the organism by the activity of reading, as well as the important part which reading plays in the life of the school and in society in general, warrant then the closest study of those aspects which may be related to visual fatigue.

The proper movements of the eyes in reading are learned just as the proper movements of tennis are learned by the novice on the court. There is, however, one important difference: in tennis, golf, or swimming, the learner is aware that he is learning muscular movements, whereas in learning to read, the subject is typically unaware of what his eyes are doing. Even the educated adult who does not happen to have read about current investigations of eye movements is likely to have no clear notion of what the eyes do in reading. Such an uninformed person may say that he believes that his eyes move steadily along the line of print, jump to the beginning of the next line, move steadily along that line, and so on. Actually, such is not the case. If the same individual were asked to observe another person's reading by looking through a pinhole on the page being read or by looking in a mirror beside the page, he would note that the eyes make a series of rapid jerks interspersed with longer pauses.

The study of the movements of the eyes in reading and in other visual tasks has been assisted by the development of apparatus and controlled techniques which allow the recording and measurement of the several kinds of movement that the eyes make. For example, the reading pattern has been recorded by directing a small ray of light to the cornea of the eye, from which it is reflected by the corneal surface. Suitable lens systems have been constructed to focus this reflected ray of light on a moving photographic plate or on photosensitive recording paper or film. As the eyeball moves, so also does the point of light and, therefore, its trace on the sensitive film. Samples of records taken by this method are shown in Figure 8. The methods of recording eye movements and the history of their development will be described in detail in a later chapter.

It is by the detailed study of eye-movement records that much has been learned about the nature and characteristics of eye movements. Records of the reading pattern show conclusively that the eyes actually jump from fixation pause to fixation pause along the line of print. Because the paper on which these movements are recorded is itself moving at a constant rate, the record looks something like a "staircase." Certain technical terms are now quite generally used to refer to the component movements of this pattern.

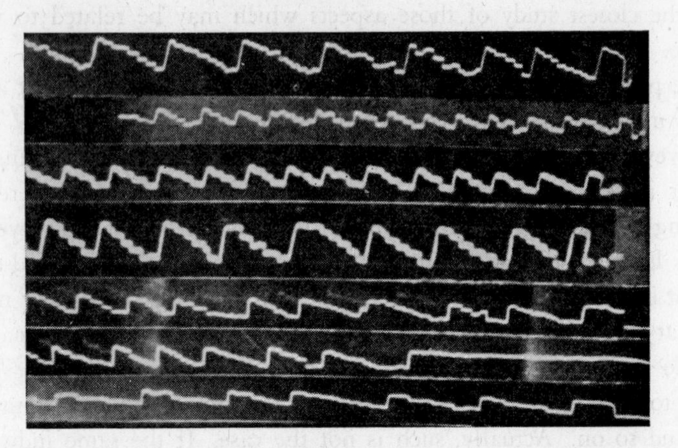

Figure 8

SAMPLE EYE MOVEMENT RECORDS—CORNEAL-REFLECTION METHOD

(After W. F. Dearborn, 78)

The term "fixation" or "fixation pause" refers to the period in reading a line of print during which the eyeball is held stationary for a given time and the retina is thus exposed to a stationary pattern of focused light differentially absorbed and reflected from the paper and print or other surface marked with letters and words. The eye is held relatively stationary during a fixation by the simultaneous contraction of sets of opposing muscles. In such pauses the eye does not remain absolutely motionless (85, 224, 270). Although the eye does not operate with mathematical precision, the pauses are effective for clear vision because the retina presents a mosaic surface of receptors. Also slight changes in the position of the eyeball relative to the fixation point may be compensated for by quick changes in the adjustments of the lens.

At the conclusion of the brief fixation pause, the eye jumps to another part of the line of print, ordinarily in a forward direction, for another fixation. This jump is called a saccade or a saccadic movement, for the reason that it is a thrown or jerked movement. A thrown movement (327) of the eyeball is one which is initiated by the contraction of one set of muscles and then proceeds on its course under its own momentum until stopped by the contraction of an opposing set of muscles. The first set of muscles is referred to as agonists, the second as antagonists. When the last fixation toward the end of the line of print has been completed, the eye makes a saccadic movement back to the beginning of the next line. Because this latter type of saccadic movement is longer and in a direction opposite to those interspersed between fixations, it is often distinguished by the term "return sweep."

Normally in our culture, reading proceeds from left to right along the line of print — a fixation pause followed by a short saccadic movement of the eyeballs to the right, another fixation, another saccade to the right, and so forth, until the line has been "read." But occasionally, more often in poor readers than in good, there are short saccadic movements of the eyeball to the left, allowing the refixation of material appearing previously in the line of print. It is assumed that these movements are ordinarily made when previous material has not been adequately fixated or comprehended, and they are therefore referred to as regressive or corrective movements.

Fixations, saccades, return sweeps, and regressions are all conjugate movements of the eyeballs. This, it will be remembered, means that both eyes move in the same direction when making them, even though the printed material may be presented to only one eye. The reading pattern of eye movements, however, also includes some vergence movements.

Figure 9 is a diagrammatic reading record of each eye taken simultaneously. The varying distances between the two lines, which represent the vergence phenomena, are shown in this diagram in an exaggerated manner. The eyeballs tend normally to be relatively diverged at the end of reading a line of print. During the return sweep, they tend to converge; this convergence represents, on the average, a one-degree shift in the line of regard of the eyeball. Thus, the distance between the two records labeled A will be longer than the distance B. While reading the line of print, the eyeballs tend to diverge again — thus, distance B is shorter than distance A′. During each fixation pause, there is a tendency for the eyes to diverge — indicated by the fact that distance B is shorter than distance C, distance D is shorter than distance E, and distance F is shorter than distance A′. Most of this divergence occurs during the first fixation — thus, the difference between distances B and C is greater than the difference between D and E or F and A′.

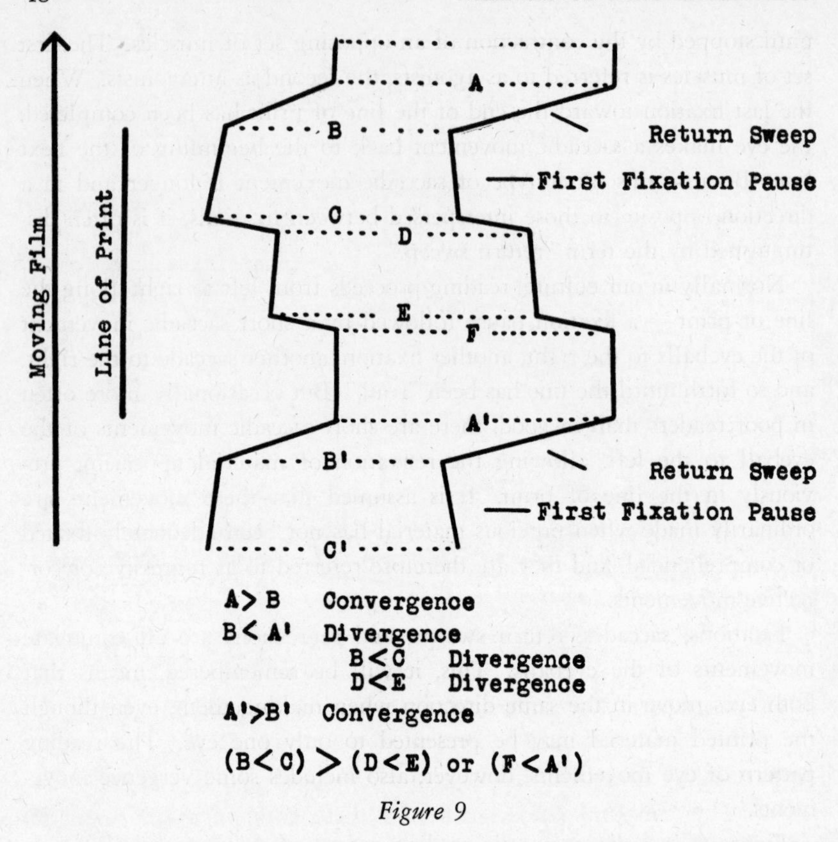

Figure 9

DIAGRAMMATIC READING RECORD EMPHASIZING VERGENCE PHENOMENA

For convenient review, a stylized drawing of a typical eye-movement record is shown in Figure 10. Each line represents the conjugate movements made by an eyeball; the distance between the lines can be used to measure vergence phenomena. The vertical lines are the recordings of fixation pauses. The long horizontal lines are the record of the saccadic return sweep made from the last fixation of one line to the first of the next line. The short horizontal lines in the opposite direction represent the saccadic movements made from one fixation pause to another. Short horizontal lines in the same direction as the return sweep indicate regressive movements.

The time or duration of each of these component movements can be determined from the vertical distance of the record of that movement,

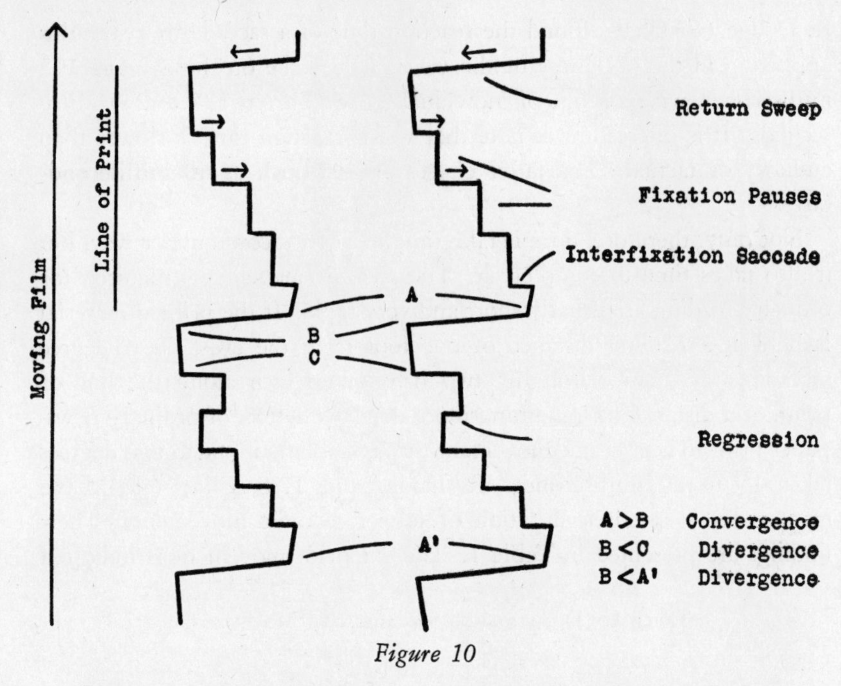

Figure 10

DIAGRAMMATIC RECORD OF EYE MOVEMENTS DURING READING

if the recording film is moved at a constant speed and if that speed is known. The temporal characteristics of these component movements of the reading pattern are only an instance of what can be learned by study of the eye-movement records. In fact, much of what is known of the reading pattern has depended on the refinement of techniques for recording eye movements and the analysis of the accurate records of such movements.

The reaction time or latency [1] of the saccadic movement is about the same, for example, as the reaction time of the hand to a visual stimulus when a key is to be pressed by a subject as soon as he sees a light flash on. This latency is around 180 milliseconds or sigma.[2] A. R. Diefendorf and

[1] Latency is the time between the presentation of the stimulus and the first appearance or beginning of the response being observed. It is essentially a measure, in this case, of the time required to activate the sensory endings in the eye, the afferent and efferent peripheral nerves and tracts, the appropriate centers of the brain, and the muscles.

[2] A sigma is a unit of time equal to a thousandth of a second or one millisecond. The term millisecond is used in this book except in direct quotations from the older literature in which the word sigma is used.

R. Dodge (82) have found the reaction time of a saccade to a stimulus appearing in the periphery of the visual field to be on the average 195 milliseconds, with a range of individual averages from 125 to 235 milliseconds. It is interesting to note that visual reaction time is slower than auditory or tactual. The latter classes are as much as 40 milliseconds faster.

Not only, therefore, does it take time to get a saccade under way, but it also takes time to complete it. The saccadic movements required for ordinary reading are usually short and very rapid. If the printed material is held at a reading distance of one foot from the eyes, a two-degree saccadic movement is roughly two-fifths of an inch along the line of print, or a distance of something more than five letters of ordinary newspaper print. The saccadic movement through an arc of one to two degrees takes 15 to 20 milliseconds. R. Dodge and T. S. Cline (90) have measured the speed or duration of longer saccadic movements. Their findings are presented in Table 1. The extent of movement is indicated

TABLE 1. DURATION OF SACCADIC EYE MOVEMENTS

Extent of movement	Duration of movement
5°	29 ms
10	39
15	48
20	55
30	80
40	100

(After R. Dodge and T. S. Cline, 90)

by the number of degrees of arc through which the eyeball has been moved. It will be noted that as the extent of the saccadic movement increases, the magnitude of the increment in duration of movement decreases. For the same individual and the same extent of movement, it is reported that the duration is nearly though not perfectly constant. A reader cannot voluntarily control the speed of the saccadic movement, even though he can make a saccadic movement at will by looking from one object to another. This fact is of great importance in evaluating the experiments on the change in the functions of the visual mechanism after prolonged activity. It is not possible by "consciously driving oneself" to modify certain aspects of the reading pattern even if, for example, the subject might wish to compensate for "fatigue" by increased exertion.

Sensations of movement related to impulses initiated in receptors or sense organs in the eye muscles themselves and in the tissues of the eyeball and its surrounding structures are very slight and give no reliable indication of when the eye is still and when it is moving. This is especially true of very short and rapid movements; the saccades are only imperfectly felt by the reader if at all. In fact, the reader is not able to count the number of saccadic movements he makes while reading a line of print.

Regressive movements are a special instance of saccadic movements. They have the same characteristics as the more usual interfixation saccades except that the corrective saccades are, of course, made in the opposite direction. It is assumed by most students of reading that these regressive movements are made when some difficulty or interesting detail is encountered while a line of print is being read. G. Fairbanks (99) has demonstrated that certain of the regressive movements are due to misreadings of the line of print which are corrected by a second fixation. The comprehension did not "make sense," and the material had to be re-viewed. Even the expert reader makes a few regressive movements, especially toward the beginning of the line after the long return sweep. The number of regressive movements made per line, however, typically decreases during school years with the age and experience of the reader. The first column of data in Table 2 shows that the average number varies

TABLE 2. THE EFFECT OF AGE UPON THE CHARACTERISTICS OF EYE MOVEMENTS

	Age of reader	Average number of regressions per line	Average number of fixations per line	Average duration of fixation pause
IB	6	5.1	18.6	660 ms
IA	7	4.0	15.5	432
II	8	2.3	10.7	364
III	9	1.8	8.9	316
IV	10	1.4	7.3	268
V	11	1.3	6.9	252
VI	12	1.6	7.3	236
VII	13	1.5	6.8	240
Fresh.	14	1.0	7.2	244
Soph.	15	0.7	5.8	248
Jun.	16	0.7	5.5	224
Sen.	17	0.7	6.4	248
Coll.	18	0.5	5.9	252

(After G. T. Buswell, 53)

from 5.1 in young children to 0.7 to 0.5 in adult readers. E. Bayle (21) in a further analysis of the reasons for regressive movements has described six different "patterns." Two are of the nature of corrective adjustments; for example, she shows that regressive movements near the beginning of the line are related to the distance of the initial fixations from the edge of the line of print. The other four patterns are the result of the reader's need to examine clues to the meaning of the material being read and to indicate difficulties in comprehension or in interpretation of the text. Evidence is presented for specific word, phrase, line, or sentence "analysis patterns of regressions."

The number of saccadic movements that are made depends of course upon the number of fixations the reader requires in comprehending a line of print. The second column of Table 2 indicates that the number of fixations made per line decreases with the age of the reader. This implies that as the reader becomes more expert, the number of fixations required is decreased and that the perceptual span, or what is seen during the fixation, is increased.

The duration of the fixation pauses similarly decreases with age, as shown in the last column of Table 2. On the average, the fixation pause made by young children is about 660 milliseconds, or around two-thirds of a second. Among college freshmen, the average duration is about 210 milliseconds for good readers and 260 milliseconds for poor readers (5). It will be noted, however, that after a child reaches the age of 10 or 11 years, the duration of the fixation remains relatively constant at about one-fourth of a second (250 milliseconds). There seems also to be a kind of personal equation governing the duration of the fixation pauses. The duration of the pauses is relatively unaffected by the conditions which either increase or decrease the number of fixation pauses.

That the duration of the pauses varies less than the number of fixations made is shown by Figure 11. These graphs compare the duration and the number of fixations made in relation to the increasing difficulty of the material read. When reviewing these graphs, the reader should make careful note of the size of the units on the vertical or *y* ordinate. The graph for *duration* of fixations has only a slight slope, indicating that duration is relatively constant despite the increase in difficulty. The other graphs, however, indicate that the *number* of fixations and regressions increases. The graph for fixation time per line has the steepest slope because what change in duration does occur in relation to the

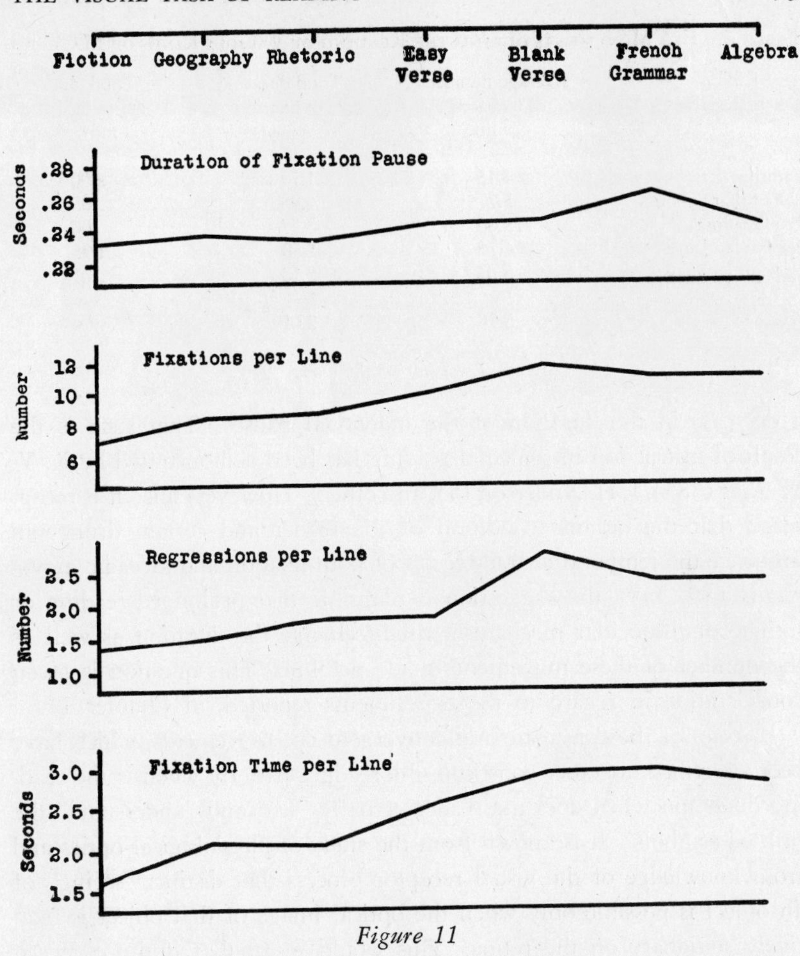

Figure 11

CHARACTERISTICS OF EYE MOVEMENTS DURING THE READING OF MATERIALS OF VARYING DIFFICULTY

(After M. Luckiesh and F. K. Moss, 203, from data by C. H. Judd and G. T. Buswell, 166)

difficulty of material read is superimposed on the increase in the number of fixations made—the latter factor being predominant. The above findings are supported by similar data shown in Table 3.

The general conclusion to be drawn is that fixations are rather constant in duration but vary much more in frequency in a given unit of reading. It would seem, then, that improved reading skill is typically related to a decrease in the number of fixations the reader requires rather than to

TABLE 3. EYE MOVEMENTS DURING THE READING OF VARIOUS KINDS OF MATERIAL

Kind of material	Average number of fixations per line	Total duration of fixation pauses	Total duration of saccadic movements
Familiar	4.45	1.70 sec.	.090 sec.
Unfamiliar	5.27	1.93	.105
Proofreading	15.00	3.77	.300
Native language	4.74	1.58	.095
Foreign language	5.04	2.18	.101
Average	5.78	2.01	.116

(After B. Erdmann and R. Dodge, 97)

a decrease in the duration of the individual pauses. That such is the result of instruction in remedial reading has been demonstrated by R. Y. Walker (385), I. H. Anderson (5), and others. However, since it is recognized that the organic condition of the reader and certain drugs can influence the temporal characteristics of both fixation and saccadic movements (89, 235), the suggestion is plausible that prolonged reading or fatigue of the ocular mechanism might change the duration as well as the number of these movements made per line. This question is given consideration in regard to the experiments reported, in Chapter 11.

If series of the conjugate and convergent eye movements, which have been described, together constitute the reading pattern, when is the reading done and when does the reader actually "see" and "understand" the printed symbols? It is known from the study of physiological optics and from knowledge of the visual receptor process that distinct "seeing" of an object is possible only when the optical image of that object is relatively stationary on the retina. This would mean that if the object is stationary, so must the eyeball (retina) be stationary; or if the object is moving, the eyeball must keep pace by moving proportionally. If one or the other of these relationships does not hold, vision is blurred, unless the movement of the eye or of the object is very slow. Since the line of print is relatively stationary in space and since the eyeball is held fairly stationary during a fixation, it is clear that the first step necessary to the actual perceiving or seeing of the printed symbols is done during the fixation pause.

During the saccadic movements the print is stationary, but the eyeballs are moving; therefore, the optical image of the print is moving across the retina. From what has just been said of the conditions required for distinct vision, it follows that saccadic movements do not provide clear images but, at most, only streaks and blurs which are of very brief duration because of the speed of the saccadic movement. These impressions are ordinarily not disturbing; in fact, they are overlooked or disregarded by the reader even as the momentary darkness during a wink is overlooked, or as afterimages,[3] or the blurring that is present during ordinary movements of the eyeball, or as the specks or fleeting particles (*muscae* or *mouches volitantes*) in the aqueous and vitreous humors of the eye are disregarded. That these entoptic specks or "flying gnats," as they have been called, can be seen when one is not "set" to disregard them is evidenced by the familiar observation of their projection as one looks up into the blue sky. Dodge (84) has reported, as the result of a painstaking observation, that gray bands of the blurred lines of print can be seen under certain experimental conditions. Thus, as R. S. Woodworth has remarked:

> . . . we can see what the retina has to show during saccadic movements, but . . . usually there is very little to see. (405, p. 591.)

There has been much speculation as to the lack of experience of blur as the eye moves in reading. The term "central anesthesia" has been invented to describe this fact. E. B. Holt (145) has discussed this matter, as have Dodge (84) and Woodworth (405). Whatever the explanation, it may be said that the reader learns to "neglect" or to fail to see what he might otherwise see during the saccadic movements, doubtless because such perception interferes with the main business of the moment—that of reading.

The average duration of the return sweep in reading newspaper print is about 40 milliseconds. The total time required to read a line of print or a whole selection can also be determined from a typical record. With these data the percentage of time required for each of the component movements can be calculated. Such calculation (78, 311, 354) demonstrates that most of the time is spent in the fixation pauses—90 per cent or even more. The ocular mechanism, therefore, operates with very high efficiency, for 90 per cent or more of the "reading" time is devoted to seeing the material presented and only 10 per cent or less of the time is required for the operation of the "seeing machine" of the visual

[3] A visual experience which continues or appears after the stimulus has ceased but continues during receptor activity initiated by the stimulus.

mechanism. Other factors which limit the speed and efficiency of the total normal reading process must evidently lie elsewhere, presumably in the central nervous system. The general efficiency of reading itself as a total physiological and psychological function must depend in large measure upon the nature of the neuromuscular mechanisms involved and the total action of the organism when reading takes place.

An investigation of the fixation pause raises the problems of just what part of the line of print the reader fixates, what is perceived during a fixation pause, and how much is seen. A particular record of eye movements can be projected onto the page of print originally read and the fixation pauses accurately located exactly when and where they occurred. This technique makes possible a study of the relation between the eye movements and the characteristics of the material that has been read. Figure 12 shows several lines of print upon

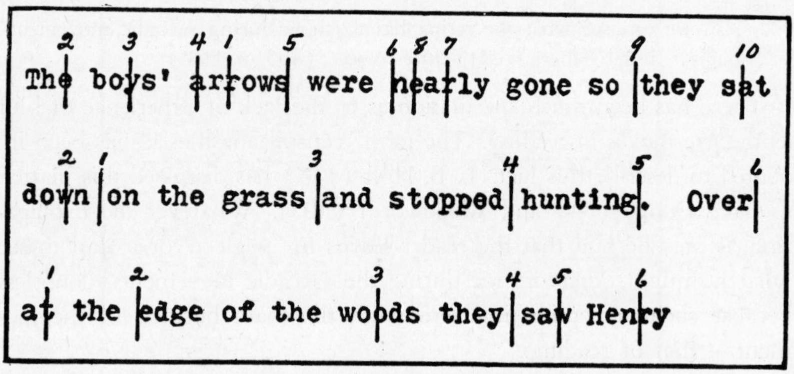

The boys' arrows were nearly gone so they sat
down on the grass and stopped hunting. Over
at the edge of the woods they saw Henry

Figure 12

LOCATION OF SUCCESSIVE FIXATION POINTS IN THREE LINES OF READING

(After G. T. Buswell, 52)

which is indicated the location of the fixation pauses made during a particular reading of the selection. The order of the fixation pauses is also indicated. It will be noticed that in the reading of the first line of print shown, the second fixation preceded the first; a regressive, saccadic movement was therefore made between these two fixations. A corrective movement was also made between the seventh and eighth fixations. A sample of fixation pauses made during the reading of newspaper print is indicated in Figure 13. (The numbers above the fixation dots indicate the duration of each pause expressed in milliseconds.) This is the record of a mechanically better reader; it will be noted that proportionally fewer fixations are made per line.

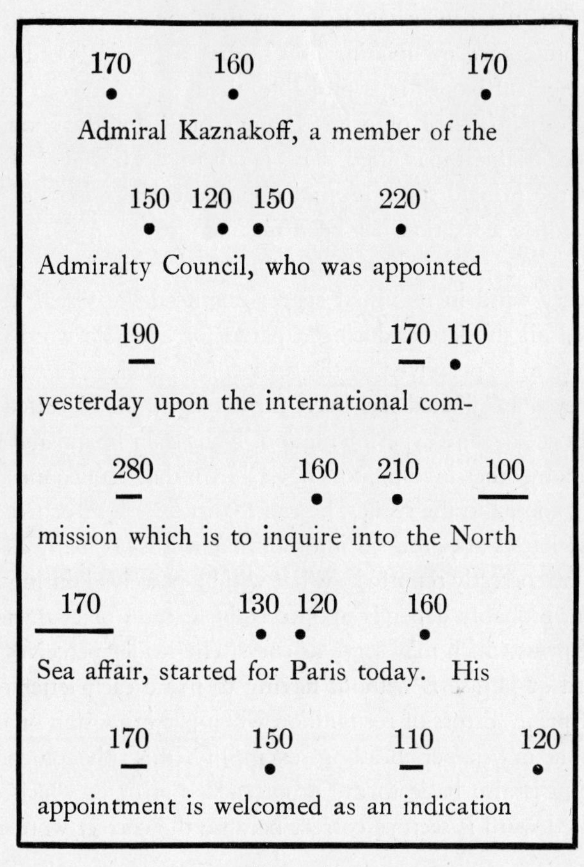

Figure 13

LOCATION OF FIXATIONS OF A RAPID READER IN SEVERAL SUCCESSIVE LINES OF A NEWSPAPER

(After W. F. Dearborn, 78)

More interesting, however, is the relationship between the location and number of fixations and the comprehension of the content of the material being read. There is the suggestion in these records that the reading of familiar phrases requires very few pauses. Proper names and titles tend to require more fixations than the rest of the prose, though the eye usually tends to avoid capital letters. The records show, however, that the eye does not always stop at the same point in space for every line of print. From the study of a great many eye-movement records (53, 78, 166), the conclusion is drawn that the eye seems to have no particular preference for fixating any special part of a word or type of letter or length of word. It is probable, then, that the exact location of fixation pauses in a line of print depends only slightly upon how the general space of the line is filled. This is not to say, however, that certain features of the printed space are not important determiners of the reading process once a fixation has been made.

The evidence clearly indicates that the eye does not fixate every letter or even every word in its visual space; nor need the visual mechanism have fixated all the letters during a pause for a whole word or even a whole phrase to be perceived by the reader. The analysis of what goes on while the eyes are fixated has been furthered by the so-called tachistoscopic or short exposure experimentation. Thus B. Erdmann and R. Dodge (97) and many other investigators have shown that if unconnected letters are briefly exposed to the reader, he can report only four or five of them; but if those letters are grouped into familiar words, as many as 12 to 20 letters can be correctly reported. What will be perceived during a fixation pause, then, probably depends upon certain features or characteristics of the line of print which may serve as cues. The reader perceives what the whole word or phrase is without having to fixate each letter or unit of the line of print. Errors of recognition when passing a sign or in a quick glance at a newspaper heading exemplify this phenomenon. This phenomenon is also basic to the proofreader's error in which an incorrectly spelled word is seen as correct because the correct word is so well known.

Several characteristics of the line of print have been suggested as possible cues which the reader uses to comprehend the printed material. The external or over-all shape of the words, the pattern formed by the letters of a familiar word, or the dominant letters in a word or phrase may give the reader the requisite cue to what he is reading. For example, it may be necessary for the reader to "see" only the few letters adjacent to the fixation point, or just the first and last letters of a word, to perceive what is in the whole space of the fixation. It is also true that the position of letters which project above or below the line and the varied location of the rounded letters and oblique lines may give to a word or phrase a distinctive appearance or configuration by which it is perceived without the recognition of its constituent parts.

The moving eyeballs as they make brief fixation pauses, separated by even more brief saccadic movements, serve as a device for presenting to the brain the nerve impulses resulting from the clear, brief exposures of printed material. To test, then, the significance of the cues listed above, the tachistoscope immediately suggests itself. This experimental device, as mentioned above, is an instrument for exposing visual material for short and known periods of time. Tachistoscopic exposure is typically so short that the reflex-controlled eye mechanism does not have time to move while the stimulus is present. Presenting material tachistoscopically is, therefore, like having the eye make a single fixation. Of course the eye seldom, if ever, does make a "single" fixation in ordinary reading, and what is perceived in any given fixation is affected by what has been perceived in previous fixations and, presumably, by what is yet to come. These facts have to be kept in mind in applying the results of the usual tachistoscopic experiments to reading.

F. Schumann (313), R. Heller (139), and W. Künzler (176) tachistoscopically presented unconnected letters to observers, with the instruction to try to grasp the whole series as if it were a long word. The letters correctly reported as having been seen were not closely grouped about the fixation point, but were more often near the ends of the series. O. Kutzner (180), G. Ipsen (153), and J. Wagner (383) performed similar experiments using very long series of unconnected letters. Figure 14 shows a graph of the number of letters correctly reported plotted against the position or distance of the letters from the fixation point (indicated by the arrow). Again, it may be concluded that the observer perceived the first and last part of the series more often than the middle part.

Familiar letter groups often appear in print, especially as parts of long words. An experiment by M. C. Wilkins (398) shows that when readers perceived a familiar letter group, they reported a familiar word having that letter combination. The words actually presented, however, were nonsense words such as Psychment Departology (reported as Psychology Department), talder powcum (reported as talcum powder), and Washout at Irvington (reported as Washington Irving).

The evidence from experiments (for example, 288, 409) on the im-

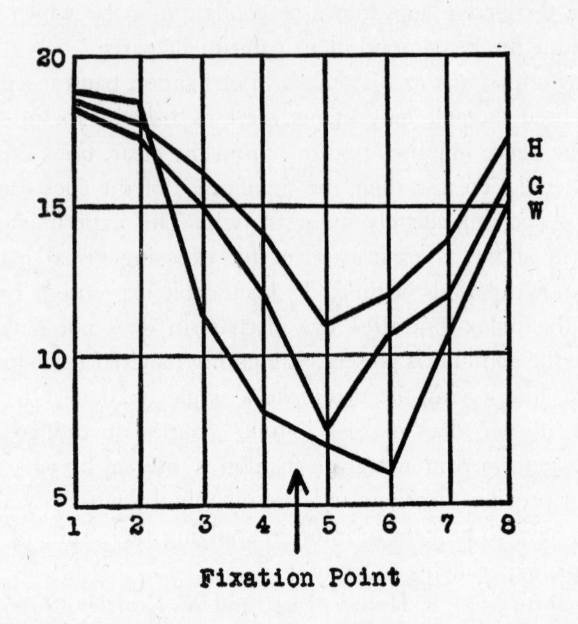

Position of the Letter in an Eight-Letter Nonsense Word

Figure 14

NUMBER OF LETTERS CORRECTLY READ AT DIFFERENT DISTANCES FROM THE FIXATION POINT

(After J. Wagner, 383)

portance of dominant letters in a word as cues to perceiving is conflicting. No general conclusions can as yet be drawn.

Kutzner (180) and F. Grossart (125) offer evidence from which it may be concluded that the words reported as seen by the observers are similar in general shape to the nonsense or actual words presented tachistoscopically to them. The printed material, however, was presented at a distance from the reader. When the tachistoscope was close to the reader, the general shape of the word seemed to be far less important.

Even though the experimental data are as yet too inconclusive to prove definitely the adequacy or predominance of a particular cue, the evidence does show that the eyeballs do not pause for each letter, nor is each letter directly seen during a single fixation pause. The inference, then, is that not all the letters are seen by the fovea of the eye (the central portion of the retina where detail vision is clearest). Some use is evidently made of the periphery of the retina; that is, some portions of the "fixated" space of the line of print must be viewed indirectly.

It is difficult to answer the question of how much a reader apprehends during a fixation pause, if only because it is extremely likely that more has been seen than will or can be reported. Cues from the print on either side of the fixation point may have been grasped which, though they are not reportable, are useful in the perception of what has been read during the fixation pause or of what will be read during the next fixation pause. Peripheral vision may also aid in the determination of where the next fixation pause is to be located. A question which immediately suggests itself, however, is how far out from the fovea the optical image of a letter can be and still be recognized by the reader.

The context of the line above and the line below seems to play a larger part in reading than is ordinarily recognized. W. F. Dearborn (78), in fact, observed that in the reading of short lines of print, as in a newspaper, this "vertical" perceptual span facilitates comprehension since material on the line above or the line below has an immediate bearing on the line being read, but that in very long lines the perception of the lines above and below may interfere with comprehension because the materials seen are not related. In this connection it has been noted that in the rapid reading by the blind of Braille (raised print), some readers move the "nonreading" hand over the lines not being read in a continuous wandering motion. A plausible explanation is that the nonreading hand serves as a substitute for peripheral vision. An excerpt from K. E. Maxfield is relevant here:

> To most seeing people, and even to many blind people, it is incomprehensible that anyone can *read ahead on a lower line with the left hand before the right has finished the preceding line.* Nevertheless, it is a fact that many of the best readers do read in exactly that way, although some of them do so quite unconsciously. One girl who reads with an unusually high degree of accuracy, speed, and comprehension vowed that she could not possibly read ahead with one finger because her mind could not carry two sets of ideas at the same time. A little later, when this girl was asked to read some fairly difficult material, she was discovered reading so far ahead on the next line with her left hand that her two forefingers met in the middle of each line.

The Uniform Type Committee found that only fifteen out of 1200 readers went ahead on the next line with the left hand before they finished the preceding line with the right. Twelve of these fifteen were in the faster group of readers, however. Whatever the cause for the change, the number of readers who follow this policy has increased noticeably. It may be that many more blind children are being taught to read with both hands, or it may be that there have been other changes in reading methods which could account for the improvement. In the 1925 experiment, which was modeled after the one conducted by the Uniform Type Committee, it was found that nine of the twenty fastest readers went ahead on the next line and that none of the twenty slowest readers did so. In a careful observation of the free reading of pupils in the fourth, fifth, and sixth grades of Perkins Institution, it was found that a number read ahead a short distance on the next line. Some read ahead only a few letters, others read ahead as much as two or three words. (223, pp. 50-51.)

The average fovea is assumed by Luckiesh and Moss (203) to subtend a visual angle of 70 minutes. The average macular area is assumed by these writers to subtend a visual angle of 12 degrees. These authors have calculated the number of letters of several sizes of type which could be included in the sizes of visual angle mentioned above; that is, how many letters of a particular type size are included in the particular distance on the printed page which is subtended by a visual angle on the retina of either 70 minutes or 12 degrees. The calculations for a reading distance of 14 inches are presented in Table 4. It should not

TABLE 4. APPROXIMATE NUMBER OF LETTERS IN A SINGLE HORIZONTAL LINE WHICH MAY BE SEEN WITH FOVEAL AND MACULAR VISION AT A READING DISTANCE OF FOURTEEN INCHES

Size of type	Foveal vision 70 minutes	Macular vision 12 degrees
6–point	6	66
8–point	5	51
10–point	4	45
12–point	3.5	38

(After M. Luckiesh and F. K. Moss, 203)

be overlooked that the eye does not always "see" or react to all that its optical or *physical* dimensions might encompass.

W. C. Ruediger (306) presented tachistoscopically to his observers a white card on which was printed at varying distances from a central fixation point an "n" or a "u." The card was 30 centimeters from the reader's eye — a distance a little less than the normal reading distance of about 35 or 36 centimeters used in the Luckiesh and Moss calculations. It was found that indirect vision was still satisfactory for perception of 11-point type when the letter was about 2½ centimeters (one inch) on either side of the central point. These data would suggest that the external boundaries of the range of indirect vision include 24 to 30 ordinary printed letters. That resolving power at these boundaries is not so good as at the fovea is indicated by the curve given in Figure 15 showing decreased acuity at different degrees from the fovea.

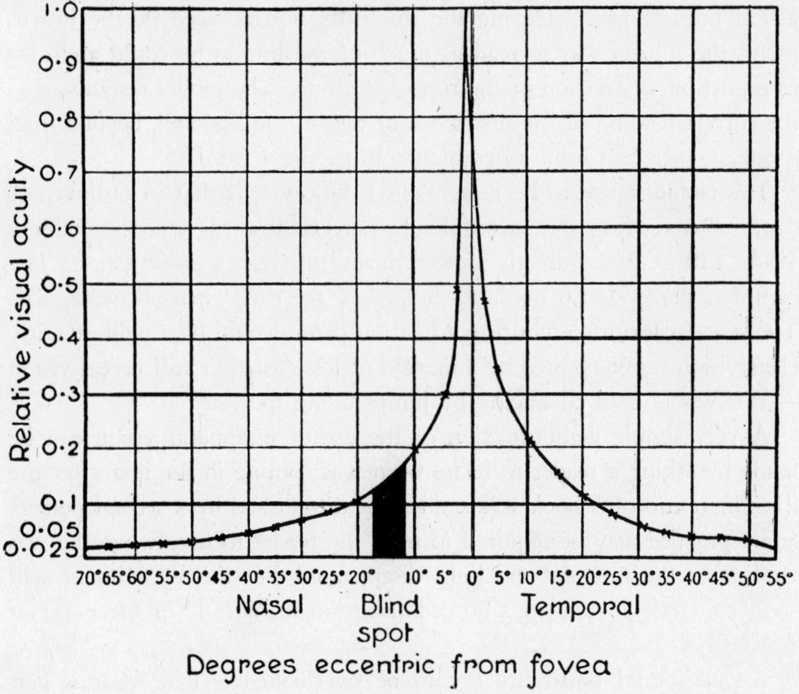

Figure 15

CURVE SHOWING VISUAL ACUITY AT SEVERAL DEGREES ECCENTRIC FROM THE FOVEA

(After W. S. Duke-Elder, 95)

W. Korte (175), however, found that isolated letters (for example, Ruediger's stimulus card) could be read farther away from the central point than could groups of letters. When groups of letters formed words, it was found that the longer the word was, the closer it had to be to the fixation point to be correctly reported. The conclusion may be drawn that the range of indirect vision is shorter for words than for isolated letters. This may be because letters in groups "mask" each other in some way, or the perception of one letter interferes with the perception of another. The fact that the first and last letters of a group are more often correctly reported than the letters in the middle of series supports this contention.

F. M. Hamilton (134) has more directly related the usefulness of indirect vision to the problem of reading by tachistoscopically presenting actual lines of print. During the single fixation allowed by the instrument, the subject was to read as much of the line as he could and also to report his impression of the rest of the line. The modal response was the correct reading of the first word or two of the line and, beyond that, a guess which had some resemblance to the next word.

The circumstance to be remembered, however, is that in ordinary or continuous reading the incompletely perceived words seen by indirect vision will be those directly viewed during the next fixation pause. The complete perception is no doubt helped by the earlier partial perception. The space of print seen during a fixation pause would be a field of fairly clear vision supplemented by a margin of less clear but still useful vision — this whole field advancing by jumps along the line.

A very simple demonstration of the use of peripheral vision can be made by asking a reader to recite what was coming in the text after the illumination on his book was suddenly extinguished by a second person. Some practice may be required to train the reader to note where he was reading at the moment the light disappeared, but this experiment will soon convince anyone that he ordinarily "reads ahead" of his point of fixation.

An additional possibility not to be overlooked is that what is perceived during any particular fixation pause may in large measure depend upon what has been comprehended during previous fixation pauses. It is the context of what is read and understood that gives meaning. If the reader is following the sequence of thought expressed by the printed material, he may expect certain words or phrases to appear and therefore needs only partial or much abbreviated cues for their recognition.

If direct methods for observing the perceptual processes of the central nervous system were available, much confusion would be cleared away and more definite knowledge of the reading process could be gained. But for the present we must depend almost entirely upon the peripheral approach to the problem. From the evidence at hand, it would seem that there is a "cue value" in the general shape of the words, but that the portion of print clearly perceived is more probably or more often the letters (particularly at the beginning and end of words) and familiar letter groups in words or phrases. It may be that during a particular fixation certain letters or groups are seen clearly by the central portion of the retina, while stimulation of the periphery of the retina may be basic in noting the general shape of the words or even letters to come. These indirect visual cues would assist the perception of words during the next fixation pause when that area of the line of print is directly viewed.

Some further ramifications of the problem of indirect or peripheral vision have been reported by C. W. LaGrone (181). He found that while in general a given subject or reader is more accurate in his perceptions in the right peripheral field (that is, right of the line of regard) than he is in the left, nevertheless it is the accuracy of perception in the *left* visual field which characterizes "good" readers as compared with "poor" readers. Good readers "prefer" the left visual field, whereas preference for the right visual field may be associated with disability in reading. This experiment supports in general the earlier findings of studies as summarized by I. H. Anderson (6). The significance of these findings is by no means clear. Further experimental observations and analysis of the right and left visual fields will be required to give full meaning to this observation so far as reading is concerned. Preference for the left visual field might lead to greater accuracy in the return sweep of the eye and possibly contribute to the habit of looking at the beginnings of words rather than at their endings, since the beginnings of words are to the left of their endings.

Of course, LaGrone may simply have the cart before the horse, to wit, that instead of good readers' having any natural preference for the left, they have learned better than poor readers to look first well to the left and then to the right (just as well-trained children do, at least in America, before they cross the street). If this is the case, we would subscribe to the recent comments of M. A. Tinker:

> The author misses the point that in tachistoscopically exposed material the long practiced habit of reading material from left to right is dominant.

> It is logical to infer that such a habit is more effective for good than for poor readers. (363, p. 103.)

On the other hand, could it be that children do have preference for visual fields before they learn to read? It is unlikely that there are any preprimary patterns that would account for the above findings, but the matter would bear checking. We may also stress a further point made by Tinker that

> a short exposure test of peripheral vision is not an adequate measure of peripheral vision as it operates in the normal reading situation where the successive fields of vision overlap. (363, p. 103.)

Such is the nature of the behavior which enables the human individual to read. This is the activity in which the eyes are engaged during the long and frequent hours we spend in reading in school and college, in our vocations, in learning what has gone on or is now going on in the world, in sheer enjoyment, or in fighting off boredom when no other occupation presents itself.

The reading pattern, however, is by no means an isolated phenomenon. It is rather a kind of work performed by that amazing *system* which we call the human organism. The reading pattern, therefore, will be modified, determined, or influenced in certain respects by the characteristics of the organism at given times and by its environment, even as other behavior patterns of the human individual may be affected. The characteristics of the reading pattern in the last analysis are a function of innumerable factors, many of which themselves interact in such a way that experimental isolation is most difficult. Reading may proceed at a different rate or have different qualities when done under one level of illumination as opposed to another. Since the characteristics of the performance are always determined by the pattern of radiant energy which stimulates the visual mechanism, the efficiency of the reading pattern may vary in relation to the format of the reading material, the print type that has been used, the arrangement of words on the page, the color of the ink or paper, and so forth. In many scientific and quantitative studies of reading behavior, it may be that the efficiency of the observed performance is in part influenced by the apparatus and procedure used to record the eye movements. Some recording procedures may make the experimental situation very unlike that of normal reading and thereby introduce "artifacts" in the data.

The present study is interested primarily in the "fatigue" changes which may occur in the reading pattern concomitant with or following prolonged activity. Our fundamental experimental variable, therefore, is time or continuous activity. If valid conclusions are to be drawn as to the influence or effect of time, then scientific methodology demands that the other factors which may affect the reading pattern be held as constant as possible. Such arrangement for control, however, depends upon knowledge of how these other variables may influence the reading pattern. Where such evidence is available, the present investigation has attempted to arrange the experimental situation so that the interference or variation introduced by variables other than time is held at a minimum.

The following chapters will review the evidence demonstrating the nature of the effect certain environmental variables may have upon reading behavior. Some studies of ocular behavior have been made previous to the ones reported in this book in which prolonged activity or work is regarded as the principal variable. (These are reviewed in Chapter 3, Reading and Fatigue.) Reading behavior has also previously been observed in experiments which have varied the format of the reading materials. (These are summarized in Chapter 4, Reading the Printed Page.) The efficiency of performance has been investigated in relation to the amount of light or level of illumination required for reading. (These studies are reviewed in Chapter 5, The Problem of Illumination.) The history of the methods of recording eye movements will be reviewed in some detail in Chapter 6 as a background for the choice of apparatus and procedure used in the present investigation. The general problem of fatigue, of course, is not to be lost sight of in the discussions of the variables which may be present in any visual fatigue study involving the reading process; it is clear, however, that the study of visual fatigue in reading cannot be made without a knowledge of these other factors. It is also hoped that the reader of this book will find a review of the factors which influence the efficiency of reading interesting and valuable.

Chapter 3

Reading and Fatigue

FATIGUE phenomena have been observed and studied in a number of experimental situations and by investigating many of the behavioral functions of which the human organism is capable. Functions observed in studies purporting to be of fatigue have ranged all the way from the changes that may occur in the physical chemistry of the substances of living muscles to the modification of intellectual capacity over a period of time. The time variable has been a unit expressed in thousandths of a second or a period of time measured in days, months, or even years in so-called chronic fatigue. For the reader who is interested in the general problems of fatigue or in the changes in efficiency that may occur in the performance of some particular task, excellent reviews of fatigue studies, especially from the psychological point of view, are available. See E. S. Robinson (298), covering experimentation from 1912 to 1920; Bills (29), C. W. Darrow (75), and L. T. Spencer (324) for work published between 1921 and 1927; a review by Bills (30) for the period 1927 to 1929; fatigue studies up to 1933 as discussed by Robinson (299); K. R. Smith (319), for studies done between 1932 and 1941; and a more recent publication by Bills (36).

Of particular interest to the present investigation, however, are the experiments that have been made to test the possibility that the reading pattern or some of its component movements may show characteristic changes when activity is prolonged or when the ocular mechanism has been made to work for very long periods of time. The human organism must do physiological and psychological work, no matter how it is defined, in order to read, and if fatigue is the result of work, then work output should be studied if the factors determining its efficiency are later to be understood and controlled. Luckiesh and Moss have estimated that:

> In the case of the typical adult reader, the ocular muscular mechanisms may be "started" and "stopped" about seventy thousand times during the course of an eight-hour period of reading. . . .
>
> If, for each fixational step or movement of the eyes, a person took a step in walking, the task of reading for eight hours would be equivalent to walking about thirty-three miles during a day's march . . . at army cadence, in about ten hours. . . . Obviously, if the visual task of reading is as severe as this analysis and analogy indicate, it is to be expected that the reader would experience fatigue and would demand frequent rest periods. (215, p. 511.)

Reading is a far more complex and involved task, however, than just the operation of a peripheral neuromuscular machine. It is conceivable that fatigue may change the ratio of operating time to "seeing" time in such a way as to devote more time to just the peripheral mechanics of reading. But, as previously noted, the calculation that in ordinary reading only 10 per cent of the time is required for peripheral movements as opposed to 90 per cent for fixation pauses certainly emphasizes the importance of the activities occurring during the pause. Even the fixation is not so simply determined as might be expected. It might be said that the time required for adequate peripheral exposure of material to the eye (so-called retinal resolution time) would determine the duration of a fixation. But tachistoscopic experiments have demonstrated that considerably less time than the average fixation pause is ample for the retinal process. All the fixations could be as short as 50 to 100 milliseconds (or, under strong illumination, only a few milliseconds) so far as the demands of the retina are concerned; instead, they are typically about 250 milliseconds. It has also been demonstrated that the more difficult the reading matter, the greater is the number of fixations made. But the evidence of indirect vision experiments shows that only two to four fixations would have been enough to cover the same amount of space. As pointed out in Chapter 2, the peripheral aspects of reading, particularly with regard to speed, may be governed by such factors as immediate understanding and general comprehension. Both the retina and the extrinsic eye muscles are capable of greater speed of performance than they customarily show during reading.

The reading pattern, therefore, is more than just a series of eye movements. It is an objective indication of work being done by an organism which is performing activities ordinarily called "psychological" as well as "physiological." Any alterations in the peripheral pattern of recorded eye movements over a period of time or during prolonged activity may be taken as indicative of changes in the efficiency of reading. Fatigue studies have been made of the saccadic movements of the eyeball, of the whole reading pattern, and of certain ocular movements which may occur while reading is done without necessarily being part of the reading pattern itself. The majority of the latter studies have been concerned with the relation of blinking movements to the work done in reading or other visual tasks.

The investigations of saccadic movements may first be reviewed here because this type of movement is one of the primary components of the reading pattern. Also, modifications observed in saccadic movements offer a convenient measure of the efficiency of the extrinsic ocular mechanisms which move the eyeballs and of the mechanisms which, after prolonged activity, may change in function regardless of the factors, central or peripheral, which determine the observed modifications.

Dodge (86) presents evidence of a breakdown in the saccadic movements following prolonged, continuous activity. The subject was required to move his eyes horizontally through an arc of 60 degrees, fixating alternately two knitting needles placed 30 degrees on either side of the primary line of regard. A record was made by a point of light reflected from the cornea of the subject's eye onto a moving photographic plate. The light ray was regularly interrupted by an alternating current circuit; thus the record line was a series of dashes, each representing one phase of the alternation, a time interval of about eight-thousandths of a second. Four samples of the continuous record are shown in Figure 16: a portion from the beginning, two in the middle of the period of continuous activity, and a sample at the end just before the breakdown in performance.

To quote from Dodge's discussion of this record:

> The succession of eye-movements in the records that are here reproduced was as rapid as practicable with subjectively adequate successive fixation of the two fixation marks. Some of the more characteristic fatigue phenomena which they show are: (1) The speed of movement becomes less toward the end of the series; (2) the fixations become less accurate; (3) and finally

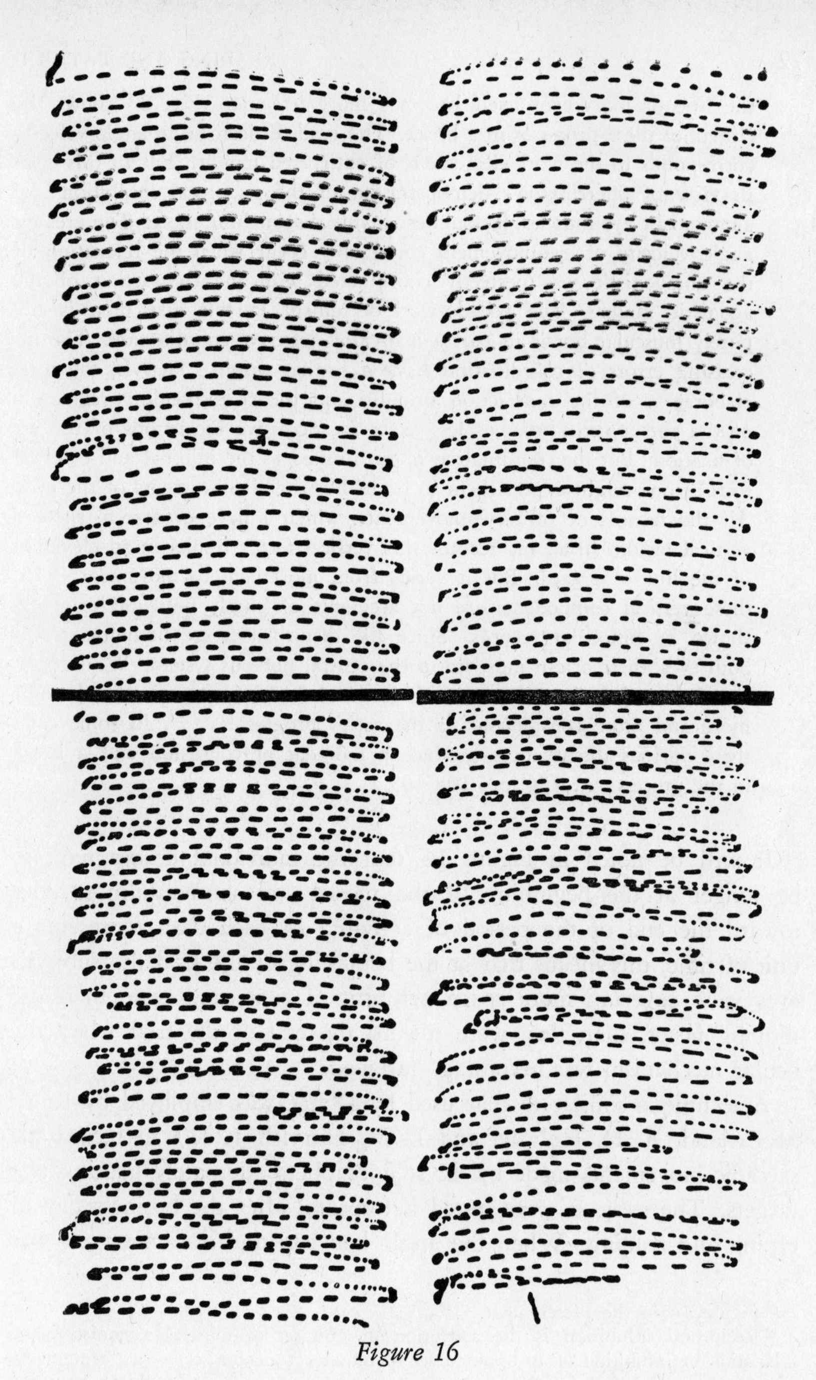

Figure 16

SAMPLES FROM THE CONTINUOUS RECORD OF ALTERNATE FIXATIONS

(After R. Dodge, 86)

> the line of movement itself becomes more irregular. Fig. 2[1] shows the climax of these processes in a break. The gradual decrease in angle velocity corresponds to the work decrement of extirpated muscle. But in this case, in view of Sherrington's demonstration of the reciprocal inhibition[2] of antagonistic eye-muscles, it doubtless involves something more. The greatest angle velocity of eye-movement could only occur when the relaxation of the antagonistic was perfectly coördinated with the contraction of the agonistic muscle. The pseudo-work-decrement in this case then is not purely muscular but is in part a matter of defective coördination. The increasing errors of coördination have a similar origin. That is, the total elaboration of the contraction impulse and the corresponding relaxation of the antagonistic becomes less exact in successive repetitions of the act of fixation. But the coördination is not limited to the internal and external recti as one might expect them to be in horizontal movements of the eyes. All the records of 60″ eye-movements, which I have ever seen, show a vertical factor. In all my records this vertical factor results in an elevation of the line of regard. But it varies from movement to movement. That these vertical components are not accidents of purely muscular origin is shown by binocular records. Since the disturbances are homologous for both eyes, their origin must lie in the central nervous system. While occasional gross disturbances occur early in the series of movements, they become more and more conspicuous as the series progresses. . . . In some cases these various disturbances produce a moment of confusion and a break in the process . . . (86, pp. 108-109.)

It will be noted in Figure 16 that the individual dashes tend to be longer at the beginning of the record and shorter, almost dots, toward the end of the period of activity. As each dash represents a unit of time, this means that at the beginning of the trial the subject's eyes were covering more space per unit of time, and were therefore moving faster, than they were toward the end of the trial when the ocular mechanism was becoming "fatigued."

A technique similar to that used by Dodge was employed by R. A. McFarland, A. H. Holway, and L. M. Hurvich (227) to record the saccadic movements made by 42 stenographers alternately fixating two targets. The subjects were tested before and after the business day of typing and reading. When the angle between the fixation targets was

[1] Figure 16 in the present text.

[2] Reciprocal inhibition is the activation of one set of muscles (agonists) and relaxation or inhibition of an opposed set of muscles (antagonists) — a phenomenon of nervous innervation for the efficient execution of a movement involving opposing sets of muscles.

15 degrees, no significant[3] differences were found between the speed of performance in the morning and in the evening. The angle was then increased to 30 degrees. The results of this experimental situation suggest that the saccadic movements were slower in the evening than in the morning, with group difference in performance not so great as individual differences. These experimenters, however, question the sensitivity or precision of the recording procedure:

> It is our belief that . . . the apparatus we used was not sufficiently sensitive to record the changes in frequency and amplitude of the binocular vergence tremors occasioned by prolonged periods of sustained visual work. (227, p. 137.)

H. Specht (323) recorded the eye movements of truck drivers before and after their driving hours to determine whether the speed of the saccadic movement varied with the number of working hours. The time required to make a saccadic movement was found to be significantly longer in men who had driven nine or ten hours than in men who had not driven at all since sleeping. Errors in fixation were also more frequent. The ability to maintain the fastest rhythm of eye movements was poorest in men who had driven the longest.

W. R. Miles (237) and W. R. Miles and H. R. Laslett (249) have observed similar changes in the saccadic performance of subjects who were very sleepy or had been deprived of sleep for 66 hours. The subjects were required to fixate alternately two dots horizontally arranged 40 degrees apart.

> . . . The speed of saccadic eye-movement under these conditions was about 30 per cent slower than the average for comparable subjects on the same eye test, but was not so slow as to interfere seriously with vision.
> . . . The subjective condition of sleepiness modified the visual fixations more profoundly than it did the eye-movement velocity.
> . . . Corrective movements for fixation were larger and less exact in the sleepy individual than is normal, and double corrective movements even in the same direction were sometimes found to be present.

[3] The word "significant" is here used not in its ordinary sense of important or consequential, but as a statistical term meaning that a difference or change (either increase or decrease as the case may be) can be statistically demonstrated as probably due to circumstances other than mere chance variations. Depending upon the standards one requires, this demonstration of a significant change is tantamount to regarding the difference or change as due to something other than chance, which "something other" may be sought for among the factors operating in the experimental situation. In any particular instance these causal factors are assumed to be the variables of the experiment. Differences not demonstrated to be significant are regarded as due to chance — the variation to be expected in a group of individuals.

> . . . Wavering of fixation and slow drifting of the eye, to the right or left, during supposed fixation, was characteristic behavior for the sleepy men. Since eye-movements themselves remain fairly adequate, it is assumed that the difficulty with fixation is due to retinal or central changes. (249, p. 12.)

> . . . the motor apparatus may continue functioning or activity may even be initiated in it during sleep. The visual areas rather than the oculo-motor nuclei are first to succumb. . . . a subject, although strongly motivated to remain awake, went to sleep during the eye movement test. The eyes remained open for a few seconds, the typical saccadic movements which had been very slow now changed into a rolling movement gliding back and forth as if following a slow pendulum, and all evidence of fixation disappeared. (237, p. 140.)

Changes in the speed and other characteristics of eye movements have been frequently associated with certain organic conditions regarded as being essentially similar to what is referred to as fatigue. Studies of the effects of alcohol on eye movements by R. Dodge and F. G. Benedict (89), Miles (235), and C. F. Scofield (314) have shown that this drug in certain dosage decreases the speed of saccadic movement. Miles has written:

> . . . while voluntary, so far as original initiation is concerned, the saccadic shifts of the eyes are withdrawn from such control in respect to their actual duration. This being the case we may expect saccadic speed to reflect changes in neural condition. Such results have been conspicuous in experiments with alcohol. (237, p. 126.)

The several experiments that have just been reviewed are concerned with saccadic movements induced by alternate fixation of targets at varying distances from each other. The results of these investigations are at least inferentially applicable to the present problem of the fatigue following reading, however, because a saccadic movement is one of the components of the reading pattern, even though its limits are determined by fixations which may be variously located along the line of print. A more direct approach to the fatigue of the eyes after reading is obviously to study reading itself. It should be noted that the tasks just reviewed required the eyes to respond in a manner that is not typical of any regularly required eye movements of everyday life. We spend years acquiring our eye-movement pattern in reading, and in so well established a pattern it is possible that work is less likely to show a decrement than in the unusual tasks of the laboratory. Investigations of the entire reading pattern have been made under conditions similar to those under which the fatiguing saccadic movements have been observed.

The physiologist M. Verworn (382) drew the conclusion, based on much experimental evidence, that the states of asphyxiation or anoxemia, narcosis (stupor induced by drugs), and fatigue are in many respects the same, differing only in regard to their histories. That is, the agents inducing these conditions or the events preceding these organic states may be different, but not the essential nature of the resulting organic condition. In most respects this observation is plausible. Other scientists have since supported similar views. A recent summary of the evidence available includes the statement:

> Every effect of alcohol which has any social significance can be produced by some degree of fatigue. Even with respect to intimate details of physiology, the two conditions appear to be essentially the same; and both are possibly but special instances of cell-asphyxiation. The two conditions are physiologically equivalent. (164, p. 193.)

Bills (32, 33) artificially induced a state of anoxemia (condition resulting from lack of a sufficient amount of oxygen) in his subjects by reducing the oxygen content of the air they breathed. These same subjects were also "fatigued" by the continuous performance of mental tasks. Comparison of the results of performance under these two experimental conditions shows a striking resemblance between the effects of the fatigue and those of the oxygen deprivation.

Because of this observed resemblance, experiments on the effects of oxygen deprivation may be included in this review for the clues they may give as to the nature of the changes in reading performance which may occur under conditions of visual fatigue. R. A. McFarland (225, 226) has reviewed and discussed investigations of the relation between anoxemia and the efficiency of performance of several ocular tasks. Of particular interest here, however, are the several experiments done by R. A. McFarland, C. A. Knehr, and C. Berens (228, 229) on the effects of oxygen deprivation on the reading pattern.

In the first of these experiments (228), 10 subjects, varying in age from 19 to 34 years and having no visual anomalies as shown by a complete eye examination, were tested in a Barach portable oxygen chamber. (This is a chamber in which the partial pressure of gases as well as the temperature and the humidity can be controlled.) Each subject was tested for an hour at a time in three experimental situations: under control conditions in which the oxygen content of the chamber was equivalent to that of the outside air, in 12.5 per cent oxygen content, and in 10.5 per cent oxygen content. The latter two experimental conditions correspond respectively to about 13,500 feet and 18,000 feet above sea level. In each situation, the subjects read six paragraphs, and during the reading their eye movements were photographically recorded. The first two paragraphs were read 15 minutes after the subject entered the chamber, the second pair after half an hour, and the third at the end of an hour.

The 10 subjects as a group showed a significant increase in the average time required for reading six lines of print. At the end of the experimental trial individual scores were wider apart than they were for the first control conditions; that is, the variability of the group increased. The subjects who were the fastest readers of the group under control conditions tended to keep their relative positions under diminished oxygen conditions. The increase in the number of fixations was slight but significant in the third experimental situation. The number of regressions per line showed no change for the group. The individuals tended to maintain their same relative positions in the group of regression scores in all three experimental conditions. The binocular adjustments (vergence movements) at the beginning and end of lines showed a slight decrease in amplitude, with a slight increase in the variability of the group and less tendency for the individuals to maintain their relative positions. The same is true for the binocular adjustments during the first fixation. The average binocular adjustment during all fixations significantly decreased in both diminished oxygen conditions, with, however, individual rank orders maintained. Qualitative changes in the record were evident as a decrease in the precision of movement and in the maintenance of fixations. Rhythmical wavering or nystagmoid movements appeared in most of the records in varying amounts. Sample records are shown in Figure 17. Ratings on comprehension of material read showed a decline, but poor comprehension was not evident until the third experimental situation.

The procedure of the above experiment was repeated (229) with a control group of eight normal subjects and an experimental group of 12 patients whose ocular examination gave evidence of refractive errors, phoria (a latent, abnormal imbalance in the action of the muscles moving the eyeballs), and heterotropias (apparent "cross-eyedness" or

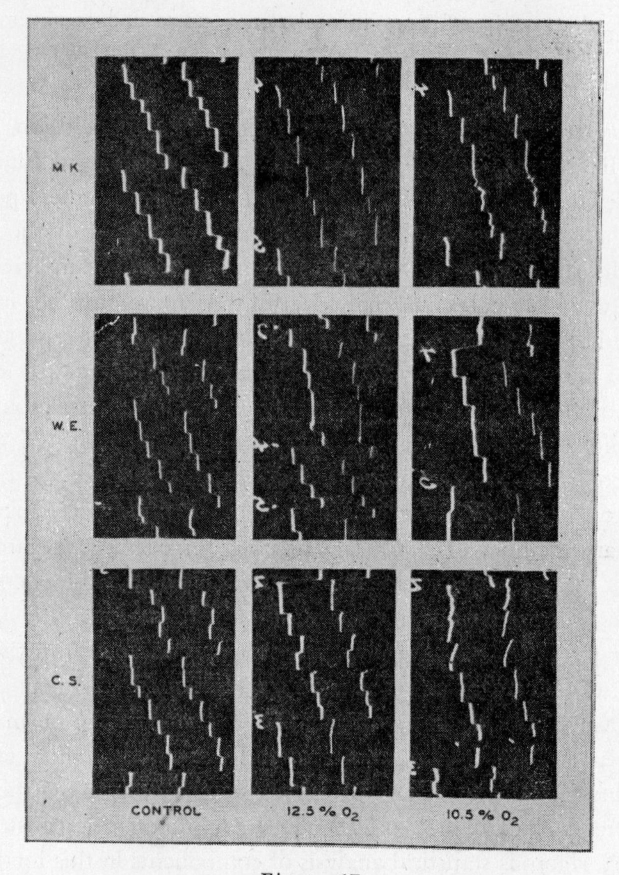

Figure 17

SAMPLE RECORDS OF EYE MOVEMENTS UNDER CONDITIONS OF ANOXEMIA

(After R. A. McFarland, C. A. Knehr, and C. Berens, 229)

"wall-eyedness") beyond the normal range. The refractive properties, characteristics of muscle balance, and so forth, of the normal eye are not precise or exact, but may be expected to vary within a certain range; the ocular deviations of these 12 patients were beyond that range in any particular case. The results of this experiment corroborate those of the previous experiment, except that the accentuation of reading anomalies was greater for the experimental than for the control group.

From both experiments it was concluded that:

> The decrease in efficiency in ocular movements under anoxemia is attributed to the diminished amount of oxygen being delivered to the nervous tissue. (228, p. 24.)

There is no direct evidence in the experiment for this conclusion, but it is the most likely one to draw in view of the experimental procedures.

In reviewing the results of these studies, the experimenters point out that, in the case of some of the component movements of the reading pattern, the statistical mean of the group indicated the same changes as did the data of any particular individual in the group. In other instances, however, the behavior of the individual scores is not best represented by the group means, since the individual variations acted in such a way as to cancel out each other's influence on the calculation of the group mean. The validity of this opinion depends to some extent upon what fatigue is considered to be. If fatigue is a particular condition of the organism having properties or characteristics peculiar to itself wherever found, then the ordinary methods of statistical analysis (for example, regarding the average or mean as the most representative indication of the phenomenon under observation) are appropriate in fatigue studies. If, however, fatigue is just a generic term referring to circumstances which depend upon the characteristics of the individual's total organic makeup, then much valuable evidence as to the nature of fatigue may be masked or completely lost unless statistical methods are used which take into account individual variation. For reasons given in Chapter 1 the present writers prefer to treat the term "fatigue" as a descriptive construct, and therefore a rigorous statistical analysis of components in this total pattern is all the more important.

If the physiological conditions of narcosis, anoxemia, and "fatigue" are as similar as they have been suggested to be, the experimental results derived under the two former conditions should be expected to support or corroborate the changes in the reading pattern observed under conditions of prolonged activity. In the experiments which have been done by a number of investigators, several procedures have been used in the attempt to induce the fatigued condition in relation to which changes in the reading behavior may be studied. In some experiments the individual was "fatigued" by other work and then required to read; in others, the individual was simply required to read for a prolonged period of time. It might almost be said that some experimental situations were set up so as to measure the effects of fatigue *on* the reading pattern, and others to measure the effects of fatigue *in* the reading pattern. For purposes of review, it is convenient to distinguish experiments which required the subjects to read after at least a subjective condition of fatigue had been induced by exercise and by depriving the experimental readers of sleep, from experiments which assigned various visual tasks or exercises at the conclusion of which reading performance was measured, and from experiments in which the "fatiguing" task itself was reading.

J. E. Lebensohn (187) reports that during pathologic sleep (for example, in lethargic encephalitis), vision is blurred and often double (diplopia), the eyelids droop (ptosis), the pupils frequently tend to be abnormally dilated (mydriasis), and the convergence mechanism may be paralyzed or impaired. He reports further that during prolonged vigil patients complain of itchiness, burning, dryness, and grittiness about the eyes, all of which "feelings" are exaggerated by attempts to read. The eyelids are kept open with difficulty, and when they are closed the patient tends to sway (Romberg sign); the lids themselves become edematous (characterized by swelling due to infiltration of fluids from the blood); and dark circles appear about the eyes. Convergent movements tend to fail, and fixations become unsteady.

In an experiment by Clark and Warren (62) three college students maintained a 65-hour vigil. Visual tests during this time showed no consistent reduction or deviation in astigmatism, depth perception, or phoria. Every 10 hours the subjects read short selections from material that was easy for them; records were taken of the eye movements during this reading. Statistics for evaluating differences are not reported, but a study of these records shows no uniform change either in the number of fixations and regressions per line or in the average fixation time. Although the greatest number of fixations per line was made in the final test, there was no consistent change up to that time. The amplitude of the binocular adjustment at the beginning and end of fixation pauses and during the reading of a line of print remained relatively constant. However, the time required to complete the divergent movements at the beginning of the line was considerably longer on the final tests; the speed of the return sweep itself also decreased sporadically. The experimenters conclude that:

> Although there were certain marked changes in the behavior of individual subjects, in general, these changes were uniformly temporary and sporadic, rather than regular. . . .

> It is clear that the vigil was not prolonged to the point of exhaustion. The changes which did occur may be explained as a temporary failure to overcome the greater subjective threshold of attention and effort. (62, pp. 388-389.)

In the experiment just reviewed, the reading was done every 10 hours. But during the intervening time, the subjects were free or were given tasks to perform only some of which were predominantly visual. This raises the question of what the effect on the reading pattern would have been if the visual mechanism had been required to work continuously during the interval between tests of reading performance.

The trial period in the experiments by McFarland, Holway, and Hurvich (227) was only about half an hour long, but during the period between reading tests, a definite visual task was assigned the subjects. The general procedure of each of the several individual experiments was essentially the same. The reading material was from Form A of the Nelson-Denny Reading Test. From 6 to 18 adult subjects were used. Records of eye movements were made during an initial and a terminal test of reading; the half-hour interval between these two tests was spent in some form of visual exercise. At the end of every experimental trial, each subject was given a standardized true-false comprehension test. It was found that comprehension was good despite the rather difficult nature of some of the reading material. The indices of reading performance used were the number of fixations, the number of regressions made, and the time required to read 10 lines of the reading matter.

In one of the experiments, the exercise period was spent in the difficult and unusual task of making 25-degree saccadic movements at the rate of 90 per minute. In another, the exercise period was spent in making repeated convergence-divergence movements at the rate of 60 per minute with targets placed at distances of one-half foot and one foot from the eyes. In a third experiment, the frequency of blinking was controlled during the half-hour of exercise. The subject was instructed to blink or was kept from blinking either by instruction or by a lid-restraining device attached to the eyelids and brow. The results of these experiments show in general a small increase in the number of fixations and in the number of regressions after the required work. In the case of the vergence exercise, reading time also increased slightly. There was also a small increase in the variability of the group after exercise. None of these differences between initial and terminal performance, however, was statistically significant.

> Repeated trials for the same individual tend to show a similar pattern of responses. . . . The individual values for the three indices . . . have, therefore, been divided into two groups, one in which the scores increase and the other in which the scores decrease following exercise. Average scores for the two groupings have been obtained. This was done to determine whether changes in the same direction are statistically significant ones. (227, p. 117.)

In no case, however, were significant differences demonstrated except perhaps in the case of subjects who showed a decrease in number of fixations following vergence exercise.

It is the opinion of the present authors that the most direct approach to the problem of fatigue in reading is the prolongation of reading behavior itself. It is proposed that the best evidence of fatigue would be changes in the subject, whether in his responses or in his subjective feelings, which take place while the reading pattern is in continuous activity and the body in the typical position for reading. To the authors' knowledge the use of this approach has hitherto been made only in preliminary investigations.

Kurtz (179) required six subjects between the ages of 20 and 30 years to read paragraphs of 150 words at the beginning and at the end of a half-hour of reading. The cards used were printed in fine type and the subjects wore minus lenses (which increase the demands made on the accommodatory functions). During the initial test, the reading time varied from 19.0 to 28.0 seconds; during the terminal period, from 20.0 to 32.3 seconds. The decrement in the number of words read per minute ranged from 24 to 74, with a mean of 52.0 words per minute. This difference is statistically significant. It will be noted that the exercise period was only 30 minutes long, but fine type was used and the subjects wore minus lenses.

In another preliminary investigation, Dearborn (78) recorded the eye movements of one subject who had been reading proof for several days. Tests were made in the morning and again after a day's proofreading. There was no significant change in number of fixations but an increase in reading time, that is, a decrease in reading rate. In a second study, two subjects read selections of long lines and of short lines. With the long lines of printing, there was noted a progressive retardation of the saccadic return sweep.

> A study of several other records would tend to show that this increase of time is but a more marked instance of what occurs in a much less degree in the short lines. After a short succession of movements of decreasing rate, a fresh start is taken with a return to the normal or to an accelerated velocity of movement. (78, p. 127.)

The results of these studies fit into the general picture indicated by the results of the other experiments reviewed in this chapter. Evidence is perhaps not sufficient or conclusive enough to permit the drawing of definitive conclusions, but the implication is that certain changes may occur in the reading pattern under conditions of continuous exercise. These experiments suggest that the variability of eye-movement performance may increase. A decrement may or may not occur in the efficiency of comprehension. More time may be required to read a particular selection, indicating a decrease in the rate of reading. Not only may more fixations be required, but they may also be less accurate and effective. Saccadic movements may become slower, more irregular, and less rhythmical, particularly the return sweep from the end of one line to the beginning of the next. More or less exact regressive movements might be made; this type of movement, however, seems to be the least affected component of the reading pattern. All of the above suggests a picture of less efficient reading, a poorer adaptation to the visual symbols that are to be comprehended.

Study of the reading pattern focuses attention on the six extrinsic ocular muscles which conjugately or convergently move the eyeballs. There are other muscles, however, which may be thought of as part of the oculomotor system. Their movements do occur while the individual is reading, even though they may not necessarily be a part of the reading pattern as here described. Of these movements, particular attention has been given to the blink or wink, the characteristic movement of the muscles which control the eyelids. A blink may be defined (41) as a temporary closure of one or both eyes, involving movements of the upper and lower eyelids so that the pupil is momentarily hidden from view. Under normal conditions, both eyes close with each wink.

The movement of the eyelids, however, is not all that occurs during a blink. Miles (238) and H. M. Halverson and S. M. Newhall (133) have shown that coincident with the lid movements are certain movements of the eyeball. Miles used a photographic method to record the light reflected from the cornea of the eyeball and from spherical mirrors attached to the eyelid. Samples of these records are shown in Figure 18.

> . . . At winking the cornea moves upward from 10° to 15°. The upward movement is accomplished in about .05 second and the return downward in .11 second or longer. The corneal movement appears to be accomplished in rather less time than is required for the complete lid movement. . . . The renewal of fixation after winking is by a slow downward drift of the eyeball, not by a saccadic corrective movement. (238, p. 331.)

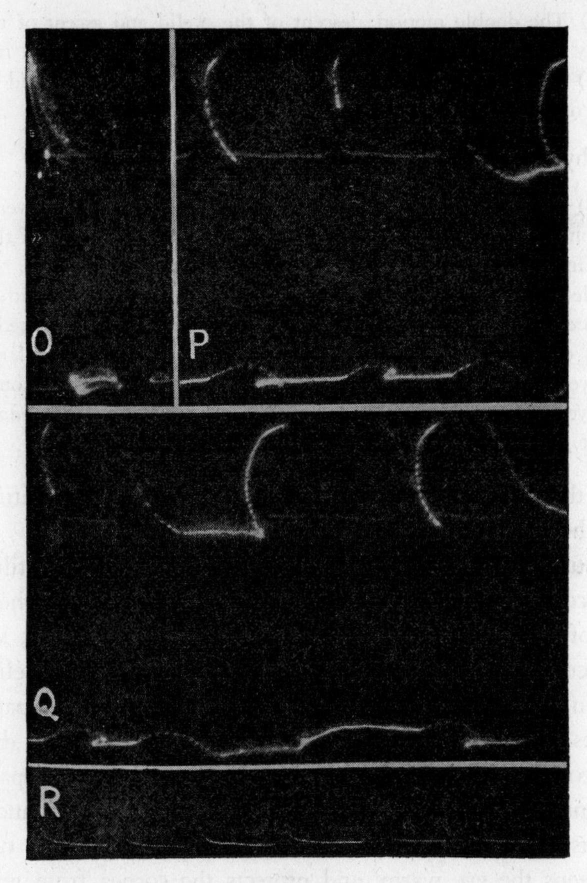

Figure 18

SAMPLE RECORDS OF THE ELEVATION OF THE EYEBALL IN BLINKING

(After W. R. Miles, 238)

Sir Charles Bell (238; see also 56) many years ago suggested, with his usual clarity of insight, several biologically useful reasons for this rapid, insensible, upward motion of the eyeball during blinking. According to the summary made by Miles, they are:

> (*a*) A stationary eyeball would not be well served by the eyelids that we have, because their edges do not touch completely together; therefore, certain portions would be left untouched.
>
> (*b*) The untouched area would be a place for the deposit of tear fluid and dust directly across the center of the cornea, so that winking in place of carrying this away would suffuse it.
>
> (*c*) The double motion, descent of the eyelid and ascent of the cornea, greatly increases the rapidity with which the eye escapes from injury.
>
> (*d*) The double motion facilitates the discharge of fluid from the lachrymal ducts. (238, p. 329.)

To these hypotheses Miles has added:

> (1) The external recti secure relaxation from strain of convergence and fixation; the corollary of this is a renewal of the sensitiveness of the muscles to changes in tension and in their response to visual cues. (2) More complete darkening and thus resting of the retina is secured with the result of renewing somewhat its sensitiveness to stimuli, and of reducing the effects of visual adaptation. (3) Winking serves for a general massage of the eye, promoting venous circulation. (4) By double motion winking, the eye avoids constantly pausing the tightly-fitting tarsal edges of the lids at points on the apex of the cornea. (238, pp. 329-330.)

Injury to the curve and shape of the cornea by the tightly fitting tarsal edges of the lids is thus avoided.

Many students have written about the general biological utility of the blink. According to W. S. Duke-Elder (95) blinking serves the fourfold function of protectively moistening and cleaning the cornea, increasing the intraocular pressure, aiding in tear drainage, and possibly eliminating the blurring of images during eye movements. H. M. Peppard (286) emphasizes the importance of the lachrymal fluid which is distributed over the cornea during a blink. This fluid, according to Peppard, has a definite antiseptic and cleaning action, improves the brilliance of the eye and its ability to reflect light, helps to remove particles of foreign matter, keeps the eye warm, and protects the cornea from wind. The blinking movement assists in the circulation of lymphatic fluid around the eye and enables the eye to move slightly so as to improve the tonus of the rectus muscles and allow them momentarily to relax their tension.

The rate of blinking has received special attention because of the suggested possibility that it bears a definite relationship to fatigue, particularly to fatigue of the visual mechanism. In these descriptions several aspects are to be distinguished; they are probably not mutually exclusive, but they have been different enough to influence the experimental approach to the problem of the blink rate. It has been suggested that the organism does work in blinking, and therefore it may become fatigued from the effort required. Blinking may be a mechanism for relieving strain and tension by producing a shift in the intensity of the visual stimulus and a change in the tension of the eye muscles. Or, blinking may be regarded as a function of the eye which may undergo change during prolonged activity, just as any other function of the visual mechanism is assumed to do. The opinion has been offered that the rate of blinking is a sensitive indicator of the condition of the "fatigued" organism, and as such may be used as a sort of peripheral behavioral "yardstick" to measure the internal state.

An evaluation of the validity of any of these suggested relationships requires description of the characteristics of the blink rate in the normal individual, demonstration of modifiability in various conditions of work, and, fundamentally, knowledge of the causes and determiners of the blink rate. The review to follow presents the evidence now available for this evaluation of the suggested relationships between blink rate and the fatigue condition.

E. Ponder and W. P. Kennedy (292) performed experiments to determine the normal blinking rate in normal human adults. The subjects read light literature for from 30 minutes to two hours, the first 10 or 15 minutes of which were used for adapting the subjects to the experimental situation. The number of subjects is not mentioned, but from the data presented it may be concluded that the samples in each case were large. The experimenters measured the interval of time between blinks (interblink period); thus, if the interblink periods were short, rate of blinking was rapid; if the interblink periods were long, blinking was infrequent. The interblink period data were assembled in a frequency distribution for each subject.

On the basis of these distributions, samples of which are shown in Figure 19, it was found that blinking patterns could be classified into four groups. The majority of the subjects showed J-shaped distributions; that is, most of the interblink periods were very short (frequent blink-

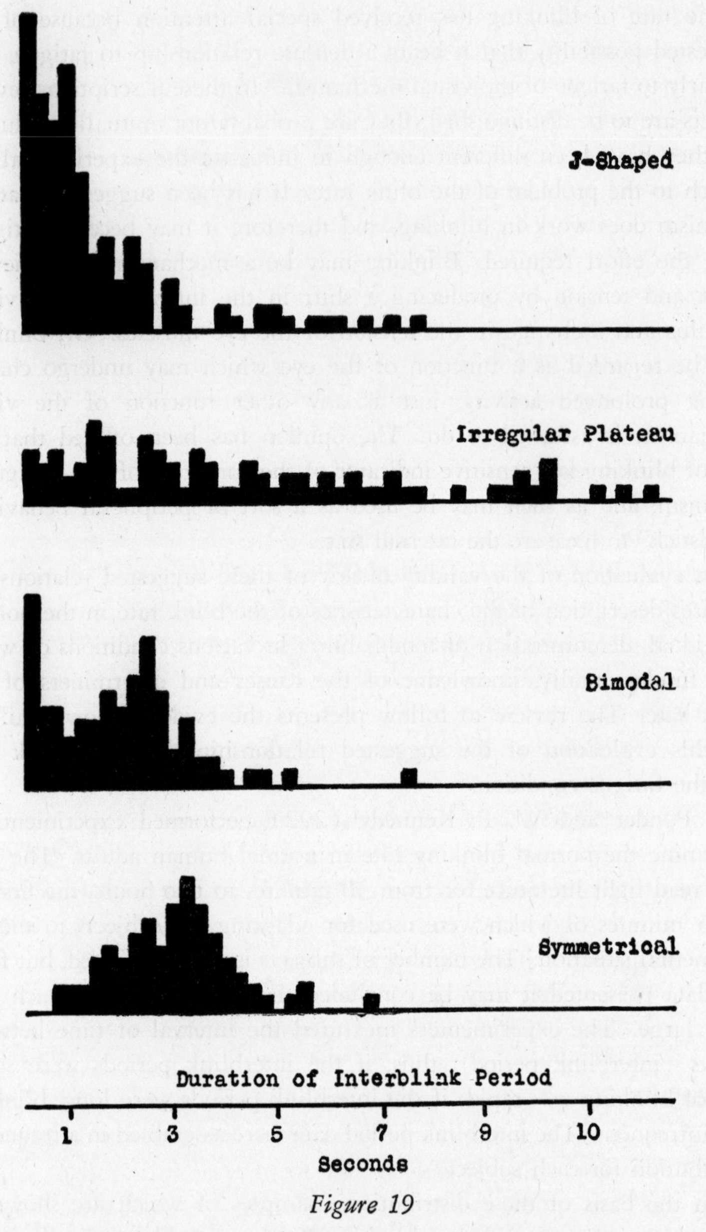

Figure 19

SAMPLE DISTRIBUTION OF INTERBLINK PERIODS

(After E. Ponder and W. P. Kennedy, 292)

ing) with a rapidly decreasing number of longer interblink periods. The distributions of the second group showed irregular plateaus indicating the presence of both long and short interblink periods. A lesser number of subjects had bimodal distributions, that is, either very long or very short interblink periods with very few of intermediate duration. The distributions for the least number of subjects were symmetrical, indicating that blinking rate was fairly regular but not rapid. The experiment does establish the fact that normal adult subjects do show individual differences in their normal blinking rate.

It was also found that if the conditions were kept constant, the mean blinking rate and the form of the distribution of interblink periods for each subject did not change significantly. J. Peterson and L. W. Allison (287) also found a high consistency in the number of blinks during a certain period of time. Both sets of experimental results, however, stress the dependence of this consistency on constant experimental conditions; for example, if reading is stopped by even a moment's conversation, the rate changes. The experiments of Peterson and Allison also show that the number of blinks made by a subject in a given period can be counted with a high degree of reliability by direct observation without the assistance of recording apparatus. This conclusion is indicated by the consistency of counts made by four different observers.

Not only does the blinking rate vary among individuals, but it has been shown also to vary with the experimental situation; that is, the task assigned the subjects may differentially influence the blinking rate.

In the experiments of C. W. Telford and N. Thompson (336), four individuals were subjected for five minutes in each case to tasks of mental arithmetic, reading, and conversation. The differences between the average number of blinks for each situation were all significant. These results were corroborated with 36 other subjects. The least number of blinks was observed in the reading situation, and the greatest number in doing mental arithmetic.

With 17 women college students, Peterson and Allison (287) studied the effects on the blinking rate of reading a scientific selection, canceling vowels, fixating a distant object, and fixating a near object. All the differences between the number of blinks made in each of these situations were significant. More blinks were made in reading and fixating a near object than in fixating a distant object and many more than in canceling vowels.

Though they do not extend the generalization to include various *types* of visual tasks, Luckiesh and Moss (210) believe that the rate of blinking is a function of the duration and severity of a *specific* visual task. The basic data from which Luckiesh and Moss drew certain of their conclusions were derived from five experiments using from 10 to 18 subjects. In the first experiment, the number of blinks was observed during the first and last five minutes of an hour of continuous reading under 10 footcandles of illumination. The variable of the second experimental situation was type size; the third introduced a glare source; the fourth required the subjects to fixate alternately two near objects; and in the fifth experiment, the subjects read while wearing various ophthalmic corrections. It is demonstrated that the number of blinks increased significantly as the duration or severity of the several tasks increased.

In the experiment by McFarland, Holway, and Hurvich (227), rate of blinking during each five minutes of a 15-minute interval was observed in 11 subjects who alternately fixated intermittent neon lamps 25 degrees apart. The data suggest an increase in blinking during the 15 minutes, which is, however, probably not statistically significant. The rate of blinking during five minutes in the morning as opposed to the rate during a five-minute test after a day's stenographic work also showed no significant difference. In an experiment by A. C. Hoffman (142) requiring 30 subjects to read continuously for four hours, the rate of blinking was significantly increased after an hour's reading and in the remaining three hours showed a further significant increase. This finding suggests that in the McFarland experiments the task was either not difficult enough or not continued long enough to affect the blinking rate.

The above-cited experiments suggest that the rate of blinking is influenced by variations in the visual task. That there are also other factors which may affect the rate of blinking has been disclosed by further experimentation and observation.

Thus Telford and Thompson conclude from their experiment on reading, mental arithmetic, and ordinary conversation that:

> . . . the decreased winking found during reading is not due to the mental activity involved but possibly to several other factors, such as the visual fixation involved in reading, the eye movements, and the fact that excessive winking interferes with the process of reading. . . . It is possible that the increased rate of winking found while working mental arithmetic was due

> to the excitement and emotional tension involved. One fact which suggested this is that subject A . . . was the most complacent and did the problems the most rapidly of the four subjects in the group, and he also did not show an increase in winking rate while doing the mental multiplication. (336, pp. 536-537.)

Miles in his discussion of the function of blinking in connection with perception in general has suggested that:

> It provides an opportunity for a new visual deal; adaptation is for the moment interrupted; stimuli are sharpened in outline and intensified in color. The more striking stimuli within the range of the visual field, with every wink, get a new opportunity to claim the attention of the observer. Negative after-images can be retained longer by occasional winking than by steady fixation. Winking which falls naturally between lines of reading fixations reduces the senseless visual blur. Finally, fluttering the curtains of the eye is one of the efficient ways of keeping awake and visually active. (238, p. 329.)

It is the opinion of McFarland, Holway, and Hurvich that:

> A high blink-rate may mean neither an increase in fatigue, nor an increase in difficulty of seeing. It may, for instance, be an anticipatory protective action. The eyes' indulgence in this normal function may simply enable them to perform their tasks more efficiently. In our opinion, *the normal functioning of vision requires blinking in order to prevent the occurrence of strain. Failure to blink facilitates strain, which in turn requires blinking to relieve the strain.* (227, p. 85.)
>
> The conclusion that blinking can be employed by normal subjects to prevent, or to delay, the occurrence of eye strain and perhaps other fatiguing effects leads to the hypothesis that a properly relaxed blink may be used as an aid to vision in general. The consequences of such a hypothesis may be subjected to experimental test. For example, if a properly executed blink actually does serve as an aid to vision, then the visual near-point for both young and old subjects should reflect such benefits. So, also should the diameter of the natural pupil. The visual acuity of normal individuals, both young and old, should accordingly be better under the conditions of relaxed blinking than it is under conditions in which blinking is restrained. (227, p. 87.)

The test made of this hypothesis was the comparison of performance in the several measures mentioned above during trials with and without "relaxed blinking."

In the visual acuity tests, the subjects were instructed to fixate a target either without blinking at all or after making a "relaxed blink." It was concluded from this study that:

> Blinking appears to be of little importance for young people (19-23) whereas, it occasions a marked facilitative effect for older persons (35 and over). (227, p. 106.)

The data for two subjects in the 19-to-23-year age group are shown in graphs E and F of Figure 20. The effect for the 35-to-49-year age group is indicated by graphs A to D.

In the experiments of these authors on pupillary size it is pointed out that when fixation is held for 15 minutes there is near the end of the period a dilation. This dilation follows a minimal point which has been

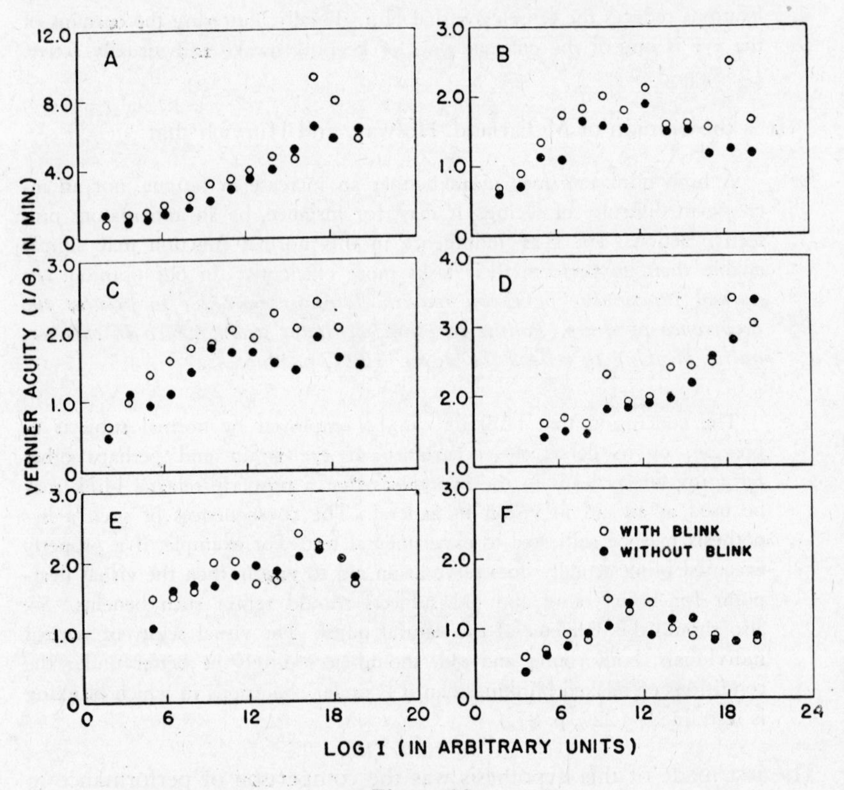

Figure 20

THE EFFECT OF RELAXED BLINKING ON VISUAL ACUITY

(After R. A. McFarland, A. H. Holway, and L. M. Hurvich, 227)

reached following the constriction which takes place as soon as fixation begins. Under all these conditions blinking is said slightly to reduce pupillary size. On the basis of this fact the authors see a support for their view that blinking may be used as a means of preventing fatigue of the visual mechanism. In evaluating this evidence, one should note that the graphs for the six subjects (Figure 21) show that the size of the pupil was slightly reduced by blinking in only three instances, remained the

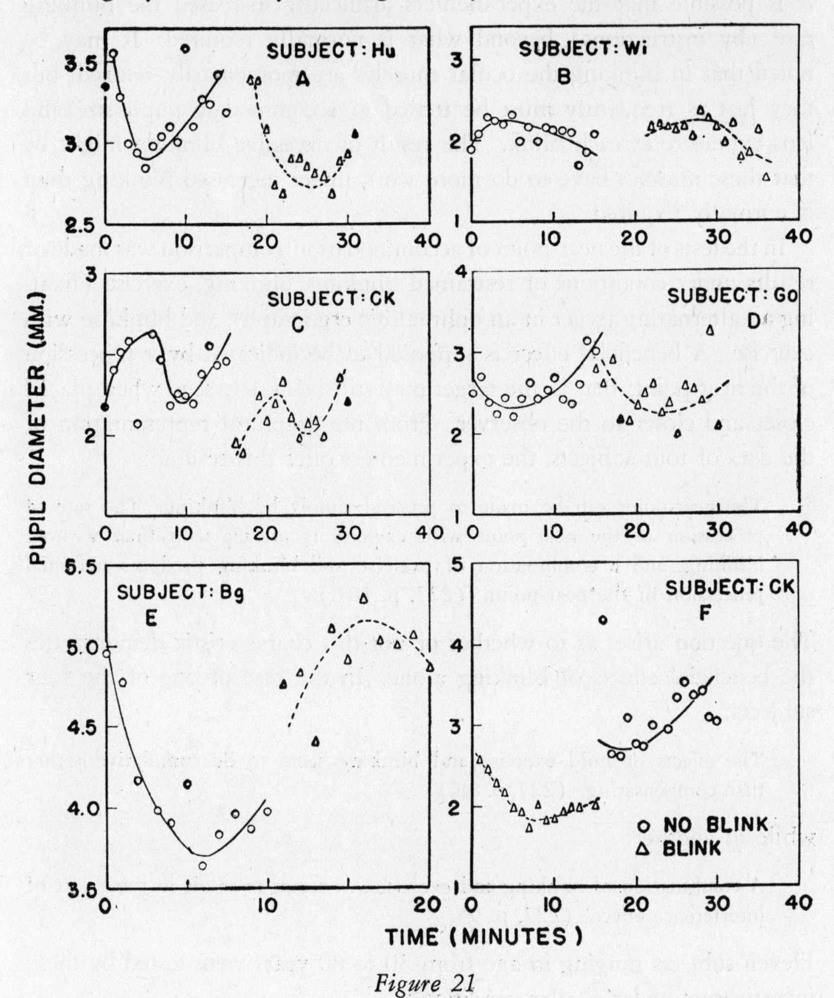

Figure 21

THE EFFECT OF RELAXED BLINKING ON PUPIL DIAMETER

(After R. A. McFarland, A. H. Holway, and L. M. Hurvich, 227)

same in two subjects, and was more dilated with blinking in the sixth subject. The experimenters remarked that:

> . . . an alternate constriction and dilation of the pupil recurred during the experiment . . . due . . . to lid closure which momentarily reduces the illumination, and relaxes the iris, the ciliary, and the extrinsic muscles of the eye. (227, p. 103.)

It is possible that the experimenters artificially increased the blinking rate (by instructions) beyond what is normally required. It may be noted that in blinking the ocular muscles are momentarily relaxed, but they just as frequently must be tensed to accommodate pupil size and lens curvature at each blink. The result of excessive blinking might be that these muscles have to do more work under increased blinking than is normally required.

In the tests of the near-point of accommodation, comparison was made of results under conditions of restrained blinking, blinking, exercise (fixating an alternating target in an ophthalmic ergograph), and blinking with exercise. A beneficial effect is supposed to be indicated by a procession of the near-point; that is, the target may still be clearly seen when placed closer and closer to the observer. From the graphical representation of the data of four subjects, the experimenters offer this résumé:

> The near-point can be made to proceed simply by blinking. The rate of procession of the near-point with exercise is greater with than without blinking, and a combination of exercise and blinking produces maximal procession of the near-point. (227, p. 101.)

The question arises as to whether or not this characteristic demonstrates the beneficial effects of blinking alone. In the case of one of the four subjects:

> The effects of mild exercise and blinking seem to be cumulative rather than compensating. (227, p. 88.)

while in another:

> A combination of blinking and exercise . . . seems to result in some sort of interference effect. (227, p. 95.)

Eleven subjects ranging in age from 30 to 60 years were tested by these investigators under similar conditions.

> An examination of individual differences in regard to the effects of blinking shows that (*a*) the most marked differences are observed in those subjects

> for whom the near-point originally receded with exercise, and (*b*) the effects of blinking are least for those who showed a procession under normal conditions. (227, p. 101.)

Samples of these results are presented in Figure 22.

These same investigators are very careful to require the subjects to use what they term a "relaxed blink."

> . . . the subjects were instructed to blink in a manner that would produce relaxation. They were asked to employ slow, relaxed blinks, and to move the lids as if they were on the verge of falling asleep. (227, p. 87.)

> During the first exercise curves . . . the near-point receded. This recession occurred even with the introduction of blinking. However, it was noted that the subject was not following instructions. The blinks were tense and abrupt. This subject was then aided (coached and prompted) to modify the original blinking from the tense, mechanical type of blink to the slow, gradually relaxing type of blink. (227, p. 91.)

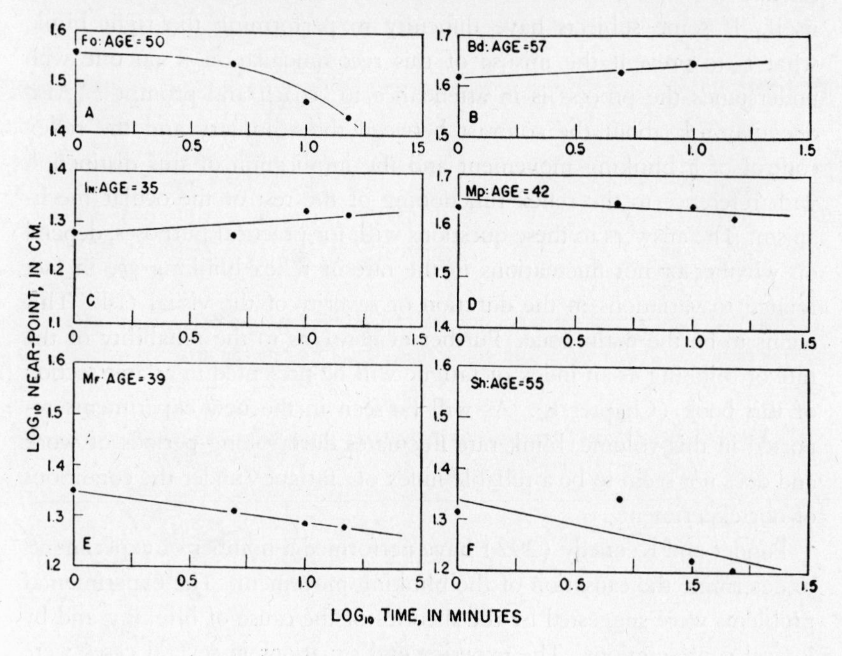

Figure 22

THE EFFECT OF RELAXED BLINKING ON EXERCISE OF THE NEAR POINT

(After R. A. McFarland, A. H. Holway, and L. M. Hurvich, 227)

> The subjects were instructed to fixate the target (*a*) either without blinking at all, or (*b*) to execute a *relaxed* blink and then to fixate the target. (227, p. 105.)

> It should again be emphasized that the kind of blink employed is very important. Helpful results are obtained when the blink is slow and relaxed, not when it is abrupt and tense. (227, p. 106.)

> These facts support the recommendation that blinking be used as a preventative measure with respect to certain aspects of visual fatigue. (227, p. 108.)

Since increased blinking is presented as a practical recommendation to be used in attempting to maintain the most efficient and hygienic use of the eyes in everyday tasks, it deserves careful consideration. In the first place, the question may be asked as to whether or not it is possible to preclude the conclusion that it was the relaxation or the attitude of relaxation which was the beneficial factor, rather than the actual blinking itself. If some subjects have difficulty in performing the right blink, what is to prevent the misuse of this recommendation if no one who understands the process is in attendance to "coach and prompt"? Also one may ask about the contrast between the voluntary and the reflex control of a blinking movement and the implication of this distinction with reference to the reflex functioning of the rest of the ocular mechanism. The answers to these questions will, for practical purposes, depend on whether or not fluctuations in the rate of reflex blinking are in fact related to variations in the duration or severity of the visual task. This seems to be the main issue. Further evidence as to the reliability of the rate of blinking as an index of fatigue will be presented in a later section of this book (Chapter 8). As will be seen in the new experiments reported in this volume, blink rate fluctuates during long periods of work and does not seem to be a reliable index of "fatigue" under the conditions of our experiment.

Ponder and Kennedy (292) have performed a number of experiments to determine the causation of the blinking movement. The experimental problems were suggested by the theories of the cause of blinking and by logical considerations. The experimental situations in several cases were very elementary, but since so few studies are available, all will be mentioned.

Irritation of the cornea as a cause was tested by noting the effect of smoke from a cigarette held continuously between the lips. The rate of blinking was accelerated. To study the allied condition of dryness of the cornea and conjunctiva as opposed to their more usual moist state would require observation of the number of blinks in a moist atmosphere with a minimum of evaporation and in a dry atmosphere with a maximum of evaporation. The authors found no significant differences in blink rate using as experimental situations a botanical hothouse and a Turkish bath. There was no significant difference from the normal either in the form of the distribution or in the mean length of the interblink periods when the superficial parts of the eye were completely anesthetized with cocaine solution.

There is the possibility that blinking may be due to stimulation from the movements of other parts of the face, an effect mediated via the fifth nerve. However, in some cases of bilateral removal of the Gasserian ganglion of this nerve, no significant change in blinking rate was noted.

Blinking movements may be related to retinal impulses carried by the optic nerve. But it was found that the rate of blinking continues unaltered in a wide range of light intensities and even in total darkness. Only transient effects are produced by darkening a well-lit room or suddenly changing the illumination. Of over 200 patients examined in a hospital for the blind, not one was observed in whom blinking did not occur, and in only one individual was the rate so slow as to be outside the normal limits.

Another possible mediation path besides the optic nerve is the nerves which supply the extrinsic muscles of the eye.

> The principal argument against it, and one which cannot be set aside, is that in blind persons in whom the eyes are either fixed in the cadaveric position or where there is continuous slow nystagmus, the movements of blinking occur at the normal rate. In such cases there is no co-ordination between the eye-muscles, on fixation, and no continued tension in the muscles which blinking might relieve. It is difficult to account for the blinking movements in such subjects as being responses to afferent impulses arising from muscular tension.
>
> ... We have been unable, indeed, to find any evidence that the movements are reflex at all in the ordinary sense of the word, for there appears to be no afferent path, destruction of which causes blinking to cease. (292, pp. 100-101.)

The validity of this argument might be questioned on the ground that the functions of all these nerves were not simultaneously excluded.

Concluding that no peripheral mechanism entirely or even primarily accounts for the blinking, Ponder and Kennedy suggest that:

> The movements appear to be centrally originated, and caused by a periodic and more or less regular discharge of impulses through the seventh nerve. (292, p. 101.)

It is known that in the disease known as postencephalitic Parkinsonism, one of the most conspicuous features of the syndrome is the almost complete absence of blinking. In this case the lesion is in the so-called basal ganglia, especially in the caudate and lentiform nuclei. This region is probably associated with the innervation of normal blinking.

Even with this hypothesis of the causation of blinking, the problem remains of how and why this normal rate is affected so as to show the significant changes which have been demonstrated. It seems that neural impulses arising from bright lights, irritation of the conjunctiva and cornea, auditory stimuli, protective adjustments, and so forth, must somehow impinge upon the neural center or centers originating the blinking movements so as to change the rate and other characteristics of the normal discharge pattern of the center.

But Ponder and Kennedy believe that a more general set of causal factors may be regarded as the modifier of the normal blink rate.

> In general all that is necessary to occasion a change in the rate of blinking is a change in the degree of attention of the subject, using the word in its psychological sense. (292, p. 102.)

The authors support this contention with the data from observations of the number of blinks made by witnesses on and off the stand in courts of law, men and women on streetcars, and men and women in study rooms. The general finding is that more blinks are made during an "emotional" or "tense" situation, and fewer during concentrated attention.

At its final propounding, the Ponder and Kennedy theory of the modification of the normal blink rate regards such changes as manifestations of mental tension [4] having no other convenient mechanism of expression.

> (1) A state of abstraction, "or, more accurately, absolute blankness of mind," is associated with a slow rate of blinking. The mental tension, as

[4] Should the mental tension of which Ponder and Kennedy speak bear any relation to muscular tension (28, 73), the experiments by H. Peak (284, 285) and by F. A. Courts (72) on the effect of "set" and tension on the eyelid response might contribute to the present discussion.

> we term it, is at a low level; there is therefore no necessity for relief through the facilitated path. (2) A state of intense, but internally directed, mental activity, such as when a mathematical problem is being solved, is also associated with a slow blinking rate. Here the "mental tension" is entirely diverted into internal channels, and again there is no necessity for relief through the facilitated path. (3) A state of mental tension which has no internal or external outlet, as impotent rage, anxiety necessarily accompanied by inactivity, or excitement which cannot be shown and expressed by physical movements is accompanied by a rapid blinking rate. Here the "mental tension" is relieved through the facilitated path.
>
> . . . we may mention that in persons or animals in which some other path than that controlling the movements of blinking is the most facilitated, a state of mental tension is relieved through that path and not through the path controlling the movements of the eyelids. (292, p. 108.)

It is difficult to apply this "release of mental tension" hypothesis directly to an experimental situation in which continuous reading is done. The ocular movements of the reading might be regarded as the facilitated path for release of tension. Thus, according to the above theory, the normal blink rate should not be changed. Yet the prolonged reading and activity of the eyeball muscles may cause a fatigue condition in the individual which might find expression in an increased blinking rate. It is even conceivable that the reading movements may adequately dissipate tension until it reaches such a degree that the rate of blinking is also affected. That care must be exercised in interpreting objective data in favor of one or the other of the above alternative explanations is obvious.

A convenient summary of this discussion of the causation and function of blinking may be made by reviewing the several theories discussed by W. P. Blount (41). Among the usual theories of the reason for blinking is the notion that blinking serves to distribute evenly the secretion of the lachrymal glands and to clear the cornea of foreign material. Doubt is cast on this hypothesis by the data of Ponder and Kennedy, which in their opinion show no alteration in the blink rate under the various conditions of temperature and humidity used. Blinking may occasion alteration in the tension of the ocular muscles and thus eliminate early fatigue by allowing momentary relaxation.

> The suggestion that the impulse to blink arises in the ocular muscles which seek in the momentary movement of the eyeball a periodic short respite from maintaining a constant fixation point, finds some confirmation in the fact that a movement of the eye to a new point of fixation averts the desire to

> blink if the normal rhythm is suppressed, but must be abandoned as a fundamental cause of the phenomenon . . . (95, p. 636.)

The fact that blinking rate is not significantly affected (as shown by Ponder and Kennedy) in anomalous conditions of the ocular muscles suggests that at most this hypothetical factor is but secondary, influencing blinking rate only in special instances. The hypothesis that blinking protects the eye from external injury would not by itself account for the relatively rapid rate appearing in some animals; for example, the ostrich has been observed to blink about once a second (1.1-second average interblink period). The contention that blinking guards the eye against continuous exposure to strong light cannot alone explain the apparently normal rate in blind animals and men.

Blount concludes that the above reasons are inadequate for a complete explanation of the blinking phenomenon. Observations of different types of animals indicate that blinking may be due to other factors in addition to threatened injury or auditory stimuli, or it may be a component of facial movements and postural adjustments of the head in general.

> Assuming the eye to be focused on some definite point, any considerable alteration in the position of the head will necessitate a readjustment of the lens. In order that this may be done, and to prevent unnecessary blurring of the image, the eyelids close involuntarily . . . When the eyelids reopen, a focusing of the new field of vision occurs. (41, p. 123.)

Recall in this connection the statement by Miles (238) that blinking offers "an opportunity for a new visual deal." Blinking movements may originally be the result of stimuli or impulses having a central origin. This type of theory would include the contentions of Ponder and Kennedy. Blount emphasizes the conceptual notion that the central stimuli may be the specific instigators of the blinking movements, but they themselves may be due to impulses arising from various nerve centers.

In much of the discussion of the blinking movement, the blink rate has been regarded as a criterion of strain, tension, fatigue, or similar phenomena. The implication has been that blinking is a peripheral indication of some condition of fatigue in addition to or even apart from being simply a mechanism which may be fatigued. It must be noted, however, that what has been experimentally demonstrated is only that the blink rate varies with the individual, with the assigned task, with the conditions or severity of a particular task, and in some instances with the duration or prolongation of a task. The rest is hypothesis. In the literature thus far reviewed, there is little evidence against regarding blink rate as a criterion of the presence or condition of fatigue, and equally little for it. Two recent studies are, however, more definite in results, one as to the reliability and the other as to the validity of the blink rate as a measure of visual efficiency. Tinker (362) has determined the reliability of the rate of blinking during reading as a measure of readability or the ease and efficiency with which material is read. He finds that as between adjacent five-minute periods of reading the reliability coefficients are "substantially high" — fluctuating, in his experiment, between .74 and .91 — but that when one five-minute period is separated from another by an interval of as much as 20 minutes of continuous reading the reliability is relatively low — *circa* .49 to .56 — and that the minimum reliability requirements are reached at the end of 30 minutes of reading. The inconsistencies in blink rate would obviously rule it out as a measure of fatigue in such long intervals of reading as are employed in the present experiment. Further, there are marked individual idiosyncracies in blink rate which would seem to exclude its use as a measure of either readability or fatigue. In this respect the earlier findings of McFarland, Holway, and Hurvich (227) are confirmed: Some readers maintain the same blink rate, some decrease, and others increase their blink rate as reading continues. Study of the scores of various individual subjects reveals even more inconsistencies, for example:

> Subject K decreases rather consistently, while H rises and then decreases, F shows little change for five periods [of five minutes each] and then increases nearly 100 percent, and E increases by several hundred percent. (362, p. 422.)

Bitterman (39) has produced experimental evidence of lack of validity in the frequency of blinking (as well as of heart rate) as indices of visual efficiency. Bitterman's investigation stems directly from a controversy between Luckiesh and Moss and D. G. Paterson and M. A. Tinker in regard to the best means of measuring variations in reading performance. Luckiesh and Moss have maintained that the speed of reading as employed by Paterson and Tinker is insufficiently sensitive as a measure of the variations in performance. They believe that the organism attempts to maintain relatively constant output in spite of unfavorable conditions and that this inner or "hidden" cost to the organism which involves expenditure of its resources needs to be measured. As a measure of this effort to maintain output in the face of approaching fatigue, Luckiesh and Moss have, as noted elsewhere in this volume, proposed a number of involuntary "psychophysiological" processes, such as heart rate, frequency of blinking, and peripheral muscular tension.

The frequency of blinking was determined by the action potentials from the superior orbicular muscle of the nondominant eye measured continuously during the experimental session. The experimental variable was the size of type, and it was determined that variations in the latter did not affect the frequency of blinking (or the heart rate). Because of the possibility that these negative findings might be a function of either the short periods of work required or the directions for speed given to the subjects, a second study using the level of illumination as the variable was undertaken. In this instance the reading periods were divided into eight five-minute intervals, and the frequency of blinking as well as the heart rate during the midperiod of the interval was computed. Findings were again negative, leading to the conclusion that the rate of blinking has little value as an index of visual fatigue or of visual effort.

As noted above, this problem has been further studied in the present experiments as reported in Chapter 8 of this book.

Chapter 4

Reading the Printed Page

THE immediate function of the movements of the eye in reading is to bring into the optimal visual area of the retina the patterned light reflected from the page and the printed symbols that are to be fixated and read. Print is the external focal point, so to speak, of the reading process; it is in relation to it that the reading is done. It might be thought that the characteristics of reading behavior, including its efficiency, depend entirely upon the reader's perception of what the printed symbols are or may mean. But this is to assume that the eye simply sees the printed symbols and that the nature of these symbols as print has no effect on the ease of seeing and bears no relation to the efficiency of reading. Paterson and Tinker (282), however, comparing eye movements of subjects reading good and bad typography, found that rate of reading, number of fixations, and pause duration are all adversely affected by nonoptimal typography. Thus a study of reading performance reveals that modifications in the format of the printed page occasion definite changes in the reader's reactions. In an investigation of visual fatigue, therefore, it is necessary to specify carefully the printed format in order to control the conditions of the experiment. Format, as well as other factors, must be held constant if changes observed in performance are to be considered as due to time or prolonged activity alone. This chapter does not attempt to summarize all the relevant work on the effect of the characteristics of print on reading efficiency but rather attempts merely to outline the problem and give some typical results.

Many features of the printed page have been studied for their possible effect on visibility or readability. Readability may be defined as the ease and accuracy with which comprehension of meaningful material takes place. The color and finish of the paper on which the symbols are printed have been varied in relation to the color of the type. The style and size of the type face have received much attention. The boldness and form of the type face have also been varied to study their effect on readability. The length of the line of print and the distance between the lines of print are other variables of printed format which have been considered. These several characteristics of the printed page will be defined and described as they are discussed below. For the reader who may be interested in the more general problems of printing, the reviews by D. B. Updike (377), J. H. Parsons (271), Tinker (346), and Paterson and Tinker (278) are suggested as additional source material.

Unexpected divergencies in experimental results still exist in this field. These differences may be due to the experimental methods used as well as to the uncontrolled effects of interdependent typographic variables. Among the methods most used may be mentioned the following: (1) tachistoscopic methods, which allow the presentation to the reader of words or letters, variously printed, which he recognizes or fails to recognize after a brief exposure. The time of the exposure in such experiments is typically under 100 milliseconds. This time is regarded as being less than the time required for a reflex movement of the eyes. (2) distance methods, which vary the distance of the stimulus card from the subject until he can just recognize the printed material or is just no longer able to discern the printing. The apparatus is usually a bench at reading height along which card holders or carriages may be conveniently moved. (3) a method, which is a modification of the above, in which print of various sizes is presented at a constant distance. This has also been widely used, especially in test charts. (4) measures of the speed of reading or reading rate, made on the assumption that rate is a function of the format of the material read.

Paterson and Tinker, for example, in their extensive investigations of the readability effects of various typographic variables, have often used this latter method. Since the results of several of their experiments will be discussed below, it may be convenient to describe their typical experimental procedure at the outset. The reading material has been taken from the Chapman-Cook Speed of Reading Test, Forms A and B. This is a test of short paragraphs; in each case one word is incorrect and is to be crossed out by the reader. Reading time for this test is 1¾ minutes only. In the case of any particular experiment, the material was printed in the format being studied, or a particular typographic feature was varied in Form A and Form B. In evaluating their method, these experimenters point out that:

> . . . demonstrated equivalence for duplicate forms of published standard tests cannot be accepted as valid except for the first trial. Experiments involving several trials and dependent upon continued equivalence in difficulty of duplicate test forms should be carefully controlled with respect to such variable practice effects. (273, p. 217.)

Therefore, rather than retest subjects with the same forms of the Chapman-Cook test, Paterson and Tinker tested a new group of subjects whenever a new variable or a new variation of the same typographical characteristic was introduced. Unless otherwise stated, these procedures have been used in the experiments conducted by Paterson and Tinker that are reviewed below.

The type faces used in printing have several characteristics, each of which may be varied in arranging the format of a particular page. *Style of type,* or sometimes just *type face,* refers to the design of the type. Various styles usually have traditional or trade names, for example, Old Style, Cheltenham, Bodoni, Roman, and American Typewriter. Figure 23 is a printed sample of several of the type faces to be mentioned below; they are listed according to their commercial designations. *Size of type* is measured according to the point system. A point is equal to .0138 inch. Thus there are approximately 72 points to a printer's inch. A point may also be defined as one-twelfth of a pica. The pica or pica body was the standard unit in the French system of printing, of which the American system that is in general use is a modification. The pica is now a 12-point type. It is also still used as a standard measurement, there being roughly 6 picas in a printer's inch. A type face is referred to by size as 8-point type, 11-point type, and so forth. Samples of graduated sizes are shown in Figure 24. Type sizes in common use vary from 6-point to 14-point type; the size of ordinary typewriter type, for example, is pica or 12-point type. The type face may vary also in boldness, even though it is of the

American Typewriter

Lorna Doone told me all about everything I wished to know, just as I questioned her; except indeed that point of points, how Master Ridd stood with her.

Antique

Lorna Doone told me all about everything I wished to know, just as I questioned her; except indeed that point of points, how Master Ridd stood with her.

Baskerville

Lorna Doone told me all about everything I wished to know, just as I questioned her; except indeed that point of points, how Master Ridd stood with her.

Bodoni

Lorna Doone told me all about everything I wished to know, just as I questioned her; except indeed that point of points, how Master Ridd stood with her.

Caslon Old Style

Lorna Doone told me all about everything I wished to know, just as I questioned her; except indeed that point of points, how Master Ridd stood with her.

Cheltenham

Lorna Doone told me all about everything I wished to know, just as I questioned her; except indeed that point of points, how Master Ridd stood with her.

Figure 23

SAMPLES OF TYPE FACES

same size and style, depending upon the width of the lines in its design. *Boldness* of the several type faces shown in Figure 25 is expressed as light, medium, bold, or extra-bold, with the heavier lines, of course, used in the latter. Type may be printed in several *forms.* Letters may be small or capital — referred to as lower case and upper case respectively. They may be straight up and down, as is usually the case, or they may slope toward the right, being then referred to as italics.

It is difficult to compare the experiments by various investigators on style of type and, therefore, to use the results for a final conclusion as to

Cloister Black

Lorna Doone told me all about everything I wished to know, just as I questioned her; except indeed that point of points, how Master Ridd stood with her.

Garamond

Lorna Doone told me all about everything I wished to know, just as I questioned her; except indeed that point of points, how Master Ridd stood with her.

Gothic

Lorna Doone told me all about everything I wished to know, just as I questioned her; except indeed that point of points, how Master Ridd stood with her.

Kabel Light

Lorna Doone told me all about everything I wished to know, just as I questioned her; except indeed that point of points, how Master Ridd stood with her.

Old Style

Lorna Doone told me all about everything I wished to know, just as I questioned her; except indeed that point of points, how Master Ridd stood with her.

Scotch Roman

Lorna Doone told me all about everything I wished to know, just as I questioned her; except indeed that point of points, how Master Ridd stood with her.

Figure 23 (continued)

SAMPLES OF TYPE FACES

the best style to be used for various utilitarian purposes. In experiments by various investigators in this field, conditions were not the same, the variables were not similarly controlled, nor were the same type faces studied. Also, similar standards of comparison have not been used in a number of such experiments.

H. Griffing and S. I. Franz (124) presented Gothic letters and Roman letters to readers by a tachistoscopic method. They determined the number of letters of each style that could be read in a single exposure, how long letters must be exposed to be correctly read, and what intensity of illumination was necessary for the recognition of each style of letter.

4 Point

Lorna Doone told me all about everything I wished to know, just as I questioned her; except indeed that point of points, how Master Ridd stood with her.

6 Point

Lorna Doone told me all about everything I wished to know, just as I questioned her; except indeed that point of points, how Master Ridd stood with her.

8 Point

Lorna Doone told me all about everything I wished to know, just as I questioned her; except indeed that point of points, how Master Ridd stood with her.

10 Point

Lorna Doone told me all about everything I wished to know, just as I questioned her; except indeed that point of points, how Master Ridd stood with her.

12 Point

Lorna Doone told me all about everything I wished to know, just as I questioned her; except indeed that point of points, how Master Ridd stood with her.

14 Point

Lorna Doone told me all about everything I wished to know, just as I questioned her; except indeed that point of points, how Master Ridd stood with her.

Figure 24

SAMPLES OF TYPE SIZES

The results favor the Gothic letters as requiring less exposure time and making possible a wider perceptual span. H. R. Crosland and G. Johnson also used a tachistoscopic technique but compared various letters all of the same style and size — 10-point, Caslon body, lower case.

> Small, almost negligible, differences in legibility occur between vertical, curved-vertical, diagonal, and curved letters. The largest difference exists between the vertical and curved-vertical letters. . . .
>
> Seriphed letters are more legible than unseriphed letters. . . . (74, p. 121.)

K. Breland and M. K. Breland (45), also using a tachistoscopic method, have shown that when the same newspaper headlines are printed in capitals and in lower case, they can be read better in lower case.

LIGHT	Lorna Doone told me all about everything I wished to know, just as I questioned her; except indeed that point of points, how Master Ridd stood with her.
MEDIUM	Lorna Doone told me all about everything I wished to know, just as I questioned her; except indeed that point of points, how Master Ridd stood with her.
BOLD	**Lorna Doone told me all about everything I wished to know, just as I questioned her; except indeed that point of points, how Master Ridd stood with her.**
EXTRA-BOLD	**Lorna Doone told me all about everything I wished to know, just as I questioned her; except indeed that point of points, how Master Ridd stood with her.**

Figure 25

SAMPLES OF TYPE BOLDNESS

This demonstration of the variable effects of letters themselves is corroborated by B. E. Roethlein, using a distance method. It was found that certain letters of every style are much more legible than other letters of the same style. This apparently intrinsic difference is even more pronounced when letters are presented in isolation rather than in groups. Sixteen different type faces were studied. However, the conclusion was drawn that, from style to style:

> . . . the form of any given letter of the alphabet usually varied between such narrow limits as to constitute a relatively insignificant factor in the determination of its legibility. (304, pp. 33-34.)

It is apparent, then, that legibility is a *product* of several factors, including the style of the letter, the size, the boldness of the face, the width of the white margin which surrounds the letter, the position of the letter in the letter group, and the shape and size of the adjacent letters. Relatively bold types, initial position in a group of letters, and distinction from adjacent letters proved advantageous for legibility. In evaluating these results, it is important to recall that a distance method of presenting letters was used.

H. E. Burtt and C. Basch (51) also employed a distance method by which letters were presented in a so-called focal variator. Legibility was evaluated in terms of the degree to which a letter or a group of letters could be thrown out of focus and still be recognized. Cheltenham, Baskerville, and Bodoni type faces were used; each style was compared with the other two. The experimenters concluded in favor of the Cheltenham type. Again it is to be noted that comparison was made by a distance method of type faces which varied in thickness of design; the stroke in Bodoni and Baskerville type is particularly light. Using a distance method, Tinker (343) found Old Style numerals to be more legible than Modern numerals when presented both in isolation and in groups. Under ordinary reading conditions, however, Modern numerals were read just as fast and as accurately as Old Style.

H. A. Webster and M. A. Tinker (390) determined the relative legibility of 10 type faces by the distance method. Significant differences were found when Scotch Roman type was compared with American Typewriter, Cheltenham, Antique, Old Style, Caslon Old Style, or Garamond; no significant differences in distance of recognition were found in the comparisons of Scotch Roman with Bodoni, Kabel Light, or Cloister Black (Old English). However, when those same 10 type faces were compared (276) with respect to their effect on reading rate, *no* important differences were found in the comparisons between Scotch Roman and Garamond, Antique, Bodoni, Old Style, Caslon Old Style, Kabel Light, or Cheltenham. But reading material printed with American Typewriter type was read 5.1 per cent more slowly than text printed with Scotch Roman, and Cloister Black retarded the rate even more than American Typewriter type.

Thus, Scotch Roman seemed the best type face for speed of reading but the poorest for distance reading, whereas American Typewriter was one of the poorest for speed but the best as judged by a distance method. Certain features of these type faces evidently increase *perceptibility* of words at a distance but reduce *speed* of reading. Results will differ, then, depending on the method used to measure the legibility of type, that is, whether speed or perceptibility at a distance is the paramount consideration. With the distance method

> Analysis has shown that the legibility of letters is increased when the size of the letter is increased, when the lines in the letter are widened, when the area of white space around or within the outline of the letter is increased, when the contrast of shading and hair lines is lessened, and when the outline of the letter is made simpler. It is possible that some of the

> factors promote legibility as measured by distance, but reduce legibility as measured by speed of reading. (390, p. 49.)

It will be noted that these statements regarding various styles of type are similar to those made by Roethlein in regard to various letters of the alphabet. These conclusions are supported by the fact that American Typewriter face has the characteristics mentioned in the statement above and is legible at a distance, but under ordinary reading conditions, as Paterson and Tinker have shown, it does not lead to rapid reading.

It would seem that as far as speed of reading is concerned most of the common type styles now in general use in printing are, with few exceptions, about equally legible. Whether or not the characteristics improving distance perception contribute also to readability under ordinary reading conditions remains to be determined. It may be said further that the crucial consideration seems to be either the letters themselves (and not necessarily their style), or certain type faces in relation to other features of the typographical setup. If it is the interdependence of typographic variables that is crucial, then it would be expected that any change in the format without a corresponding change in some other features of the printed page would interfere with optimum readability. It may be that the statistical technique of factor analysis will provide an experimental design which is needed to help solve the problem of optimum type style.

The reading materials in an experiment by Luckiesh and Moss on boldness of type face were printed with four weights of Memphis type — light, medium, bold, and extra-bold — composed in 21-pica lines with two points of leading.

> . . . the maximum differential in rate of reading these materials did not exceed 3.5 percent . . . a maximum differential of about 12 percent in rate of blinking was observed during the reading of these materials. (209, pp. 265-266.)

It is doubtful whether one should conclude that significant differences were established by this experiment. Roethlein, however, has asserted that:

> The relatively heavy-faced types prove to be more legible than the light-faced types. The optimal heaviness of face seems to lie in a mean between the bold faces and such light faces as Scotch Roman and Cushing Monotone. (304, p. 34.)

It must not be forgotten that in the case of these conclusions, the experimental method used may be the decisive factor. The former experiment involved a speed-of-reading method, the latter a distance method.

Burtt and Basch (51) and Tinker (345) used a distance method to determine the effect of type form on perceptibility. In the comparison by Burtt and Basch of 14-point Bodoni, Baskerville Roman, and Cheltenham Medium type faces previously reviewed, differences were statistically significant only for Bodoni *versus* Cheltenham when both type styles were presented in lower case. All differences, however, were significant when these styles were compared in upper-case form (capital letters). Tinker found that both letters and words in upper case were read at greater distances from the subject than were letters or words in lower case. Unrelated letters and words were both read at about the same distance when printed in upper case; but when presented in lower case, words could be read at a greater distance than could a series of unrelated letters.

> These findings indicate that total word-form is more potent in the perception of words in lower case than in all capitals where perception seems to occur largely by letters. . . .
>
> The greater influence of total word-form on perception of words in lower case in comparison with words in capitals is an important factor contributing to the faster reading of text in lower-case type. (345, pp. 173-174.)

Tinker and Paterson support this conclusion by using their speed-of-reading method.

> Text printed in all capitals is less legible than material in lower-case letters and slows down speed of reading to a very marked degree. . . . Text printed in italics is slightly less legible than material in lower-case letters and decreases speed of reading somewhat. (364, p. 368.)

The distance method of experimental study and the factors contributing to perception at a distance have naturally focused attention on the size of type face as a possibly significant typographic variable. The results of experiments on size of type seem to be conflicting. It is the opinion of the present authors that much of this confusion may be due to the very short time allowed for reading and comparing various samples. Individual variation in ability to adapt quickly to a new typographical format after having just briefly read another may account for at least some of the differences in results from experiment to experiment. Long periods of continuous reading and a number of subjects are required if conclusions in this field are to be fully satisfactory.

Griffing and Franz (124) compared 0.8-millimeter-high and 1.6-millimeter-high Roman letters (roughly, 2.5- and 4.5-point type) and 0.9-, 1.6-, 3.1-, and 6.0-millimeter-high Gothic letters (roughly, 3-, 4.5-, 9-, and 17-point type). They found that the larger types were, in every instance, more legible. These results were obtained by tachistoscopic methods.

A. R. Gilliland (120) compared eye-movement records taken while his subjects read material printed in type sizes ranging from 3 points to 90 points. The sizes of type did not seem to be particularly effective, even though rereading the same material in different formats was not characterized by very similar eye-movement patterns. The number and location of fixations, for example, varied from reading to rereading but not in a way suggesting any consistent or regular relationship to the size variable. A similar procedure with children involving the reading of some relatively easy paragraphs suggested that size of type is evidently not so important a factor in the reading of children as has sometimes been supposed. Luckiesh and Moss (211), however, report that the number of characters seen per fixation decreases from 8.50 to 7.84 as the type size is increased from 4 to 10 points. In another experiment (202), they report that for their subjects the number of blinks made while reading 12-point type was less than that made while reading 6-point type. Paterson and Tinker (280) compared the eye movements made in the reading of 6-point and 14-point type to those made in the reading of 10-point type. With 6-point type the number of fixations increased, total perception time greatly increased, and the number of regressive movements slightly increased. With the 14-point type, there was a striking increase in the number of fixations made, but less time was taken per fixation, and the number of regressions slightly decreased.

In Gilliland's experiment, adults were required to read paragraphs printed in 3-, 4-, 6-, 9-, 12-, 18-, 36-, 54-, 72-, and 90-point type. According to the quoted results of this experiment:

> The reading of the average adult is not greatly affected by changes in the size of type between the limits of 36 point and 6 point type. Above 36 point type or below 6 point type, the rate of reading begins to decrease for a majority of the subjects. (120, p. 146.)

Individual differences, however, were noticeable. Some subjects were not affected by even greater sizes of type. Subjects with visual defects and low visual acuity had difficulty in a few cases in reading small type. Slow ocular movements or a narrow span of the visual field also decreased the rate of reading large type.

Tinker and Paterson (368) printed Form A of the Chapman-Cook Reading Test in 7-point type, 12½-pica line length (about two inches). Form B was reduced in size, by planographic methods, to 80 per cent, 50 per cent, and 30 per cent of Form A, with which these reductions were compared. Significant differences in reading rate appeared in the reading (for 1¾ minutes) of the 50 per cent reduction. However

> At the present time, one would be justified in concluding that reductions to half-size may be made without undue loss of legibility. (368, p. 531.)

Such a finding would definitely minimize the importance of type size for readability.[1] However, in another experiment Paterson and Tinker (272) compared speed of reading 10-point type (line length, 80 millimeters) with the speed of reading 6-, 8-, 12-, and 14-point type. All comparisons showed significant differences ranging from a 5.2 per cent to a 6.9 per cent decrease in reading speed. See also Paterson and Tinker (281) for an experiment which shows some little superiority for larger as contrasted with smaller type (11-point *versus* 8-point and 11-point *versus* 6-point type) when optimal line widths were used.

Paterson and Tinker regard even a 6 per cent decrease in reading speed as important, considering

> The increasingly important rôle of reading in all phases of modern life . . .
> The results obtained in this experiment justify the conclusion that, for a line length of 80 millimeters and for the comparisons here made, 10 point type yields the fastest reading and is thus the optimum size of type (in comparison with other sizes used) for efficient reading. (272, p. 130.)

For want of more conclusive data, this optimum size of type was accepted in choosing the format of the reading material used in the new experiments reported in this book.

In addition to the variable characteristics of the type face, there is also to be considered the arrangement of the symbols on the printed page. Letters are arranged in lines, but those lines may be long or short, close together or widely separated, regular in length, or broken by illus-

[1] That there are real hazards in the photographic reduction of size of type is witnessed by the experience of the Association of Research Libraries in reproducing the Library of Congress catalogue by a photolithoprint process. See A. I. Bryan (49).

trations, and so forth. The *length of a line* of print is usually expressed in millimeters or picas (a pica is equal to .17 inch or 4.22 millimeters). Figure 26 compares line lengths varying from 9 picas (38 millimeters) to 43 picas (180 millimeters). The term *leading* refers to the distance between the lines of print. For example, an 11-point type on an 11-point body would mean that the distance between the lines was 11 points, the same as the size of the type. Eleven-point type on a 12-point body would mean that the distance between the lines of print was one point wider than the size of the type. The former instance is referred to as solid set, the latter as one point of leading. Samples are shown in Figure 27 of solid set, 1, 2, 3, and 6 points of leading. The necessity for taking account of the relations of these various factors in any experimental study of the relative merits of different arrangements of the printed page is clearly brought to the fore in an experimental investigation by B. R. Buckingham (50). This investigator brings to his study of the relation of typography to readability an intimate knowledge of the requirements and the practice of printing. It does not do much good to specify typographies which just cannot be put into print, or which, if set in type, would produce either ridiculous results or results which no printer, versed in the arts of his trade, would tolerate. Thus, as regards E. R. Shaw's recommendations Buckingham comments:

> . . . first, that so-called 'standards' which have subsequently been uncritically adopted by educational people have apparently been plucked out of the air; and second, that these standards have little reference to present printing conditions. (50, p. 99.)

And, as regards some of J. H. Blackhurst's findings about a quarter of a century later:

> This separating of size of type, length of line, and interlinear spacing as Blackhurst has done is wholly artificial. None of these exists by itself. No length of line, for example, can be said to be most desirable, independent of these other characteristics of the type page. For example, the 103 mm. line which is recommended without regard to size of type or interlinear space would be intolerable if the type were six-point, set solid. (50, p. 103.)

Again, in commenting on "one especially good investigation" made a few years later which recommended an 80-millimeter line of 10-point type:

> One cannot even say (although the investigators in this case suggest it) that a line of 80 mm. is best for ten-point type. The results are valid only for the interlinear spacing employed, and the investigators do not

9-PICA LINE LENGTH (38 Millimeters)

Lorna Doone told me all about everything I wished to know, just as I questioned her; except indeed that point of points, how Master Ridd stood with her.

13-PICA LINE LENGTH (55 Millimeters)

Lorna Doone told me all about everything I wished to know, just as I questioned her; except indeed that point of points, how Master Ridd stood with her.

19-PICA LINE LENGTH (80 Millimeters)

Lorna Doone told me all about everything I wished to know, just as I questioned her; except indeed that point of points, how Master Ridd stood with her.

29-PICA LINE LENGTH (122 Millimeters)

Lorna Doone told me all about everything I wished to know, just as I questioned her; except indeed that point of points, how Master Ridd stood with her.

43-PICA LINE LENGTH (180 Millimeters)

Lorna Doone told me all about everything I wished to know, just as I questioned her; except indeed that point of points, how Master Ridd stood with her.

Figure 26

SAMPLES OF LINE LENGTHS

tell us what that is. Widen the spacing and the probability is that a longer line may be employed to advantage. In fact, the situation is more complicated; the results are valid only for the series of type used with its characteristic shape of the letters, its height of the type face on the body (all ten-point type is not of the same height), its expansion or right-and-left spread-outness, and its width of heavy and light strokes. Accordingly, the printer, not knowing what series of type he may use, nor the spacing he may have between the lines, must be very sanguine if he suppose that merely by setting ten-point type on an 80 mm. line he is attaining desirable results. As a matter of fact, he supposes no such thing. He realizes that essential items are missing and probably wonders how the investigators 'got that way.' (50, p. 105.)

SOLID SET

Lorna Doone told me all about everything I wished to know, just as I questioned her; except indeed that point of points, how Master Ridd stood with her.

1 POINT OF LEADING

Lorna Doone told me all about everything I wished to know, just as I questioned her; except indeed that point of points, how Master Ridd stood with her.

2 POINTS OF LEADING

Lorna Doone told me all about everything I wished to know, just as I questioned her; except indeed that point of points, how Master Ridd stood with her.

3 POINTS OF LEADING

Lorna Doone told me all about everything I wished to know, just as I questioned her; except indeed that point of points, how Master Ridd stood with her.

6 POINTS OF LEADING

Lorna Doone told me all about everything I wished

to know, just as I questioned her; except indeed that

point of points, how Master Ridd stood with her.

Figure 27

SAMPLES OF LEADING

This review of previous studies leads to the conclusion that investigations attempting to study a single variable with "other factors constant" are not practicable. If one took only "seven pointings of type from eight to eighteen inclusive, eight lengths of line . . . and an appropriate number of interlinear spacings, say ten . . . there would be . . . 560 different specimens . . ." (p. 105). With only four of the most typical type series the number of specimens mounts to 2240, which, if tried out on, say, 200 students in four different school grades, would produce 1,792,000 returns.

Buckingham, however, finds a way out by which the requirements of experimentation are maintained but given a different application. For each series of type, single variables such as the total cost of the book, the cost of paper and press work, or the total area of type pages (each of which, incidentally, is found to correlate with the others to the extent of *circa* r = .90) may be employed, since "Any actual specification as to size of type, length of line, and amount of leading for a book of a given length works out to require a definite area of type pages . . ." (p. 106), the cost of which can be precisely estimated. The real skill, however, seems to lie in setting up materials "according to a few well-recognized specifications so described that the printer can reproduce them" (p. 106) and then finding the readability of each of the specifications. One face of type, known as Monotype No. 8, "having normal 'set' and medium expansion," three sizes of type — 18-, 14-, and 12-point, three lengths of line — one of 24 picas (or 101.5 millimeters) called the "A" line, one of 21 picas (or 89 millimeters) called the "C" line, and one of 14½ picas (or 61.5 millimeters) called the "E" line, and three amounts of leading — 5-, 4-, and 3-point — were employed. The resulting 27 specifications or specimens were reduced to 18 by the elimination of the "E" line in 18-point type "because it is impracticable to set such large type in so short a line," and by dropping 5-point leading in the case of 14- and 12-point type because "such wide leading is generally regarded as appropriate only for larger type" (p. 107).

In addition to the wisdom shown in the selection of typographic materials, a second characteristic which makes Buckingham's investigation outstanding is the wealth of experimental evidence secured. Three stories of approximately the same length (325 words) and vocabulary load and of equal and high "interest value" were set up in the 18 typographical forms. "Each story was equipped with twelve multiple-choice questions for testing comprehension" (p. 111). The subjects were over 2000 second-grade children; each child read three stories, each story being set in a different typographical form, and was individually timed on the reading and then given as much time as necessary for answering the multiple-choice questions. The total number of usable returns was 2337, representing the readings of 779 children.

Three criteria were employed to appraise the results: speed of reading, comprehension, and speed and comprehension combined. The specimen described as "12 E 3," which means 12-point type in the short E (61.5 millimeters) line with three points' leading, was read more rapidly than any other. Specimen "12 C 4," that is, 12-point in the medium C (89 millimeters) line with four points of leading, was second, and a close third was 14 E 3; 12 E 4 was fourth. Thus, 12-point type, especially if set on a short or medium length of line which has generous leading, makes the best showing.

The comprehension questions did not prove to be a clear-cut delineator of typographical differences. Although again the 12-point type made a better showing than 14- and 18-point type, there was no sure trend as to the preferred length of line. The reason may be that the comprehension questions were not difficult enough to bring out differences.

When speed and comprehension are combined into a single measure, 12-point type with a short line is still clearly advantageous. Twelve-point type in a short line with 4-point leading, or 12 E 4, which was fourth in rank as measured by speed alone, takes first rank, and 12 E 3, which was first according to speed alone, is well up on the list, as is 12 C 4, the 12-point, well-leaded intermediate line.

Finally, as to the relation of readability to area and cost, since the materials presented show that size of type and interlinear space may to some extent be substituted for each other (for example, when 14-point type is replaced by 12-point type and given an added point of leading, its ranking is improved in five out of seven cases), it is possible "to think of all the factors which affect the area covered by a fixed amount of matter . . . as the *spread* of the printed matter" (p. 120). Spread is obviously closely related to cost. These considerations lead to what Buckingham rightly calls an amazing result:

> If, now, we place beside the figures for area, the ranks of the different specifications according to readability we are startled by the similarity in the ranking. In fact . . . there is a substantial correlation between area and

> speed of reading and likewise between area and the combination of speed and comprehension. (50, p. 122.)

Thus, "considerations of economy actually enforce those of readability . . . " (p. 122). Examples of this fact are as follows:

Twelve-point type which covers a relatively small amount of area has three specimens which rank in terms of speed of reading among the first four of the entire 18; 14-point type holds second place; and 18-point type, a very poor third. The conclusion of the matter is stated in the following practical terms, which are in part dictated by the prevailing if false notion of school officials that young children need to have extra-large type in their textbooks:

> If a publisher uses this series of type (Monotype No. 8), the figures indicate rather conclusively the superiority of the twelve-point type set on a short line. If a publisher is unwilling to adopt a fourteen and one-half pica line he can still use the C line (twenty-one picas) with good economy and high readability. In other words, he can adopt 12C4. If he dares not risk the publication of a second-grade book in twelve-point type and is willing to take fourteen-point type, his best selection will be 14C3. (50, p. 123.)

Tinker and Paterson varied the size of type and the line length simultaneously. Reading material was printed in 6-, 8-, 10-, 12-, and 14-point type with line lengths respectively 68, 72, 80, 97, and 115 millimeters. A comparison of each with the 10-point-type, 80-millimeter line showed that rate of reading was significantly retarded only in the case of the 6-point-type, 68-millimeter line. But the experimenters make the statement that:

> The experiment yields evidence that, within certain limits, neither size of type nor line length as single variables can be relied upon in determining optimal typographical arrangements. Both factors (and perhaps others as well) work hand in hand and must be properly balanced to produce a printed page which will promote a maximum reading rate. (366, p. 78.)

Since the reading materials of the present experiment were printed in 10-point type, the studies reviewed below are concerned with variations in line length when the size of type is held constant at 10 points.

The reading material in line-length experiments by Luckiesh and Moss was printed with 10-point Textype, with two points of leading, in black ink on nonglossy white paper, and read under a uniform diffuse illumination of 10 footcandles. The line length was varied in each five-minute trial period: 13 picas, 17, 21, 25, and 29 picas (roughly, 55-millimeter to 122-millimeter lines). It was calculated (211) from eye-movement records that the number of 10-point type characters included in an average fixation increased from 8.14 to 9.31 as the line length was increased. The statistical significance of the differences observed (209) in reading rate and in rate of blinking was not determined. However, the authors conclude:

> The data pertaining to the rate of involuntary blinking reveal relatively large differentials as compared with those involving rate of reading. Furthermore, the results obtained with the two criteria are not even in qualitative agreement. For example, the criterion of rate of reading indicates that the readability of 29 pica lines is the same as that of 13 pica lines; while the criterion of rate of blinking indicates a marked superiority of the 13 pica lines. (209, pp. 268-269.)

Paterson and Tinker (279) compared the eye-movement records made in the reading of 180-millimeter lines of print (43 picas) and 37-millimeter lines (9 picas) with those made in the reading of 80-millimeter lines (19 picas). The results of reading 19- *versus* 9-pica lines showed differences in eye-movement performance to be statistically significant except for the number of regressions; all differences for 19- *versus* 43-pica lines were significant.

> One may characterize the oculomotor patterns in reading an excessively short line by saying that the number of fixations is increased, the span of perception is decreased, the mean duration of the fixations is increased, total perception time is greatly increased, but the number of regressions is approximately the same. . . . The . . . factor that could account for the decreased efficiency in reading the short line would appear to be the difficulty in making maximum use of peripheral vision in the horizontal direction. . . . fixation frequency in reading the long line is definitely increased, whereas the average number of words per fixation is decreased. Furthermore, the average time devoted to fixations (pause duration) is slightly increased and, of course, total perception time is increased as well. A most striking difference occurs with respect to the number of regressions. . . . These come chiefly at the beginning of each line. . . .
>
> We interpret the results to mean that an excessively long line width gives rise to a major difficulty in swinging back to the beginning of successive lines. . . . It is entirely possible that this difficulty so upsets the reading process that the re-establishment of the most efficient oculomotor patterns in reading each line is impossible. (279, pp. 574-576.)

The reading materials in another experiment by Tinker and Paterson

(365) were also set in 10-point type. Material with a line length of 80 millimeters was compared with material printed in line lengths of 59, 97, 114, 136, 152, 168, and 186 millimeters. The reading rate in the case of each comparison was significantly retarded. This was found for fast as well as slow readers, with evidence that the fast readers were retarded relatively more than the average or slow readers. These authors concluded, as indicated on page 112, that, for 10-point type, 80 millimeters is the optimum length of line for efficient reading.

Paterson and Tinker conclude from their several studies:

> that line widths can be varied to a surprising degree without any appreciable adverse effect on speed. That is, a definite range of optimal line widths exists. However, lines shorter than or longer than the optimal range definitely retard reading speed. (279, p. 572.)

The results of the above experiments are taken by the present authors to indicate that the 88-millimeter (21-pica) line length for the 10-point type used in the present experiment is within the optimum range, at least as far as the criterion of reading rate is concerned.

M. Bentley (25) used reading material printed in 12-point type with from 0 up to 9 points of leading in certain studies. Seven-point leading was found by him to permit the most rapid reading. The rate increased steadily with greater width of leading from solid set to 3 points, remained about constant up to 6 points of leading, increased considerably with 7 points, and decreased markedly thereafter. An experiment by Luckiesh and Moss presented material in 10-point Textype arranged in 21-pica lines (about 88 millimeters) with five different degrees of leading. Their conclusion is:

> It is evident from our data . . . that the *maximum* speed of reading 10-point and 12-point types is not significantly influenced by the factor of leading when the latter is varied from zero to 6 points. (204, p. 147.)

Paterson and Tinker (275) used material printed in 10-point type, 80-millimeter line, with leading varied from solid set to 1, 2, and 4 points. Only the 2-point leaded text significantly increased reading speed. However,

> The advantage of 2 point leading may hold only for the particular size of type and width of line used in this investigation. (275, p. 397.)

Further experiments which vary size of type in relation to points of leading are required.

H. T. Hovde (147, 148) varied not only size of type (6 to 8 points) and leading (½ to 1 point) but context as well. He found:

> . . . that the context of the reading material is a more important factor in its effect on the reading rate, and consequently upon legibility, than the sensory material. Changes in size of type and leading are not as dominant an influence as changes in the context of the reading material. Because of the dominance of context, no conclusion can be drawn from the relative effects of changes in size of type and leading. Experimental evidence by those who have studied reading habits corroborates this conclusion.
>
> . . . The readers' preferences and opinions of legibility differ from the amount of reading as measured by the reading rate. The readers' preferences for larger type and leading probably are due to an impression that more material has been read because more space has been covered in the reading, although the reasons for the preferences are given in terms of sensory content. Reasons for the choice of larger sensory units in some instances are confused with context, but opinions of legibility are stated largely in terms of sensory content. The results of this experiment do not warrant specific recommendations for the use of a particular type size or leading for newspaper columns within the limits of the type size and leading that have been tested. (148, pp. 70-71.)

However, Tinker and Paterson (371) conclude from their very well controlled series of investigations on line width, type size, leading, and type faces in newsprint that variations of type size and leading (the "sensory" variables studied by Hovde) affect legibility least. They also show that type face affects legibility most. These findings suggest that context, then, would be expected to be the most variable factor in Hovde's experiments. Also, when type faces have been varied in different orders of presentation (369), results have not changed. From this finding it was concluded that "set," which may include the preference of the subject, does not necessarily influence the differences obtained when variations in typography are introduced. These latter findings do not necessarily negate nor perhaps even weaken the conclusions drawn by Hovde with regard to the significance of context as a reading variable, but neither do Hovde's findings minimize the importance of all typographical factors.

Crosland and Johnson (74) have studied a problem related to leading. They investigated the effect of interletter hair spacing, that is, the space between letters of the line of print, rather than the distance between the lines of print (leading). Interletter spacing of one-half point did not appreciably affect the legibility of the letters presented in a tachistoscope.

However, for letters whose shapes do not contrast greatly, for example, p, d, b, and q, the effect of the hair spacing was greater.

It may possibly be concluded that, within certain rather wide limits, the number of points of leading is not a crucial consideration in arranging the printed page. However, it would seem that, as is evidently true of line length, the variable effects of leading are so intimately associated with the other typographic variables that no general conclusion as to optimum points of leading should be drawn. Rather, for each size and style of type or for each line length, there may be an optimum in the number of points of leading that can be used. In the 10-point-type, 88-millimeter-line format used in the present experiment, one point of leading was used, although two points of leading might have been preferable.

Words and letters are not things apart from the paper or other surface on which they are printed. The reader reacts to visual symbols which are figures on a background. Actually, in black print on white paper the light stimulus is received primarily from the white paper, the black print absorbing radiation and thus producing the pattern of gradients which stimulates the receptive surface of the retina. It is always likely that a real modification of the background may have some effect on the perception of the figures, even as changes in the characteristics of the symbols have been found to affect the perceptual processes. Paterson and Tinker (274) found that the rate of reading was significantly better for black print on a white background than for other combinations with which they experimented. The color of ink or print in relation to the color of the background may thus be considered as a significant variable in the study of the reading process.

Striking differences in readability have indeed been demonstrated depending on the color schemes used in printing. K. Preston, H. P. Schwankl, and M. A. Tinker (293) compared several color combinations of ink and paper to black ink on white paper by measuring the farthest distance from the eyes at which single words could be recognized. Blue print on white background was found to be the most legible, black on white ranked fourth in legibility, and red on green was last of the 11 combinations studied. Tinker and Paterson studied the effect of similar color combinations on the rate of reading. Despite the notoriously unstandardized and unsatisfactory color terminology used by printers, the results were very much the same as those of the above experiment, except that the rate of reading black on white, as already noted, was the fastest. The following list is offered by Tinker and Paterson as a rough guide:

> Providing good legibility: Black on white, grass green on white, lustre blue on white, and black on yellow.
>
> Providing fair legibility: Tulip red on yellow, tulip red on white.
>
> Providing poor legibility: Grass green on red, chromium orange on black, chromium orange on white, tulip red on green, black on purple. (367, pp. 478-479.)

From the results of both experiments, similar conclusions were drawn. Tinker and Paterson state:

> The evidence in this experiment justifies the following rule: In combining colors (color of ink and paper) care must be taken to produce a *printed page* which shows a maximum *brightness contrast* between print and background. (367, p. 479.)

Preston *et al.* conclude:

> In general, the greater the luminosity or brightness differences between symbol and background, the greater the legibility of the print. (293, p. 461.)

Black print on a more or less white background is, then, the commonly used optimum, no doubt because it represents the extreme in brightness contrast. Tinker and Paterson (372) have studied the effect of minimal contrast (red on dark green) as contrasted with maximal contrast (black on white). Span of perception, number of fixations, and regressions in the subject used all showed the advantage of the high-contrast situation.

Luckiesh and Moss (205) used reading materials printed in black ink on white, cream, yellow, and red papers. The average number of words read per minute (during five-minute trial periods) for each of the papers in order was: 284, 273, 266, and 268. Using their own visibility meter, they judged black print on cream-tinted paper to be the optimum printed surface. For the same papers, the frequency of blinking was: 29.2, 28.8, 32.4, and 34.6. The authors again judged the readability of black print on the cream or yellow paper to be about the same as that of black print on white paper, with the red slightly inferior. C. E. Ferree and G. Rand (106, Pt. II) found that subjects preferred a yellow-tinted paper. They conclude that unsaturated and light shades are better than saturated and dark shades. E. A. Betts (27) also found cream-tinted paper to be associated with high visibility.

The paper used in the books read in the present experimental sessions was "mill natural," which has a cream-tinted surface.

The results of experiments by Roethlein (304), F. N. Stanton and H. E. Burtt (325), and Paterson and Tinker (277) all agree that the quality and texture of the printing surface (paper) are insignificant variables, or at least much less significant factors than has been supposed. Stanton and Burtt used a white, glossy-coated paper as the standard with which were compared papers with so-called dull-coated, white-antique, and ivory-antique (India) surfaces. No significant differences were found. Paterson and Tinker compared egg-shell paper to white-enamel, artisan-enamel, and flint-enamel paper. These papers represent degrees of gloss from 22.9 per cent for egg-shell to 95.1 per cent for the flint-enamel. Again, no significant differences were demonstrated. Paterson and Tinker caution the reader, however:

> . . . to accept the findings as being true only for relatively short periods of reading. It is probable that relatively long periods of reading print on glossy paper will result in eyestrain and fatigue. (277, p. 131.)

No evidence for this conclusion concerning fatigue has been presented by these experimenters or by any other investigators known to the present authors. However, this variable deserves further study.

A description of the most legibly printed page must at this time be regarded as tentative. The evidence which has been reviewed, however, suggests that certain recommendations can be made which are much more than simply esthetic. The situation may be simplified somewhat by establishing one variable as a sort of anchor and defining the others in relation to it. Convenience and frequency of use have led us to decide that the size of type face upon which we shall base our other variables will be 10-point. This is the type used in Figures 58, 59, and 60, on pages 240 ff.

The readable page, then, may be printed in any of several styles of type, preferably those which are fairly simple in design. The width of the lines of the type design may be medium to bold in thickness. The majority of the letters will be lower case and not italicized. The lines of print may be around 80 millimeters or 19 picas in length, solidly set or with up to two points of leading. The printing ink should be black on a cream-tinted paper of dull finish.

It is not said that the above description is necessarily *the* optimum or the only desirable combination,[2] but rather that it represents one of the good formats and certainly a page that will in general be read with ease.

In conclusion, then, it may be said that in any experiment on fatigue in reading it is important to consider the characteristics of the paper used in the book that is read. It is also important to describe in detail the type in which the book is printed, the color of the ink used, and the way in which the type is set in regard to leading and other characteristics. A good standard form of print has been described above, which is the one adopted in the experiments reported later in this book.

In the next chapter we turn to a consideration of the evidence concerning the illumination of the printed page and related topics.

[2] This book is set in 11-point linotype Garamond, with 2 points of leading.

Chapter 5

The Problem of Illumination

WHEN one reads an ordinary printed book, light is reflected into the eye from the printed page in such a way as to allow the formation on the retina of a sharply focused pattern of brightnesses determined by the differential absorption and reflection of the light by the surface, as noted in Chapter 1. It is the recognition of the contours, shapes, and colors of that pattern as it varies from fixation to fixation which makes possible the reading of printed symbols. It might be assumed that as long as that pattern can be "seen," that is, as long as it is adequate to initiate receptor activity, light as a variable which may affect the efficiency of the reading process need be given no further consideration. It has, however, been found by experimentation that "light," that is, the radiant energy of the visual stimulus, has certain variable characteristics which may contribute to or interfere with the efficiency of reading.

First of all, the efficiency of reading may be affected by the over-all level or intensity of illumination. The individual may read in the light from a single small candle in an otherwise dark room, or in full and clear noonday sunlight. The light may be evenly distributed and of proper intensity, or brighter or dimmer patches may be present on or beside the printed page which might interfere with the ease of reading. Much reading is done in the natural light from the sun which reaches the page not directly but by reflection from walls and other natural and artificial objects, including the sky. Frequently, however, we read in artificial light. The question has been raised as to whether we read as well in artificial as in natural light, and also what the effective optimal characteristics of light are for many special visual tasks.

In experiments on visual fatigue such as those reported in this book, it is important to arrange proper lighting for the reading situation. To make this arrangement, it is necessary to know the effects of the characteristics of illumination so as to control them properly. In fatigue studies it is important to remember that, if the experimental variable is to be prolonged activity, it would be unfortunate to adopt an atypical lighting condition, or to vary the illumination of the books read, without taking cognizance of these factors. C. A. Veasey (378) points out that, in attempting to consider what is adequate artificial lighting, besides the actual amount of light, other factors such as size of object, contrast, speed, duration, sensitivity, and visual acuity must be considered.

The intensity of illumination has perhaps been the most widely studied of all reading variables. Evidence is also available for controlling the effects of "glare" and for a recommendation of the proper color and composition of light to use. Useful clues to the problem of reading illumination may be derived from experiments on various ocular functions in addition to the reading pattern; the review to follow, therefore, is not confined to investigations of the reading process alone.

Experiments on the color of type in relation to the color of the printing surface have supported, as was previously shown, the general recommendation of using black ink on white or cream-tinted paper. This leaves still unanswered, however, the question of whether or not the color of the light differentially absorbed or reflected from this black (dark gray) and white or near-white field is a significant variable. The natural light from the sun is essentially a mixture of all the wave lengths of radiant energy to which the human eye reacts and of much invisible radiation as well. Many artificial lights now in general use attempt to reproduce this natural light. However, almost all artificial sources have been found to differ from sunlight to a greater or lesser extent in color composition. Light from reading lamps may emphasize wave lengths in the yellow, or the reader may elect to use special light bulbs, filters, or fluorescent tubes which produce a bluish or other tinge. Since so much reading is done in artificial light, variations from daylight must be taken as important variables in the reading situation.

Ferree and Rand (105, 106) have concluded from their experiments that the best illumination for work is natural daylight. This does not mean direct sunlight but "north-sky light" at its best. By the same token, artificial light closely approximating daylight in color, composition, and diffuseness also approaches the optimum in illumination. When the artificial light varies in composition from natural light, it has been found that mixtures of daylight and artificial light seem to be more satisfactory than only artificial light.

For approximating the effectiveness of daylight, blue light bulbs and sodium lights have been suggested—the latter suggestion is a generalization from traffic experiments. Luckiesh and Moss (200) compared the amplitude of convergence before and after an hour's reading under sodium-vapor and under tungsten-filament lights. The amplitude was found to be slightly more reduced under the sodium than under the tungsten illumination, suggesting that the more usual tungsten-filament bulbs are better for reading. Ferree and Rand (105) have concluded that blue bulbs may be less satisfactory than ordinary lamps, especially the "blue" bulbs which transmit green in excess. After experiments with Mazda light bulbs, they recommend an artificial light produced by such bulbs and filtered through so-called daylight glass, or what is commercially called "whiterlite glass." This type of light was used in arranging the illumination for the experiments reported in this book.

Glare ordinarily means that too much brightness for comfort in seeing is present. More generally, the term has been used, it seems, to refer to bright patches of light coming from the visual space being viewed or from its "surround" in such a way as to act in an unfavorable manner on the eyes and thus reduce the effectiveness on the retina of the light coming from the page the subject wishes to see. Thus, glare often results when there is an uneven distribution of brightness within the field of vision of such intensity or character as to be noticeable or to cause discomfort, annoyance, or interference with "seeing."

The opinion has been expressed that it is a fallacy to assume that all glare hinders visibility and ocular comfort. Peripheral glare, if less intense than the figure observed, may improve visual functions (193). The interpretation and value of the above statement depend upon what its author meant by glare. If the term is used to refer to a certain range of illumination intensities and, as the last sentence suggests, a certain relationship between the center and the surround of the material being viewed, then the term may be superfluous in a professional vocabulary. If, however, the term is to mean the effect on the eye of certain extremes of intensity and of brightness especially in contrasting situations, then the above statement requires further elaboration.

Light sources have been introduced in addition to those required by the reader in experimental studies of glare to determine the effect of such additions on visual functions. The data have shown that the resulting glare does interfere with ease of seeing or visibility. Luckiesh and Moss observed the rate of blinking during reading. From trial to trial the brightness of the center field, for example, the open book, was varied in relation to the brightness of the surrounding field. The rate of blinking increased when contrast was increased. They conclude:

> . . . that the processes of reading are accomplished with a minimum of effort or under the most favorable conditions when the brightnesses of the central and surrounding fields are approximately equal. (206, p. 582.)

Analysis of the data presented by Luckiesh and Moss (214) showed that in the presence of glare sources the rate of blinking significantly increased. The rate of blinking was found to vary with the brightness of the glare source, even though the over-all illumination at the eye remained constant. Luckiesh and Moss (198) have also found that the pressure "unconsciously" exerted on a recording button by the finger of the reader increased in the presence of glare sources. This is regarded as an indication that the "tension" or perhaps even "effort" of the reader is increased by glare. It must be pointed out that all such experiments are a function of the method used and that blinking is a process that must be carefully considered before it is taken as a sure index of fatigue, as has been indicated in Chapter 3. M. R. Harbinson and F. C. Bartlett (135) presented patterns of dots to subjects by means of a tachistoscope, the exposure time of which could be varied. Introducing glare or speeding up exposure time under glare conditions was associated with subjective discomfort and poorer perception.

Glare is evidently a factor in lighting which should be reduced or eliminated to promote efficient reading. As a method of controlling glare in local lighting, Ferree and Rand (106) suggest arranging light sources so as to have the brightest light on the plane of work near the level of the eyes and the rest of the light decreasing gradually above and below this level. One form of this arrangement was used in the experiments reported in the chapters which follow in this book.

Perhaps the most important consideration, certainly the one most widely discussed at present, is the level or intensity of illumination that is best for efficient reading. Light intensity may be measured or expressed in a number of different ways depending upon what feature of intensity is the primary concern of the experimenter. Standard books dealing with photometry describe and discuss these general measures. The photometric unit most frequently used in the experiments to be reviewed below is the footcandle. A footcandle is an intensity of illumination equal to the density of luminous flux upon a surface placed at right angles one foot from a light source of one candlepower, or, conversely, a standard candle placed one foot from a surface will illuminate that surface to an intensity of approximately one footcandle. The intensity of light falling on an ordinary book page from a 60-watt Mazda lamp in a desk reading lamp is about seven footcandles.

To put the problem concretely, it may be asked what the wisest recommendation is that may be made, based on experimental evidence, concerning the number of footcandles at the page of print required for most satisfactory reading. Experiments pertinent to this problem and the conclusions drawn from them are the concern of the following review.

The classical study of the relationship between visual acuity and illumination was made by A. König (173). This work shows that visual acuity varies with the logarithm of the intensity of the illumination in a definite manner. The resolving power of the mosaic of retinal receptors gradually increases up to nearly 100 times its initial value as effective illumination increases. Ferree and Rand (101, 102) measured visual acuity under illumination varying from 0.0001 to 20.0 footcandles. They report that visual acuity increased as intensity was increased up to 5 footcandles; thereafter, the increase in visual acuity was relatively small, and hardly noticeable when the intensity level was raised to 20 footcandles. Subjects with astigmatism were poorer at lower intensities than normal subjects, but acuity performance was much the same for both groups at the higher levels of illumination. T. Klein (171) measured visual acuity in a range of intensities from 0.04 to 1000 footcandles. He concluded that 0.5 footcandles is adequate for ordinary acuity tests and that, in general, an illumination intensity of 2.5 to 10.0 footcandles is desirable for most ocular work. Those of his subjects who were myopic (nearsighted) showed some increase in acuity with intensities of illumination above 10.0 footcandles. Cobb (65) concluded that the logarithmic relationship holds between visual acuity and illumination intensities of from 0.064 to 30.4 footcandles. Toward the higher intensities, however, visual acuity improves even less than would be expected from this exponential formula. Tinker (361) has studied the preferred illumination intensities for reading. He found great individual differences, varying from 10 to 84 footcandles in a group of 30 subjects who were required to make five choices under a direct local light.

After reviewing several experiments relating visual acuity to intensity of illumination, L. T. Troland made the summary statements:

> The question which is of the greatest interest in the above discussion is that of the level of intensity at which visual acuity becomes substantially constant. It is generally admitted that the acuity ceases to increase after a certain level has been reached and that at certain higher intensities it begins to decrease once more. The work of König (1897) still appears to be the most convincing of extant studies concerning the dependency of acuity on intensity, and this leads us to place the intensity level in question at 66.5 footcandles or thereabouts. . . . However, if we take the average of all available estimates other than König's as to *the point at which there is no longer an appreciable gain in acuity,* resulting from intensity increase, we arrive at a value of 6.5 footcandles. . . .
>
> The discrepancy between the findings of different investigators is probably attributable to differences in the exact conditions under which their measurements were made, as well as variations between the individual observers whose reactions were tested. (376, pp. 136-137.)

Troland, however, notes that an appreciable gain in acuity is secured by increasing the intensity above 6.5 footcandles. The fact that the crucial intensity named above is relatively low is of importance in relation to the rest of the present discussion.

The relationship between accommodation and illumination has been studied. The intrinsic and extrinsic muscles of the eye adjust for the distance of the fixated object in the visual space by changing the curvature of the lens (accommodation) and convergently moving the eyeballs. H. E. Israel (154) determined the distance through which an object could be moved before the adjusting apparatus of the eye would respond. This distance he referred to as the "error." Under illumination as low as 0.0117 footcandles, the average error of accommodation alone was found to be only one twenty-third of the total distance for which the eyes can accommodate. The average error for both convergence and accommodation was as low as one fifty-eighth part of the entire distance.

Dilation and constriction of the pupil are obviously related to illumination. In normal subjects these actions can vary the diameter of the pupil between about two and eight millimeters. It is known that visual acuity is reduced at both of these extremes. P. Reeves (295) reports data which show that in an illumination intensity of 10 footcandles the pupil has an average diameter of five millimeters. This is well within the range of pupillary diameters in which visual acuity will not be disturbed. The pupil itself will react, however, to light of very minimal intensities. E. Engelking (96) has shown that the absolute threshold for the pupillary light reflex with a dark-adapted eye is at about 0.003 footcandles. Other studies have been made of the relationship of illumination and certain other ocular functions such as brightness discrimination, flicker, and movement and depth discrimination. These are not reviewed here as they do not bear directly on the reading problem.

It may be concluded from these studies of visual processes that the proper functioning of the external and internal ocular muscles requires intensities of illumination which fall within definite limits. This implies that too little or too much light may well be a disadvantage in reading.

The experiments reviewed above have been concerned with the relation of illumination intensity to some particular ocular function. It is likely, however, that the performance of certain visual tasks may demand higher intensities of illumination than others. P. W. Cobb and F. K. Moss (66) required subjects to follow for half an hour a spot of light moving in a circle. At the end of this exercise the muscular balance of the eye was tested. It was found that under conditions of both five and 100 footcandles, the result was the same—an increase in esophoria (tendency of the eyes to turn inward). The experimenters take this finding to indicate that the lower intensity has no disadvantage over the higher, nor does the higher illumination have any advantage over the lower in the performance of this particular task. L. R. White, R. H. Britten, J. E. Ives, and L. R. Thompson (395) determined the rate of mail sorting under illumination intensities varying from 2.5 to 10 footcandles. The rate increased with increase in illumination, but after eight or nine footcandles had been reached, little or no additional improvement was noted. These experimenters also found that, under the illumination intensities used, recognition of briefly viewed (tachistoscopically presented) figures was not affected by degree of illumination.

E. W. Atkins (11) administered a number-work test (a routine clerical task of crossing out numbers), a co-ordination test (the subjects were required to draw a line through a narrow path), and a chain association test. Each task was done under five different intensities of illumination: 9.6, 24.6, 53.8, 66.5, and 118.0 footcandles. Each of the five subjects worked for approximately one hour a day. From the data the tentative conclusions were drawn that a brightness of about 34 footcandles gave the greatest efficiency, and that the higher and lower brightnesses were less comfortable to the subjects. However, the differences in performance reported were very small. An examination of the data shows that on the number-work test there was no change in efficiency from 9.6 to 118.0 footcandles of illumination.

Luckiesh and others (216) observed the rate of perceiving letters on a rotating drum under illumination varying from 0.39 to 25.0 footcandles. They found an increase in speed with an increase in illumination up to about 11 footcandles or perhaps higher, but the increase in speed was not very marked after the intensity level was raised above seven footcandles.

Troland (376), after making a review of many tasks involving the use of the eyes, offers the following tentative recommendations: For most industrial tasks of a gross nature one-footcandle illumination is probably sufficient, but fine, detailed work may best be accomplished under as much as 200 or 300 footcandles, depending on the conditions under which the work is to be done. The Illuminating Engineering Society makes similar recommendations for various industrial tasks (151, 333). The problem remains, however, of determining just where the task of ordinary reading falls in this sequence, that is, how much illumination is required for optimal reading conditions. This specific problem has been variously investigated, with, unfortunately, varying conclusions and hence with varying recommendations of a practical nature. Some of these studies are reviewed below.

In an experiment by McFarland, Knehr, and Berens the basal metabolism and pulse rate of 21 subjects were compared during reading periods of one hour under one footcandle and one hour under 50 footcandles of illumination. On a succeeding morning, the experiment was repeated with the order of illumination reversed. The experiments were carried out in an air-conditioned darkroom where the temperature and humidity could be kept constant. No apparent relationship was observed between the basal metabolic rate and the level of illumination.

There was a general tendency for the pulse rate to decrease slightly during the two-hour period of reading, irrespective of the level of illumination. The experimenters conclude that:

> . . . It is questionable whether reliable criteria for determining adequate levels of illumination for tasks such as reading during short periods of time (approximately 2 hours) can be obtained in terms of oxygen consumption and heart rate, since the amount of tissue involved in the eyes and brain is relatively small in relation to the total amount of tissue in the body. The changes, if any, might be expected to be relatively small and consequently concealed by uncontrollable variables. (230, pp. 74-75.)

Another approach to the problem of optimal intensity of illumination for reading has been to note subjective preference. Ferree and Rand (106, Pt. II) report that most of their subjects found it comfortable to read under an illumination intensity of from 10 to 40 footcandles. M. Osumi's experiment (268) on feeling-tone during reading led him to conclude that illumination of from 3.7 to 15.2 footcandles was most suitable — the data are actually reported with respect to brightness, measured in terms of *lux* (one footcandle equals 10.764 lux).

Tinker (359) concludes, however, that preference may be determined by adaptation, and therefore noting a reader's preference for a particular illumination intensity is not a satisfactory method of determining the intensity of light needed for efficient visual work. Tinker had subjects choose light intensities for comfortable reading after adaptation to eight footcandles and to 52 footcandles. He found that the intensity preferred was closely related to the level of illumination to which the subject had adapted. In another experiment Tinker (360) reports that the maximal speed of perception in reading is reached at about 10 footcandles when the subject has adapted for only two minutes. When, however, a 15-minute period of adaptation was used, performance was no less efficient under only 3.1 footcandles.

Tinker conducted an experiment the purpose of which was to study the effect of changes in illumination intensity upon the speed of reading. The reading material consisted of Forms A and B of the Chapman-Cook Speed of Reading Test read under light intensities of 0.1, 0.7, 3.1, 10.3, 17.4, and 53.3 footcandles. There were three parts to the experiment, of which two are reviewed here. In the first part of the experiment, speed of reading was measured when the eye had had only *two minutes* to adapt to the intensity of light used. Six groups of 82 university sophomores each were subjects. From the critical ratios computed, it was concluded that:

> In general, when the eye is adapted for only two minutes to the brightness of light used, speed of reading increases with increases in intensity up to a point which lies somewhere between 3.1 and 10.3 footcandles. Further increases in brightness of light produced neither faster nor slower reading than that found at 10.3 footcandles. (357, p. 564.)

In the second part of the experiment, the speed of reading was measured when the eye had had *15 minutes* to adapt to each light intensity before the reading began. Six groups of 72 readers each were subjects.

> It is usually stated that the major portion of retinal adaptation has taken place by fifteen to twenty minutes. If the results in Part II differ from those in Part I, it should be due to the difference in adaptation time . . . when light intensity is increased, reading rate increases from 0.1 to 3.1 footcandles, but no more when the brightness is raised above the 3.1 footcandle level. . . . The contrast in results from Parts I and II emphasizes the importance of providing adequate visual adaptation to the illumination intensity under which the eye is to work. (357, pp. 565-566.)

Of interest here is the fact that the speed of reading was not increased by raising the level of illumination above three footcandles after adequate adaptation.

Reviewing his own and related experiments Tinker concludes that:

> When discrimination of rather fine detail is required in reading, a minimum intensity of about eight to ten foot-candles is essential. . . . In ordinary reading, however, a wide range of intensities may be employed without discomfort or fatigue although the speed of reading may become less at the lower intensities. If distribution is adequate, reading may be safely done under illuminations of from two to forty foot-candles. (348, p. 677.)

With this general recommendation Ferree and Rand would also agree, assuming of course that other variables were adequately controlled (103, 104).

Luckiesh and Moss recommend:

50 to 100 footcandles for severe and prolonged tasks such as proofreading, difficult reading, etc.

20 to 50 footcandles for moderately critical and prolonged tasks, such as clerical work, ordinary reading, etc.

10 to 20 footcandles for moderate and prolonged tasks of office and factory, and when not prolonged, ordinary reading, etc. (203, p. 350.)

However, these same writers also assert:

> It has been definitely established that intensities of illumination as high as 100 footcandles are desirable for such a visual task as reading ordinary black print upon white paper. (201, p. 273.)

Again, they say:

> . . . it is indicated that the ideal level of illumination for reading even large type excellently printed is above 100 footcandles. Therefore, ten footcandles on 8-point type is a very conservative standard of visibility. (203, p. 343.)

These same investigators (203, 212) support their recommendations by using in some instances the Visibility Meter (shown in Figure 28) which they designed. This device is intended to determine the amount of illumination required to see a particular test object as "easily" as a standard test object can be seen.

> This instrument . . . consists essentially of two colorless photographic filters with precise circular gradients in density which may be rotated simultaneously in front of the eyes while looking at an object or while performing a visual task. The observer holds the instrument in approximately the same position that eyeglasses are worn, and with a finger of the right hand slowly turns a disk which rotates the circular gradients until the visual threshold or limit in the performance of the visual task is reached. The procedure is quite similar to that employed in operating a visual photometer. . . .
>
> The gradient filters . . . not only reduce the apparent brightness of the visual field due to absorption, but also lower the contrast between the object of regard and its background due to the slightly diffusing characteristics of the photographic film which produce the effect of a "veiling" brightness over the field of view. The brightness of the retinal image may be varied by the actual filters used, over a range sufficient to alter the size of the threshold stimulus by a factor of two. (203, pp. 168-170.)

It has been said of this instrument that:

> The measurements with the visibility meter consist in interposing between observer and test object a variable filter. The test consists in resolving two vertical bars while the total illumination reaching the eye is varied by means of the filter. Of course, the same result, so far as illumination is concerned, might be obtained simply by varying the intensity of light on the test object. The visibility meter, however, does something else: it introduces another variable through the progressively increasing scatter or fogging effect of the filter. To overcome this combined result of reduction

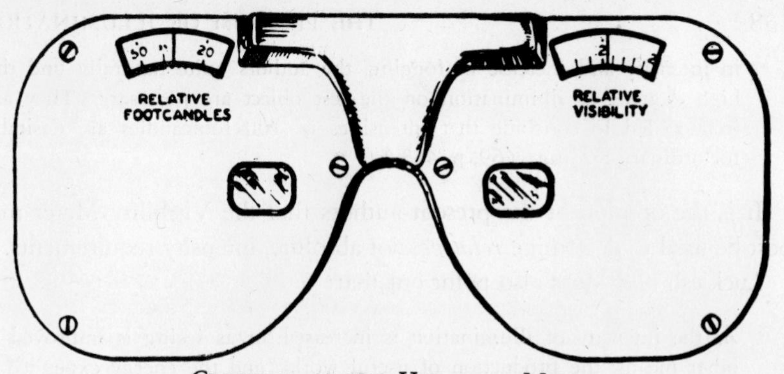

Close-up of the Visibility Meter

(After M. Luckiesh and F. K. Moss, 203)

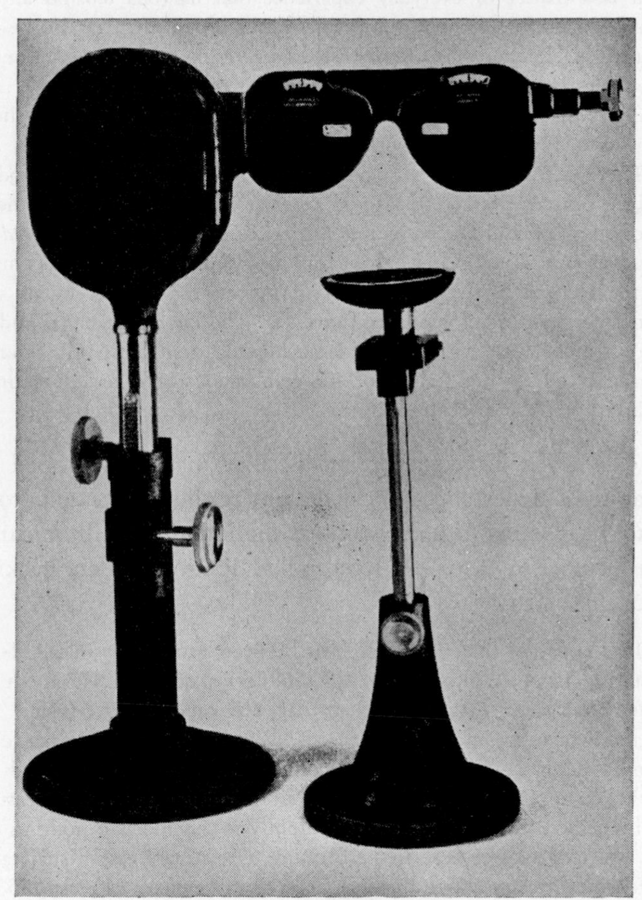

Figure 28

The Luckiesh & Moss Visibility Meter

(After M. Luckiesh and F. K. Moss, 212)

> in intensity and increase in fogging, the authors quite naturally find that high degrees of illumination on the test object are necessary. They are, in fact, led to conclude that intensities of 100 footcandles are desirable for ordinary reading. (69, p. 463.)

It is the opinion of the present authors that the Visibility Meter may best be used to determine *relative,* not absolute, intensity requirements.

Luckiesh and Moss also point out that:

> As the intensity of illumination is increased, or as seeing is improved by other means, the production of useful work (and the energy expended in useful work) increases and eventually reaches an optimum. . . .
>
> It is a matter of everyday experience that nervous tension and fatigue commonly cause a tightening of certain muscles. . . . It may also be observed that muscular energy is often wasted as a result of strain or fatigue which originates remotely from the place where it may manifest itself. . . . In this case, an inadequacy in conditions for seeing is manifested in the useless expenditure of muscular energy.
>
> The muscular strain, using the term in its usual sense, produced by fatigue or strain is referred to as *nervous muscular tension* in the present discussion. Measurements of this factor are designated as *indicated nervous muscular tension,* since we have no means of knowing the completeness or the accuracy with which this criterion appraises or measures these internal psycho-physiological reactions. . . . The method evolved and used in the research . . . consisted in measuring the changes in muscular tension as registered by the fingers of the left hand which rested naturally and lightly upon the knob of a concealed key. (197, pp. 541-543.)

The data given in geometric means show that the indicated nervous muscular tension developed incidental to reading decreased from 63.2 grams to 54.1 grams to 43.0 grams as the intensity of illumination was increased from 1 to 10 to 100 footcandles. From their data Luckiesh and Moss conclude that:

> It is apparent that the differences between psycho-physiological reactions resulting from reading under different levels of illumination are of such definiteness and magnitude that they are capable of creating muscular strains which are measurable. . . . This *indication* of the waste of human energy due to inadequate levels of illumination may be considered as a conservative appraisal of the actual conditions. Certainly, it is measured at a point remote from its origin. Apparently it can indicate nothing else than an effect of greater ease in performing a relatively easy visual task under intensities greatly above the threshold requirements. (197, p. 553.)

In evaluating this statement, it should be remembered that muscle tension may in some instances facilitate behavior. It is also true that learning changes the amount of tension shown in different tasks.

It may be valuable to consider the recommendations of Luckiesh and Moss in relation to other findings. It is reported (for example, 233) that glare interferes with visual acuity. It is known that the possibility of glare interference begins at around 25 footcandles (376). Ferree and Rand (106, Pt. II) report that glare may interfere at even lower intensities when artificial light (Mazda lamps), rather than daylight, is used for illumination, due to the yellow color and the relatively poor diffusion of the Mazda light. At the recommended 100 footcandles or more the danger of glare must always be remembered. It is also known that pupillary diameter or size depends in large measure on the intensity of illumination incident upon the eye and that the pupil constricts in the presence of bright light, especially if that light is close to or directed into the eye. At extremes of constriction, characterized by the so-called pin-point pupil, however, (as well as at extremes of dilation) visual acuity is impaired. Luckiesh and Moss (199) present data on the heart beat during reading under 1 footcandle and under 100 footcandles. The differences in heart beat are not all statistically significant, even though a decrement is shown under both circumstances. It is interesting, however, to note that the heart rate at 100 footcandles is higher than at 1 footcandle of illumination. The question is whether too high a level of illumination has been recommended.

Luckiesh and Moss object to many experiments in this field on the grounds that rate of reading is a poor criterion by which to test visibility or ease of reading.

> The results of a series of carefully controlled investigations, involving diverse visual variables, reveal that the normal rate of reading is an insensitive indicator of readability as compared with rate of blinking. Furthermore, the appraisals of readability by the two criteria are frequently in disagreement. Whether or not the criterion of involuntary blinking adequately appraises all factors involved in readability, it appears to be far more significant, from both theoretical and experimental viewpoints, than the criterion of rate of reading. (209, p. 269.)

It is a question whether this "disagreement" is a function of the carefully controlled investigations or of the technique of presentation and evaluation of data. Data on rate of reading have been published by Luckiesh and Moss (203) for one experiment in which 14 subjects read for 30 minutes in each case under 1, 10, and 100 footcandles of illumination. For another experiment (203), data are presented on the rate of blinking during reading for five minutes under each of the same illumination intensities. The mean scores for rate of reading were, respective to illumination intensity: .716, .728, and .747; for rate of blinking the corresponding mean scores were: 34.6, 34.6, and 35.4. Using the method of reporting favored by Luckiesh and Moss, these data are presented (Table 5) as 100, 101.7, and 104.3 for rate of reading and 100, 100, and 102.3 for rate of blinking. Analysis of the difference between these means permits the conclusion that reading rate under 1 footcandle is not significantly different from that under 10 footcandles, nor is that under 10 footcandles significantly different from reading rate under 100 footcandles. Rate of blinking was also not significantly different under 1 footcandle as opposed to 10 footcandles, nor under 10 footcandles as opposed to 100 footcandles. It will be noted that the conclusions from these particular experiments do not suggest making a recommendation of 100 footcandles as opposed to lower intensities. But more important at the moment is the fact that conclusions to be drawn from the rate of

TABLE 5. AVERAGE NUMBER OF BLINKS OCCURRING DURING THE FIRST AND LAST FIVE-MINUTE PERIODS OF AN HOUR OF READING UNDER LEVELS OF ILLUMINATION OF 1, 10, AND 100 FOOTCANDLES

	1 ft-c		10 ft-c		100 ft-c	
	first	last	first	last	first	last
Number of blinks	35	60	35	46	36	39
Relative rates of blinking	100	171	100	131	100	108
Percent increase	71.5±5		31.4±3		8.3±1	

(After M. Luckiesh and F. K. Moss, 207 and 210)

reading are comparable to those to be drawn from the rate of blinking—in short, no distinction is made with certainty here in the effectiveness of the two criteria. (S. J. MacPherson [217] has also used blinking rates in assessing various types of lighting while various visual tasks were performed.)

It is recognized, of course, that other data presented by Luckiesh and Moss to support the contention that the normal rate of reading is an insensitive indicator as compared with rate of blinking may warrant such a distinction as that referred to above. In an experiment by Hoffman (142) in which subjects read for four hours, the rate of reading (number of lines read) and the rate of blinking were determined from five-minute samples at the beginning of the four hours and at the end of each half-hour thereafter. Blinking had significantly increased at the end of an hour's reading; rate of reading was already significantly decreased at the end of a half-hour of reading.

The preceding statement, of course, does not imply that the blinking rate cannot be used as a criterion with which to investigate any illumination problems. Ponder and Kennedy (292) report little change in the individual's rate of blinking in a wide range of illumination intensities, including total darkness. McFarland, Holway, and Hurvich (227) offer data for three subjects which show that the rate of blinking increased as much after an hour's reading under 650 footcandles as under 0.5 footcandles.

Luckiesh and Moss (210) report an experiment in which 11 subjects read for an hour at a time under 1, 10, and 100 footcandles. The blinking rate was determined for the first and last five minutes of each such hour of reading. Luckiesh and Moss accept the tentative hypothesis of Ponder and Kennedy and others that the rate of blinking is affected by or may be indicative of the strain or tension caused in an individual by, among other things, the difficulty of a task. The assumptions, then, upon which this experiment is based seem to be that, in reading, the illumination intensity is inversely related to tension (the lower the illumination, the greater the tension) and that the degree of this tension is indicated in some way by the rate of blinking. The experiment, of course, was not designed to test these assumptions, but, accepting them, it had as its purpose the determination of the illumination intensity requisite for facile reading.

The significance of the differences shown in Table 5 has been determined by Hoffman, using the data presented on page 230 of *The Science of Seeing* (203). The t-ratios evaluating each difference are shown in Table 6.[1] They are listed according to the comparisons made between first or last five-minute intervals under 1, 10, and 100 footcandles of illumination.

The ratios in group I of this table compare the rate of blinking at the beginning and end of an hour's reading under each of the three

[1] This table is reproduced by permission from a paper by Hoffman entitled "Luckiesh and Moss on Reading Illumination," Journal of Applied Psychology, 1947, *31,* 44-53. This article in general is an expanded discussion of the work on illumination by Luckiesh and Moss as presented here.

TABLE 6. ANALYSIS OF THE DIFFERENCES AMONG THE AVERAGES SHOWN IN TABLE 5

	Five-minute periods compared	t-ratios
Group I	1 ft-c; first vs. last	2.654 *
	10 ft-c; first vs. last	2.450 *
	100 ft-c; first vs. last	2.410 *
Group II	1 ft-c first vs. 10 ft-c first	0.000
	10 ft-c first vs. 100 ft-c first	0.830
Group III	1 ft-c last vs. 10 ft-c last	2.594 *
	10 ft-c last vs. 100 ft-c last	2.251 *

* Significant at the 5% level of confidence

illumination intensities. It will be noted that in all three instances the view is tenable that blinking significantly increased. The same comment can, then, be made regarding the data of this experiment as was made regarding the experiment previously reviewed on indicated muscular tension. It may be asserted that no crucial or optimal intensity is established by this experiment; it is merely implied as being somewhere above 100 footcandles — assuming that there is advantage in further reducing if possible the rate of blinking.

The design of this experiment should be noted. Its purpose was to demonstrate the effect of the illumination variable. During the first five minutes of reading under each intensity of illumination, it is reasonable to assume that the most salient factor varied was this illumination intensity itself. In a comparison of these several sample periods, the data show no significant change from one illumination level to the next. This is indicated by the ratios in group II, which are not significant according to usual standards. The intensity of illumination, then, does not seem to be demonstrated as a significant variable as measured in these circumstances. Luckiesh and Moss, however, made comparisons after an hour of reading. In connection with this fact the recent experiment by Hoffman (142) referred to above is relevant. In this experiment it was demonstrated that there are significant changes in the rate of blinking and in other eye-movement measures of reading under *constant* illumination, *which changes already occur within an hour of continuous reading.* This leads the present writers to suggest that Luckiesh and Moss have demonstrated (group I ratios) a "work decrement" of some sort. The term decrement is used not to mean that the number of blinks decreased, but rather to imply a change of a presumably deleterious nature — the higher the rate of blinking, the worse the reading situation is assumed to be.

When, however, the decrement after reading under 1 footcandle is compared with the blinking data after reading under 10 footcandles, the latter are found to be significantly lower — group III ratios. But when the last five minutes of reading under 10 footcandles is compared with the last five minutes under 100 footcandles, a significant difference is also found. This focuses special attention on blinking performance during what may be called the last 100-footcandle five minutes as compared with the *last 10-footcandle* five minutes and with the *first 100-footcandle* five minutes. The difference in magnitude of the two t-ratios evaluating these comparisons (the second in group III and the third in group I) suggests that performance at the end of an hour's reading under 100 footcandles is more like that at the end of an hour's reading under 10 footcandles than it is like that at the beginning of reading under 100 footcandles. This suggests that decrement or the work-in-time factor may have been more important than the illumination variable in influencing the present data.

An additional comment may be made. The difference in magnitude of the two t-ratios in group III gives indication that the decrement was less for reading done under 100 footcandles than for reading under the lower intensities of illumination. The difference between the last five-minute periods at 100 footcandles and at 10 footcandles is seemingly less than the difference between those at 10 footcandles and at 1 footcandle. All the ratios in group I are significant; if the second ratio in group III had been insignificant, it could then be concluded that decrement under 100 footcandles is no different from the decrement under 10 footcandles. Therefore, 10 footcandles might seem to be just as good as 100 footcandles as far as minimizing "fatigue" is concerned. But the comparison of the last five minutes under 10 footcandles with the same period under 100 footcandles is significant. Even though the question of whether some intensity less than 100 and more than 10 footcandles would be as satisfactory is still left open, the above finding points to the conclusion that reading is less difficult under 100 footcandles than under 10 footcandles. This finding, then, is the important one that has been sought in this discussion since the recommendations of Luckiesh and Moss were first considered.

It may be of interest to some readers to know that none of the t-ratios reported in connection with the above blinking experiment would be regarded as significant if a 1 per cent level of significance had been chosen. Such a level could quite legitimately have been chosen in view of the other findings reported in this discussion of the problem of illumination. Before accepting the recommendations of Luckiesh and Moss, which are at variance with so many other conclusions, one would wish to be very confident that the recommendations were justified. Ratios insignificant at the 1 per cent level of confidence would, of course, mean that no significant differences had been demonstrated.

In a recent critique of the experiments of Luckiesh and Moss, D. G. Cogan has stated:

> Needless to say, the recommendations of this science[2] . . . have come as a considerable surprise to those familiar with man's ability to adapt himself to dark, and to those who are acquainted with previous reports showing that 10 foot-candles are adequate for ordinary purposes, and not more than 20 foot-candles for exceptionally fine work. . . .
>
> The other source of experimental data that is said to prove the necessity of light intensities considerably in excess of present conditions is the alleged correlation of different illuminations for reading with certain biologic changes. Specifically, the authors state that reading under low illumination produces increased tension of the finger on a push button, increased size of pupil, slowing of heart, decrease in amplitude of convergence, increased frequency of blinking, and more recently, changes in the rate of reading. Some of the data have been misinterpreted by the authors, and some have been contradicted by the work of others. None of the experiments are above controversy, and all are done with the wide intensity variations of 1, 10 and 100 foot-candles—in some experiments 0.1 and 10 foot-candles only were used, whereas in others only 1 and 100 foot-candles—so that deductions concerning the intermediate intensities, which are the significant ones, of 5, 10, 20 and 40 foot-candles are invalid. The criteria of comfort and work output are, according to the authors, unreliable. Thus they dispose of the considerable amount of data of previous investigators that indicate that for all practical purposes light intensities of 10 foot-candles are adequate. (69, p. 463.)

Tinker states that:

> The experiments of Luckiesh and Moss have led them to recommend what seem to be excessively high light intensities for visual tasks. . . . Re-examination of their data, however, suggests that their conclusions are not justified by their findings. . . .
>
> Although all indications suggest that the critical level for reading 10- to

[2] The science of seeing promulgated by Luckiesh and Moss.

> 12-point type is around 3 to 4 foot-candles (most certainly this critical level is below 10 foot-candles), it is suggested that any specifications made should provide a margin of safety. The conclusion is that 10 to 15 foot-candles should provide hygienic conditions when one's eyes are normal and print is legible. (357, p. 570.)

The intensity of illumination under which reading was done in the new experiments reported in later chapters of this book was 16 foot-candles. The choice of this illuminating intensity was made in the attempt to make the best generalization from the experimental evidence available. This level was judged to be satisfactory for the work of reading required.

It may seem to some readers that this chapter, which is an attempt to review the literature on the effect of illumination on reading, is unduly detailed. Unfortunately, as shown, however, there is a striking difference of opinion between experts on this matter, and it was necessary for the purposes of the present investigations to discuss these differences. It is hoped that the positive conclusions of this chapter concerning good levels of illumination for experimental work or for daily work with reading will be of value. In the next chapter we review and evaluate the methods that have been used to study eye movements.

Chapter 6

The Recording of Eye Movements

MANY of the data of the experiments reported in the later chapters of this book have been derived from study of records of the movements of the eyeballs during a long reading period. Such study and measurement are possible only when apparatus is used to record objectively the movements as they occur.

Simple and direct methods of studying eye movements have, of course, given valuable data, but the general trend of eye-movement research has necessarily been toward the development of refined methods of recording. This refinement of methodology is required in the effort to measure as accurately and as validly as possible the oculomotor behavior that is observed. Recording devices have the advantage not only of making a permanent record of the phenomena studied but also of allowing later quantitative measurement of the records of the eye movements. This procedure has made possible the solution of a whole series of problems dealing with the activity of the eyes in reading and in other tasks.

The technique used in the present experiments involves the adaptation of a recently devised electrical method of recording the movement phenomena of the eyes. In its present form it has not been used, so far as the writers know, by any previous investigators of long periods of reading. This new method, however, follows in sequence a long history of research and may be considered one present culmination of contributions to the technique of eye-movement recording. For certain purposes a refined photographic technique is probably superior, as pointed out by Tinker (363).

The principles of eye-movement recording can perhaps best be discussed by reviewing the gradual evolution of the methods which have been developed. In making such a review, one is impressed not merely by the number and complexity of the pieces of apparatus that have been used but also by the increasing awareness on the part of scientists of the requisite properties of good ocular-movement recording procedures. The methods to be reviewed here have in some instances been developed simultaneously. Emphasis will, however, be placed on the structural principles the devices represent rather than on the strict chronological order of their development, which may be determined by reference to the dates of publication given in the bibliography.

This review is primarily concerned with describing representative examples of methods developed to record the eye movements made by *human* subjects while *reading.* Several of the methods, however, were originally developed for use with animals; this is especially true of the earlier methods described by G. I. Grünberg (126) and M. D. Vernon (379). It so happens that of the methods developed, a few are applicable only to man, but many of the methods developed for use with human subjects could easily be adapted for animal experimentation. G. R. Wendt and R. Dodge (394) have discussed the problems of modification of recording methods for use with animals. Also, several methods have been developed which have been applied to the recording of phenomena of ocular behavior not related to reading.

The first methods to be developed were those by which the eye movements are directly observed without the aid of intermediate recording devices. The next methods were those in which instruments are used to supplement or facilitate direct observation but not to provide records of the eye movements for later interpretation and measurement by the experimenter. These simple eye-movement techniques were first developed when the intricacies of the methodological problems involved were not fully realized and before elaborate apparatus had been designed. The problems investigated in early eye-movement studies began with the general, qualitative classification of the larger and slower movements. These studies were made by watching the subject read, by placing a finger on the closed lid and counting the number of conjugate movements, by noting the words perceived in a line of print, and by other direct and relatively simple procedures.

Several methods of studying eye movements utilize the afterimage phenomena of the eye. S. Lamansky (183) in 1869 based his method on the principle that, when the retina of the eye is stimulated during its movement by an intermittent light, the number of afterimages that may be reported by an experienced subject is a function of the time required for the movement. The subject, in a dark room with his head held steady, looked from a fixation point on a dark screen past a prism to another fixation point. On the prism was focused the optical image of a petroleum flame made sharp and clear by a series of lenses. Between the lamp and the prism was rotated a disk with a certain number of slits which regularly interrupted the image flame. The time for the movement, then, could be calculated from the number of afterimages of this flame reported and the known rate of rotation of the disk.

G. Guillery (130) improved Lamansky's method by using an episcotister. This provided essentially a tachistoscopic instrument in which the duration and number of exposures were regulated by a sectored disk instead of by a shutter arrangement. In this instance a disk with four slits was rotated by clockwork behind a dark screen in the middle of which was a series of variously shaped openings — round, semicircular, square, or rectangular. The form of the afterimage, depending on which of these openings was illuminated during the movement, gave more reliable data than the counting of a series of similar images. A. Brückner (48) substituted for the episcotister and screen a so-called Ruhmkorff apparatus, which produced a controllable number of light sparks from two electrodes of a coil set in platinum points on a wood support. The sparks were sent through a 1.5-millimeter-square hole in a strip of black cardboard on which were a series of light-colored marks used as fixation points in ascertaining the length of the eye movement. In both these techniques, the subject's head was held in a fixed position, usually by the use of a Helmholtz biting board.

To test the hypothesis that the movement or sweep of the eyes was not a continuous excursion but rather a series of saccades and fixation pauses, A. Landolt (186) marked a line on a wall requiring a 30-degree excursion. In the middle of the line was placed a magnesium lamp. The subject fixated one end of the line. As soon as he saw the magnesium light, the subject swept his glance along to the other end of the line and closed his eyes. If the eye movements had been continuous, the afterimage would have been a straight line, but the results showed a persistent line interrupted by knotty points (*nœud*) corresponding to the saccades and to the fixations made.

E. Marx (221) determined the amount of movement during a "fixation" of the eye by placing the subject before a dark wall in which there was a hole. Behind the hole was a Nernst lamp, the glowing rods of which were hidden by a four-millimeter-diameter white card suspended on a thread. The subject, whose head was fixed with clamps, held the releaser for a shutter fitting over the hole and for the switch operating the lights in the room. When the room was lighted, the subject fixated a marker similar to the card behind the shutter, then turned off the light, held the fixation for the number of seconds determined by a metronome, and pressed the shutter key, which gave him a momentary glimpse of the card and lamp. The subject then fixated, or rather projected, the afterimage of this glimpse on a card provided and reported the point on the card which corresponded to the center of the afterimage. This center was compared with the location of the center of the originally fixated marker, and the amount of movement that had occurred could be measured.

The temporal aspects of the fixation "movement" of the eye were studied by Cobb and Moss (65) with an apparatus using a red and a green fixation light with a test object between them. The subject first fixated the red fixation point and then pressed a key which extinguished the red light and lit the test object and the green fixation light. The subject glanced at the test object and then fixated the green fixation light. The test object, midway between the fixation lights, was a black screen with 12 perforations arranged in a circle 38 millimeters in diameter. The perforations were each 2.5 millimeters in diameter. Directly behind the circle and concentric with it was a rotating disk with an opening which, as it passed behind each succeeding perforation in turn, allowed a flash of light to be emitted. The subject reported the number of these bright spots in the arc of the circle which he had seen. From these data and the known speed of the disk, the duration of the fixation on the test object could be computed.

H. Gertz (117) first studied the eye movements and their extent by noting changes in the phosphenes which he ascribed to the retinal currents of action during eye movements. Later, however, he measured the amount of movement by means of a Nernst lamp, mounted against a dark, homogeneous wall, which projected a pencil of light onto the optic disk of the subject. As the subject moved his eyes, he noted the diameter of the field he could see from appropriate markings on the fixation wall. The degree of the ocular excursion could be computed by using the known length of the diameter of the field.

It was soon discovered not only that the eyeball moves in either a horizontal or vertical direction, but also that, in addition to the general direct movement or shift in the line of regard, certain torsion phenomena appear. By torsion is meant that the eyeball also rotates slightly about its sagittal axis, somewhat in the same manner as if one were to hold a marble between the thumb and forefinger, turn the marble, and at the same time twist it slightly. A. Wichodzew (397) and B. Barnes (14) have developed techniques to measure the degree of this torsion. M. W. Loring's apparatus (196) for the same purpose consists of a large, vertical, graduated arc on which is mounted a telescope directed inward perpendicular to the arc. The whole arc can be rotated on its ends to any desired position determined by a protractor. The telescope can also be moved along the arc to any desired position and fastened there, depending on the position of the subject. The head of the subject is as firmly fixed as possible with one eye placed before a small brass ring suspended by firmly fixed iron supports. The telescope is adjusted to the position of the subject. Cross-hairs inside the telescope are turned to correspond to a suitable line on the iris of the subject's eye. The arc is then moved through a known distance as the eye is moved by the subject. The cross-hairs are then reset, and the amount of torsion is noted. One light illuminates the vernier scale for reading the circular rotation and another illuminates the eye of the subject.

The apparatus devised by R. Bárány (12) also required that the subject's head be as firmly fixed as feasible in an instrument — a mouthpiece of dental wax and head clamps were used. One eye fixated a small fixation loop. The other was well lighted by means of an adjustable electric lamp mounted beside it. Onto this lighted eye was focused a telescope by means of several screw systems. Two very fine turnable hairs in the telescope field were focused on a well-defined blood vessel of the iris, one hair horizontal and the other vertical to the vessel. The position of these hairs was measured on a circular scale around the telescope.

Then the head of the subject and the whole apparatus, including the telescope, were tilted by means of screws on the base of the apparatus; the degree of tilting was measured by a protractor. The first thread was again made parallel with the chosen blood vessel and the new position noted. The difference between this placement and the former measurement indicated the amount of torsion due to the tilting.

A problem related to torsion experiments was studied by E. J. George, J. A. Toren, and J. W. Lowell with an instrument called the Ocular Kinemometer. This instrument is designed to determine accurately a point within the eyeball through which the visual axis passes at all times during any horizontal excursion. An arc graduated from 0 at its center to 90 degrees at both ends is mounted upon two slides at right angles to each other which adjust the instrument to the subject's line of vision.

> The center of the circle upon which the arc is drawn we designate as the point 0. The arc is fitted with a sliding carriage upon which the tube . . . is mounted . . . the axis of the tube will always point to the arc center 0 for any position of the tube along the arc. . . . there is placed at the end of the tube proximal to the eye a very narrow vertical slit, and at the distal end a fine vertical needle. The centers of the slit and needle intersect the axis of the tube, and the subject's visual axis therefore coincides with the tube axis when the needle appears in the center of the slit. . . . For measuring the position of this point 0 posterior to the corneal vertex, there is mounted upon a bracket extending from the tube . . . a microscope . . . which focuses upon the cornea. The axis of the microscope lies at an angle of 90 degrees from the axis of the tube . . . so that the corneal vertex may be observed at a right angle to the visual axis. . . . Within the microscope is a graduated micrometer scale, the central graduation of which is marked 15, which graduation is coincident with the axis of the microscope. (116, pp. 835-836.)

In practice the tube is so adjusted that the axis and the line of vision are the same (the needle always in the slit through the excursion). If the center of rotation were on the visual axis, the corneal vertex would remain stationary at 15, but since it is not, the microscope micrometer measures the amount of deviation from the position 0.

The Blix Ophthalmometer (265, 334) focuses on the eye of the subject (whose head is, as usual, held as rigidly as possible) a lighting tube which reflects the image of the cornea into a second tube. This second tube is essentially a microscope, the eyepiece of which is fitted with an ocular micrometer. The position of a blood vessel in the conjunctiva or one of the striae of the iris is noted on this scale. The amount of movement of this convenient marker, coincident with the excursion of the eyeball, is then determined on this scale. The Bausch and Lomb Keratometer (328) is similar to the above-mentioned instrument except that only the tube containing the micrometer scale is involved. It is held at an angle of 45 degrees to the line of regard and is pressed against the brow of the subject to keep it stationary.

In some experimentation, direct observational techniques are still widely used for problems which do not require the elaborate equipment that is now available. Of such a simple, direct, observational type is the tube used by S. M. Newhall (260). The material to be read is placed against the short arm of an L-shaped rack. At the end of the long arm of the L is a U-shaped cut closed by a rod against which the subject rests the upper part of the lip under the nose. This is to steady the head without interfering with the ability to make verbal reports or to breathe. A table board is clamped to a laboratory standard to which in turn is clamped the observation tube and the light source which serves both experimenter and subject. The standard is brought up to the side of the subject and placed for convenience. A 20-diopter convex lens is set in the end of the tube and focused by sliding the tube back and forth in the carrier. When the distance between eye and lens is somewhat less than its focal length, a virtual erect image of the eye filling the field of view is obtained. By this means the eye may be observed as it moves in reading or in other tasks.

Miles has also developed a simple and practical technique, especially adaptable to studying the eye movements of children.

> It involves only the making of a hole about 1/4 inch in diameter somewhere near the middle of the page of copy that is to be read. The experimenter holds the copy, seating himself on a stool in front of the chair to be occupied by the reader. He holds the page in front of his face with the print toward the reader and with the small peep-hole close to one of his own eyes. The advantages of this simple direct method appear to be the following: (1) the observer is as close as possible to the eyes of the reader, (2) the eyes are seen from directly in front, and the movements are thus apparently larger than when seen at an angle through a mirror, (3) the direction of the reader's line of regard can be fairly accurately judged when the observer is looking through from the center of that field which the reader is covering, and (4) with the face of the observer thus hidden the subject reads with less distraction. (236, p. 373.)

L. E. Javal (163), who was the first to make a scientific record of observations of the peculiar saccadic movements of the eyes, finding that some methods interfered with the subject's normal reading environment, observed the movements from behind the subject by placing a reflecting surface somewhat to the front and to the right of the subject. The practicability of this technique has led to its adoption by many users. This mirror system may be rearranged to suit special experimental situations. For example, F. N. Freeman (109) observed the movements from behind the subject by means of a mirror. This was held in a frame adjustable to the subject's head at such a height that the top of the mirror was on a level with the lower edge of the subject's eyes when the head was held erect. The subject could still look over the mirror and read the material held at a level with the eyes.

The main disadvantage of direct methods of observing eye movements such as those just considered is that no permanent record of the actual movements themselves is available for measurement or study when the observation is completed. Also, many of the direct methods do not permit quantification or measurement of the constituent movements of the reading pattern or other eye behavior. Indirect methods of observation have therefore been developed involving techniques or apparatus which have the intermediary function of making eye-movement records which can later be measured, interpreted, and analyzed by the experimenter. These indirect methods, then, are primarily characterized as making possible a procedure or device for recording. Photography has been much used for this purpose and is at present perhaps the most widely known technique. Methods based on electrical phenomena have been studied and adapted to the problems of eye-movement recording. Several mechanical methods have been developed; these latter methods will be described first.

The difficult task has been accomplished of attaching levers to the eye which are then activated when the eye moves. In another indirect method delicate capsules are pressed against the cornea. The air system of these capsules is in communication with air systems that record changes on smoked or sensitive papers. Very light cups of various materials have also been fitted over the cornea and attached to it. The cup is then connected to a device suitable for recording.

For recording vertical eye and lid movements, J. Ohm (263) placed to the right of the subject two laboratory standards and a recording system using a kymograph.[1] One standard carried a horizontal aluminum lever one end of which was attached by a taut linen thread to the eyelid with a piece of adhesive tape. The free end of this lever, shaped to a writing point, pressed against the kymograph drum. Directly over this lever was the left-eye lever held by the second standard. This second lever curved over the nose and forehead and ended in a vertical arm three centimeters long set at a right angle to the other arm. The end of this lever was attached to the left eye in the same manner as was the right-eye lever.

For recording horizontal movements (264) a lever, which also recorded on a kymograph, was suspended from a pivot joint. A second curved lever was attached at right angles to the first lever and passed freely through a slot. This second lever was attached to the eyelid by a thread, or a thin glass tube was inserted in its hollow end. When the glass tube was used, a flat knob was provided which rested against the cocainized conjunctiva near the outer cornea. The tracing on the kymograph paper showed an inclination for a movement to the right and a declination for a movement to the left.

R. Cords (70) criticized the lever methods of recording eye movements by pointing out that accurate experimental results required that the lever be firmly attached to the eye with no slack between the eye and the lever, that the lever be as light and short as possible, and that pressure or pulling on the eye be avoided. Ohm (265) later modified his apparatus in keeping with these principles, using a better mechanism for controlling the movement of the lever and substituting a clamp to attach the thread to the eyelid.

The protuberance of the cornea from the rest of the eyeball has been utilized in a number of methods of indirect mechanical recording. Delicate capsules laid over the eyeball (usually with the eye closed) have been connected to recording devices in such a way that as the corneal bulge moved under the capsule, the air pressure in the system was changed. This change activated the recording device. One of the earliest investigators of eye movements to use a capsule type of apparatus was E. Buys (55). A capsule, over which was stretched a delicate gum membrane, was pressed against each eye by means of a movable lever arm attached to two standards. The two capsules were connected to a kymo-

[1] A kymograph is a revolving drum to which is usually attached smoked paper upon which a stylus may leave a tracing.

graph apparatus by rubber tubing. If horizontal, conjugate movements were to be recorded, the capsule was placed on the inner side of the eye (toward the nose); if vertical, over the eyeball. When horizontal movements were made, the recording levers activated by the capsules deviated in opposite directions.

A. Schackwitz (310) used an adjustable spectacle frame to hold the capsule against the eye. A vertical projection on the temple wire of the spectacle frame supported a brass tube (one millimeter in diameter) curved in a sort of L. The long arm of this L-tube was inserted in a fine rubber tube leading to a Marey tambour [2] behind the subject. The short arm of the tube was inserted in a soft capsule 14 millimeters in diameter with a two-millimeter rim over which was stretched a very thin gum membrane. This capsule rested gently against the lid of the closed eye and responded to the slightest movement of the cornea. Grünberg (126) used an essentially similar capsule system which, however, transmitted the variations in corneal bulge to the recording lever by direct mechanical means.

In J. Witmer's apparatus (404) the capsule was held against the cocainized eye by means of a head band and socket joints. Contact with the cornea was made by a glass bead fastened to the membrane of the capsule. Recording of the eye movements (along with a time line) was done on a revolving drum. An aluminum lever was controlled by a recording tambour in communication, by means of rubber tubing, with the eye capsule in this apparatus. L. Galley (112) developed an elaborate modification of the apparatus devised by Schackwitz. It consisted of a pneumatic relay involving several Marey tambours. The first of these, as in the apparatus made by Schackwitz, was connected, by a system of tubes and pipes, with a capsule. To this second capsule was attached a stud which controlled the movement of a small pipe. This pipe was connected at one end to the air chamber which filled the relay by an inlet. The other end of this system was shaped in the form of a small nozzle, which blew into another nozzle leading to an additional capsule and stud controlling another similar pipe nozzle, which was directed into a writing capsule. To this was attached a glass pillar controlling a lever that recorded on moving paper. The elaborateness of

[2] A Marey tambour is a capsule which responds to changes in air pressure and transforms them into mechanical motion which may be recorded, for example, on a kymograph.

this system of pneumatic amplifiers was in the interest of securing a sensitive recorder. When this system was filled with air, it was sensitive enough to pressure to respond with a vigorous movement to even a very slight change in the eye-capsule pressure.

A modified form of the eye capsule has recently been described by A. Arrigo (9). A very fine rubber sleeve is held by vacuum pressure against the lowered eyelid of one eye. On the end of this sleeve is a button with a flat surface in contact with the eyelid. The pressure changes related to the movements of the lid resulting from the eye movements below are transmitted through a rubber tube to a recording lever on a kymograph.

A. Lamare (184), who collaborated with Javal, devised a method by which eye movements could be "heard" instead of "seen." The first three fingers of one hand, placed on the face, held over the eye a small tambour. The membrane of this tambour supported at its center a small pointer or stem pressed against the eyeball. Two tubes of rubber were attached at one end to the cup of the tambour; the other ends were inserted in the ear of the experimenter. The changes in air pressure transmitted by this air system enabled the experimenter to count the movements of the eyeball. The return sweep of the eyes to the beginning of the line of print gave an intense and prolonged sound, and the saccades after the beginning of the line produced short puffs. Later Lamare (380) studied eye movements by causing the movement of the lid to break the circuit of an electric current, giving rise to sounds through a microphone.

In the older corneal-cup methods a very light concave cup connected with the first link of the accessory recording device was fitted directly on the eyeball. A. Ahrens (2) first placed a form-fitting ivory cup on the cornea of the eye after it had been strongly cocainized to relieve the great pain, excessive tear secretion, and so forth, caused by the apparatus. This cup carried a very small mirror serving to reflect a beam of light onto a screen where the movements could be observed. For permanent records, however, a bristle that traced on a smoked drum was fastened directly to the cup and the drum moved near the eye.

E. B. Delabarre (81) made plaster casts over the cornea of an artificial eye and obtained a smooth, concave surface that would fit fairly well over the curvature of the cornea of a natural eye. This cast was trimmed to a thickness that would make it as light as possible and yet retain the requisite firmness. The finished cup was pressed against the anesthetized eyeball. To record the movements he

> . . . adopted the method of casting within the plaster a thin wire ring, from one side of whose circumference a branch projected to the outside. It was then possible to make a hole through the center of the cast, of about the size of the pupil. The wire ring surrounded this hole, imbedded within the plaster, and to its projection, situated just to one side of the opening, it was easy to attach a light thread leading to a recording lever. On the side of the lever opposite to the attachment of the thread [was] fastened a thin elastic fiber, and thus the lever moved back and forth in correspondence with the horizontal movements of the eye. . . . By running the thread over a pulley, it was similarly possible to record the vertical movements. (81, p. 573.)

When this apparatus was fully adjusted and very light lever systems were arranged it made remarkable recordings of the real movements of the eyes. It must be remarked that great technical mastery of light-weight lever systems was required to make this system work and that the cup on the eye was often very painful.

E. B. Huey (149) used a plaster cup cast on a carnelian marble or a steel ball having a radius of curvature very little less than that of the cornea. The subject's head was fixed by holding the teeth in sealing wax into which the subject had bitten when the wax was warm. The recording kymograph, on iron standards, was placed before the subject. A trace was made upon it by a glass lever. This lever was connected to the cup at one end and was in contact with the drum at the other by means of a celloidin-tipped, tubular glass pointer. A holder for the reading matter was mounted on a sliding track, so that it could be at any measurable distance from the cornea. Later (150) an aluminum pointer was substituted for the glass rod, and the recorder which produced the time line was improved.

An aluminum cup in the middle of which was cut a round window for the iris was used by J. Orchansky (266). It followed the movements of the eye by adhesion to the moist cornea over which it fitted. A small mirror was attached to the side of the window in the cup by a jointed system which allowed the mirror to be turned in any convenient direction to reflect a light beam to a projection screen. There was also a small tube attached to the side of the window into which could be inserted a writing or recording lever. E. Marx and W. Trendelenburg (222) used a method similar to Orchansky's. In this experiment an aluminum shell or cup one-half millimeter thick, corresponding to the size and shape of the cornea, was used. But to avoid the frictional disadvantages of the former method, the cup was cut so that the part which went on the sclera did not interfere with lid movements. Recording was made possible by directing the light reflected from a small mirror attached beside the iris opening. The mirror reflected the light into a special camera, where it was focused on bromsilver paper moving in a track.

For lighter apparatus to be used in a rotation chair, G. Dohlman (92) placed a soft rubber cap over the cornea of the cocainized eye held open by a blepharostat. This cap was jointed to a pendulum lever on the end of which was a thin aluminum screen. This screen was interposed between a light source (fastened to a band on the subject's head) and a photocell. The screen, which at rest covered half the cell, increased or decreased, respectively, with the movement of the eye, the illumination on the photocell. The electric current generated by the illumination of the cell was conducted to a three-stage amplifier and then recorded by an oscillograph reflecting light from galvanometers onto sensitized paper.

A method, half mechanical and half photographic in technique, has been developed by F. H. Rodin and R. R. Newell for recording eye movements when it is necessary to bandage or pad the eye.

> A silver wire, about no. 18, was wound in a close helix about a mandrel about 1/16 inch (0.15 cm.) in diameter. Successive turns were cut off with scissors and straightened to form open rings. These were easily closed onto a tiny pinch of skin or conjunctiva, and they were retained well. On the completion of the test, they were easily removed by cutting the opposite portion of the ring . . . (303, pp. 525-526.)

After the eyeballs were thoroughly anesthetized, these markers were attached to the bulbar conjunctiva about two millimeters off the limbus, three of them in a semicircular arrangement and one at the external canthus by the last lower eyelash. Then, with the eyes bandaged, x-ray pictures were taken. The amount of movement was determined by the distance between the record of the bulbar markers and the marker on the canthus.

The mechanical techniques that have been described have the advantage of making a permanent record. However, involving kymographic devices for recording, as so many of them do, it is difficult to record movements of the eyes continuously over long periods of time. The kymographic record is limited to the length of time it takes the drum to revolve, or to the amount of recording paper available in a so-called long-paper kymograph. In order to meet this difficulty Delabarre devised a method which provided a continuous roll of smoked paper. Such a device is obviously difficult to use, however.

Photography, therefore, early suggested itself as a convenient technique for making continuous permanent records. The first photograph of eye movements is believed to have been made by Dodge (90) in November 1899 on a five-inch by seven-inch falling plate. This record is shown in Figure 29. It was a direct photograph of the sclera, radii of the

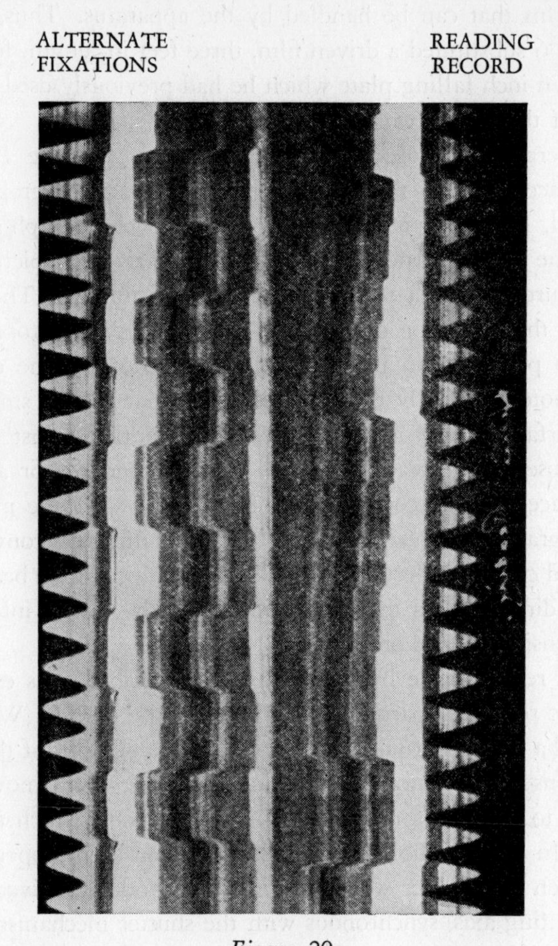

Figure 29

DODGE'S FIRST PHOTOGRAPH OF EYE MOVEMENTS

(After W. R. Miles, 239)

iris, pupils, and a swinging-pendulum time line. It included a reading record and a record of alternating fixations to the right and left. The subsequent development of this technique of photographic recording and its significant role in eye-movement research make this first successful photograph of special historical interest to all workers in this field.

Since the turn of the century, of course, photographic equipment has been improved for use in eye-movement recording in many ways. Now, for example, the length of the experimental period is limited only by the length of film that can be handled by the apparatus. Thus, Dearborn (78) in 1906 substituted a driven film, three feet in length, for the five-inch by seven-inch falling plate which he had previously used in a modified form of the Dodge camera, illustrated in Figure 30.

The general group of photographic methods may be further distinguished according to the manner in which the photographic equipment is used. Kinetoscopic or "movie" techniques photograph some small object on the eye or cornea or make possible serial still pictures of the motion-picture type of a particular structure of the eye. The same device allows the recording of the light reflected from mirrors, which in turn are so placed as to pick up light reflected from the eye. Other methods photographically record the light reflected from small mirrors or other surfaces which are themselves held gently against one eyelid, which is closed while reading is done by the other eye, or a mirror or patch is placed on the cornea itself. However, by far the most widely used photographic method, because of its reliability and convenience, is the so-called corneal-reflection method. In this procedure a beam of light is reflected directly from the natural mirror of the cornea into a camera and onto sensitive plates or films.

The first record made by Dodge, as just described, was essentially a kinetoscopic record of particular structures of the eye. O. Weiss (393) also devised a method of taking kinetoscopic photographs of the eyes and eyelids themselves by modifying the camera used. Film moved from a supply roll to a winding roll over two smaller spools which turned continuously. In order to hold the film still in front of the opening of the camera when the shutter was admitting light and thus give a clear-cut print, a rotating axis, synchronous with the shutter mechanism and having small rollers on each end, was located between the second small spool and the winding roll. As the axis rotated it struck against the film and unwound a portion from the supply roll. Then, until the winding

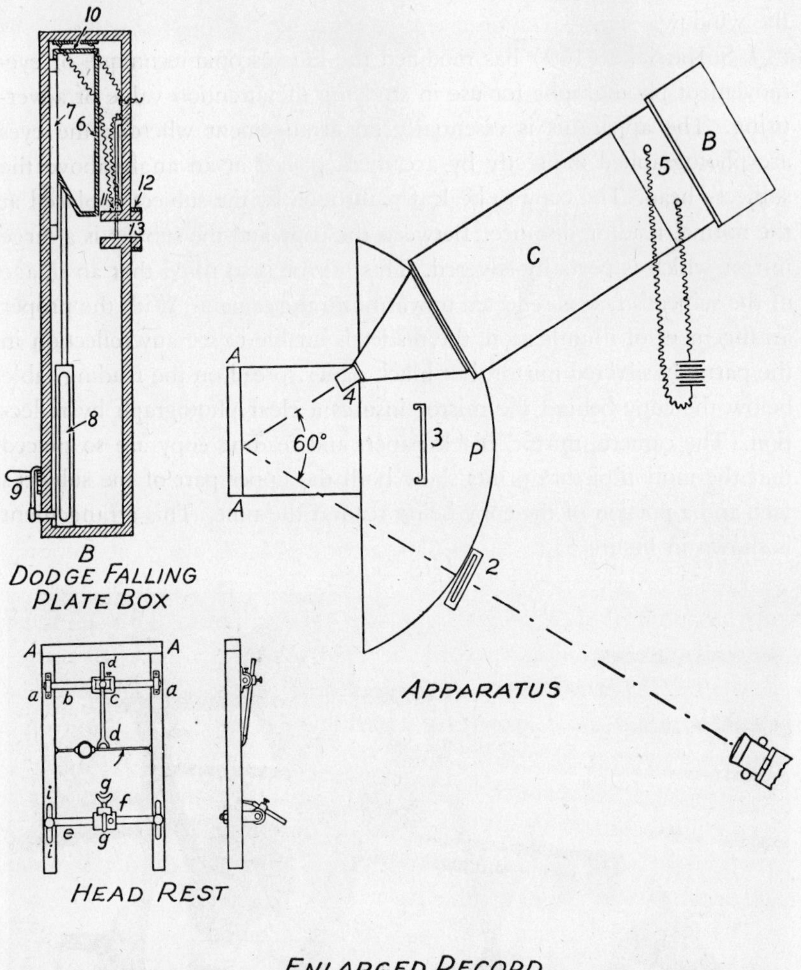

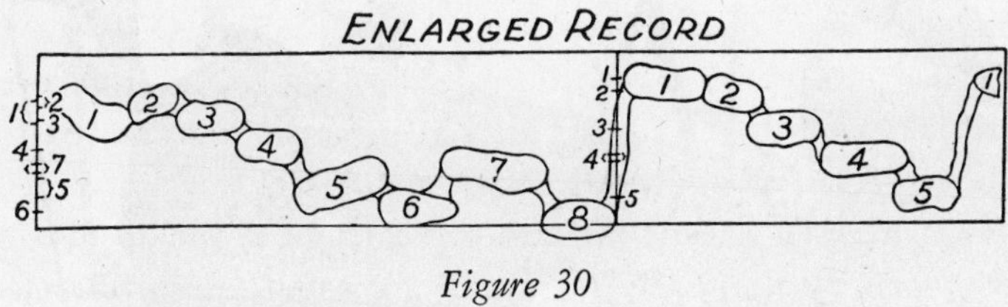

Figure 30

DODGE FALLING-PLATE CAMERA

(After W. F. Dearborn, 78)

roll had made the film taut again, the film was stationary in front of the window.

J. S. Karslake (169) has modified the kinetoscopic technique of eye-movement photography for use in studying the attention value of advertising. The apparatus is essentially an arrangement whereby the eyes are photographed indirectly by a camera placed at an angle above the subject's head. The copy to be leafed through by the subject is placed at the normal reading distance. Between the copy and the subject is a large mirror which is partially silvered. This mirror is so tilted that an image of the subject's face is reflected upward into the camera. With the proper arrangement of illumination, the reader is unable to see any reflection in the partially silvered mirror, but black paper spread on the reading table below the copy behind the mirror insures a clear photograph by reflection. The camera, mirror, black paper, and reading copy are so placed that the motion-picture prints show both the upper part of the subject's face and a portion of the copy being read at the time. This arrangement is shown in Figure 31.

Figure 31

A MIRROR AND CAMERA ARRANGEMENT FOR RECORDING EYE MOVEMENTS

(After J. S. Karslake, 169)

From the record can be determined page identification, first inspection of each page, the length of time given to any item, and the time at which the page is turned. For purposes of interpretation, these pictures are projected frame by frame upon a small screen placed in the center of each page of the experimental copy. Correlations between the reader's report of what areas were looked at in sequence and four judges' interpretation of that reader's record are high. Karslake has described (170) supplementary equipment for use in advertising experiments, for example, an exposure device, writing tables, and so forth.

C. H. Judd, C. N. McAllister, and W. M. Steele (167) photographed, instead of only the eye or part of it, a small patch of Chinese white attached to the cornea. These white flakes were prepared by spreading a thin layer of Chinese white on a thin layer of paraffin. When hard and dry, very small pieces were cut out and dipped in more paraffin and then smoothed to give a waterproof flake of white which adhered to the cornea. The subject was held stationary in a specially built chair with firm head and back supports. In front of the subject was a rigid crossbar to furnish a firm rest for the upper teeth. The subject also wore a spectacle frame to which were attached bright polished beads, small steel balls, or tiny mirrors, which were to provide points of reference on the photographic recording. This simple control made possible the discrimination of head movements as distinct from true eye movements. A kinetoscope camera was used in which was run a long, continuous roll of photosensitive, heavy celluloid. Between the lens and the film was a rotating shutter which revolved to give a series of exposures. While the shutter was cutting off the light, a sprocket wheel inside the camera, run by an intermittent gear synchronous with the shutter mechanism, drew enough film in front of the camera opening to expose a wholly new and stationary surface when the shutter again admitted light. There was a roll of film for each eye. A time line was made by a vibrating interrupter of the Kronicker type at the rate of 20 times per second. A record is shown in Figure 32.

Judd (165) later submitted a mechanical device for running the camera instead of the original manual method. McAllister also modified the original technique to counteract the possibility that the eye moved significantly during the time when the shutter was closed preparatory to taking the next image. Two camera systems were used, synchronized so that one was closed while the other was open for the exposure and *vice versa.* The film records from both were then compared.

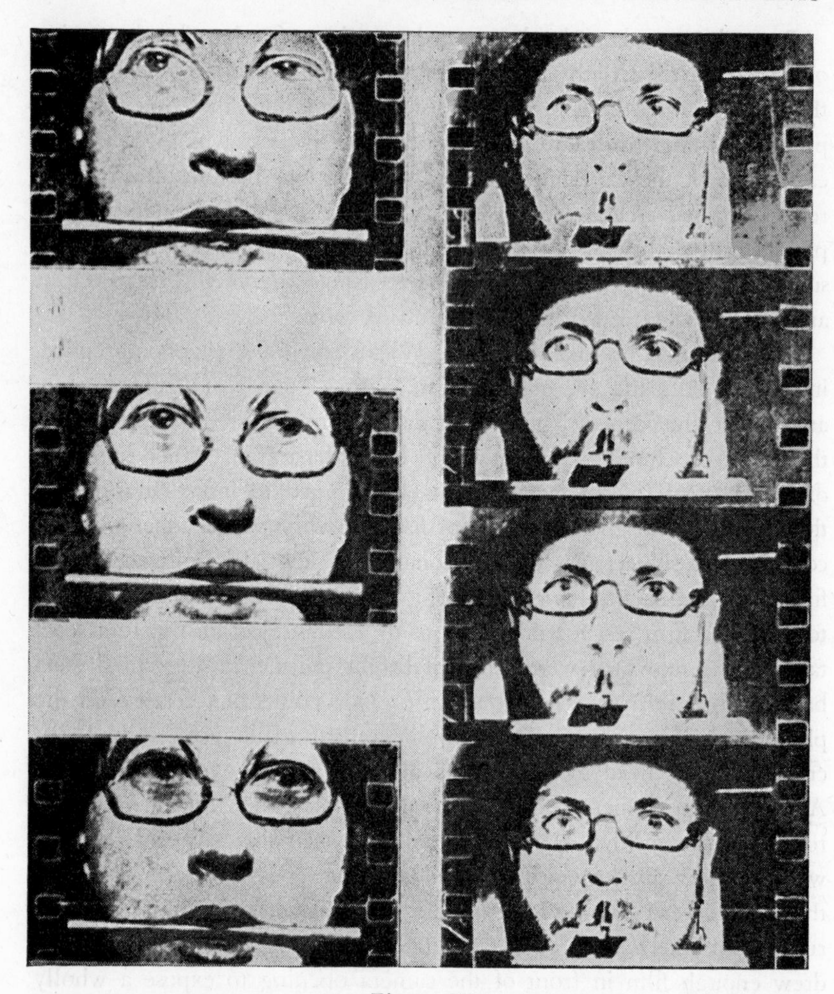

Figure 32

SAMPLE RECORDING OF AN "EYE SPOT"

(After C. H. Judd, C. N. McAllister, and W. M. Steele, 167)

Because flakes of Chinese white have a tendency to shift slightly on the cornea due to eye or lid movements and gravitational effects, E. Totten (373) has prepared another "eye spot" which reliably maintains its original position on the cornea for 15-minute intervals. Flexible collodion is spread out thin on a piece of glass and when dry painted with Chinese white laid thick enough to be densely white. After two days for drying, pieces of the desired size (up to one square millimeter) are then cut from the sheet, loosened from the glass with a thin scalpel, and again laid on the glass collodion side down. A drop of flexible collodion is placed on each white square; when dry, the superfluous portions are cut away leaving a very thin plate of white surrounded by collodion for protection. Gum arabic is boiled, a little spread out on glass, and a platelet dropped on it. With the excess gum cut away, this adhesive platelet is ready for use.

Dodge (85) compared the methods of photographing an object on the eye with the corneal-reflection method which he had developed. Instead of the Chinese white flake, he attached to the cornea a very small silver hemisphere by means of a piece of black tissue paper soaked in paraffin. As a source of illumination he used not daylight but an alternating-current arc lamp, producing a series of discrete flashes. This obviated the use of a kinetoscope camera and also made a time line unnecessary since the time of each exposure was known from the broken lines produced by the alternating light. Part of the light beam was directed to the silver hemisphere or bead and then into the camera; the rest of the light was directed from a mirror to the cornea and then into the camera. He found that the movements of the bead were slightly larger than those of the "bright spot" from the cornea but were more distorted.

A similar mechanical device for securing a photographic recording of light reflected from an object (a bright bead) attached to the cornea has been described by H. J. L. Struycken (332). The bead lay in a tripod, which was hung by fine hooks or clamps from the edge of the cornea. With a still-plate camera, the record showed the direction and size of the movement of the eyeball; and with a moving film, each separate excursion was discernible.

It is typical of kinetoscopic methods that, whether the photographing is direct or indirect, a record is still made of some relatively gross feature of the eye or of some "eyepiece" (bead, flake, and so forth), including on the photographic print an image of the rest of the eye. The more involved the print, the more difficult, of course, the interpretation and quantification of the record. In the interest, then, of refining the record, methods were developed which recorded simply a beam of light reflected from mirrors placed on or over the eye. The recording of the eye movements depended either directly on the actual excursion of the cornea or on the bulge of the cornea beneath the closed lid.

These mirror-reflection methods, however, are all instances of what has been called photokymography.[3] Photokymography is a technique used in recording phenomena of muscle tonus, knee jerks, eyelid reflexes, a variety of voluntary movements, pulse, electrocardiograms, galvanometer deflections, and so on.

Wendt and Dodge have described a universal photokymograph and the possibilities of its general application as a recording device.

> The instrument here described is an instance of a large class of instruments usually called "photokymographs." . . . A strip of sensitive paper moves behind a narrow slit through which light may pass to expose the paper. Such a photokymograph operates on principles entirely analogous to those of non-photographic recording systems. . . . If one should thrust the sharp point of a pencil through the slit and then move it back and forth along the slit while the sensitive paper was moving, a carbon tracing would be made on the paper. An entirely analogous tracing is left when a narrow band of light, crossing the photokymograph slit, is made to move along the slit. That portion of the light which falls on the slit passes through to leave its trace on the sensitive paper, and after development the result is similar to that achieved by the lead pencil. (394, p. 10.)

In photokymographic recording, one has an option of using any of several systems of introducing light to the slit of the photokymograph; mirror recording systems, however, have been the most generally useful.

Wojatschek (394) pasted a mirror to the closed lid of the subject's eye and photographically recorded the deviations of the beam of light reflected from the mirror. The mirror would tend to remain roughly tangential to that part of the corneal surface underlying it at the moment.

Dodge, in collaboration with R. C. Travis (374), has developed the standard apparatus utilizing the methods of mirror reflection and photokymography. The technique depends upon the following principles:

> 1. A mirror which is pressed lightly against the lid over the cornea will always tend to assume a position tangential to the surface of the cornea on which it rests as far as this is permitted by its mounting. . . .
>
> 2. The angular displacement of the mirror will depend on the following factors: (*a*) The angular displacement of the eye. (*b*) The geometrical relationship between the radius of curvature of the cornea and that of the eyeball. . . . (*c*) The relative position of the mirror with respect to the

[3] Instead of using levers or pointers marking on the smoked paper of a kymograph, photokymography uses a narrow band of light to record or "write" on photosensitive paper — hence the term photokymography.

> apex of the cornea. . . . (*d*) The thickness and stiffness of the intervening lid. . . . (*e*) The intercurrent movements of the lid. (87, pp. 167-168.)

The apparatus consisted essentially of a spectacle frame (shown in Figure 33) which held the mirror against the closed eyelid. Light from a 180-

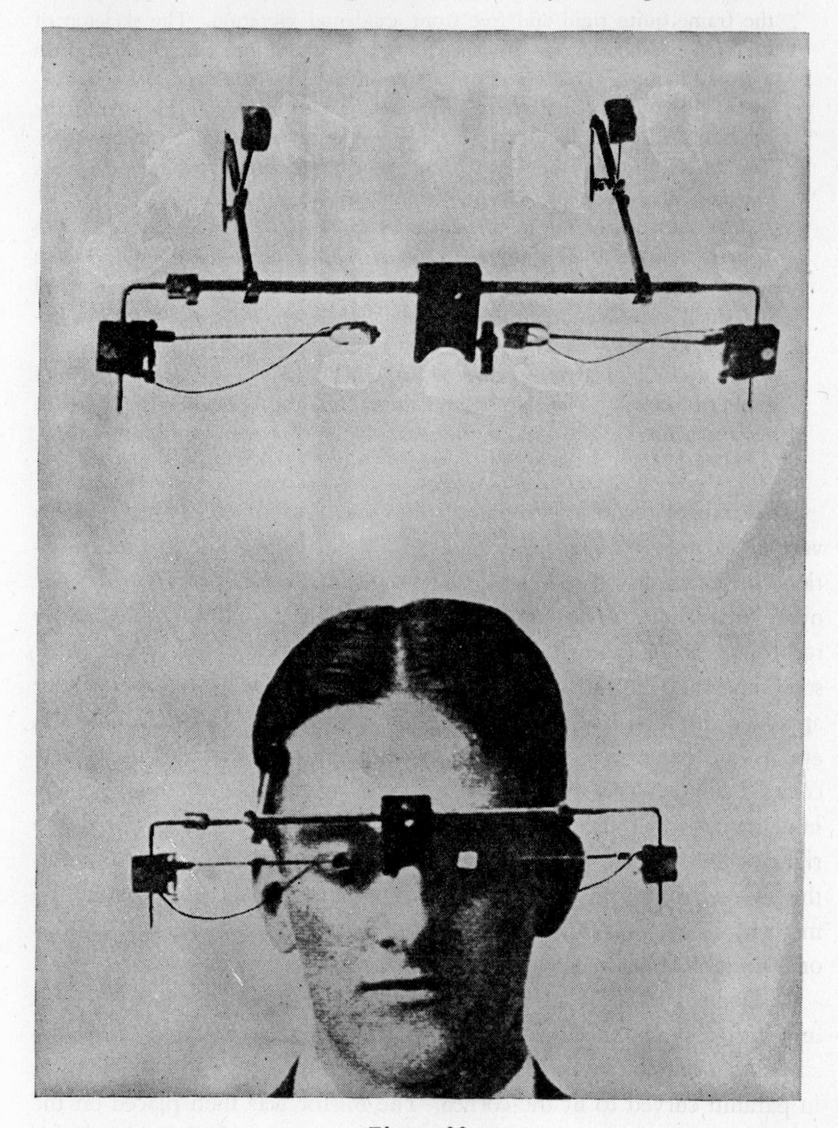

Figure 33

SPECTACLE FRAME FOR THE MIRROR RECORDING OF EYE MOVEMENTS

(After R. Dodge, 87)

watt nitrogen-filled incandescent lamp was reflected by the mirror into a suitable camera.

> The frame resembles a spectacle frame with adjustable nose-piece, temples, and secondary side supports to the head. These five supports make the frame quite rigid and free from accidental vibration. The skeleton of the frame is constructed from 1/8 in. brass tubing and resembles in form a capital letter *E.* The central offset from the stem would represent the nose-piece. . . . It is made of hard rubber, shaped to rest on the bridge of the nose, and may be clamped to the main stem at any angle to the temples. The longer offsets at the top and bottom of the *E* represent the temple tubes that hold the adjustable "riding" temple bars . . .
>
> Into the ends of the main stem tube are thrust the longer arms of two L bars. . . . On their shorter arms these L bars carry hard rubber blocks which may be clamped at various heights and angles. To these are attached the small cone bearings that carry the light steel arms on which the recording mirrors are pivoted. . . . Each recording mirror is held against the closed eyelid by a light forked, steel bar. . . . The axis of this bar is on a hard rubber block. . . . The mirror arms terminate in a fork which is drilled to receive a needle, the axis of the small block that holds the mirror. (87, pp. 172-173.)

This mirror-recording apparatus has been used to advantage with various secondary apparatus necessary for a particular experimental situation (for example, 71, 375). J. C. Fox and R. Dodge (108) used it for nystagmus studies. The same motor that moved the photographic paper recording the reflected light from the mirror rotated a wire cylinder, or sometimes a belt, concentric with the subject's head. On this cylinder appeared the stimulus patterns being tested. Scofield (314) used the left eye as the recording eye and rested the right eye against the velvet-covered edge, shaped to fit the eyeball, of a metal tube, three centimeters in diameter, which led into a small rectangular box open at the end to the right of the subject. In the box was a mirror placed at such an angle to the eye as to reveal the desired part of the visual field. As in the majority of eye-movement methods, the head was fixed by rigid clamps or adjustable blocks.

R. Dodge and W. R. Miles have devised a floating-mirror technique for use with recumbent subjects only. A concave mirror was prepared by silvering a one-to-two-millimeter square of glass wafer and embedding it in paraffin curved to fit the cornea. The mirror was then placed on the cornea in the desired position, usually with a fine badger-hair brush moistened in saline solution.

> Optimal positions for the concave mirror appear to be slightly to one side of and below the pupil, thus interfering to the least possible degree with vision.
>
> The adherence of the mirror to a given position on the cornea depends on surface tension. This is ample for the recumbent subject only. . . .
>
> The greatest variety of arrangements is permissible in conforming the optical system to the various experimental situations. . . . It seems to us also inadvisable to suspend the recording camera directly above the patient's head. This can be obviated by redirecting the deflected beam with a plain mirror to a horizontal camera slit placed at the rear. (91, pp. 125-126.)

The mirror-reflection methods require that some of the apparatus be in contact with the eye of the subject. If the subject does not become accustomed to the contact or if the mirror causes pain or inconvenience, it may influence the results secured by its use. It is an easy step, however, as noted above, to use the cornea itself as the reflecting surface instead of an attached mirror. This requires a rearrangement of the camera and optical system which has resulted in the development of the now common and valuable corneal-reflection methods.

This method of corneal reflection also depends on the curvature of the cornea and thus, indirectly, on the radius and regularity of that curvature.

> If the radius of the curvature of the cornea were infinitesimal, the apparent movement of the corneal reflection would equal the sine of the arc of movement measured on a great circle of the eyeball. If, on the other hand, the radius of the cornea were equal to the radius of the eyeball, and the latter rotated on its center of curvature, the corneal reflection would appear to remain stationary. As a matter of fact neither of the above suppositions is true; and the apparent movement of the reflection actually lies somewhere between zero and the sine of the angular movement of the eyeball. More exactly, since the average radius of curvature of the center of the cornea is 7.7 mm., and the distance from its apex to the center of rotation of the eye averages 13.5 mm., the apparent movement of a distant object reflected from near the center of the cornea will be slightly less than one half the actual displacement of the apex of the cornea but always in the same direction. More accurately, under the above conditions, the movement of the reflection will be (13.5—7.7)/13.5=(5.8)/13.5 of the actual movement . . . (85, pp. 81-82.)

G. M. Stratton (329) published the description of his technique in 1902 and a modification of it in 1906 (330). It was used to record on a single plate the eye movements following the lines of a diagram. The camera was placed directly in front of the right eye of the subject, which was the recording eye. A light to the side of the subject, from which he was shielded by a screen, was reflected onto the cornea by a mirror and then into the camera. The diagram to be followed was placed behind the subject on a rack tilted downward so as to reflect into a mirror tilted upward immediately in front of the camera slit but easily observable by the subject. The front of the camera was later modified so that these mirrors were unnecessary and the observer viewed the diagrams directly. In order to check any special effect that might have arisen from a particular position of the light or from any peculiarity in the movement of either the right or the left eye, the relative positions of the camera, diagram, light, and subject were alternated during the experiment.

Dodge and Cline (83, 90) described an improvement they had made following the same principle.

> The head rest . . . is fitted with an attachment for holding a narrow strip of white cardboard . . . which is illuminated by direct sunlight from behind the subject. It is the image of this piece of cardboard reflected from the cornea which makes the records. . . .
>
> A horizontal perimeter . . . carries the adjustable fixation points and a holder for printed matter. The perimeter was a horizontal wooden table fastened securely to the head rest, and strong enough to support the camera, which could thus be readily adjusted to the most favorable point of view, without refocusing. The fixation points were bits of white paper attached to knitting needles which could be set vertically into holes in the perimeter table. . . .
>
> The camera . . . was an ordinary 5 × 7 bellows camera fitted with a fair lens of 1⅜-in. aperture. . . .
>
> The plate-holder . . . is the vital part of the apparatus, since it must provide, not only for the regular motion of the sensitive film across the slit, but also for the registration of the time record. . . . The plate is held in a small wooden frame . . . guided by two brass rails. . . . Since there must be absolutely no lateral motion of the plate, all play is taken up on one side by a spring pressing the guide on that side against its track. The rapidity of the fall is governed by the escape of air from a cylinder into which the falling plate presses a closely fitting piston. . . . A second pump on the outside of the plate-holder . . . serves to force the plate up to the top of the plate-holder. . . . The release of the air is provided for by inserting between the valve and the inner air pump, a set of two tightly fitting brass tubes . . . A set of holes was drilled in the inner tube, and the fall is occasioned and controlled by uncovering one or more of these holes . . .
>
> The time records are produced by the oscillations of a pendulum within the plate-holder and just in front of the horizontal slit. The light at one end of the slit is intercepted at each oscillation of the pendulum, making a continuous time curve the entire length of the plate. (90, pp. 149-152.)

This apparatus soon came to be regarded as a standard piece of equipment, and subsequent developments were more often than not described as modifications of the Dodge method or modifications of apparatus originally described as a modification of the Dodge method.

Dodge (88) himself later introduced two new methods for recording time ordinates. One, by means of periodic resistance in the lighting circuit, produced a series of fainter spots on all the record lines appearing in a straight line across the film. For more frequent intervals than the two-second periods of this method, a perforated disk controlled by a fork-driven, synchronous motor was interposed between the camera slit and a secondary source of illumination. Between the years 1901 and 1903, Dodge modified the falling-plate chamber by using oil instead of air. By this means the speed of the falling plate could be reliably varied. F. G. Benedict, with W. R. Miles, P. Roth, and H. M. Smith (24), added a new device to move the falling plate laterally by small increments so as to get several records on the plate. To record stimulus presentation, a sliding contact was arranged inside the camera which completed a solenoid circuit turning the light on the subject's eye at the same instant the stimulus appeared.

Dearborn in 1906 described a modification of the Dodge apparatus, since used and modified by many other investigators.

> The light was placed at an angle of 30° to the right of the primary line of regard of the eye, and in the same horizontal plane as the eye. The camera itself stood at a corresponding angle to the left of the subject, and the pages or books to be read were then held in a book rest at a convenient distance (about 30 cm.) directly in front, so that the angular excursions of the eye to the right and left were about equal. . . . On each of the two uprights of the head rest . . . two spools of solid brass were fastened. . . . The two upper and the two lower were connected by a strong brass rod on which spools of brass were slipped. . . . These could be moved along the bars. . . . Through these brass blocks holes were drilled at right angles to the cross rod . . . and small rods inserted which could be moved up and down and were secured by thumb screws. To the end of the upper rod . . . a cross piece or "bridge" was fastened which could be adjusted to fit over the bridge of the nose much like a pair of spectacles. On the end of the lower rod was clamped a mouth piece with wax impression. This was so made that it could reach to the back teeth and be held securely. The bridge piece and mouth piece when rightly adjusted served much like a vise. The whole mouth piece and connections could finally be moved vertically in the slot . . . and securely clamped by the thumb screws at the desired height,

> that is, so as to bring the eye of the subject on line with the camera. . . . A "finder" in the form of a spectacle loop . . . facilitated in securing the right position for the eye. . . . The "finder" could be removed when the proper position was secured. (78, pp. 14-16.)

Dearborn, as above noted, later substituted for the original falling plate a motor-driven film. This apparatus is shown in Figure 34. J. Piltz (289) made records upon a film rotated by clockwork about a vertical axis instead of on the falling plate. E. Koch (172) had experimented with film moved between grooves by means of a kymograph motor. His apparatus had the additional feature of using a Nernst lamp as the source for the pencil of light which was reflected from the eyes into the camera through openings in a tube. In the side of the tube was an opening in which was inserted a prism reflecting onto the record the direct beams from an interrupted light, thus giving a time record. The side on which the camera was held depended on the plane of movement that was to be recorded. Modern photography has, of course, improved the apparatus for handling moving film, so much so that in contemporary research with the corneal-reflection method, motion-picture film or moving film rolls are used almost exclusively. It should be remembered, however, that in such equipment the film must move at a smooth and continuous rate and not stop and start as does the film in a motion-picture camera.

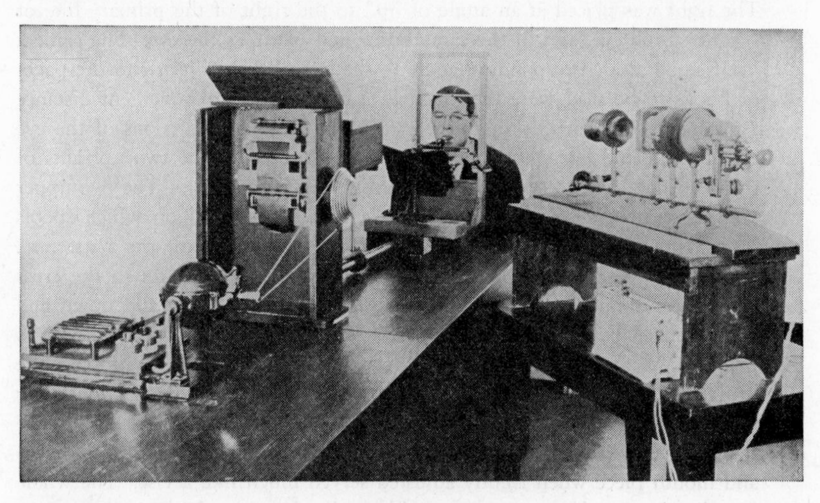

Figure 34

AN EARLY FORM OF THE DEARBORN EYE-MOVEMENT CAMERA

An apparatus developed by C. T. Gray (123), under the direction of Dearborn at the University of Chicago, included an arc light, controlled by an adjustable rheostat. These light rays were directed through a double convex lens (to concentrate the beam), a cooling tank, a violet filter (to reduce the apparent brightness), a small hole in a diaphragm (to cut off marginal light), and then onto two small mirrors just in front of the subject. These mirrors directed the beam to the corneas. To the head rest were added two cheek supports. The subject also wore a frame of the sort used for spectacles, on which was placed a highly polished bead. The reflection from this bead was always focused on the film so that any head movement was recorded simultaneously with eye movement. This is a most important addition, for it makes it possible to distinguish head-movement artifacts in the eye-movement record. The camera took simultaneous records from the two eyes. Adjustments of this optical system were made at the back of the camera box.

A. Walton has objected to the use of a carbon arc lamp because of its tendency to change in intensity, and to mirrors because of their liability to get out of alignment.

> By using an incandescent lamp projector set in a fixed position below the level of the eye, we are able to secure good records of eye-movements even when the reader wears glasses. A minimum of annoyance to the reader and to the operator results. (386, p. 593.)

Buswell modified the Dearborn-Gray apparatus (1, 52, 54) by substituting for the hand-feed arc lamp a 400-watt, three-wire, automatic nitrogen bulb which provided a beam of light constant in intensity and quality. For the 50/second vibrating tuning fork was substituted a 25/second tuning fork (providing the time line) so as to decrease somewhat the tediousness of calibration without affecting the validity of the record. For the camera system, a new mechanism to run a kinetoscope film was used to give longer reading time. A tachistoscopic device, which causes no more disturbance than turning a page, was used for holding long passages of reading material.

W. R. Miles and E. Shen (250) developed an apparatus incorporating the advantages of both the Dodge and the Dearborn-Gray methods. Two or three records could be taken on a five-inch-wide panoramic film. Though the reading was done with binocular vision, only movements of the right eye were recorded. The interrupted light from the carbon arc was directed to two small front-surface mirrors; the light was received by one, reflected to the other, and reflected from the latter to the eye. Though the whole eye was illuminated, only the sharp high light due to the curvature of the cornea was reflected into the camera. The record made by these investigators was supplemented by additional reflections from small spherical mirrors on bits of pith attached by a little gum arabic to the midpoint tarsal edge of both eyelids. For registering head movements the reflection from a bright bead on a spectacle frame was also recorded.

Another modifier of the Dodge method, who has also profited by other subsequent developments, is J. P. Guilford (127, 128). This experimenter recorded the horizontal movements by the reflection from a "bright spot" on panoramic film moving in the vertical direction giving an eye line of breaks or waves. The light from an electric arc was directed from the rear and at the subject's left along a tube (with a lens system to provide a concentrated ray of low intensity) to a mirror 18 centimeters from the subject's eye and directly below the camera lens. The light was reflected from this mirror to the subject's eye and then in turn into the camera. J. P. Guilford and J. Helson (111, 129) later substituted for the panoramic camera a motion-picture film that could be moved by an electric motor at a constant rate. To secure a simultaneous record of the eye movements and of the stimuli presented, a light was placed in circuit with the stimulus lights in such a way as to throw a pinpoint image upon the film beside the record of the eye movements.

The Vernon modification (379, 381) included the usual head and chin rest and a camera for vertically moving film. But by directing the light from the side and placing the camera over the subject, the central space in front of the subject was left free for reading racks.

> The light from the bulb . . . contained in the brass chamber . . . passes through a blue gelatin filter and the narrow aperture, 3 mm. in diameter, of a diaphragm. . . . The divergent beam of blue light passes along a brass tube . . . impinges on the right-angled prism . . . and is totally reflected on to the cornea of the subject's right eye . . . The beam is reflected by the cornea in a direction parallel to the sagittal plane, at an angle of about 50° with the horizontal; and impinges on a second right-angled prism . . . by which it is refracted and totally reflected into the brass tube . . . of the camera. . . . The divergent beam is focused by the lens . . . and after passing through the tube . . . and the aperture of the camera . . . forms an image on the film . . . (381, p. 64.)

The eye-movement camera (shown in Figure 35) developed by Tinker (344) at the University of Minnesota is now one of the

Figure 35

A CAMERA FOR RECORDING THE CORNEAL REFLECTION

(Courtesy of M. A. Tinker)

most elaborate of the large cameras. The important research findings made possible by this camera are reviewed in detail in other chapters of this book. Research using this camera has now covered many phases of eye-movement photography. The camera and head rests are mounted on a heavy oak table in a dark room. The light source and timing devices are in an adjoining room, the beam of light entering through a small wall hole directed to a mirror placed below the lenses and reading copy and then reflected into the eye. The head rest is a circle of steel with padded supports for the front, back, and both sides of the head and cheeks.

> The barrel of the camera, a brass tube 8 in. in diam., is approximately 70 in. long and is mounted on roller bearings which allow the whole camera to be moved forward and backward. . . . All adjusting is done by gears operated . . . from the rear of the camera. . . . The film and lens arrangement allow the following possibilities: (1) records from both eyes or from one eye upon either film; (2) records of one eye upon one film and the other eye upon the other film; (3) records from one eye and a reference point . . . upon either film. (344, p. 116.)

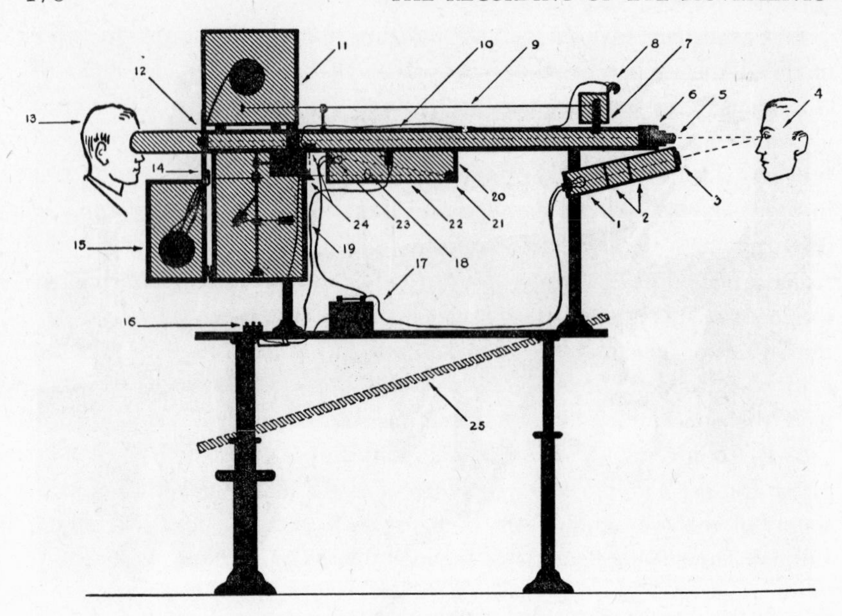

Figure 36

THE HARVARD OPTOKINETOGRAPH

1, 2, and 3 illustrate the enclosed source of illumination. The rays of light are reflected from the corneas of the eyes of the subject and are focused upon the film in the form of minute points of light.

1. Two six-volt electric light bulbs.
2. Two sets of baffle plates to eliminate indirect rays of light.
3. Lenses concentrating the rays of light upon the corneas of the eyes.
4. The subject.
5. Two photographic lenses focusing the rays of light upon the moving film.
6. A set of cams, controlled by the operator with knobs at (12), which adjust the position of the lenses to focus the light points upon the film.
7. A revolving holder for four selections of reading material. This provides enough reading material to keep the subject occupied long enough to become well adjusted to the process. Frequently, when a single paragraph is presented, the subject completes the reading before he settles into his habitual rhythm or rate of reading.

   The position of the reading material above the camera lenses was selected after finding that many readers have drooping eyelids or long lashes which interfere with the rays of light when the reading selection is below the lenses.
8. Reading lamp.
9. Control rod for reading selections.
10. The dark box or extended "bellows" of the camera.
11. Container for unexposed film.
12. A frame through which the pin-points of light may be observed by the operator during the photographing process as well as while focusing the points of light.
13. The operator. The telescope illustrated was designed to be used in a partly lighted room.
14. A cog wheel which drives the film.
15. Container for exposed film.

L. Carmichael, working under the direction of Dearborn, in 1922 modified the earlier Dearborn camera to make it more adaptable for clinical use. A camera called the Harvard Optokinetograph, illustrated in Figure 36, which incorporated a number of new and advantageous features, was developed by Comfort and Dearborn (*cf.* 335, pp. 77-79) in the years 1927-1929. The light source is placed under the lenses in this camera, a feature later adopted in the Ophthalmograph of the American Optical Company. The reading materials were placed above the lenses. This gave a wider visual span in the vertical plane and permitted more lines to the page. By a mechanical device the page, when read, was dropped out of sight and a new page exposed to view, which gave the opportunity for more prolonged reading.

E. B. Coburn in 1905 had adapted the falling-plate method of photography for the simultaneous recording of horizontal and vertical movements of the eye. Light from both eyes was reflected into the camera through lenses whose axes were inclined toward each other.

> In the interior of the box are stretched steel wires on which move two carriers . . . rolling on specially turned, grooved wheels. The carriers move at right angles to each other, one moving horizontally . . . and the other . . . moving vertically. The wires and carriers are so arranged that they are equally distant from the lenses, so that the size of the images and their movements shall be equal. The carriers are actuated by clockwork . . . and move simultaneously and at uniform speed. An attachment is provided by which the clockwork is stopped automatically when the plates have passed the focal points of the lenses. On the anterior surface of the carriers are holders for the ground-glass focusing screen and the sensitive plates. . . .
>
> To prevent the tracings of the corneal reflections of the two eyes from overlapping and interfering, a pair of 10-degree prisms . . . side by side, one with the base up and the other with base down, are interposed between the horizontal carrier and its corresponding lens. (68, pp. 1-2.)

---

16. Electric control switches.
17. Electric transformer.
18. Lenses focusing the time-line.
19. Pendulum regulator for the speed of the film.
20. A box containing the film timing device.
21. A silver ball from which the light was reflected.
22. A telechron motor with a rotating perforated disk which interrupted the light line on the side of the film making 10 points of light per second and making it possible to determine the duration of pauses of the eyes during reading.
23. The source of light for the above timing device.
24. Mirrors directing the light to the film.
25. A tilting device designed to place the reading material in a more natural position for the reader. This involved tilting the whole camera.

The Iowa eye-movement camera developed by, among others, H. H. Jasper and R. Y. Walker (161) and E. Murray (253) was modified to make simultaneous binocular records of both vertical and horizontal movements on continuously moving film. The light from the carbon arc source was directed through the usual lens system onto two adjustable front-surface mirrors and then to the eyes. But since this camera required that the light reflected from the corneas be recorded on two papers, a prism system of different strengths was interposed between the cornea and the camera to separate the light and direct it to the proper film. The entire lens unit was mounted so that it could be adjusted in three dimensions; adjustments were made in the rear of the camera by means of telescoping rods. Focusing was done on a plate of ground glass. A time line, a series of small black spots, was registered by a neon light located at the back of the camera.

H. E. Weaver (389) placed a pair of prisms before the lens of the Dodge camera in such a manner that half of the light reflected from the cornea to the lens was displaced slightly in one direction and the other half in the opposite direction. Using vertically and horizontally moving films, he secured by this arrangement records of both vertical and horizontal eye movements.

Both the above techniques required two films, one for the horizontal, the other for the vertical movements of the eye. H. F. Brandt (43) has developed an apparatus for recording the horizontal and vertical movements simultaneously on the same film. But the recording of the horizontal movements is not on the same part of the film as is the vertical record. The two records, though on the same film, are 39 centimeters apart. The film is so sprocketed that it is first presented moving horizontally, and then it is presented moving vertically. The movements which are selected for recording depend upon how the telescope lens is focused on the moving film. Reflectors on a head band direct light through another appropriate lens system simultaneously to record movements of the head.

B. Clark has modified the Dodge apparatus to record simultaneously horizontal and vertical movements of both eyes at the same place on a single film.

> The light-beam from each eye is picked up by a focusing lens . . . Beyond the lens the beam is divided into two parts, one central and one peripheral. The lens is mounted in a brass cylinder . . . 44 mm. in diam.,

> by the use of two tightly fitting brass collars. Within this cylinder a smaller cylinder . . . is fitted just loose enough to rotate. Two prisms are mounted . . . The first . . . is a total-reflecting prism of optical glass, mounted with a light brass housing which is in contact within the apex and the two non-refracting sides and also hooked under the edges of the total-reflecting surface. The housing slips into two tracks . . . where it is held in position behind the achromatic lens by a long sheet-brass spring which extends the length of the cylinder. The small cylinder is so rotated that the reflecting surface of the prism forms an angle of 45 degrees with the horizontal axis of the instrument. In the same housing a flat prism . . . 0.8 diopter in power, is placed with its base-apex line horizontal.
>
> The resultant effect of this lens system is as follows. The rays from the peripheral part of the lens are focused on sensitized paper without further change. They record horizontal movements as a *horizontal displacement.* The central rays are focused to one side of the peripheral rays, by means of the flat prism; but their motion is rotated 90 degrees by the total-reflecting prism, i.e., *a vertical movement of the eye will also cause a horizontal displacement on the film.* Thus it is possible to record the horizontal and the vertical movements of both eyes simultaneously on a single record. (60, pp. 325-326.)

It will be noted that most of the modifications of the original technique are not readily portable and must ordinarily be used in a laboratory. E. A. Taylor (335), however, incorporated many of the mechanical principles required in photographing eye movements in a portable instrument. This apparatus, known as the Ophthalmograph (3), made by the American Optical Company, is a generally useful eye-movement camera. It is shown in Figure 37. The apparatus is mounted on an adjustable standard and is provided with head and temple clamps and a chin rest. The light sources (lamps of the type used in automobile headlights) are housed in metal cases (on either side of the reading rack) in which are cut small holes through which a beam passes to illuminate the eye. The reflection from the "bright spot" on the cornea is focused, by means of two telescope-like lens systems, onto the film, using a ground glass window as a finder. The 35-millimeter film moves at a constant rate across a sprocket wheel from the supply roll into the winding chamber, from which any desired lengths may be conveniently removed, ready for developing.

F. Berg (26) has pointed out the unavoidable approximations involved in all eye-movement recording methods and the necessity for judging the worth of a particular method according to its inherent measurement errors. These arise either in the characteristics of the method itself or in

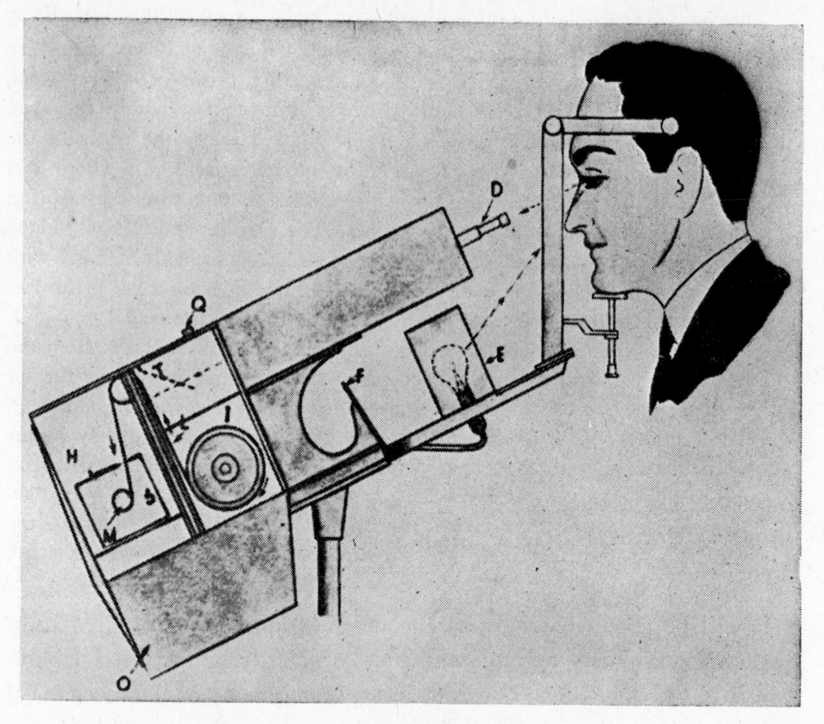

Figure 37

THE OPHTHALMOGRAPH

Diagrammatic Side View

(Courtesy of the American Optical Co.)

its application. The limitations should be met by employing in each experiment the method most applicable to the problem to be studied. Procedures can be varied in order to avoid undesirable features. In short, the question of the validity and reliability of each type of experimental apparatus is raised, as well as the problem of the form of application of the method to particular experimental situations.

With the photographic methods the angular displacement of the beam of reflected light depends on the angular displacement of the eye, the geometrical relationship between the radius of curvature of the cornea and that of the eyeball, and the relative location of the beam with respect to the apex of the cornea.

Experiments on the torsion phenomena of the eye (14) indicate that

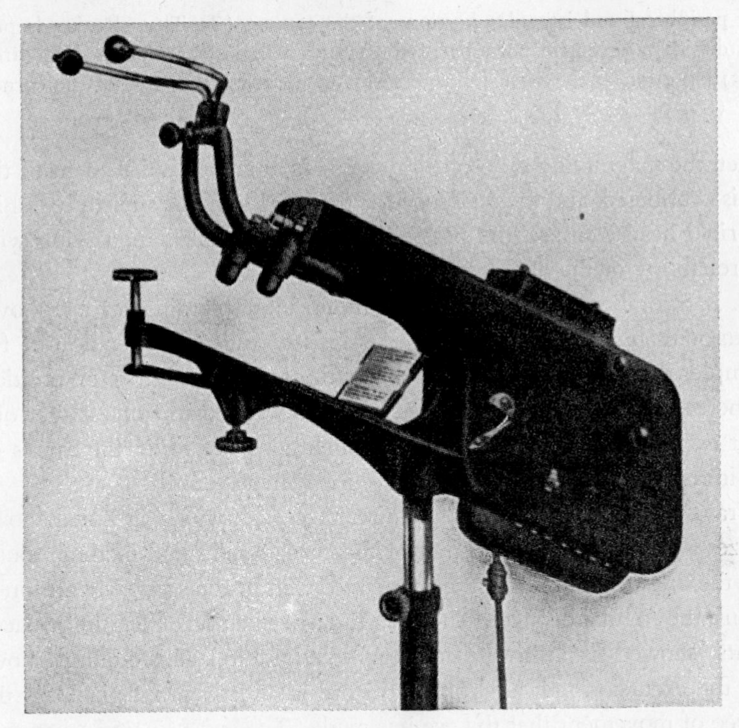

Figure 37.

THE OPHTHALMOGRAPH

Commercial Model

(Courtesy of the American Optical Co.)

the center of the axis of rotation is not a single hypothetical point or location within the eyeball; instead it tends to shift slightly and vary with the degree of excursion. It is believed, however, that for the very small degrees of excursion required for the reading movements, this effect is negligible so far as the interpretation of records is concerned.

The geometrical relationship of cornea and eyeball has been previously discussed in connection with the principles of corneal-reflection methods. As to the curvature of the cornea and its effect, Dodge states:

> Somewhat unfortunately for the purpose of photographic registration, the radius of curvature of the cornea increases slightly from its apex to its periphery, where it is highly irregular. It follows: (1) That no use of the corneal reflection is permissible which involves the use of the extreme

> peripheral and irregular portions of the cornea; (2) That all records produced by eccentric portions of the cornea will be foreshortened in direct proportion as the virtual image seems to approach the edge of the cornea. (85, pp. 82-83.)

When the magnifying ratio of film extent to angular displacement of the eye is considered, and the tendency for the head to move slightly (despite the rigid head clamps), the possibility of this variable's interfering with the reliability of the data becomes clear.

E. L. Stromberg (331) compared monocular recordings of eye movements with binocular recordings. Analysis of the records indicated, for example, that fixation pauses were not the same in number or position in the case of fast and of slow readers. He was led to suggest that one must exercise great care in drawing conclusions regarding the causes of reading difficulties from ordinary eye-movement records.

Travis (374), using the Dodge mirror recorder, which, as noted above, utilizes a principle similar to that of the corneal-reflection method, found that the distance on the photographic record in millimeters, when plotted against the angular displacement or voluntary refixation of definitely spaced points, showed a positive rectilinear relationship. This finding shows that the excursion indicated on the record is directly proportional to the degree of movement that the eye has made. Tinker (347, 353) has conducted several experiments to test the reliability of the photographic method. He concludes (349) that the technique is a satisfactory method of measuring reading performance but emphasizes that such is the case only if adequate controls are maintained and enough samples taken.

M. E. Broom (46) wished to determine the reliability of the reading record yielded by the Ophthalmograph. For this purpose he used the cards, made by the makers of this instrument, on which reading selections are printed. The reliability coefficients were regarded as being too low to permit the sure use of this technique with individuals, a conclusion in which H. A. Imus, J. W. M. Rothney, and R. M. Bear (152) concur. But, as these several authors point out, the card materials are *not* standardized. For want of control, then, of an important variable, these experiments perhaps prove nothing more than that the cards used to test the reliability of the instrument are themselves unreliable.

L. C. Gilbert and D. W. Gilbert (119) investigated the question of whether reading follows a normal course when done under the artificial conditions imposed on a subject whose eye movements are being recorded in an eye-movement camera. Forty-seven fifth-grade pupils read at an ordinary reading table and before the camera. Comprehension of material read and reading time performance were not significantly different in the two situations. Nearly as many of the subjects preferred to read before the camera as at the tables. The novelty of the method for fifth graders, however, should be considered in evaluating their subjective reports. In connection with this work, L. C. Gilbert (118) designed a projector stand to facilitate plotting or interpreting eye-movement records taken by photographic methods.

The corneal-reflection method has certain characteristics which make its use in some experimental situations difficult. Karslake has pointed out some of the objectionable factors inherent in the method:

> (1) To keep the eyes directly in front of the camera and to obtain a record of eye movements alone, head movements must be eliminated through some arrangement for holding the head rigidly in place.
>
> (2) Since undistorted reflection occurs only from the center third of the cornea, the angular field of view through which eye movement is permissible may be no more than fifteen or twenty degrees. Therefore, the selection to be read, if placed at normal reading distance, must be restricted in size; or, if it is desirable to use an area the size of a double page spread from some periodical, the material must be placed beyond normal reading distance. The larger the area, the farther away it must be placed if the photographic record is to picture movements of the eye with reasonable fidelity.
>
> (3) The reader is distracted by the presence of lights (for reflection from the eyes) within the peripheral field of vision, the general awkwardness of the reading situation, and the difficulties involved in being properly placed in preparation for taking the eye movement pictures. (169, p. 418.)

The undue restraint imposed upon the reading subject by head clamps and the necessity of elaborate apparatus in close contact with the subject make the corneal-reflection methods inconvenient to use in some experimental situations. This is especially true when continuous records must be taken for long periods of time.

It has already been noted that certain physiological functions of the human organism can be studied by registering the electrical changes that accompany the action of certain living cell systems. In some cases such recording requires only small electrodes in contact with the subject and no other apparatus in the immediate environment of the subject. The possibility of applying these electrical techniques to the study of eye movements is thus very attractive. Actually, the electrical method of eye-movement study has been a recent development. Its proper use depends on knowledge of the electrical phenomena of the eye and on a general knowledge of microelectronics and the physical means of recording very small electrical changes. The use of electrical techniques for recording eye movements is recent, therefore, because these techniques depend upon recent developments in applied electronics.

E. Schott (312) in 1922 used a spectacle frame to which was attached 0.4- to 0.5-millimeter-thick copper wires bent in spiral form with enough tension to hold the ends against the cocainized eye. These wires acted as electrodes. The electrode for the inner canthus had a two-millimeter copper button on the end of the wire; the electrode for the external canthus, a three-millimeter loop. These electrodes were connected to a string galvanometer [4] which gave a characteristic deflection for each eye movement. Schott also noted that the record of these characteristic deflections looked very much like the photographic records of movements of the eyeball.

The similarity between the records obtained and the possibility that similar physiological functions were involved suggested to I. L. Meyers that the apparatus used for recording the heart beat (the electrocardiograph) might be used to record eye movements. He reasoned as follows:

> The records, like the electrocardiogram, are based on the fact that a muscle under the influence of a stimulus, including a nerve impulse, is traversed by a wave of negativity, the so-called action current, immediately preceding its contraction. The current, if led off through a string galvanometer, produces a deflection of the suspended thread between its magnetic poles, the direction of the deflection varying with the direction of the current. A photograph of the deflection, when obtained on a moving film thus furnishes a record not only of activity in the muscles but of the origin and course along which the current is propagated. The current flows from the point of higher to that of lower potential and, accordingly, the point at which it enters the galvanometric arc of the circuit is designated the positive pole and the point at which it leaves this arc the negative pole. (234, p. 901.)

Meyers placed electrodes on the temples of both sides of the head, since this bony region, as a depository of inorganic salts, is an excellent conductor of electric current. The electrodes were connected with the electrocardiograph, the galvanometer string of which was slackened and calibrated to deflect two centimeters for each millivolt of current. The

[4] A galvanometer measures the intensity of an electric current or its presence and direction, usually by the deflection of a needle or of a wire in a magnetic field.

electrodes were made of block tin, shaped like a horseshoe three inches in diameter. The tin was covered with rubberized cloth and several thicknesses of gauze wet in saturated saline solution. These were attached to the cleansed skin of the temples by bandages with the open side of the horseshoe toward the eyes. As a rule the skin resistance measured between 3000 and 4000 ohms, and often less. When these electrodes were in place, it was found that movements in a particular plane were not recorded by a flow of current through the galvanometers unless the electrodes were located in such a way that the plane of the eye movement was between them. In recording horizontal movements, the electrodes had to be placed opposite the canthi of the eyeballs. In recording vertical movements, they were placed on the forehead or brow and the malar region of the cheek.

E. Jacobson (156, 157) also used the electrocardiograph to obtain records on bromide paper of what he too regarded as action potentials from the ocular muscles. In fact, he usually placed one electrode near the orbital ridge and the other behind the ear on the mastoid bone to record so far as possible monophasic action potentials from the ocular muscles. The electrodes were made of platinum foil, about 1×2 centimeters in size, and wrapped in cotton previously wet in a 0.9 per cent saline solution which was prevented from evaporating by a covering of "silkloid" surgical dressing. These were attached to the skin by gummed paper and connected to a galvanometer calibrated to show one centimeter of deflection for each millivolt. Elaborate precautions had to be taken because of the sensitivity and other characteristics of the amplifiers. The average of the maximal values of voltage produced varied from about 88 to about 137 microvolts. Jacobson found that:

> With a particular subject and a particular location of the electrodes, eye-movement in one direction is recorded as a photographic pattern, clearly distinctive from the patterns recorded during looking in any other direction. (157, p. 695.)

O. H. Mowrer, T. C. Ruch, and N. E. Miller also experimented with the electrical procedures for recording eye movements reviewed above. They also found that a galvanometric deflection is produced when the eyes are moved in the same plane as the electrodes, but not when the plane is at right angles to the electrodes, and that the galvanometer effect increases with the eye movement and persists as long as a given position of the eyes is maintained. They agreed, therefore, with the facts observed by the previous experimenters, but concluded that the explanation

> of these effects as due to the summation of action currents from the extrinsic ocular muscles is highly untenable . . . the only plausible remaining explanation of the results reported by Meyers and Jacobson is that a persistent potential difference exists between the back and the front of the eye and that the galvanometric effects associated with eye movements are due to change in the pattern of the electrical field which this potential difference imposes upon the neighboring anatomical structures. (252, pp. 423-424.)

That such a potential difference might exist on the eye had been indicated by A. Kohlrausch (174) in his study of the electrical phenomena of the eye. He points out that a potential difference, due to divergent metabolic rates, exists in the eye. The current may be thought of as flowing from the cornea to the fundus. On the inside of the eye, the current flows from the retina to the transparent horny tunicle or membrane of the eye. In the retina, it flows from the point of the rods to the nerve fiber layer; and in the nerve fiber layer, from the free end to the base of the sense cell. The region of more active metabolic rate is negative with respect to other less active, and therefore positive, regions. Kohlrausch also summarized the results of former investigators of this static potential (*Bestandpotential*) as measured in various vertebrate eyes.

To test their hypothesis that the electrical changes produced by the eye movements depend upon the fact that there exists a potential difference between the cornea and the retina of the living eye, Mowrer, Ruch, and Miller derived several deductions which could be experimentally tested.

The first experimental hypothesis concerned the character and polarity of the galvanometric effects.

> If movement of the eyes away from the median position to the right produced, let us say, a decrease in resistance between the two electrodes, a comparable movement away from the median position to the left should likewise produce a decrease in the resistance, and therefore a deflection of the galvanometer in the *same* direction as in the former case . . . (252, p. 424.)

The galvanometric system was so arranged that resistance changes in the grid circuit were independent of the current flowing in the plate circuit and thus would produce no detectable movement of the galvanometer. A potential difference as small as one or two microvolts, however, would produce a decided deflection.

> With the apparatus just described, it was found that eye movements give rise to galvanometric effects which are strictly comparable to those obtained when the electrodes are connected directly to a string galvanometer. This finding decisively demonstrates that these effects are due, not to resistance changes between the electrodes, but to true potential variation. (252, p. 425.)

It may be well now to analyze this experimental situation a little more closely. Let us assume that electrodes are placed on each temple and that the eyes are turned to the right. If the galvanometric effects associated with this eye movement are due to the summation of muscle action currents, then the right electrode will be negative because of its proximity to a contracted (metabolically more active) extrinsic eye muscle, and the left will be positive because of its proximity to a relaxed (metabolically less active) eye muscle. On the other hand, if the galvanometric effects are due to the changes in the intrinsic corneo-retinal potential, then the right electrode, by virtue of its nearness to the cornea (metabolically less active), should be positive, and the left electrode, by virtue of its nearness to the retina of the left eye (metabolically more active), should be negative. The latter situation is always found. This finding is consistent with the hypothesis that it is a potential difference between the retina and cornea of each eye that is being measured.

D. B. Lindsley and W. S. Hunter (191) came to the same conclusion from an analysis of the records taken with several electrode placements on human subjects. Samples of their recordings are shown in Figure 38. The bottom line in each record is a time line in seconds. The lines above show, respectively, potentials from the horizontal, vertical, temporal, and oblique leads. The insert in Record D is a key for the placement of electrodes used in all the records. L and R stand for left and right eye, respectively. For Record A the subject was required to fixate four points in succession to the right and then return to the first fixation point by the same four stages. Record B is the same except that the return was a single sweep. It will be noted that only the pair of vertical electrodes failed to pick up potential differences. Where the potential records are deflected upward, the electrode nearest the back of the eye is negative with respect to its corresponding electrode. The visual task given the subject in Records C and D was similar to that of Record A except that

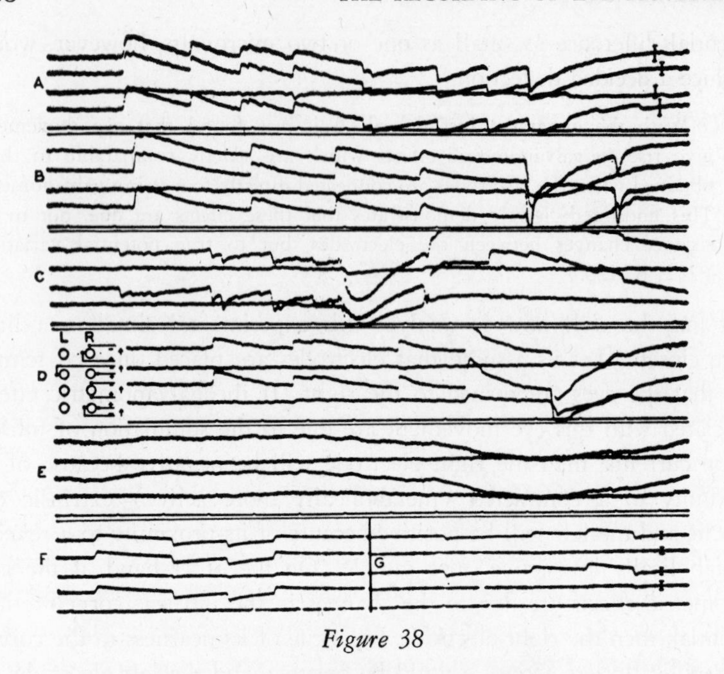

Figure 38

SAMPLE ELECTRO-OCULOGRAMS

(After D. B. Lindsley and W. S. Hunter, 191)

movement was in the vertical meridian, up in C and down in D. Here only the vertical and oblique pairs of electrodes register potential changes, with the lower electrode negative in C and positive in D.

> Inasmuch as all of the records . . . show deflections consistent with the view that the back of the bulbus is negative with respect to the front and inasmuch as these deflections are of an entirely different character from the muscle action potentials which show in some of the records [Figure 35] definitely supports the existence of an electrical polarity of the eye. (191, p. 183.)

To return, however, to the experimental tests by Mowrer, Ruch, and Miller: passive movement of the eye was tested as the second experimental hypothesis.

> If the electrical effects accompanying eye movement originate in the extrinsic ocular muscles, these effects should fail to appear when the eyes are moved passively. On the other hand, if these electrical effects arise from a corneo-retinal potential difference, they should occur with passive and active movements alike. (252, pp. 425-426.)

The latter proved to be true — the galvanometer showed characteristic deflections even for passive movement of the eyeball.

The third deduction involved experimental destruction of the retina.

> In order to anticipate the objection that the records obtained from passive eye movements in the cat might be due to action currents produced by the proprioceptive stimulation of the ocular muscles through stretching . . . (252, p. 427.)

the retina was destroyed in experimental animals by chemical means. Such destruction would be expected to diminish seriously or even eliminate galvanometric deflections, since the corneo-"retinal" potential difference would be destroyed. No potential differences were recorded after such destruction of the retina.

Miles (247) observed the polarity potentials in nine subjects who had suffered unilateral enucleation and therefore wore an artificial eye at the time of the experiment. Electrodes were placed about the active eye and about the artificial eye. The potential of the active eye corresponded closely to the values found for normal two-eyed subjects. The region about the artificial eye gave records which were in the same direction as those of the active eye, but the potential difference was smaller. It was concluded that these potentials from the region of the artificial eye arise from the spread of electrical energy through the tissues from the active eye.

Mowrer, Ruch, and Miller also obtained direct evidence of the corneo-retinal potential differences by exploring the freshly excised and the exposed but intact eye of the turtle. The exploring was done with non-polarizable silver-chloride electrodes.

> We found that our supposition is correct: there is a definite potential difference between the front and the back of the eye, the latter being consistently negative with respect to the former. (252, p. 427.)

It is, therefore, concluded by Mowrer, Ruch, and Miller that the records of eye movements obtained by the galvanometric technique depend on the potential difference existing between the cornea and the retina. Electrodes attached to the skin and at any position about the orbit measure the change in potential difference which occurs as the eyeball is moved. This is shown in very schematic form in Figure 39. That the potential difference or electrostatic field of the eye is related to the varying metabolic rates of the various regions of the eye itself is the most

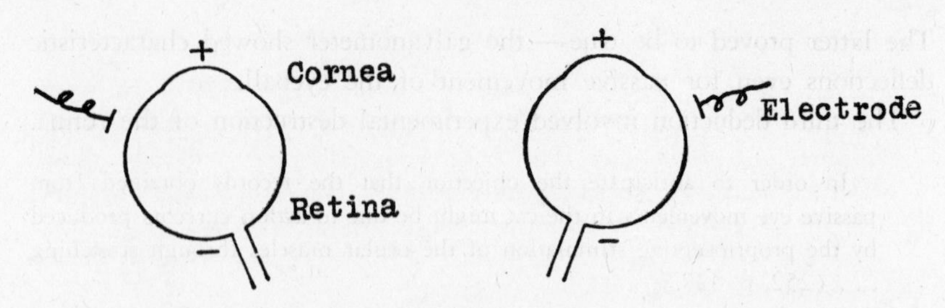

Figure 39

SCHEMATIC DIAGRAM OF THE CORNEO-RETINAL POTENTIAL

Two electrodes are indicated as placed on the skin near the temporal side of the orbits.

(After A. C. Hoffman, B. Wellman, and L. Carmichael, 143)

satisfactory general theory so far offered to explain the observed facts of the corneo-retinal potential.

Miles (241, 242, 243) investigated the possibility that the potential difference may be changed by various experimental conditions.

> In general the results indicate that the polarity potential of the eye as measured by leads from adjoining skin areas is relatively stable but possible of artificial modification. (243, p. 536.)

Potentials recorded with the eyelids closed tended to be slightly higher than those recorded when the eyes were normally open. Applying moderate pressure to the eye with the fingertips increased the average value of the potential only slightly. Massaging one eye for about 15 seconds was followed by a slight rise in the potential difference for that eye, but the potential for the other eye was lowered. Three or four drops of 10 per cent saline solution in the conjunctival sac of each eye produced a marked increase in potential difference (about 30 per cent) which lasted well beyond the time when any smarting or discomfort was reported present.

The potential slowly decreased with repeated measurements when the subject was in a relaxed position but returned to its previous level when the subject changed his posture.

> . . . The eye potential was found to conform to the pattern for blood pressure, metabolism, and other functions which decrease with relaxation and inactivity when the subject is in a comfortable posture and free from apprehension. If the subject is afraid and tense, the eye potential is increased. (242, p. 181.)

In connection with other studies, Miles reports that:

> A consistency tendency was found for the steady potential measurements to show a slightly smaller value on the second than for the first day. It is assumed that this change rests on psychological factors of mental attitude and adjustment to the laboratory procedure. This is a significant finding, pointing as it does to a relationship between the strength of the eye's steady potential and the psychological state of subjects coöperating in the experimental routine. (246, p. 137.)

Miles (248) has also shown that the value of the recorded polarity potential is significantly changed by the level of illumination, that is, under conditions of dark and light adaptation. Under constant illumination of five millilamberts, the potential value remained very steady for a given subject. The average potential for the experimental group of young men was about 1.10 millivolts. After five minutes of dark adaptation to 0.001 millilamberts, the average potential value dropped from 1.10 millivolts to 0.99 millivolts, and after ten minutes, to 0.88 millivolts. With a change back to five-millilambert illumination, the potential value increased to 1.26 after five minutes' light adaptation. A second experiment showed 0.85 and 0.76 millivolts for five and ten minutes respectively in the dark, followed by 1.14 millivolts five minutes after the five-millilambert light had been turned on. Again, the change in potential difference under conditions of light and of dark adaptation was significant. It seems that the eye in adapting from 0.001 to 5 millilamberts increased its potential scarcely at all or very slowly during the first three minutes. During the fourth and fifth minutes, the increase was accelerated, which acceleration continued for a little longer and then fell to an equilibrium value.

Because of the very small magnitude of the potential difference existing on the eye, the changes picked up by the electrodes near the orbit require the use of a very sensitive galvanometer or of amplification before the impulses are introduced into a recording apparatus. The electrical equipment used to amplify and record these electrical changes in the present authors' experiments is an adaptation of a technique that is widely used in general electrophysiology. It is similar to that used in the recording of such phenomena as muscle potentials in intact organisms, the action potentials of heart action (the electrocardiogram), and the electrical activity of the brain (the electroencephalogram). The detailed characteristics of the apparatus used in the present experiments will be discussed later. Electrical apparatus of a different type for eye-movement recording has been described in detail in several instances by other experimenters (234, 245, 246, 252). The designing of amplifiers with special characteristics and the determination of their special properties, as well as the application of suitable amplifying systems to experimental problems of eye-movement recording, are the tasks of a physicist or electrical engineer trained in microelectronics.

Five principal methods of recording have been used in published and unpublished research involving the electrical recording of eye movements. Each method has its inherent advantages and disadvantages. These methods are as follows:

I. Direct connection to a string galvanometer.

II. String galvanometer with input through a vacuum-tube microvoltmeter.

III. Moving mirror-type oscillograph with vacuum-tube amplifiers.

IV. Photographic record of the image of a cathode-ray oscilloscope.

V. Ink-writing oscillograph with vacuum-tube amplifiers (either capacitance-coupled or direct-coupled).

Method I has the advantage of simplicity of apparatus (100). It uses the recording system frequently available where electrocardiograms are taken. It has the disadvantage, however, that the sensitivity is considerably influenced by the resistance of the subject and electrodes. J. Colle and E. de Cooman (69a) have pointed out the difficulty of maintaining a relatively constant resistance in such a recording system below a certain desired level. The points at which the impulses are picked up — the electrodes against the skin — have been found to be variable in resistance.

Recent improvements in controlling the input voltage of the electrical system (upon which calibration of the record depends) have in a measure offset these variations. In Method II the disadvantage is overcome by the addition of a relatively simple piece of apparatus employing two vacuum tubes. Miles (240, 244) describes a recording system using an Einthoven galvanometer combined with a vacuum-tube microvoltmeter which causes the string galvanometer to perform as an electrometer. In this system the influence of tissue and electrode resistance is reduced, and current drainage from the recording equipment is decreased. In this arrangement the recorded deviation of the potential changes may also be slightly amplified, and the deflection speed of the galvanometer string is improved.

Methods III (191), IV (143), and V (the method of the present experiment) also have certain advantages. They are readily adapted to multichannel recording. Thus, several different phenomena may be recorded simultaneously and in correct temporal relationship. For example, both horizontal and vertical eye movements may be recorded simultaneously with general physiological phenomena, such as breathing, heart action, or brain wave, as well as other phenomena, such as the onset and duration of stimuli.

Method V, which has been developed for the present experiments, has marked advantages in economy of money and in convenience when records of long duration are desired. Photographic recording is not employed in this method, and, of course, no processing of film is required. This new method is very well adapted to continuous records which are, for example, many hours in length. If desired, short records using any of the other types of recording may also be taken at any time during the making of a long ink oscillogram for purposes of comparison.

If Method III, IV, or V is used, a high-gain vacuum-tube amplifier is required to step up the small physiological potentials sufficiently to provide a useful deflection of the oscillograph. The type of amplifier which will probably most often be used is the so-called capacitance-coupled amplifier. It has the characteristic that the coupling condensers do not allow a steady deflection in response to a steady potential in the input. This characteristic means that records of all long-continued potentials must be considered in the light of this fact. Following a brief unidirectional pulse of any magnitude, the deflection somewhat gradually returns to its base line or normal amplitude. In such a condenser-coupled amplifying system (see Figure 40), the direction and extent of potential change at the time it takes place are recorded, after which the recording oscillograph returns to the base line, even if the input potential is maintained.

The so-called direct-coupled amplifier, on the other hand, produces a sustained deflection in response to a sustained input potential. This type of amplifier is not subject to "blocking," so the effect of an excessive input potential is limited to the duration of the excessive input, which is not always the case with the capacitance-coupled amplifier. A record (shown in Figure 40) obtained with a direct-coupled amplifying system is therefore like a record obtained with, say, the corneal-reflection method, in which the position of the eyes at any one time can be determined directly from the record. A stationary position of the eyes is recorded as such.

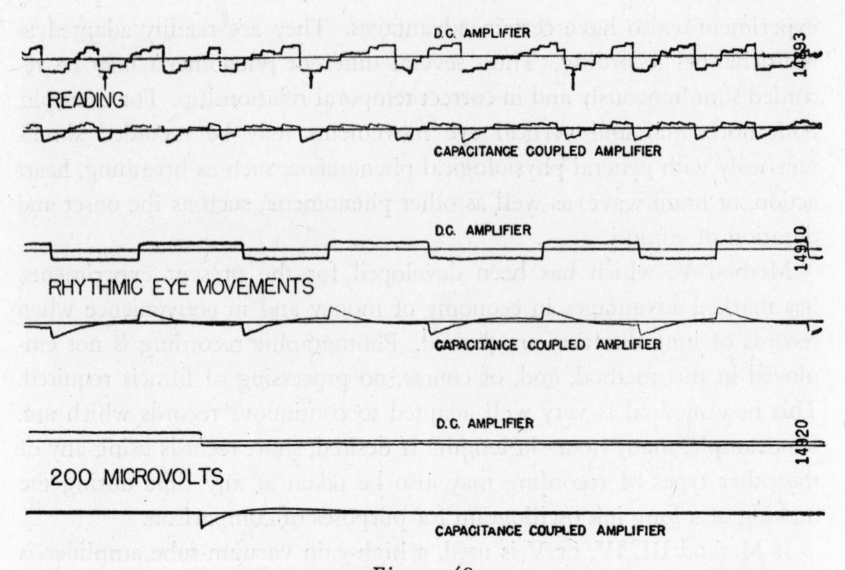

Figure 40

COMPARISON OF RECORDS TAKEN WITH A DIRECT-COUPLED AND A CAPACITANCE-COUPLED AMPLIFYING SYSTEM

For certain studies this method of recording is indicated, since several ocular phenomena (for example, convergence movements) may be recorded by its use which cannot be so well recorded by the condenser-coupled systems. The direct-coupled amplifiers, however, have certain disadvantages, such as the difficulty of maintaining a constant base line.

Electrical methods have often been objected to on the practical grounds of the expense of the equipment required and the necessity for technical service during the progress of the experiment to insure recording of accuracy and discrimination. To meet these objections, W. C. Halstead has arranged a system for the electrical recording of eye movements which he regards as relatively inexpensive to build and easy to operate. (His apparatus is shown in Figure 41.) It also does away with the usual necessity of shielding or grounding the subject.

> The method . . . involves the use of a specially constructed, portable, three-stage, capacitance-coupled amplifier with balanced input for detecting the corneo-retinal potential . . . A vacuum tube bridge circuit operated from the output of the amplifier operates in turn a recording pen which writes directly on wax coated (stylographic) paper. With the exception of

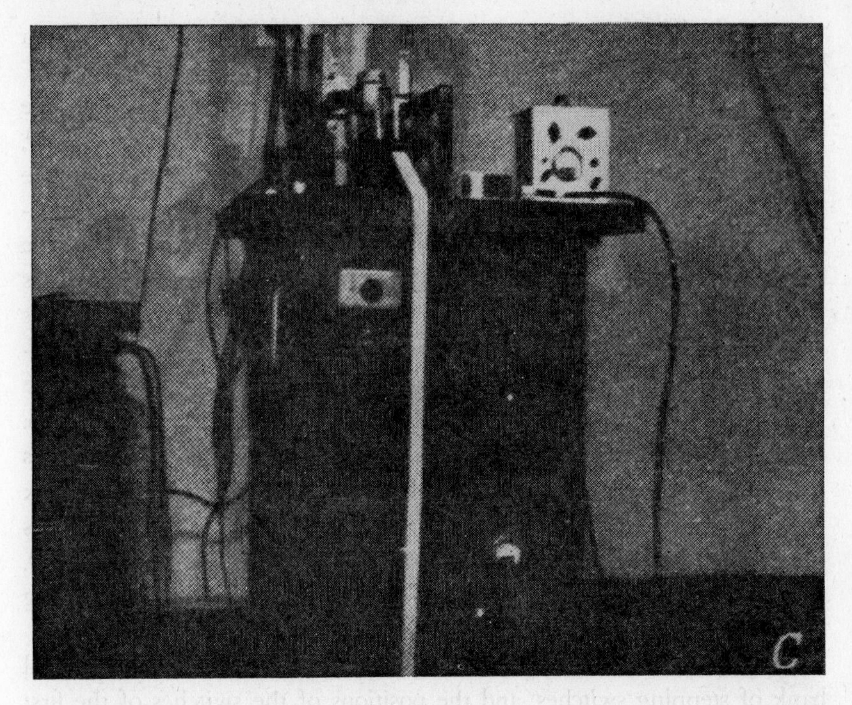

Figure 41

APPARATUS FOR THE ELECTRICAL RECORDING OF EYE MOVEMENTS

(After W. C. Halstead, 132)

> the balanced input, the machine is *AC* operated. Both direction and extent of eye movement within a visual angle of $\pm 1°$ are thus recorded directly on the tape which serves as a permanent record. By the use of two amplifiers, it is possible to follow both vertical and horizontal movements simultaneously. A single shielded cable connects the subject with the instrument. . . . Elimination of shielding of the subject is accomplished by using a common ground for the instrument and subject and by the balanced input. Small silver electrodes attached to the two temples (or above and below one of the orbits) plus a collar or neck grounding electrode are the only necessary connections to the subject. (132, pp. 178-179.)

A further refinement in technique, to facilitate the interpretation of the record, has been developed by Bertram Wellman in the Laboratory of Sensory Psychology and Physiology at Tufts College in connection with the experiments reported in this book. This apparatus is intended to produce a direct *typewritten* record of the number of heart beats, blinks, lines read, fixations, and regressions during each one-minute period of a six-hour reading test.

The typewriter is actuated by 12 solenoids, one connected to the type bar corresponding to each of the 10 digits, and one to the space bar, while the twelfth solenoid is used to return the carriage and advance the platen. Two banks of 11 stepping switches are used to control the typewriter. One group of three stepping switches in each bank gives the count of fixations. The first, or units, stepping switch of this group is advanced one step at each fixation. On the tenth fixation, a contact is made which advances the tens stepping switch one step. The tens stepping switch is mechanically interlocked to the units stepping switch so that at the same time that it advances, it resets the units switch to zero. It, in turn, advances the hundreds stepping switch when it reaches its final position and is in turn returned to zero by a mechanical interlock with the hundreds switch. Thus the positions of these three switches indicate any number of impulses received by the units switch up to 999. For each of the other four functions to be counted, a pair of stepping switches capable of counting to 99 is used.

At the end of one minute, the impulses are transferred to the second bank of stepping switches, and the positions of the switches of the first bank remain fixed. A multicontact, motor-driven switch then energizes the typewriter solenoids so that the appropriate numbers are typed on a strip of paper. The typewriter carriage is then returned, and the platen is advanced so that the typewriter is ready to type the next line of figures, and at the same time all the stepping switches of the first bank are returned to zero, ready to resume counting at the end of the minute, when the count of the second bank of switches will be ready to be recorded by the typewriter. In this way, by using two banks of switches, one bank can be actively counting during each minute while the other bank remains fixed and has its count recorded by the typewriter.

In spite of its seeming complexity, this system of recording involves a smaller outlay than the purchase of a commercially available recording counter. It has the additional advantage of giving a direct record of the count of several important eye-movement phenomena during each minute without the necessity of subtracting.

The relays which provide the impulses for actuating the stepping switches are energized by special amplifiers and control tubes. Each control tube is a gas discharge tube, which discharges a condenser through the relay coil, and a circuit designed to hold the relay closed for the proper length of time, regardless of the type of impulse received from the amplifier channels. Each of the five control tubes is triggered by an amplifier tube whose grid is connected to the recording amplifier circuits through a high resistance, so that only an insignificant amount of current will be taken from the recording amplifiers, and no appreciable change in their characteristics will be produced. The amplifier tubes for the heart beats and blinks are simply connected to the appropriate recording channels with the appropriate polarity, and the gain (of the auxiliary amplifier) adjusted until satisfactory operation of the relays is obtained. The operation of the line recorder is similar, except that care must be taken to have the gain such that the return sweep at the end of each line will actuate the trigger tube but regressions or backward motions within the line will not operate it because of their smaller magnitude. The regression-counting circuit is similar to the line-counting circuit, except that the gain is higher; and it is arranged so that when a line is counted, no regression is counted.

Since the count of fixations requires that both forward and backward motions of the eyes be counted, a rectifier is used so that each impulse from the horizontal eye-movement channel is registered regardless of its polarity.

The frequency response of each circuit must be carefully adjusted so that reliable action is secured and false registration caused by spurious voltages such as muscle action potentials is minimized. The apparatus just described was developed for possible use in collecting the data of the experiments on which the present book is based but was not in a fully satisfactory working state by the time these experiments were begun. The apparatus used in the current experiments is described in detail in Chapter 7.

The previous discussion has been generally concerned with what is being electrically recorded. There remains the question of how accurately the eye movements are recorded by these methods. We have seen that studies have been made of the photographic methods to determine their reliability and validity. The reliability and validity of the electrical technique must likewise be investigated to ascertain whether the changes in corneo-retinal potential as recorded electrically are correlated sufficiently with the degree of ocular excursion to give a useful record of eye movements in reading.

W. O. Fenn and J. B. Hursh provided a partial answer to this question by investigating the relation of the potential changes to the degree of excursion of the measured eye movements. The excursions made by their subjects were much wider than those required in ordinary reading. The potential changes observed varied between 0.20 and 0.84 millivolts. The experimenters plotted the voltage, as indicated by a string galvanometer, against twice the sine of the angle of each excursion.

> The graphs are good straight lines affording therefore a strong confirmation of the theory of corneo-retinal polarization, and proving that the method is a reliable one for the purpose of recording eye movements. (100, p. 8.)

They also found that the slope of each of the lines was characteristic of the individual making the eye movements. These individual differences, they believe, depend upon differences in polarization of the eyeball or differences in the effectiveness of the surrounding tissues in short-circuiting the potential, rather than on age, sex, or other similar characteristics.

Miles (246) measured the ocular polarity potentials of three groups of normal females and of a group of 14 mixed normals ranging in age from 21 to 37. Ten different eye potential measurements were made, using five electrode placements, and each subject was tested on each of two days. The reliability coefficients of correlation between the same measure on each of two days are reported for his entire group of 56 cases. All the coefficients are positive and range between 0.39 and 0.75. The latter coefficient is for the placement across the temples, which gives the highest potential. On that lead the younger girls showed a coefficient of 0.81, the school girls, 0.77, the mature women, 0.59, and mixed normals, 0.78. It is to be noted that these are coefficients for individual groups rather than for the entire experimental group, for which the highest correlation was 0.75.

> The coefficients indicate that the ocular polarity potential measurement is a fairly reliable one.
>
> . . . Rather marked individual differences were found in the steady potential of the eye. Some subjects show potentials three or four times as high as other subjects, and some are much more variable than others from day to day. The causes of these individual differences are still unrevealed. Subjects were found to vary more markedly from each other in body potentials than in eye potentials.
>
> . . . The steady potential of the eye gives no indication of correlating positively or negatively with the potentials of the tissues surrounding the eye. (246, p. 136.)

Data from another study of the polarity potential of the normal eyes of 15 subjects led Miles to similar conclusions:

> . . . Galvanometric deflections registering the steady polarity-potential of the eye show no evidence of action currents from the extraocular muscles, but do frequently show action current spikes from voluntary and reflex winking.
>
> . . . Data . . . show the presence of certain simple relationships existing between the lateral measurement leads and the ascertained potentials. These relationships may be reduced to simple equations indicating equivalence of certain combinations of leads. The results support the hypothesis that the eyeballs and their orbital and interorbital tissues act, at least under the conditions of minimal current drainage, as one homogeneous bioelectrical field.
>
> . . . A steady potential from the eyeball can be isolated for measurement from the potentials of the skin and surrounding tissue by making use of the eye's motility.
>
> . . . The eyes are unique not in having steady electromotive force, probably a characteristic of body tissues generally, but rather in having rapid and accurate motility which makes the isolation and measurement of their potentials practicable.
>
> . . . The measurable ocular polarity-potential of the human eye *in situ* is in the order of 1 millivolt when the eye rotates laterally 30 degrees from the primary line of regard; the range found between supposedly normal subjects is from about 0.3 to 2.5 millivolts.
>
> . . . The potential can be measured, without discomfort to the subject, by means of small metal foil electrodes placed on the skin near the eye . . .
>
> . . . The potential exhibited by the eyeball is closely proportional to the sine of the angle of rotation of the eye, and therefore is to prove useful as a means of measuring eye movements in connection with a variety of scientific problems. (245, pp. 35-36.)

An experiment by A. C. Hoffman, B. Wellman, and L. Carmichael (143) demonstrated the correlation between recorded voltage and the very small excursions of the eyes involved in reading. Simultaneous electrical and photographic records were taken of the eye movements made while subjects were alternately fixating pairs of horizontal or vertical dots. Figure 42 represents the stimulus cards used. The binocular photographic record, regarded as the criterion, was made with the Ophthalmograph. The electrical record was made by a Westinghouse Type PA Mirror Oscillograph and capacitance-coupled amplifiers. Small silver solder disks (shown in Figure 43) attached to the skin with an adhesive washer served as electrodes. Figure 44 shows the arrangement of

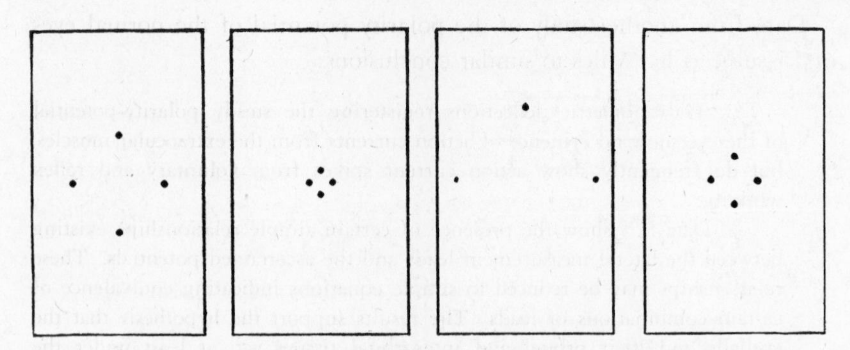

Figure 42

DOT PATTERNS USED AS GUIDES FOR EYE-MOVEMENT EXCURSIONS

(After A. C. Hoffman, B. Wellman, and L. Carmichael, 143)

the electrodes about the eyes of a subject; Figure 45 shows the subject in the experimental shielded room. A further test of the reliability of the electrical method was made by determining the possibility of variation in the relation between the electrical and photographic records due to different placements of the electrodes about the eyes of the subject. The electrode placements investigated are schematically shown in Figure 46.

The results of this experiment show that the potential difference recorded is characteristic of the individual subject. No significant variations in the data due to electrode placement were demonstrated. The placement of electrodes may, therefore, it seems, be chosen, within appropriate limits, in any particular experimental situation on the basis of convenience or according to the movement plane required by the experimental procedure. Voltage change was found to be correlated closely with the degree of ocular excursion. This finding agrees with the conclusion of Fenn and Hursh for larger excursions. It was concluded that the changes in the corneo-retinal potential, as recorded by the electrical technique, are sufficiently consistent and highly enough correlated with the degree of ocular excursion, as recorded by the corneal-reflection technique, to constitute a reliable method of recording eye movements of the sort characteristic of reading.

The electrical method of recording as developed by Hoffman, Wellman, and Carmichael (143) has special advantages which suggest its use in a number of experimental situations. A Kodachrome motion-pic-

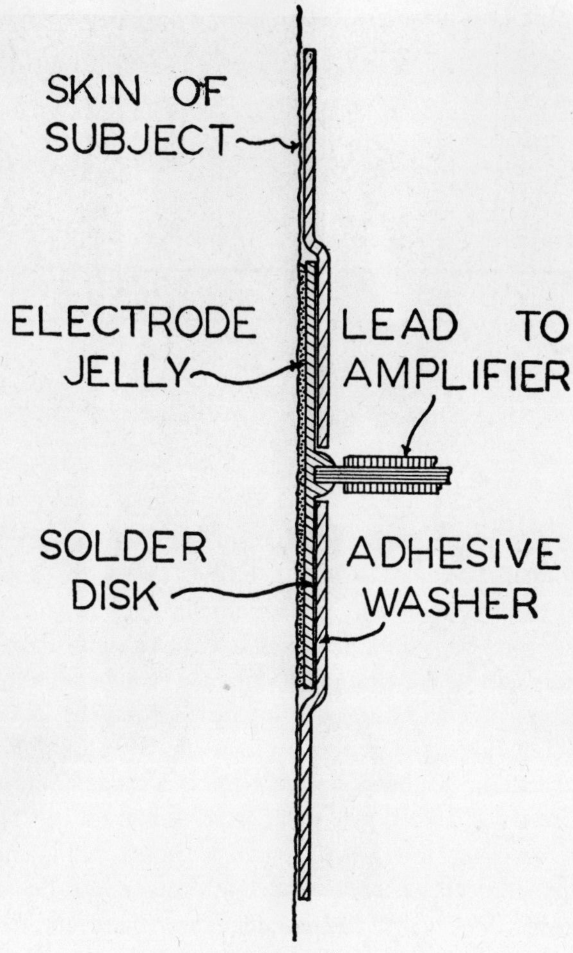

Figure 43

DIAGRAM OF THE TYPE OF ELECTRODE USED IN THE STUDY BY HOFFMAN, WELLMAN, AND CARMICHAEL

(After A. C. Hoffman, B. Wellman, and L. Carmichael, 143)

ture film[5] entitled "The Electrical Recording of Eye Movements," by L. C. Mead and L. Carmichael, has been made which illustrates the apparatus and experimental technique already described. This electrical procedure has subsequently been applied to advantage in experimental

[5] This film is listed as PCR-75K by the Psychological Cinema Register of Pennsylvania State College, from which it may be rented or purchased.

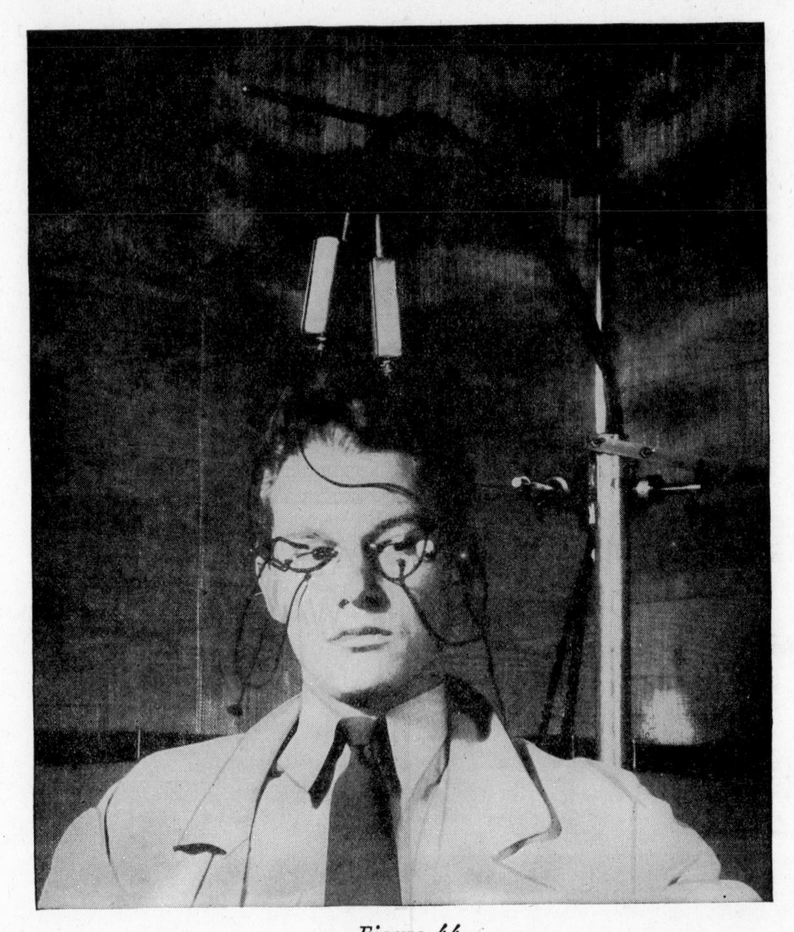

Figure 44

FRONT VIEW OF SUBJECT SHOWING ELECTRODES IN PLACE

(After A. C. Hoffman, B. Wellman, and L. Carmichael, 143)

situations where eye-movement recording was heretofore inconvenient or impossible. Some of the useful features of this new method, especially when used with ink-writing oscillographs, are noted in the next paragraph.

The subject or reader is typically quite unrestrained. Only electrodes with fine lead wires of suitable length are in contact with the subject. Movements of the eyes in emotional situations and in experiments of which the procedure requires the subject to move his head, or indeed his whole body, may thus be conveniently studied. It has, for example, been

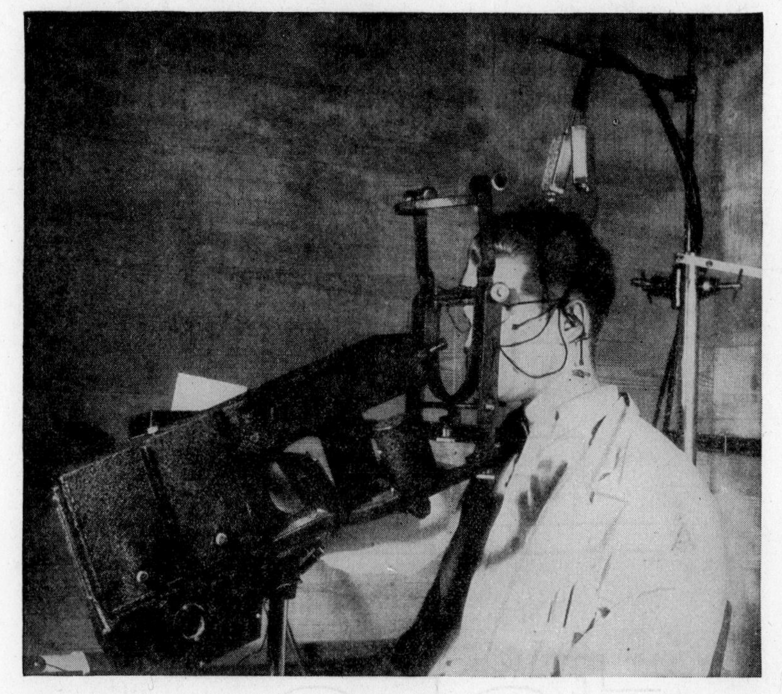

Figure 45

SIDE VIEW SHOWING SUBJECT READY FOR SIMULTANEOUS ELECTRICAL AND PHOTOGRAPHIC RECORDING OF EYE MOVEMENTS

(After A. C. Hoffman, B. Wellman, and L. Carmichael, 143)

suggested that the normal eye movements of motorists while driving in various traffic situations could be recorded and measured by this technique. This procedure could also be used in the study of the eye movements of an airplane pilot as he glances at the landing field and his instrument panel. It had a number of applications to war problems in the study of the eye movements used in operating optical instruments, such as height finders or radar equipment.

These electrical techniques of eye movement recording have also been used by the present writers in testing the visual mechanism of newborn infants and of animals. Carmichael was first interested in this technique in connection with certain studies of the visual mechanism of the fetal and newborn guinea pig and rabbit. The technique has been used by him as an objective method of studying quantitatively the degree of "night

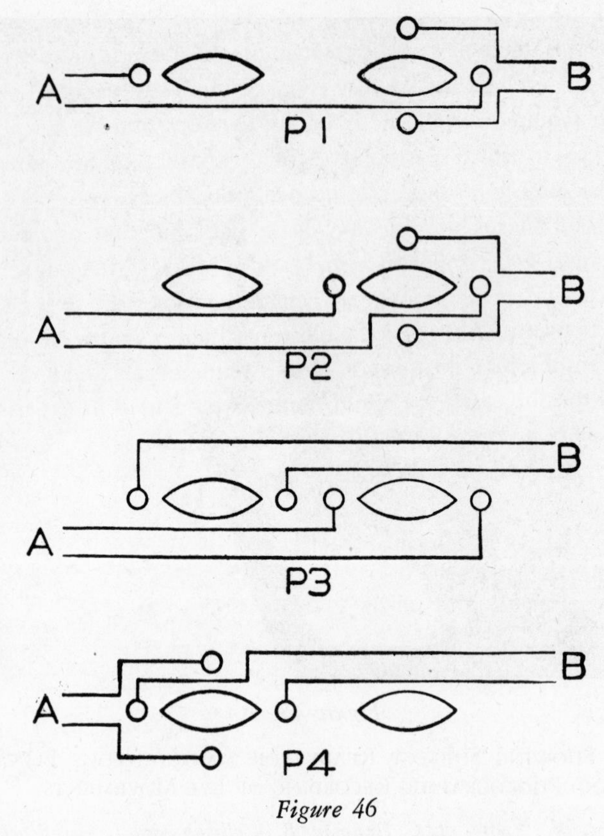

Figure 46

FRONT VIEW DIAGRAMS OF ELECTRODE PLACEMENTS STUDIED BY HOFFMAN, WELLMAN, AND CARMICHAEL

A and B indicate the two amplifying systems.

(After A. C. Hoffman, B. Wellman, and L. Carmichael, 143)

blindness" resulting from Vitamin A deficiency in newborn human infants long before any other objective or subjective method could be employed. It has also been used in color discrimination and acuity tests in animals. The technique is also applicable in studying eye movements in states of aphasia, fantasy, and imagination. Soon after the electrodes have been fastened to the subject's skin, he typically forgets about them much as the ordinary person quickly comes to ignore the feeling of a ring on his finger.

The electrical methods in general do not require light for recording.

The eyes of the subject may therefore be either open or closed. It is thus possible by this method to study some of the reflex adjustments and reactions of the eye in a totally dark room or in an experimental situation such as that required for the study of the so-called autokinetic phenomena of the eye, in which a stimulus light of minimal or low intensity is seen by most subjects to make "subjective" movements.

This method makes possible the direct determination of fixation in mapping central and peripheral visual fields. Miles (248) suggests that the modifications of the potential which he observed depend upon retinal functions, in which case the electrical method of recording offers promise of an objective measure of certain retinal states and activities to supplement the subjective threshold methods long used in experimental studies of vision.

Chapter 7

The Methodology of the Present Experiments

THE DESCRIPTIONS in the preceding chapters of the concept of fatigue, of the nature and characteristics of the reading process, of the materials and optimal illumination and other conditions for reading, of the part played by the eye movements, and, finally, of the methods of recording these movements, have given the reader the necessary details and background for the new experiments to be described here. These experiments were undertaken in order to study the effects of prolonged reading of books or microfilm in causing what is popularly termed "visual fatigue." Stated in other words, the problem to be investigated is the determination of how long a normal human subject can continue to read before there are significant changes in his reading behavior.

Obviously, as has been previously noted, there is a direct experimental approach to the solution of this problem. This attack on the problem calls for the recording and then the measurement and evaluation of such changes in behavior as may be observed in the records of eye behavior during periods of prolonged reading. The applied study of visual fatigue can therefore, it seems, best be approached by providing scientifically controlled conditions, a sufficient number of subjects, and the requirement that the subjects read continuously. The records of the eye movements must be made with as refined a method of observation as possible and for as long a period of time as may be needed to reach valid conclusions as to the changes in the eye behavior or other activity of the human organism resulting from such prolonged reading. The present experiments, we believe, meet most of these conditions.

Previous research has suggested some of the variables which should be controlled in a study of visual fatigue in reading. An effort to measure "fatigue" suggests that the continuity of behavior in time is important. It was clear, therefore, from the first that it would be desirable to study continuous reading. It was also clearly desirable that the conditions under which the reading was done should be constant, although of course variation of such conditions as part of a planned experiment may be important. The period of the prolonged activity should be longer than the amount of time one normally spends in reading. By adapting these conditions, a reasonable opportunity for "fatigue" effects to appear will be provided. The number of subjects should be large enough to insure a reasonable sample of normal reading behavior. It is especially important also that the number of subjects be large enough to give reasonable precision to the statistical conclusions which may be drawn. The methods of observation must have such validity that they will give an accurate record of reading behavior itself. Techniques must be refined enough to measure the whole range of changes that may occur in reading behavior at all times and especially as the activity is prolonged. These characteristics, of course, are the requisites of experimental physiological and psychological methods when applied to many specific problems.

The experiments on fatigue in relation to prolonged reading, as previously reviewed, do not satisfy all or even most of the stipulated conditions required for an adequate investigation of visual fatigue during reading in a normal situation.

The experiments of Dearborn, of McFarland and his collaborators, and of Clark and Warren may be taken here as typical examples of visual fatigue experiments previously done. These experiments are considered below in the light of the "ideal" requirements just discussed. It must be remembered in reviewing these experiments that some of them were conducted before the electronic techniques used in the present experiments were available.

In the experiment performed by Dearborn (78), the reading task was a prolonged one and was assumed to be continuous at least for several hours at a time. However, tests were made only at the beginning and at the end of a day and only a few subjects were observed. In certain experiments conducted by McFarland and his associates (228), the reading was neither continuous nor prolonged. The subjects read only six paragraphs at a time. These reading periods were separated by intervals of other activity. It must be remembered that these experiments were performed to determine the effects of oxygen deprivation; they were not meant to be a direct attack on the problem of visual fatigue except for the possible similarity between anoxemia and "fatigue." The experiment by Clark and Warren (62) was essentially an investigation of the effects of prolonged wakefulness. The period of the subjects' activity was therefore prolonged, but the actual reading was not continuous (a sample was taken only every 10 hours). As far as the subjects' attitude was concerned in this experiment, the reading was just one of several tasks they were required to perform. Also, the other tasks did not always require work that was primarily visual.

The above representative experiments have been mentioned to indicate that, so far as the authors have been able to determine, a direct approach to the problem of reading fatigue had not hitherto been made. The experiments to be reported in detail below attempt to investigate the problem of reading fatigue more directly and in a more normal situation than any experiments previously conducted of which the authors have knowledge.

The subjects were required to read continuously for six hours. College students and high school students were used as subjects. Each subject read from two books differing in content but presented in similar typographical format either as a book page or as microfilm reproduction. In view of the increasingly wide use of microfilm and the report that some readers have found the reading of the projected film more fatiguing than ordinary reading, the experiment included an equal use of microfilm reproductions and of ordinary reading materials. One book was an "interesting" historical novel, the other a "dry" eighteenth-century treatise on economics. (It is recognized that all individuals will not agree with the value judgments "interesting" and "dry" as used here.) The books read are described in detail on page 236. The subjects were divided into four experimental groups depending on their educational status (college or high school) and on the way (normal or microfilm) in which the two books were presented. Comprehension of the material read was tested at intervals during the reading period, and a more general test was given at the conclusion of each six-hour session.

Before the reading period and again after it, the visual and the stereoscopic acuities of the subjects were tested. During the reading period, continuous recording was made of eye movements. At the same time and also continuously, records were made of heart beat (the electrocardiogram) and of the electrical potentials of the brain (the "brain waves" or electroencephalogram). The specific "reading" functions of which continuous records were made were the patterned movements of the eyes dependent on the activity of the six extrinsic muscles which move the eyeball. Due to the fact that the eyeball turns upward when the lid is closed, continuous records of blinking were made on a special recording channel used for this purpose alone.

The present experiments, as just noted, involved the recording and measuring of several functions of the subjects as they read continuously for the six-hour period. The term "function" is here used to refer to some particular pattern of movement, to some component of the movement pattern, to some particular activity performed by the subject, or to some other measurable process which takes place during reading. The term "measure" will be used to refer to the data or record kept of the performance of any function which is subject to objective measurement and quantification.

The eye-movement functions chosen for study in the present experiment included, first of all, blinking. A full blink is defined as a temporary closure of both eyes, involving movements of the upper and lower eyelids, so that the pupil is hidden from view. This is a behavioral definition such as would be used by an observer. Actually recorded by the electrical apparatus used in the present experiments was the short upward movement of the eyeball in its socket, which has been demonstrated (238) to occur with the typical blink.

The incidence in time of these temporary deflections (blinks) was the measure used in the present experiments. This measure will hereafter be referred to as "Blinking Number."

Besides blinking, the present study has analyzed and quantified certain of the lateral eye movements which constitute the so-called behavioral reading pattern of the eyes. A description of this characteristic pattern has already been given in Chapter 2.

Conspicuous in the recording of such eye movements are the records of fixation pauses. As already noted, the general term fixation refers to the act of holding the eyeball stationary to look at a stimulus object without changing the line of regard. However, as descriptive of an ocular function to be observed in this experiment, the term fixation or fixation pause is used to refer to the specific instance of fixation as a component of the reading pattern. It has been well described as the time in reading a line of print during which the eyeball is held fixed and the retina is thus exposed to a stationary stimulus pattern of energy gradients such as are reflected from background paper and the printed symbols upon it. The short saccadic movement which separates the fixation pauses changes the orientation of the eyeballs in relation to the line of print. This movement thus makes possible the presentation of a new and again still or fixed stimulus pattern to the retina when the next fixation pause occurs.

Three fixation measures were analyzed in the present experiment. The number of fixations made during a five-minute sample period will hereafter be referred to as "Fixations Number." Another measure was derived by dividing the total number of fixations made by the number of lines read in the same interval of time. This measure is referred to as "Fixations per Line." The phrase "Fixation Sigma Score" refers to the standard deviation of the number of fixations per line. This is a statistical measure showing the amount of variation in the number of fixations which are made during the reading of each line of print. As such, it indicates how reliable, in a statistical sense, the mean number of fixations per line is. The use of the standard deviation measure was suggested by the finding in other experiments that changes in variability of performance may occur during prolonged activity even though mean performance does not vary. That finding also focuses attention on the indices of variability derived by statistical analysis of all the measures used in this experiment.

The so-called regressive movements of the eyes have also been investigated in this study. Normally, reading proceeds from left to right along the line of print. A fixation pause is typically followed by a short saccadic movement of the eyeballs to the right. Then another fixation pause occurs, then another saccade to the right takes place, and so on. Regressive, or corrective, movements are saccadic movements of the eyeball to the left. Such movements allow refixation of material already read or fixated.

The measures of this ocular function used were the incidence of these regressive movements during a five-minute sample period ("Regressions Number") and the number of regressions per line. The latter score was

Figure 47

THE TELEBINOCULAR

(Courtesy of the Keystone View Co.)

derived by dividing the total number of regressions made by the number of lines read in the same interval of time. This measure will be called "Regressions per Line."

Another function measured in the present experiment was the number of lines read. The number is shown by the record of the eye movements as taken in this experiment. This measure is essentially an index of speed and has been frequently used as such in other reading experiments. It will be referred to in this study as "Lines Read Number."

Certain rapid tests were made of the subjects' visual acuity and stereoscopic acuity before and again after the six-hour reading period. Some tests that might have been used would have imposed so severe a task on the visual mechanism that the reading immediately following such tests might have variably affected the experiment. The functions were measured by means of a Telebinocular and stereograms prepared by the Keystone and the Zeiss companies. The Telebinocular, shown in Figure 47, is a convenient viewing instrument the focal length of which can be adjusted by the subject to his own convenience.

Two sets of Keystone cards were used. One set of stereograms (a sample of which is shown in Figure 48) is designed to test visual acuity.

Figure 48

A KEYSTONE STEREOGRAM FOR TESTING VISUAL ACUITY

(Courtesy of the Keystone View Co.)

Several targets are so arranged on the stereogram that the illusion of distance is created; thus, a retreating series of targets is presented. The subject is required to report on which side of a central dot another dot may be found. The target in a series for which the subject can no longer correctly report the location of the crucial dot marks the limit of visual acuity. This limit may be expressed in terms of refractive error or of distance. Three such retreating series of targets were presented. The score used was the average apparent distance of the last target just before the dots on two consecutive targets could not be correctly located.

The other set of Keystone stereograms is designed to test stereoscopic acuity. Three rows of letters and numerals are presented on each of 20

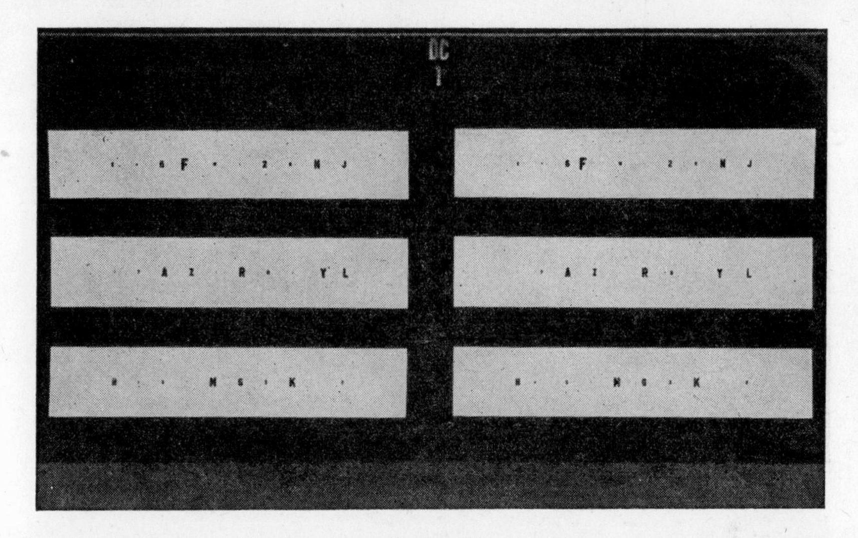

Figure 49

A KEYSTONE STEREOGRAM FOR TESTING STEREOSCOPIC ACUITY

(Courtesy of the Keystone View Co.)

cards. A sample stereogram is shown in Figure 49. These symbols are of varying size, but only one stands out in depth or relief from the rest of the line. L. C. Mead (232) has shown that, despite the variation in size of the symbols, the number of correct judgments decreases as the tridimensionality effect becomes smaller. The subject was required to report in each case which of such figures seemed nearest to him. The stereograms were progressively more difficult as the apparent distance between the crucial letter and the rest of the line became progressively smaller. If a subject gave the correct response to any of the three lines on each card, the entire card was scored as "right." When a subject failed two consecutive cards — that is, when he had made six consecutive errors — the test was stopped. The total number of "rights" was the score used. This score can be translated into a measure of stereoscopic acuity. Evidence as to the reliability or validity of these particular tests is limited to the fact that the scores agreed in general with the results of a complete ophthalmological examination made of several of the subjects.

The Zeiss stereograms (Figure 50) present a series of architectural designs. At the top of each design is drawn a circle, a cross, and a balloon, in such a way that each appears at a different distance from the subject.

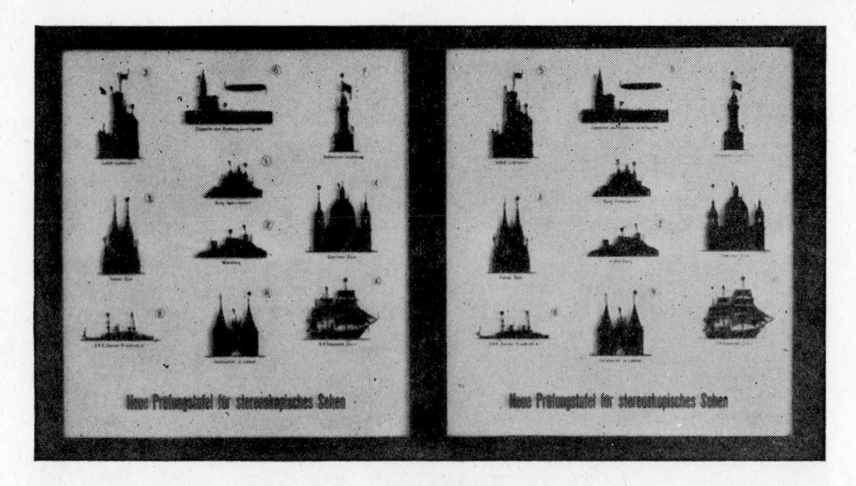

Figure 50

THE ZEISS STEREOGRAM FOR TESTING STEREOSCOPIC ACUITY

The subject is required to report the correct distance order of these objects The three objects are represented progressively closer together as the subject proceeds from design to design. When the order of distance in the case of two consecutive designs was incorrectly reported, the just preceding design was taken as crucial. Since the number of the design was known, the stereoscopic acuity represented could be determined from charts supplied with the stereoslides.

More general functions of the subject were also recorded in the present study. A record was made of the heart beat throughout the six-hour reading period. The pulse or heart beat has usually been measured by recording the indirect effects of the contractions of the heart muscles (for example, by a plethysmograph, by "counting the pulse," and so forth). In the present experiments, the electrical phenomena of the contraction of the heart muscles themselves were recorded — the electrocardiogram. The record of a single heart beat has been called the PRT wave (diagrammatically shown in Figure 51). It is essentially a wave recording with three components. Auricular contraction begins at the P-wave and finishes near the beginning of the QRS wave. The sweep of excitation over the ventricles gives rise to the QRS wave. The T wave is correlated with the latter part of the ventricular contraction when blood is being expelled into the large arteries. No particular measure of these components of the heart-beat recording was used in the present experiments,

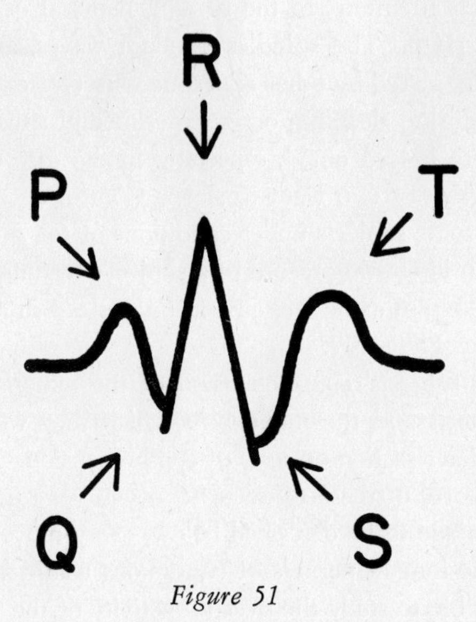

Figure 51

THE ELECTROCARDIOGRAM — THE PRT WAVE

but they did provide an interesting check on the variations in heart rate during reading which seem to be related to other alterations in behavior. Casual observation of these six-hour-long electrocardiograms seems to indicate a greater variability of heart rate and of the form of the electrical wave than would have been anticipated. A later complete study of these six-hour-long continuous records may provide some new information in regard to normal heart function. It should be noted that the lead used was not one of the standard leads used in most clinical electrocardiographic work.

The electroencephalogram was also continuously recorded during the reading period. Because of the nature of the experimental procedure of the present investigation, these records are not typical of those secured during less complex activity of the subject. In this instance the records are like those obtained when the eyes are open and the subject is doing visual work in a lighted environment. Since the optimal procedure for analysis of such encephalograms made with the eyes open is still undecided, no general quantification was made of these records in the present experiments. The record was kept, however, not only for future reference, but also because of the possibility that it would show when the subject was not "paying attention" to the reading material or was drowsing or even going to sleep. The spindles, random waves, and true bursts of "alpha waves" observed by other experimenters (for example, 194) during drowsing, during sleeping, or in experimental situations of minimal stimulation were indeed noted, especially in the case of a few subjects who for a moment or two went to sleep. Control encephalograms have been made on some subjects under conditions of relaxation and minimal stimulation. An interesting record of a subject's reading and concomitant electroencephalogram as he was just falling asleep in a series of drowsy spells is given as Figure 99.

Tests of the subjects' comprehension of the material read were also made. These tests and the manner in which they were given will be described in a later section on tests of comprehension. Percentage values were used as scores of these tests.

By the technique to be described below, every movement of the eyes, even during the longest periods of continuous reading, can be recorded. Thus, it is possible to study the over-all activity of the visual mechanism during prolonged periods of work. Any change in this eye activity resulting from alterations in the organism concomitant with the passage of time during work is also recorded.

An analogy may make the underlying plan of this new technique more clear. If it is desired to determine the efficiency of an internal combustion gas engine, it is possible to attach a recording dynamometer to the crankshaft of the motor. Measurements may be made of the work of the motor during experimental periods. In this way the performance of the engine in relation to various grades of fuel or to the time characteristics of electrical ignition may be studied. The record of the dynamometer will accurately indicate changes in the level of performance, for such records provide an objective measure of the alterations in the efficiency of the motor. Later investigations may be undertaken to note the correlation between special fuels or other isolated factors such as ignition timing and alterations in the recorded brake horsepower, but any change that is significant in the total mechanical system will be recorded as a change in the work recorded by the dynamometer.

By analogy with this mechanical system, it may be said that the present experiments describe the use of a technique by means of which a total, functional, visual activity may be recorded and then later its functional components studied in relation to interposed experimental variables. Thus, any change in eye movements brought about by so-called general fatigue of the organism, by an alteration in the sensitivity of the retina to light, or by a change in the external eye muscles, to take but a few examples, must be reflected in an objective and measurable alteration in the final eye-movement record if the changes in the system are important enough to alter the efficiency of the total mechanism.

The apparatus and methods for recording eye movements have been brought to a high degree of accuracy and successfully employed in investigating many phenomena of eye movements, as we have seen in detail above. Not any or all of these methods, however, should be used interchangeably. In many instances certain methods are limited in applicability and reliability by the conditions imposed on the adequate recording of eye movements by a particular experimental situation or procedure. In the case of the present experiments, each subject was to read continuously for six hours under conditions that were relatively normal, and complete objective records of this behavior were to be made.

Because of this requirement certain of the older methods which have been reviewed above were regarded as inappropriate. The results derived from the simple, direct methods of observing the eye movements, for example, could easily be reduced in reliability because of subjective errors either in the original observation or in the recording, the former primarily because of the speed of the ocular movements, the latter because of the lack of permanent records. Another disadvantage of this method would have been the inconvenience or indeed impossibility of directly observing the eyes of a subject for six hours.

In using the mechanical methods, there is always the question of the degree to which the apparatus interferes with the eye movements, and of the amount to which the recorded excursions are due to the actual eye movements or to the mechanical characteristics of the instrument. For example, any type of cup fitting over the cornea is subject to frictional and adhesive variations. Also, such devices often interfere with lid movements. Any lever or similar device attached to the eyeball may impede the normal excursion of the eye. Since many of these methods require the anesthetization of the cornea, the narcotics may cause deviation in the normal movement, even though these effects may be minimal.

Those methods which require one eye to react to the stimulus situation and record the conjugate movements of the other, particularly where apparatus is in direct contact with the second eye, share with similar photographic methods the disadvantages of possible variations in excursion of the two eyes. This would be especially true because of the unequal illumination of the eyes. These variations may also be due to mechanical interference with the movements of one of the eyes or to unilateral oculomotor dysfunctions of the subject. The variable factors in the corneal-reflection methods arise primarily in maintaining the beam of light at the correct point on the cornea. While the curvature of the cornea is the prerequisite of these methods, it may at the same time be irregular enough to vary markedly the results should the fixation of the light beam not be accurate or constant. The primary difficulties are, however, those of the laboratory—the undue restraint on the subject for so long a period of time and the necessity of particular lighting conditions.

As a means of surmounting these difficulties and others that will occur to the reader, the electrical method of recording was selected for the present experiments. With this technique the only apparatus in immediate contact with the subject is the lightweight electrodes necessary for picking up the changes in the corneo-retinal potential. All extrasituational recording apparatus may be far removed from the subject's immediate experimental environment. Relative freedom is, therefore, given to the movements and posture of the subject. Records of the electrical phenomena of the brain and the wave of electrical activity occurring with each heart beat can be made simultaneously with the record of the ocular behavior, and for all this recording one type of apparatus can conveniently be used.

The complete apparatus required, of course, is more than just the electrodes to pick up the electrical changes and the oscillographic device to record them. The potential differences and other electrical phenomena observed are so small as to require high-gain amplification. In turn, however, the necessary amplifiers are so sensitive that they will respond in addition to aberrant or extraneous electrical changes. Proper shielding and control of the experimental room and of the amplifiers are, therefore, also required.

The apparatus in the Tufts College laboratory involves the use of miniature electrodes attached to the skin of the subject, four high-gain, noninterfering, amplifying channels, and a fifth channel of amplification with less high gain. Each of these five amplifying systems is attached to an appropriate ink-writing oscillograph which has been so developed that continuous records of as many hours' length as desired may be made. The apparatus as constructed at present could without modification record continuously for 56 hours. The motion picture film by Mead and Carmichael, referred to in Chapter 6, shows the apparatus used in the present investigations and the technique for introducing a subject into the experimental situation. Also shown are some typical, appropriately labeled eye-movement records, electrocardiograms, and electroencephalograms.

The relatively nonpolarizable electrodes used in these experiments were of the so-called silver-hat type, made of chlorided silver. Continuing the analogy of the term, the brim was 10 millimeters in diameter and the small dome-shaped crown 5 millimeters in diameter. At the top of the crown was a small hole 2½ millimeters in diameter. To the brim was soldered a fine, insulated, wire lead attached at its other end to a radio or "banana" plug. The lead wires were long enough for the subject to move about conveniently without interference.

The plug of each electrode was inserted in the appropriate place on a plug box or electrode board. A system of switches (on the pre-amplifier box described below) connected to this plug board was so arranged that any pair of electrodes might be grounded or introduced to a particular amplifying channel as desired. The electrode board was in the experimental chamber out of view of the subject. It was the only part of the recording apparatus in the chamber. In the plug box were fuses in each circuit to protect the subject from possible stray and deleterious electrical currents.

Before an electrode was attached, the skin was cleansed with ether to remove skin oil and dirt, which would have interfered with the electrical contact to be made. Collodion was spread on the fabric washer attached to the inner surface of the electrode brim. The electrode itself was then held to the skin until the collodion was dry. To insure adequate contact, the skin beneath the dome of the electrode was then lightly irritated with a blunt instrument (a toothpick) inserted through the small hole in the electrode.

The dome-shaped crown of the electrode was filled with a commercial electrode jelly (an agar and acid compound), to facilitate electrical conduction. Each electrode was then tested for resistance by means of an ohmmeter constructed for this purpose. If the resistance was found to be over 10,000 ohms, the skin was further irritated or the electrode reapplied. Resistances greater than the above amount would have interfered to a significant degree with the recording of the potential changes. In the present experiments the resistances were, in general, considerably less.

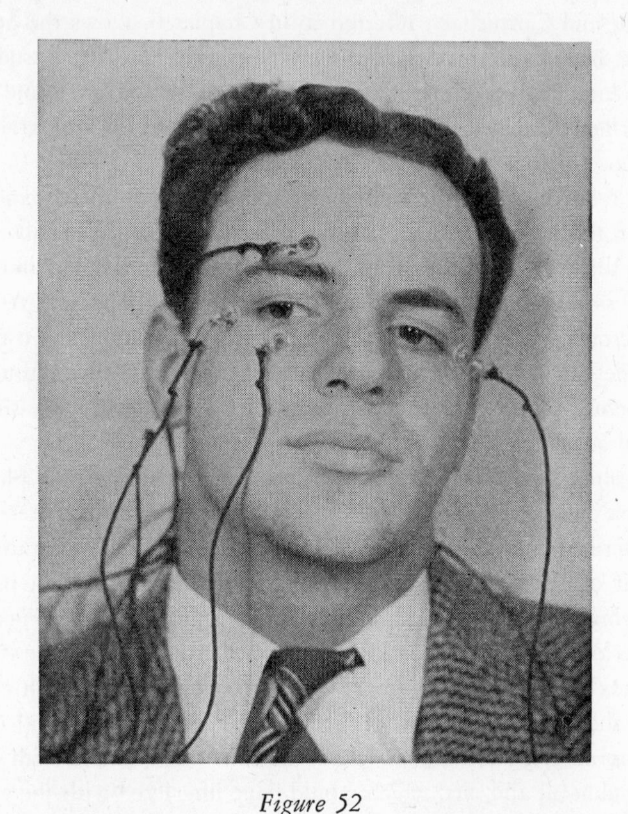

Figure 52

PLACEMENT OF THE ELECTRODES FOR THE ELECTRO-OCULOGRAM

Eight electrodes were used for the recordings made in the present experiments. As shown in Figure 52, an electrode was placed on the skin of the face at the external canthus of each eye. One electrode was attached on the bony ridge above the right eyebrow, and another on the ridge beneath the right eye. The first two picked up the electrical shifts which recorded the horizontal movements of the eyes; the latter two were used in the present instance to record the upward, vertical movements of the eye made during blinking.

The other four electrodes used were for the electrocardiogram and the electroencephalogram. As mentioned previously, many different electrical techniques have been applied to the study of problems in addition to the recording of ocular potentials. In the case of eye-movement recording, electrodes are placed in pairs about the ocular orbit, depending on the plane of movement to be observed. In the case of the electrocardiogram, the placement of the electrodes has been the subject of much study. Certain leads are now generally agreed upon for clinical test purposes. In the present experiments, the pair of electrodes was placed so that the heart was also on the line roughly between them. One electrode was attached to the lobe of the right ear and the other was placed upon the ankle of the left leg. The electrodes were placed at some distance from the heart for reasons of recording efficiency. The oscillograph record from these electrodes is the characteristic PRT wave previously described.

In the study of brain waves, the question of using either bipolar or monopolar leads from the electrodes to the amplifiers immediately arises. Bipolar leads would mean placing two electrodes in close proximity somewhere on the skull; monopolar leads implies that one electrode is in contact with the skull, the other being an "indifferent" electrode placed elsewhere on the skull or body.

H. H. Jasper (160) has summarized the merits and disadvantages of these placements as used in brain-wave recording. Records taken with bipolar leads are distorted by three chief artifacts: interference between simultaneously active cortical cells beneath each electrode, diphasic artifacts due to conducted disturbances, and zero potential differences due to a source which equally affects both electrodes. Due to the proximity of the two points (at the electrodes) between which potential differences are set up, it is not possible to pick up disturbances at a distance from the electrodes. These disturbances would tend, rather, to affect each electrode equally.

The principles involved in the monopolar leads are not so well understood. It is supposed that the concentration of the lines of current which flow under the "active" lead are so great in relation to those which flow under the "indifferent" lead that the potentials in the immediate vicinity of the "active" lead predominate. Some experimenters (17) believe that no truly "indifferent" lead is possible and that the so-called monopolar leads, even when both electrodes are placed directly on cortical tissue, may also give rise to diphasic and even triphasic artifacts.

Jasper (159) took simultaneous electroencephalographic records from bipolar leads one millimeter apart and from one of these same electrodes as a monopolar lead with a diffuse electrode on the skull. He reported that fundamentally the same general type of activity from a local cortical area was recorded with one type of lead as with the other. He also noted that similar cortical activity was recorded with both bipolar and monopolar leads following the local application of strychnine and in response to afferent stimulation. At present it is, of course, difficult to evaluate the data of electrode placement until more is definitely known about the characteristics of the cortical activity which the electrodes are to pick up and record.

The electrode placements for the electroencephalogram in the present experiment were over the right cerebral hemisphere. One electrode was placed two centimeters to the right and on the line with the inion or back protuberance of the skull; the other was placed two centimeters to the right of the midline of the skull at the vertex or top of the skull. This particular electrode placement was chosen because previous studies had shown that from bipolar recording of this sort, a good index of the special low-frequency characteristics of sleep is easily secured in some subjects. It seemed especially important in this study to make a record, if possible, of any periods of drowsiness in the subject.

The amplifiers used for all recording, whether of eye movements, electrocardiogram, or electroencephalogram, were of the paired, noninterfering, resistance-capacity coupled type. This equipment was capable of recording the absolute magnitude of potential shifts but not of the recording of maintained potentials. The pre-amplifier and power amplifiers (Figures 53 and 54) were housed in shielded cages separate from each other.

The controls on the pre-amplifier box were of two types: some were concerned with electrode distribution, and the others with the calibration of the record. Calibration of the recorded voltages made it possible to determine the amount of potential causing any given excursion on the record. The switches for the selection of electrodes were mounted on the panel of the pre-amplifier box. Each switch had 16 points cor-

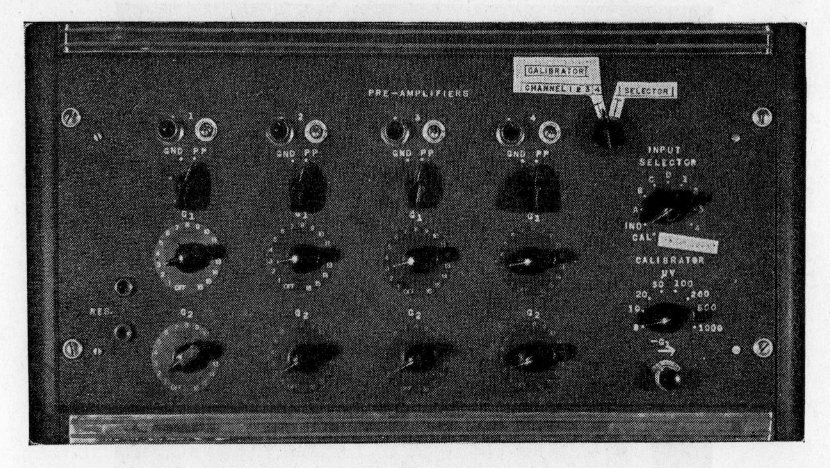

Figure 53

PRE-AMPLIFIERS USED IN THE PRESENT STUDY

responding to the 16 receptacles on the electrode board. Each channel had two switches. One would throw any of the 16 electrodes onto the grids of the input stage, and the other would connect any of the 16 electrodes with ground. Thus any combination of electrodes might be conveniently led to the amplifiers. The apparatus was so controlled that there was virtually no interference from extraneous electrical sources such as the 60-cycle power current of the laboratory.

The amplification of the potentials could be altered by the two gain controls on the power amplifiers. One was a continuously variable control; the other, a step control. With these controls the total amplification was regulated so that recording might be accomplished without distortion. The higher the amplification, the smaller was the potential necessary, of course, to cause a deflection of the oscillograph. There were also two filter switches on the power amplifier; one progressively cut out low frequencies, and the other, high frequencies. These switches could have been used to reduce the interference of muscle potentials when an electrode happened to have been placed on an active muscle group.

The ink-writing polygraph consisted of five individual oscillograph units and a constant-speed, paper-feed mechanism. The polygraph is shown in Figure 55. The oscillograph units were built something like very large, dynamic loudspeakers. The peak-to-peak linear amplitude of each pen was about 15 millimeters. That is, the total linear amplitude

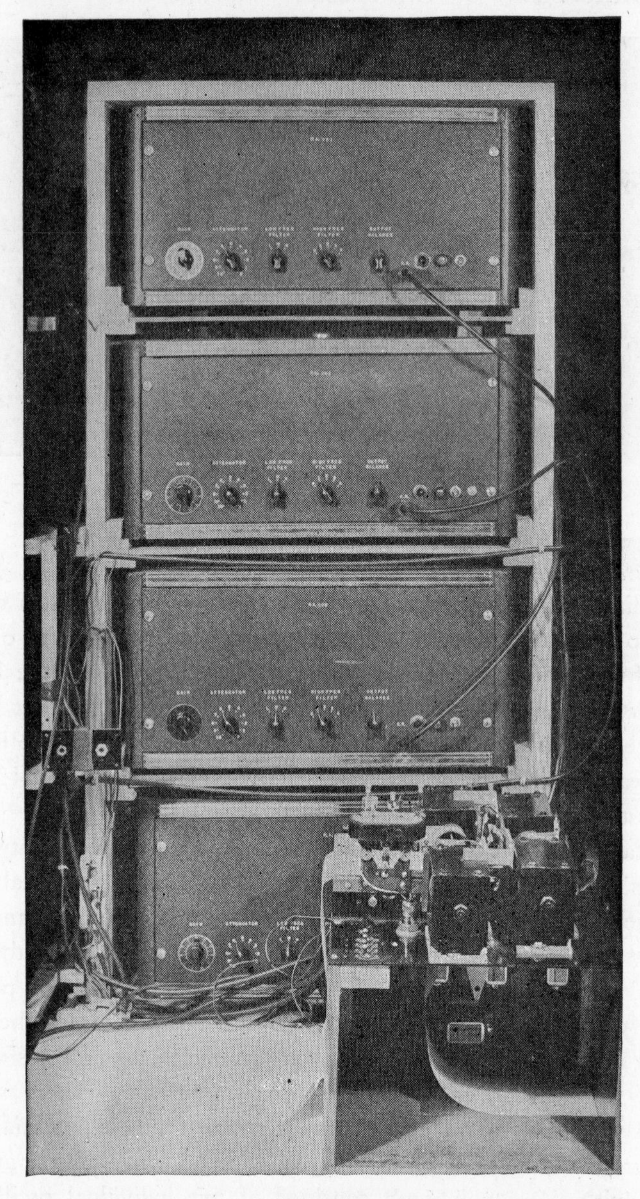

Figure 54

AMPLIFIERS USED IN THE PRESENT STUDY

Figure 55

INK-WRITING POLYGRAPH USED IN THE PRESENT STUDY

of the excursion might be 7 to 8 millimeters on each side of the base line. The units were so arranged that the pens just touched the paper and produced a smooth, clear-flowing ink line. The pens were also properly spaced apart and correctly aligned on the writing surface so as not to interfere with one another.

The pens were made of stainless steel tubing. In the body of the pen, the inside diameter was 0.02 inch. The tip was drawn out to an even finer diameter so as to give a thin, distinct line of writing. Special ink was developed for this experiment because it was necessary to have a very constant and free-flowing fluid for the long records required. The new ink was a 1 to 2 per cent solution of methylene blue in distilled water to which a little oil was added to prevent clogging in the capillary pens. The ink was protected from the air of the room to avoid the formation of microscopic molds which sometimes form in such fluids and clog the pens.

The paper was run in paper guides to keep it flat and smooth under the pens. The paper-feed mechanism was capable of running at three constant speeds. For these experiments the mechanism was adjusted so that the paper moved at the rate of 1½ centimeters per second. The recording paper was 10 centimeters wide. It was divided by perforations into consecutively numbered lengths of 30 centimeters each. Heavy red lines further divided these lengths into 3-centimeter sections; light red lines divided each section into five equal portions. The paper was folded by the printer so that as it ran through the recording device it fell in even, flat, but continuous strips.

Figure 56 is a sample of a record made with the apparatus described above. The first oscillograph unit recorded the heart beat. The second

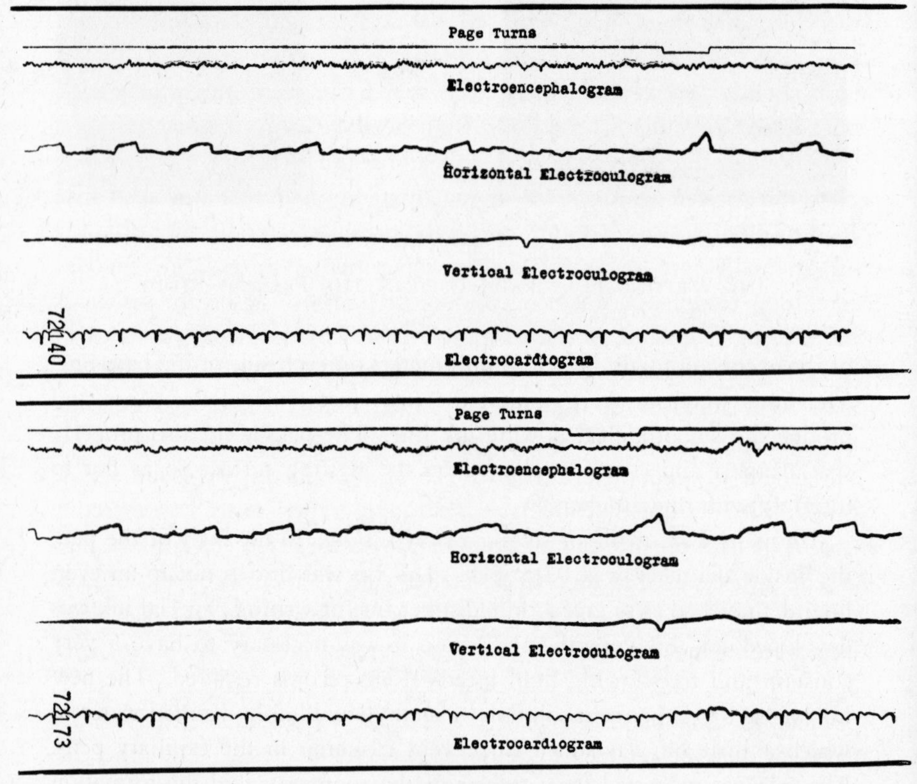

Figure 56

SAMPLE OF RECORD TAKEN WITH THE TUFTS COLLEGE APPARATUS

was a record of the vertical blink movements; the third, a record of the horizontal eye movements. The fourth channel recorded brain potentials. The fifth channel, referred to above as the one with less high gain amplification, was used to record the turning of the pages by the subject. This channel was activated by an "electric eye" set, consisting of a suitable light-condenser system, beside the subject's book. The slight flash of light produced by the turning of each page activated a photoelectric cell, which in turn produced a deflection on the same continuously moving paper on which the other records were being simultaneously made.

In the present experiments, reading had to be done in an enclosure because of the wish to reduce noise from the laboratory and because of the desirability of having a grounded room to shield the recording electrodes on the subject from stray electrical currents. The reading, therefore, was done under artificial light. The light sources were two grounded "baby spot" lights with 60-watt bulbs and an overhead 60-watt bulb slightly behind the subject. The spot lights were on either side of the subject, directing a light beam from overhead onto the bookstand.

Following the suggestion of Ferree and Rand (106, Pt. I) to reduce glare effects, the arrangement of the three light sources was such that most of the light was concentrated on the reading material; the rest faded off gradually into the black of the experimental room. Any marked brightness contrast between the amount of light falling on the center of the reading page and on the surrounding area of the book was not discernible. The artificial light was filtered through daylight or "whiterlite" glass. The intensity of illumination under which reading was done in the present experiment was 16 footcandles. This fact was checked by a Macbeth illuminometer. This choice of illuminating intensity was a generalization from the findings of available experiments (reviewed in Chapter 5) on the intensity of illumination required for efficient reading.

The subjects used in these experiments were 40 men who had not previously been used in any prolonged reading investigations. Ten subjects were included in each of four experimental groups; the distinctions between these four groups will be discussed in a later section on the experimental situation. Twenty of the subjects were students in Harvard College; they are referred to below as "college students." The other 20 subjects were students in the high school at Arlington, Massachusetts; they will be referred to as "high school students." All these subjects came to the Laboratory of Sensory Psychology and Physiology at Tufts College, where all the experimental work was done.

Before the experimental reading period began, each subject filled out the first part (Questions 1-18 inclusive) of the questionnaire which is reproduced on the following pages.

Please make the following judgments. It is not expected that your judgments will be finally valid but that they will merely represent an indication of your best estimate.

1. I believe that my parents or teachers report that I learned to read
   (*a*) at an unusually early age. ....
   (*b*) at a rather early age. ....
   (*c*) at about the usual age. ....
   (*d*) at a little later than the average age. ....
   (*e*) at much later than the average age. ....
2. In my junior high school years, that is, in the years immediately preceding my four years of high school, I probably read
   (*a*) much more than most of my companions. ....
   (*b*) somewhat more than most of my companions. ....
   (*c*) about the same amount of material as my companions. ....
   (*d*) somewhat less than my companions. ....
   (*e*) much less than my companions. ....
3. In my last year in secondary school, that is, my last pre-college year, I probably read
   (*a*) much more than most of my companions. ....
   (*b*) somewhat more than most of my companions. ....
   (*c*) about the same amount of material as my companions. ....
   (*d*) somewhat less than my companions. ....
   (*e*) much less than my companions. ....
4. It is my opinion that I now read
   (*a*) much more than most of my companions. ....
   (*b*) somewhat more than most of my companions. ....
   (*c*) about the same amount of material as my companions. ....
   (*d*) somewhat less than my companions. ....
   (*e*) much less than my companions. ....
5. Reading is now
   (*a*) one of my principal pleasures. ....
   (*b*) a real pleasure. ....
   (*c*) neither a pleasure nor an annoyance. ....
   (*d*) something I avoid if I can. ....
   (*e*) difficult and unpleasant for me. ....
6. In my opinion, in comparison with others of my age and general educational level I read
   (*a*) much more than most individuals. ....
   (*b*) somewhat more than most individuals. ....
   (*c*) about the same as most individuals. ....

(*d*) somewhat less than most individuals. ....

(*e*) much less than most individuals. ....

7. I find that

(*a*) I never notice any symptoms of fatigue, eye strain, or headache even after a long period of reading. ....

(*b*) I notice some few symptoms of fatigue, eye strain, or headache after a long period of reading. ....

(*c*) Fatigue and eye strain serve as an indication that I should stop reading. ....

(*d*) I am troubled by fatigue and eye strain after ordinary reading in connection with my college work. ....

(*e*) Fatigue and eye strain are a constant accompaniment to the use of my eyes. ....

8. After long periods of study and reading I often have the following unpleasant subjective, that is, personal, feelings and reactions. (Please write briefly.)

....

....

....

....

....

9. In study and reading I sometimes read without interruption for

(*a*) more than 6 hours. ....

(*b*) more than 4 hours. ....

(*c*) more than 2 hours. ....

(*d*) more than 1 hour. ....

(*e*) more than ½ hour ....

10. When I am reading in my own room I ordinarily "stretch my legs" or break the period of study every

(*a*) 6 hours. ....

(*b*) 4 hours. ....

(*c*) 2 hours. ....

(*d*) 1 hour. ....

(*e*) ½ hour. ....

11. If it is available I eat some candy, drink some milk, or take other nourishment about every

(*a*) 8 hours. ....

(*b*) 6 hours. ....

(*c*) 4 hours. ....

(*d*) 2 hours. ....

(*e*) 1 hour. ....

12. My head feels more clear for reading and study
    (*a*) immediately after arising. ....
    (*b*) in midmorning. ....
    (*c*) immediately after luncheon. ....
    (*d*) in midafternoon. ....
    (*e*) in early evening. ....
    (*f*) in late evening. ....
13. At the present time
    (*a*) My head is very clear and I feel like reading and studying. ....
    (*b*) My head is reasonably clear and I feel like reading and studying. ....
    (*c*) I feel a little tired but I know that I can read and study. ....
    (*d*) I have a headache or feel some annoyance at the thought of reading and studying. ....
    (*e*) The idea of reading and studying in my present condition is revolting to me. ....
14. My average amount of sleep at night is .... hours.
15. Last night I slept .... hours.
16. Please note any special occurrences during the last 48 hours that might influence your physical condition so far as your ability to read and study is concerned.

....

....

....

....

....

17. (*a*) I have never worn glasses. ....
    (*b*) I wear glasses now and have worn them continuously for about .... years.
    (*c*) I wore glasses once beginning at about age .... and continuing to about age ....
    (*d*) I wear glasses only when I read. ....
    (*e*) I should like to make the following comments concerning glasses:

....

....

....

....

....

18. I have had the following trouble with my eyes:

....

....

....

The treatment which I have carried out was, briefly:

....

....

....

AFTER READING

19. Following the experience that I have just had in prolonged reading in one position I feel that

(*a*) After a half hour's rest and some food I could do an evening's studying without inconvenience. ....

(*b*) I could do some studying, although with reluctance. ....

(*c*) I could study and read effectively if required to do so. ....

(*d*) I doubt my ability to do any further reading or studying. ....

(*e*) I would absolutely refuse to use my eyes again until after a night's sleep. ....

20. Briefly describe below the subjective feelings that you noticed during the period in which you were reading in the experimental room.

....

....

....

....

....

From these questionnaires, information was available concerning the subjects themselves and the subjective reports of their attitudes toward visual work before, during, and after the experiment.

Of the college students, 11 reported that they had never worn glasses. Four wore glasses. Two of these had worn them for two years, one for three years, and one for six years previous to the experiment. Five of the college students wore glasses only when reading. Of the high school students, 16 reported that they had never worn glasses. Two had worn glasses for eight years previously. Two wore glasses only when reading. The subjects who wore glasses wore them during all the reading periods.

It is recognized that many of the questions asked the subjects were general and relatively simple.[1] The questionnaire was designed to give an outline description of the subjects, especially with regard to their reading habits. It was felt that some information, even though subject to the unreliabilities of memory and introspective report, would be better than none. Also, a more elaborate interview with the subject would have unduly prolonged the experimental period and would have required procedures the complexity of which was not warranted by the purpose of the present experiments.

Certain comments may be made about the general reading habits of the subjects as they were reported to the experimenters. Eight college students reported that they had learned to read "at a rather early age." Eleven said that they had learned "at about the usual age." One reported that he had learned at "a little later than the average age." Seven high school students had learned to read "at a rather early age," twelve "at about the usual age," and one "a little later than the average age." The modal response for both sets of subjects was that they had learned to read "at about the usual age." This may be, of course, an unreliable finding, for it is based merely upon the subjects' own reports, but it is given as a record of the subjects' beliefs about themselves as recorded.

As may be seen from the questionnaire, the subjects were also asked to compare from memory the amount of time they had spent in reading to that spent by their college and high school companions. Five college students reported that they thought they had read much more than their junior high school companions, eight somewhat more, three about the same amount, and four somewhat less. For these same categories, respectively, the number of high school students reporting in each was five, five, eight, and two. The modal response for the college students was that they had read "somewhat more than most of my companions"; for the high school students the modal response was "about the same amount of material as my companions." In comparison with their senior high school companions, the number of college students reporting in each category was three, five, ten, and two; the number of high school students in each was two, seven, seven, and one. The modal response for the college students was about the same amount of material read as their companions. The modal response for the high school students was about the same or

[1] In some instances not all the subjects answered all the questions; hence the number of reports indicated is not always 20.

somewhat more material read than their companions. Again, the validity of these results depends on the subjects' understanding of the question and the reliability of their reports in answer.

At the time of answering the questionnaire, two college students believed they read much more than their college companions, five somewhat more, five about the same amount, and eight somewhat less than their companions. In these same categories, the number of high school students was two, eight, six, and three. The majority of the college students believed that they read somewhat less than their companions; the majority of the high school students somewhat more than most of their companions.

Six college students reported that they regarded reading as one of their principal pleasures, seven found reading a real pleasure, six regarded reading as neither a pleasure nor an annoyance, and one avoided reading if he could. Three high school students regarded reading as a principal pleasure, nine as a real pleasure, and eight as neither a pleasure nor an annoyance. The modal response for both sets was "reading is now a real pleasure."

In comparison with other acquaintances of their own age and general educational level, it was the opinion of two college students that they read much more, seven that they read somewhat more, six about the same amount, and five somewhat less. The number of high school students reporting in these same categories was one, eight, eight, and three. The modal response for the college students was "somewhat more than most individuals" (the mean response, however, would be lower) and for the high school students, "somewhat more" or about the same. The general impression given by these replies is that, considered as samples of their respective populations, both groups of students were somewhat better than average in reading interests and probably in reading skills.

In answer to the questions about their study habits, three college students and five high school students reported that they never noticed any symptoms of fatigue, eyestrain, or headache even after a long period of reading. Fifteen college and twelve high school students reported that they noticed a few symptoms of fatigue, and so forth, after long reading periods. This was the modal response for both groups of subjects. Two college and three high school students reported that they regarded fatigue and eyestrain as indications that they should stop reading.

In reply to the question as to how long they studied or read without interruption, two college students reported more than six hours, five reported more than four hours, ten more than two hours, and three more than one hour. The number of high school students reporting in the same categories was two, five, eight, and four; one student reported that he did not study for more than a half hour at a time. The modal response for both groups of subjects was reading and studying without interruption for more than two hours. The usual period of uninterrupted study for the group as a whole was thus considerably less than the six-hour experimental period of continuous activity required in the present experiments.

When the subjects were asked, however, how soon the period of study was broken momentarily by other activity, the modal response was that such breaks occurred every hour. One high school student reported that a break was made every four hours; five college students and five high school students reported a break every two hours; thirteen and nine, respectively, every hour; and two and four, every half hour.

The majority of the college students reported that their heads felt more clear for reading and study in the early evening or in midmorning. The high school students preferred for studying, the midmorning, immediately after arising, or the early evening. The time of the present experimental reading periods was late afternoon and early evening.

Since the experimental period extended from midafternoon through the dinner hour into midevening, some questions were asked about the subjects' general regimen. Four college students and one high school student reported that they took some form of nourishment every six hours. Seven college and three high school students ate every four hours; five and eight, respectively, every two hours; and three and five, every hour. The modal response for the college students was the taking of nourishment every four hours; for the high school students, every two hours. No interruption, of course, was allowed during the six-hour experimental period. Chewing might under certain conditions have interfered with the record of reading.

According to their reports, five high school students slept on the average ten hours at night; three college and six high school students slept nine hours; eight and nine, respectively, eight hours; eight college students, seven hours; and one, six hours. On the night before their first experimental trial, one high school student slept eleven hours; two slept ten hours; two college students and eight high school students, nine hours; seven and five, respectively, eight hours; five and four, seven hours; four college students slept six hours; and two college students slept five hours. Whereas the modal response for the average amount of sleep of the college students was seven or eight hours, and of the high school students, eight hours, the modal number of hours slept before the experiment was eight for the college students and nine for the high school students.

Other information than the questionnaire data was also available for these subjects. The college students were, as noted above, Harvard undergraduates and were included in a group of students which had been intensively studied from a psychiatric and clinical point of view in the so-called Grant Study — a study of the normal college student. The high school students were Arlington, Massachusetts, High School students selected from a group which had also had the advantage of being studied, by the Harvard-Arlington Guidance Study — a program for improving vocational and educational placement. The subjects of the experiment were thus chosen because they had previously been scientifically studied from many different points of view. It was felt that any idiosyncracies in performance which might possibly appear in the present study could more readily be related to the known characteristics of the subject in question than if an unknown group of subjects were used.

Psychometric and psychiatric data available from the Grant Study of the 20 college subjects are presented in Table 7.[2] It will be noted from the charts that these subjects represented a fairly homogeneous group within themselves. The scores reported are with respect to the mean of the group studied by the Grant Study and not necessarily with respect to the general population. The tests used were those developed for the purposes of the Grant Study and so are not general psychometric instruments. The 20 individuals were chosen in such a way as to provide for the present experiments a fairly balanced group with respect to intellectual and emotional traits and with respect to manual and scholastic skills. No extreme ocular refractive errors are reported for this group of 20 college students.

Similar psychometric data were available for the high school subjects from the Harvard-Arlington Guidance Study. The balance in this experimental group was also achieved not only by selecting individuals about

[2] Tables 7-75 appear in the Appendix.

average in any particular score but also by including individuals whose scores were found in the neighborhood of both extremes of the range tested. This was true especially in the case of scholastic aptitude and reading achievement scores. The tests used in the Arlington Study have been standardized for more or less general use among high school populations. The scores reported, therefore, allow a comparison of the performance of these high school students with the performance of high school students in general.

One basic difficulty, as pointed out above, in a study of what has been called visual fatigue is that such a phenomenon involves much more than simple physiological and mechanical changes in the visual system. The psychological reactions of the subject, such as those called "interest" and "attention," must always be considered, as well as the more definite facts of the physiology of specific muscular work. In the present experiments, for example, two types of literature were read by each subject. It is possible that factors of interest, comprehension, and even so-called fatiguing effects might be different in the two instances. Other facts concerned with the motivation of the reader also required consideration. In the present experiments, for example, tests of comprehension (to be described later) which were used as a means of assuring the experimenters that the reader kept to his task may also have affected the reader's attitude toward the task.

The aim of the present experiments was to use reading materials in which "difficulty of comprehension" was experimentally varied but the typographical format of the reading selections remained essentially the same so as to control as much as possible the conditions from one experimental situation to the other. The two books which the subjects read for six hours each were from the Everyman series: *Lorna Doone,* by Richard Blackmore, and *An Inquiry into the Nature and Causes of the Wealth of Nations,* Volume 2, by Adam Smith. These two books will be referred to as Lorna Doone and Adam Smith, or, more simply, as D and S. Lorna Doone is a pastoral, historical novel in which an adventurous plot is developed, rather than a series of arguments, such as is Adam Smith, an eighteenth-century treatise on economics, which was intended to be the more difficult of the two books.

The typographic format of all books included in the Everyman series is not the same. The two here selected are almost identical. The books are printed in black, 10-point, Old Style type of medium boldness, solid set, on dull-finished, cream-colored paper. The length of the lines of print is 88 millimeters. The size of the pages is 106 by 172 millimeters. There are 44 lines per page, and about 12 or 13 words per line. This particular format was chosen as conveniently representing a good format, as determined by experiments previously reviewed on size and style of type, leading, color of paper, and other features of the printing setup. The more closely this format represents the optimum, the better, it is believed, reading variables were controlled in the present experiments.

Twenty of the subjects read the books directly, under essentially normal reading conditions, as described above. For the other 20 subjects, the books were reproduced on microfilm. The reproductions of the books used in the experiments were read in a microfilm apparatus (shown in Figure 57), manufactured by the Spencer Lens Company, and altered in the present use to make the "turning of pages" more convenient. The apparatus is essentially a tall box, shaped like a truncated pyramid, with one open side. At the top of the black box (which is above the reader's head) are film holders and a lens system which projects an image down upon a "reading pad" lying on the base of the box. The projection of the microfilm was such as to reproduce the same format as in the books which were directly read, even to exposing two pages at once like an open book. To "turn the page," the subject simply pressed a lever within easy reach. The reading pad mentioned above was a tablet of white paper. The use of this tablet facilitated the taking of comprehension tests of the multiple-choice type. The subject marked his choice on the paper and at the completion of the test tore that sheet off. These sheets could then be conveniently corrected by placing a stencil over them. The microfilm apparatus was placed on a table at such a height that the reading pad upon which the reproductions were projected was as far from the subject as the actual book would have been. The distance between the reading pad and the lens system was, of course, fixed to insure proper focus and the typographic format of the actual books.

Previous studies of microfilm reading (for example, 4) have described instances of subjects who reported feelings of eyestrain and visual "fatigue" when microfilm reproductions were read, even for relatively short periods of time. McFarland, Holway, and Hurvich observed the number of blinks made by six subjects during five-minute intervals at the beginning, half-way through, and at the end of an hour's reading. The reading was done under three sets of conditions: (*a*) microfilm reading,

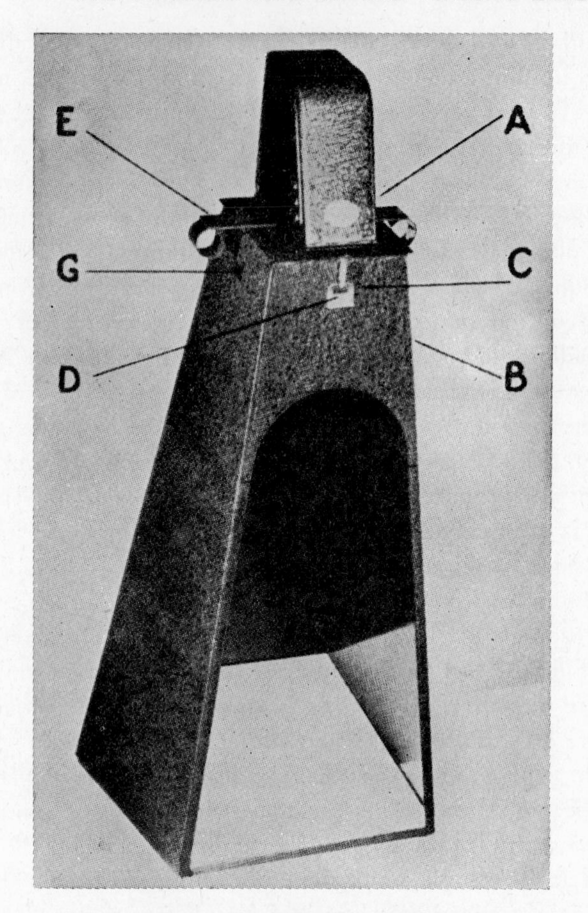

Figure 57

MICROFILM APPARATUS

A — Projection head
B — Projection case
E — Glass filmbook

(Courtesy of the Spencer Lens Co.)

(*b*) reading of the original book in the normal position under approximately the same illumination as in the microfilm reading, and (*c*) reading of the original book placed in the microfilm stand. The level of illumination was approximately 15 footcandles in all three instances.

The absolute blink-rate for the three different reading conditions is

> least in the case of the microfilm reader. The differences, however, are hardly significant. . . .
>
> As regards the preferred mode of reading, our protocols indicate a high degree of agreement among subjects. With one exception, microfilm was rated last. (227, p. 78.)

In a somewhat elaborate experiment (142) on visual fatigue preliminary to the present study, each of 30 subjects was given standardized instructions to read steadily, without skimming, throughout a four-hour period. No check was made in this preliminary experiment of the subject's comprehension of what he read. This was done in order that the subject might be the more inclined to read in his normal manner and to keep the "fatiguing" task as homogeneous as possible. It was, however, regarded as essential to the present visual fatigue study that some check be made on the subject's comprehension of the material read. At the same time it was recognized that these checks might, as above noted, affect the attitude of the subject or his mental "set" toward the task of reading.

Standardized tests were first suggested, since they contain reading material of known difficulty and level of comprehension. Alternate forms could have been used at the beginning and end of the reading period. Validity, reliability, and similar necessary measures would have been statistically determined and thus available in interpreting the data. However, it was recognized that using standardized tests would require the subject to stop his reading of one kind of material (the books previously described) and, for a few minutes, read other material. The tests might also be materially decreased in value if not used under circumstances similar to those under which they were standardized. The combined effect of the above variables on the data of the present experiment could not be determined without extensive investigation beyond the scope of the present study.

It was, therefore, considered preferable in planning the present study to prepare comprehension checks specifically for this experiment. A comprehension test was administered at the end of the six-hour reading period, and regular comprehension exercises were interspersed during the reading period. Both types of tests consisted of items in the form of multiple-choice questions (four alternatives) on the material (Lorna Doone and Adam Smith) actually read by the subjects. The final test was devised to determine how well the subject comprehended all the material

You are to *encircle* the number in the left margin which corresponds with the number of the word or statement which best fits the sentence. Remember that this book was written in the 18th century, and your answers should come from Adam Smith, rather than from any present-day information.

1 2 3 4 — 1. Drawbacks were supposed to encourage (1) importation, (2) cheating, (3) exportation, (4) short-selling.

1 2 3 4 — 2. Before 1776 Great Britain had a monopoly on the (1) tobacco, (2) potatoes, (3) corn, (4) whisky from the American Colonies.

1 2 3 4 — 3. (1) Income taxes, (2) bounties, (3) the gold standard, (4) Spanish trade encouraged merchants to export goods.

1 2 3 4 — 4. Adam Smith used the (1) wine, (2) wool, (3) tobacco, (4) corn market to illustrate his discussion of bounties.

1 2 3 4 — 5. A bounty on exportation is more favorable to merchants and manufacturers than a bounty on (1) production, (2) importation, (3) farming, (4) trading.

1 2 3 4 — 6. At one time in European history (1) artificers, (2) farmers, (3) middle-men, (4) manufacturers were prohibited from operating in the corn market.

1 2 3 4 — 7. The commerce treaty mentioned between Portugal and England was concerned with (1) leather and corn, (2) wines and woolens, (3) wood and coal, (4) silk and wool.

1 2 3 4 — 8. The gold which Portugal sent to Britain came originally from (1) Brazil, (2) Spain, (3) France, (4) the Virginia Colonies.

1 2 3 4 — 9. Almost all of Britain's gold came from (1) France, (2) America, (3) Italy, (4) Portugal.

1 2 3 4 5 6 7 8 — 10. Ancient Greece and Rome established colonies because of (1) necessity or utility, (2) religious pressure, (3) greed or exploitation, (4) political pressure, whereas the other nations were interested in colonization solely as a chance to find (5) room for their prisoners, (6) new land for their rulers, (7) gold and silver mines, (8) markets for their produce.

1 2 3 4 — 11. (1) The Roman Law, (2) The Agrarian Law, (3) The St. John's Law, (4) The Division Law divided the land into certain proportions among the citizens comprising the state.

1 2 3 4 — 12. The West Indies got their name from the mistake of (1) Vasco de Gama, (2) Isabella, (3) Columbus, (4) Marco Polo.

1 2 3 4 — 13. Columbus represented St. Domingo as a land abounding in (1) potatoes, (2) animal life, (3) cotton, (4) gold.

Figure 58

PORTION OF FINAL COMPREHENSION TEST, *Adam Smith*

he had read; the interspersed comprehension exercises were designed to offer a progressive check of comprehension as the subject was reading, in addition to serving the further purpose of keeping the subject at his task.

The questions of the final comprehension test sampled so-called thought units; in the case of both books several pages at a time were usually required to complete such a unit. The interspersed comprehension checks *included one question per page* up to the three-hundredth page. About 25 pages were covered in one exercise, the exact number of questions depending on the convenience of dividing the story or argument. Twelve such exercises were prepared for Lorna Doone and 13 for Adam Smith. Each exercise was inserted in the books between the appropriate pages. The reader took each test as he came to it, signaling to the experimenter (and thus recording on the paper just before and after taking a test) by a series of rapid blinks. The interspersed exercises for both books comprised about 600 questions, and the final tests included 138 questions, making about 738 questions in all.

Figure 58 presents a page of the final comprehension test taken after the reading of Adam Smith. Figure 59 is an example of an interspersed

A. After the harvest party John slept: *a.* under the table. *b.* in his own room. *c.* outside. *d.* by the pump. B. Huckaback confided the purpose of his visit to: *a.* John. *b.* John's mother. *c.* Lizzie. *d.* no one. C. The sisters wanted John to: *a.* follow Huckaback. *b.* revisit Glen Doone. *c.* like Ruth. *d.* watch his mother. D. Upon finding Fry in Annie's room, John threatened to: *a.* call the parson. *b.* call his mother. *c.* tell his wife. *d.* cuff him soundly. E. Annie's first ruse to trace Huckaback was to: *a.* send John after him. *b.* send Fry after him. *c.* tie a ribbon on the pony. *d.* tie a bag of bread crumbs under the pony. F. Sending Fry was suggested by: *a.* Ruth. *b.* Annie. *c.* John's mother. *d.* Lizzie. G. Fry had followed Huckaback primarily because of: *a.* Annie's sake. *b.* his own curiosity. *c.* the money to be given him. *d.* fear of John. H. The part of the mountains through which Fry followed Huckaback was: *a.* habited by shepherds. *b.* desolate in the winter. *c.* avoided during harvest. *d.* always avoided. I. Fry was frightened by: *a.* white smoke coming from the quagmire. *b.* black smoke coming from a hollow tree. *c.* a man coming out of a pit. *d.* a man slinking through the trees. J. Fry stayed long enough by the quagmire to: *a.* just see the man's head. *b.* make sure it was a man. *c.* make out the man's features. *d.* see who the man was. K. The wilds of Exmoor were an excellent place for smuggling because of: *a.* the general desolation of the place. *b.* ravines running inland from the sea. *c.* the uncharted sea beyond it. *d.* no vigilance

Figure 59

INTERSPERSED COMPREHENSION EXERCISE, *Lorna Doone*

along the sea-coast. L. Should a Protestant rising occur, it is likely that the Doones would: *a.* have nothing to do with it. *b.* side in with the Papists of their birth. *c.* fight with the Protestants. *d.* at this time be unpredictable. M. Huckaback left Plover's Barrow: *a.* as suddenly as he had come. *b.* after confiding in his daughter. *c.* with much ostentation. *d.* by night. N. Carver was a handsome man to John except for his: *a.* scars on his cheek. *b.* matted hair. *c.* cruel eyes. *d.* jutting jaw. O. Carver thought the gifts were from: *a.* John. *b.* Charlie. *c.* Counsellor. *d.* Lorna. P. John, while waiting for Lorna, was almost shot by: *a.* a Doone sentinel. *b.* Doones returning from a foray. *c.* Counsellor. *d.* Carver. Q. What restrained John from boldly entering Glen Doone was: *a.* fear of the Doones. *b.* Carver's gun. *c.* Annie's prayers. *d.* his mother's counsel. R. Betty gave John her message: *a.* after he had fed the pigs. *b.* as soon as they were outside. *c.* when John's mother had gone to bed. *d.* when Annie joined them. S. Betty told John to: *a.* spy on Charleworth. *b.* see if Sir Ensor had died. *c.* go to Glen Doone in the morning. *d.* watch out for Carver. T. On the morning when John went to see Lorna, he philosophized about: *a.* right and wrong. *b.* the sun. *c.* the dew. *d.* Lorna. U. John thought that Lorna was: *a.* purer than the morning dew. *b.* clearer than the moon. *c.* sweeter than the violet. *d.* deep as the ocean. V. Lorna's answer to John's proposal was: *a.* "Yes, I shall marry you." *b.* "Darling, you have won it all." *c.* "I suppose I must." *d.* "Wait awhile, and then put your question again."

Figure 59 (continued)

INTERSPERSED COMPREHENSION EXERCISE, *Lorna Doone*

comprehension exercise used with Lorna Doone; an example for use with Adam Smith is presented in Figure 60. Except for the necessary numbering of the questions and the alternate choices (one of which the subject encircled in each case), these exercises were printed in the *same* format as the original reading materials.

Although the questions on these exercises may be objectively scored and have the advantage of appropriateness to the experiment, they are not standardized testing material. Hence, technically their validity and reliability were not and are not known. After the questions were prepared and before they were printed, three psychologists who are acquainted with the requirements of test construction reviewed and discussed the

A. Most schools and colleges receive their subsistence from: *a.* taxing the students. *b.* endowments. *c.* grants from the king. *d.* grants from the public treasury. B. According to Smith, prohibiting teachers to receive fees: *a.* is of benefit to the students. *b.* improves their efficiency. *c.* reduces the number of teachers. *d.* decreases their application. C. An extraneous authority over the professors: *a.* but forces them to give so many lectures. *b.* insists on the improvement of teaching. *c.* determines who is a good teacher. *d.* can more wisely rule a university. D. The privileges of graduates in arts and sciences: *a.* encourages students to learn. *b.* improves the quality of teaching. *c.* forces students to college regardless of its merit. *d.* are granted to the college of the greatest merit. E. The discipline of most colleges and universities: *a.* is for the ease and benefit of the masters. *b.* is required by the negligence of the pupils. *c.* merely ends in force and restraint. *d.* should begin when the pupils are twelve or above. F. The generally best taught parts of education are those: *a.* offered by the universities. *b.* learned in the public schools. *c.* for which there are no public institutions. *d.* demanding the highest fees of the students. G. Greek and Hebrew were seldom taught to churchmen because: *a.* the Pope had decreed that they should not be. *b.* good teachers of these languages were scarce. *c.* the people saw no reason to learn them in order to read the Bible. *d.* the Latin translation was given divine authority. H. The study of Greek was gradually introduced because of: *a.* the finding of new biblical documents. *b.* new interest occasioned by the Reformation. *c.* effects of the Renaissance. *d.* the requisites of a classical education. I. Moral philosophy: *a.* studies the rules and maxims of conduct. *b.* arranges morals into a system. *c.* investigates the principles of a moral system. *d.* lays down rules of conduct. J. Metaphysics developed from: *a.* Logic. *b.* Theology. *c.* Moral philosophy. *d.* Natural philosophy. K. When moral and natural philosophy became subservient to Theology: *a.* emphasis shifted to the life hereafter. *b.* physics began to come into its own. *c.* happiness in this life received consideration. *d.* both began to crumble. L. With respect to adoption of new improvements in philosophy, the richest and best endowed universities were: *a.* usually first. *b.* in general slowest. *c.* most apt. *d.* constrained to adopt. M. The custom of travelling after leaving school grew out of the: *a.* lure of finer universities abroad. *b.* discontent among

Figure 60

INTERSPERSED COMPREHENSION EXERCISE, *Adam Smith*

the young men of the day. *c.* defects of the universities. *d.* increased wealth of the gentry. N. Music was taught in the Greek school to: *a.* increase the culture of the society. *b.* improve the public morals. *c.* add a note of refinement to the rigors of war. *d.* counterbalance the physical training. O. In the Greek and Roman republics teachers were: *a.* paid only by their pupils. *b.* highly subsidized by the state. *c.* partially subsidized by the state. *d.* slaves under state control. P. At Rome the study of the civil law: *a.* was provided for by the state. *b.* was left to the instruction of families. *c.* received some state support. *d.* required attendance at certain schools. Q. The regularity and orderly system of Roman law is due to the: *a.* control by the state. *b.* diligence of the teachers. *c.* attention to practice and precedent. *d.* moral character of the people. R. A discouragement to private teachers arises from: *a.* the high salaries they must demand. *b.* inferior teaching in the public schools. *c.* strict control by the state. *d.* the privileges of graduation. S. According to Adam Smith the utility of a woman's education is due to the: *a.* public institutions which teach her. *b.* existence of no public institutions for women. *c.* necessity to train her in certain abilities. *d.* wise control of the state. T. The division and specialization of labor: *a.* develops the initiative of the laborers. *b.* keeps alive an interest in efficiency. *c.* reduces the necessity of general education. *d.* degrades the laboring classes. U. The education of the common people requires the: *a.* attention of the public themselves. *b.* interest of people of rank and fortune. *c.* interest of the people of high rank. *d.* attention of the best educated themselves. V. According to Smith the schools for the public should be: *a.* paid for by the public. *b.* financed by the pupils attending them. *c.* maintained by both public and pupils. *d.* paid for by endowments. W. Smith suggests as encouragement for acquiring an education: *a.* premiums granted by the public for proficiency. *b.* high salaries to the teachers who teach best. *c.* higher salaries to teachers with the best pupils. *d.* the force of state law. X. The practice of military exercises: *a.* should be encouraged by the people. *b.* seems to require the support of government. *c.* depends on the spirit of the people. *d.* may be left to a chosen few. Y. From the instruction of the inferior ranks of the people the government should: *a.* expect no advantage. *b.* be put in a dangerous position. *c.* derive considerable advantage. *d.* receive considerable revenue.

Figure 60 (continued)

INTERSPERSED COMPREHENSION EXERCISE, *Adam Smith*

questions. All were eliminated which they did not consider satisfactory.

A subjective analysis of this sort is not sufficient, and a statistical analysis will later be undertaken. Unfortunately, the circumstances of the present experiments have not yet permitted the standardization of these tests. A statistical analysis of the tests would require the administration of the questions to a sufficiently large and representative sample of students, some of whom had read the books and some of whom had not. From the data of these administrations, the statistical worth or value of each question could be determined and new comprehension exercises of known validity, reliability, and so forth, prepared. It is, however, believed that the subjective analysis of these comprehension checks by "test-wise" psychologists in some measure achieved the same results as an objective evaluation would have.

The subject, with electrodes attached to his skin, may easily pick up certain stray voltage shifts. Because of the sensitivity of the apparatus used in this experiment, it was therefore considered wise to require the subject to read in an electrically shielded room. Every part of the room, including the lights and the electrical apparatus, was adequately grounded. The experimental chamber, then, is spoken of as a grounded or "shielded" room. Figure 61 shows a subject in the experimental room.

The shielded room used in this experiment was a wood framework to which was attached the metal shielding. This enclosure was four feet wide, eight feet long, and eight feet high. One side wall was a closely fitting door. In two of the other sides were screened windows (two feet high and a foot and a half wide) with shutter flaps. A ventilating system made it seldom necessary to have these flaps raised. The walls of the room were painted a dead black. The reading table (three feet by two feet) and the lower table supporting the microfilm apparatus were covered with paperboard of the same black. Once the book stand or microfilm apparatus had been adjusted to the preference of the subject, it was not changed during the six-hour reading period.

The shielded room was built on a platform resting in turn on large rubber cushions to deaden the vibrations and sounds from the outer laboratory. Disturbances from the laboratory were kept at a minimum. Further to insure constant conditions, the room made of metallic shielding was enclosed in a sound-resisting room seven feet wide, twelve feet long, and ten feet high. The atmosphere of the experimental chamber,

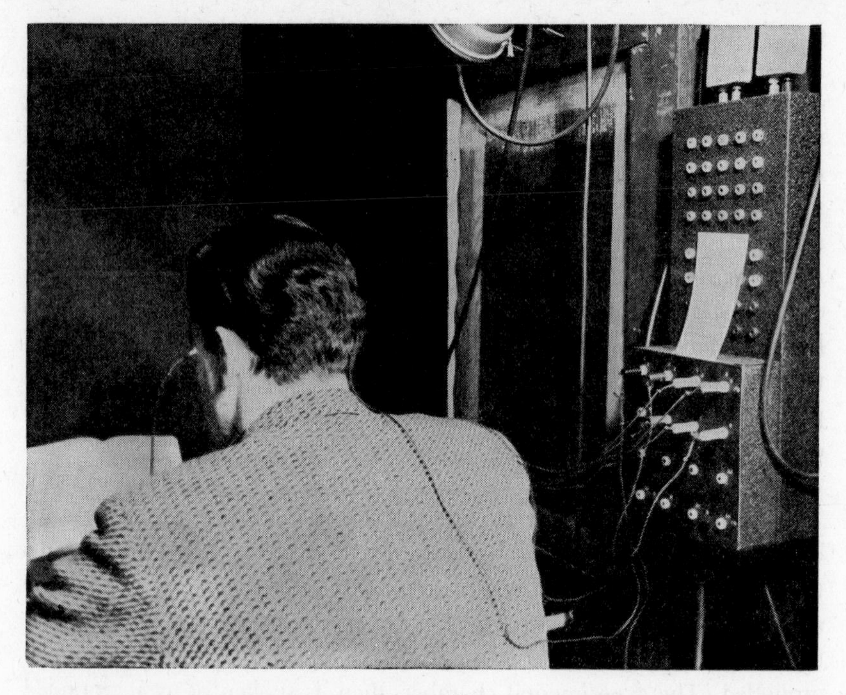

Figure 61

SUBJECT IN THE READING ROOM OF THE PRESENT STUDY

therefore, was not unlike that of an ideal reading cubicle in a university library.

The light on the reading material, as noted, came from three light sources placed above the subject. Measurement indicated that the level of illumination on the page read was approximately 16 footcandles. The illumination on the reading pad in the microfilm apparatus also approximated this same level. Records of the temperature and humidity in the grounded room were taken before and after each experimental period. Changes in these measures during the six hours were relatively slight. For the 80 reading periods of this experiment, the temperature averaged about 70 degrees Fahrenheit, and the relative humidity varied from 35 per cent to 50 per cent. The ventilating system in the shielded room changed the air completely every 60 seconds or less. The new air entered from the regular laboratory room.

These temperature and humidity records were kept because of the general interest in the possible effects of ventilation on work output and especially on blink rate. It would seem from a review of the literature of industrial psychology that the chemical contents of the air in their various proportions are not so important as direct factors as they are in their association with the temperature and humidity of the surrounding air and with air movements. Industrial psychologists have discussed the problem of ventilation and in some instances (309, 404) have found significant changes in work output associated with changes in ventilation, especially when extremes of ventilation and heavy muscular work are involved.

It is recognized, of course, that in a particular industrial situation, the optimum temperature or humidity depends upon the nature of the work performed. Many of the industrial findings may not, therefore, have particular bearing on the "work" performed in the present experiments, which may be regarded as of the type popularly called "mental." In a series of experiments making use of a testing room in which the temperature and humidity could be controlled, it was found (407) that the optimum temperature is around 65 degrees Fahrenheit for normally clothed individuals at rest or otherwise engaged in light activity in still air. The temperature in the present experiments was never below 65 degrees and was usually a few degrees above this level. Additional experimental evidence suggests that for performing "mental" work of various kinds (reading, arithmetic tasks, cancellation tests, and so forth), temperature and humidity variations within a not too extreme range around the optimum do not significantly affect the accuracy or speed of the results or, in most cases, the subjective report of the individuals doing the work.

Several experimenters report (19, 20, 340) that, within the limits of their controlled variations, ventilation by recirculating the same air instead of by introducing outside air occasioned no observable deleterious effect upon the intellectual processes involved in the work. E. L. Thorndike and others (337) observed no significant differences in efficiency of performance in supposedly favorable conditions of ventilation and in conditions assumed to be unfavorable. The experimental conditions used by Thorndike's group involved a temperature of 68 degrees Fahrenheit, 50 per cent relative humidity, and a temperature of 86 degrees Fahrenheit, 80 per cent relative humidity, respectively. L. I. Stecher kept temperature constant and compared the relative humidity conditions of 50 per cent and 20 per cent. Subjective reports and scores from 10 tests alike fail to show any significant effects. The concluding statement is made by this experimenter that with regard to mental work:

> Psychology has given its answer, as far as it can in the present state of the science, to the question as to whether the ventilation conditions commonly found have any effect on the practical activities of life. If this absence of demonstrable effect is due to a constant adjustment of the organism that will eventually result in strain, it is for physiology to trace any subtle, long-time ill-effects that may have escaped the behavior tests. (326, p. 85.)

The 40 subjects of this experiment who each read for two six-hour periods in the electrically shielded room under the conditions described were divided into four experimental groups. Since each group is different in some respect from each of the other groups, these four groups will be referred to as the four experimental situations.

Ten of the college students made available by the directors of the Harvard College Grant Study read the printed pages of the books in relatively normal circumstances. This group will be referred to hereafter as the *Grant Study Subjects (normal reading),* or, more simply, as *G.S.*

Ten of the high school students supplied by the directors of the Harvard-Arlington Guidance Study also read the printed pages of the books under relatively normal conditions. This situation will be referred to as *High School Subjects (normal reading),* or as *H.S.*

Ten additional Grant Study subjects read the microfilm reproductions of the two books used. This group will be referred to hereafter as *Grant Study Subjects (microfilm reading),* or, more simply, as *G.S.M.*

Ten additional high school subjects also read the microfilm reproductions of the two books used. This situation will be referred to as *High School Subjects (microfilm reading),* or as *H.S.M.*

From these four experimental situations, six comparisons of performance can be made:

1. Grant Study Subjects (normal reading) *vs.* Grant Study Subjects (microfilm reading)
2. High School Subjects (normal reading) *vs.* High School Subjects (microfilm reading)
3. Grant Study Subjects (normal reading) *vs.* High School Subjects (normal reading)
4. Grant Study Subjects (microfilm reading) *vs.* High School Subjects (microfilm reading)

5. Grant Study Subjects (normal reading) *vs.* High School Subjects (microfilm reading)
6. Grant Study Subjects (microfilm reading) *vs.* High School Subjects (normal reading)

In each of the first two conditions above, the type of reading is varied. The first condition permits a comparison (within the present experimental circumstances) of the efficiency of normal as opposed to microfilm reading by subjects of relatively high educational attainment. The second comparison allows a consideration of normal as opposed to microfilm reading by subjects of lower educational level. The next two conditions test the influence of educational level when the type of reading is held constant. The third condition permits a comparison of the efficiency of normal reading by subjects of a relatively high educational age as opposed to subjects of a lower educational age. The fourth compares the microfilm reading of college subjects and of high school subjects. Assuming that the efficiency of reading increases with educational level or "age" and with the normal character of the reading material, the fifth condition juxtaposes the normal reading of college students and the microfilm reading of high school subjects to make a comparison when the differences in performance might be expected to be large. The sixth condition offers a test of the assumption that the differences in performance will be small because of the subjects and the type of reading compared.

Planning the experimental procedure of a "fatigue" study such as the present one, which required continuous activity throughout a period of time equivalent to a good part of a subject's normal working day, involves to some extent the problem of possible diurnal changes in efficiency of performance. Since H. D. Marsh's early study in 1906 (219), experimenters have regarded diurnal variations either as signs of fatigue following work or simply as indications of variations in efficiency. For example, some investigations have been concerned with the effect of a day's activities on the subjects (138, 220), whereas others were to determine if possible the hours of the day during which work would be most efficient (114, 115, 399, 400, 401). However, those interested in diurnal variations as indicators of fatigue have realized the complexities introduced by the concept of fatigue itself, and those concerned with periodicity of efficiency have pointed out the dependence of variation in performance upon the type of occupation or task in which the subjects were engaged.

L. A. Robinson (302) and others have reported that the mental efficiency of school children rises during the morning, is low early in the afternoon, and then shows a rise, probably to be followed by another low point. H. L. Hollingworth (144) and T. Arai (7) found a decline in mental efficiency as the day proceeds. Muscio (256) found that feelings of fatigue increased during the day except for an early afternoon recuperation. H. P. Maity (218a) reports a decline in rote memory during the day. In a review of the problem of diurnal variation, E. S. Robinson has made the following telling comments:

> Such findings are not to be criticized as facts and as facts they probably may be used to advantage under certain peculiar conditions. Nevertheless, they cannot be considered as broadly typical of diurnal fluctuations. . . . One can explain these differences in terms of the subjects employed, the nature of the day's work, changes in temperature and other atmospheric conditions, meals and the like. If this is true, it seems reasonable to believe that, in so far as there are differences in the efficiency of work at different hours, these differences are themselves to be explained in terms of the subjects, the work, etc., rather than in terms of the characteristic natures of different times of day. Each time of day, like each time of year, covers such a host of psychological possibilities that it seems futile to work out its correlates except for some extremely practical and immediate purpose. It may, of course, be well worth while for employers and educators to know the specific diurnal variations of specific groups of employees or students working under conditions which for them are standard. (298, pp. 477-478.)

Considering the characteristics of the present experiment, D. A. Laird's study may be cited. One hundred and twelve college students were given tests of immediate retention of a selection read, the reading time of the selection when read with the intention of remembering it, single and two-column additions, a substitution test, Part III (Comprehension) of the Thorndike Intelligence Test, and delayed retention of the selection first read. The tests were administered according to a schedule which made it possible to compare performance either for the days of the week or for the hours of the day. The hours (40-minute trial periods) at which the tests were administered were: A.M., 8 and 10 o'clock; P.M., 1, 4, 8, 9, and 10 o'clock.

> It has been found that the performance was at its peak on Wednesday, that it gradually approached the high point on this day and abruptly declined on the day following to a very low level. In general, all of the individual tests followed this curve of rise and fall.

> From 8 A.M. until the period from 4 to 5 P.M. there was found a steady decline at the hours studied. From 8 P.M. until 10 P.M. there is a rise, which, however, scarcely comes up to the average of the day. From 10 to 11 P.M. there is a loss.
>
> These conclusions apply, not necessarily to every individual student, but represent accurately the average performance of a large group, or the 'typical student.' It may be that there are individual exceptions to these findings as the result of habits of study and work. It is doubtful if there are variations as a result of one student being intrinsically and apart from habits of work different from others. (182, p. 62.)

To offset the possible uncontrolled influence of these variables in the present experiments, subjects were studied each day of the week, with very few exceptions, but always at the same hours each day. The experimental period began at 2 o'clock in the afternoon. The actual reading began around 3 in the afternoon and lasted for six hours. The subject usually left the laboratory around 9:30 P.M.

As soon as the subject came to the laboratory, he was given the Keystone Visual Acuity Test Form DB, the Keystone Stereoscopic Acuity Test Form DC, and the Zeiss Stereoscopic Acuity Test. Responses were recorded on a sheet, an example of which is shown in Figure 62.

Immediately following these tests, the subject was asked to complete the first part of the questionnaire which has been previously described and which is reproduced on pages 228-231. This portion of this questionnaire, it will be recalled, was discussed in describing the subjects of the present experiment. The latter part, which was completed at the conclusion of the experimental period, consisted of two questions, Numbers 19 and 20.

The electrodes were then placed on the subject as described previously, and the subject seated himself in the experimental chamber before the reading stand. During the reading of a preliminary book, the amplifiers were set so as to give the desired "gain" of voltage, and the apparatus was otherwise adjusted.

The instructions read to the subjects at this point in the experimental procedure were as follows:

> This is a study of the way the eyes work in reading. It is hoped that this experiment will provide significant results for both pure and applied science, and therefore we ask you to co-operate with us in following these directions to the best of your ability.
>
> You are asked to read the books that you find on the reading stand in

Subject ______________________ Date ______________________

Zeiss Stereo.

Fig. No.	Before Far---Near				After Far---- Near			
1								
2								
3								
4								
5								
6								
7								
8								
9								
10								

Keystone Stereo.

Card No.	Before Top	Before Mid	Before Bot	After Top	After Mid	After Bot
1						
2						
3						
4						
5						
6						
7						
8						
9						
10						
11						
12						
13						
14						
15						
16						
17						
18						
19						
20						
21						
22						
23						

Keystone Acuity

	Before 1	Before 2	Before 3	After 1	After 2	After 3
1						
2						
3						
4						
5						
6						
7						
8						
9						
10						

Figure 62

VISUAL TEST RECORDING BLANKS

this cabinet. *Please read every word of the book.* Do not skim or skip words, lines, or pages. Do not let your glance wander from the book!

Please keep your hands away from your face as much as possible and especially never touch the electrodes. Do not rest your chin on your hands if you can avoid it. In general try to avoid unnecessary head or body movements. At the end of the whole six-hour period you will be given a test to determine what you remember of the material you have read. This test will involve ideas both large and small, but it will have as few "catch" questions such as unusual proper names, etc., as possible.

During the six-hour period there will also be short comprehension tests appearing in the book. These occur about every 25 or 30 pages. You are to take them as you come to them, and *do not* look back for the answers. Before starting *each* short test and after finishing *each* of them, wink rapidly 8 or 10 times. This signals to the experimenter so that he may know when you are taking a test. You are not expected to study the book in preparation for the test but to read the book in a straightforward way, with the understanding that you are to be tested upon its contents. Please do not reread any page or sentence. Also, please do not turn back to previous pages for rereading after you have once read them.

To the high school students, the additional comment was made that if they felt they could not continue for the full six-hour period, they could quit, but would be paid only half their fee. This provision was made for fear some of the younger subjects might find the task too exhausting. On the other hand, the "half fee" was intended to preclude too ready quitting. All subjects finished the six-hour period. The college subjects from the Grant Study group were paid $4.50 per experimental trial, making $9 in all for reading both books, each for six hours. The high school subjects were paid $4 per experimental trial.

The two doors of the electrically shielded and sound-resisting chamber were closed, and the continuous recording of eye movements, heart beat, brain waves, and page turns was begun. Forced ventilation was always maintained. In the case of the normal readings, half the subjects read Lorna Doone during their first six-hour reading period and the other half read Adam Smith first. In the case of the microfilm reading, all the subjects of a particular group read one of the books first. The subject signaled when he began and finished a comprehension check by blinking eight or ten times rapidly. This made a definite mark on the record which can be distinguished from other features of the recording. The sheet shown in Figure 63 was used for recording the adjustments of the apparatus and the time at which the comprehension checks were taken.

As soon as the six-hour reading period was over, the subject left the experimental chamber. Before the electrodes were removed, the subject again took the visual acuity test and the two stereoscopic acuity tests previously referred to. He then took the general comprehension test on the material which he had read in the six hours' time. This test examined him in a more comprehensive and general way on the same material

Subject ________________ Date ____________

Channel	Gain	Atten.	LFF	HFF
1				
2				
3				
4				

Pages read ________

Test No.	Start Time	Section	Finish Time	Section	Score
1					
2					
3					
4					
5					
6					
7					
8					
9					
10					
11					
12					
13					
Final					

Figure 63

TRIAL SHEET

upon which were based the detailed questions he had answered during the reading period. Immediately following the taking of this test, the subject filled out the latter portion of the questionnaire, relating to his experience during the six-hour period.

After each oscillograph record was made, it was edited in preparation for the reading of appropriate sample periods. The portions of the recording made while the subject took the interspersed comprehension checks were marked for possible future reference and so that these portions would not be sampled when the record was read.

Each six-hour record was divided into 30-centimeter lengths (representing 20 seconds of time) by perforations at the edge of each "page." Each total record was almost one-fifth of a mile in length. This whole record was first divided into half-hour units by tearing the record at the appropriate perforations. Each section of the record so divided was marked by the code number of the subject and the capital letter D or S, depending on which book the subject had read during the six-hour reading period. The half-hour sections were numbered in Roman numerals. Each half-hour section was further divided into five-minute units and lettered from a to f. Thus, for example, that section of the record of the seventh Grant Study subject reading the microfilm reproduction of Lorna Doone representing the third five-minute interval of the eighth half-hour of his reading would bear the citation G.S.M. 7D, VIIIc.

It was the plan of the present experiment to read those eye-movement portions of the record representing the first five-minute interval (Ia) and the last five-minute interval of each half-hour (If, IIf, IIIf, and so forth, to XIIf) of the six-hour experimental period. Figure 64 diagrammatically represents this time sampling of the six-hour period. If any of these intervals included the recording of a comprehension exercise, it was not sampled; in its stead the nearest five-minute unit to it was used. Subsequent use of the word "record" will ordinarily refer to the 13 sample portions rather than to the entire oscillograph record. The sample

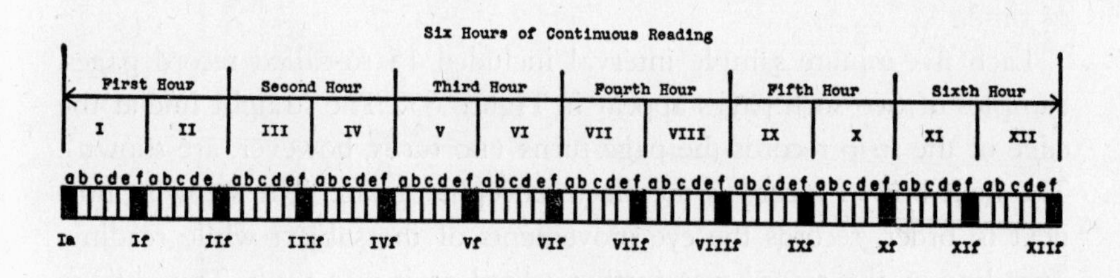

Figure 64

DIAGRAM OF THE TIME SAMPLING USED IN THE PRESENT STUDY

record, then, includes a total of 65 minutes of the entire reading period.

The selection of the time at which sample periods were taken was based upon the results of an empirical study in a preliminary investigation and on the recommendations of other experiments. In the opinion of Luckiesh and Moss (207), their general experience indicates that a period of five minutes is adequate for sampling, although in some cases it is advisable to repeat the series of measurements and use the mean value for interpretation. Tinker (353), by means of test-retest evaluation of photographic records, has found that 20 or more lines of reading by the subject are necessary for individual diagnosis. When group comparisons, however, are to be made, adequately reliable data may be gained from the reading of only five or six lines of print. Since the sampling procedure of the present experiment included from 61 to 225 lines of reading at a time, five-minute sampling was considered adequate.

It is, of course, important to note that these five-minute sample periods were "true samples," for the subject and the experimenter alike did not know in advance what portion of the entire oscillograph record was to be selected or that a given period was a "sample run." The records were all complete and continuous. Thus, these samples are *not* to be considered as comparable to any samples taken, for example, by photographic techniques in which records are made only of the sample period, allowing thereby changes in motivation and other attitudes during the arranging of the apparatus for each sample period. In the present experiments, care was also taken not to give the subject any information concerning the period that was to be sampled. The subjects were not allowed to have watches or any other means of objective knowledge of the passing of time.

Each five-minute sample interval included 15 so-called record pages. Samples of two such pages appear in Figure 65. The straight line at the edge of the strip records the page turns (no turns, however, are shown). The next line of record is the electroencephalogram. The stepwise line, next in order, records the eye movements of the subject while reading. This line of the record was further edited as it was read. The oblique lines on the record line itself were made by the editor at the end of each line of print read by the subject. The two lines in each case perpendicular to the record line mark the beginning and end of a "break" in reading — or at least a portion of the record during which it is assumed the subject was not reading normally. The irregular series of short lines between the

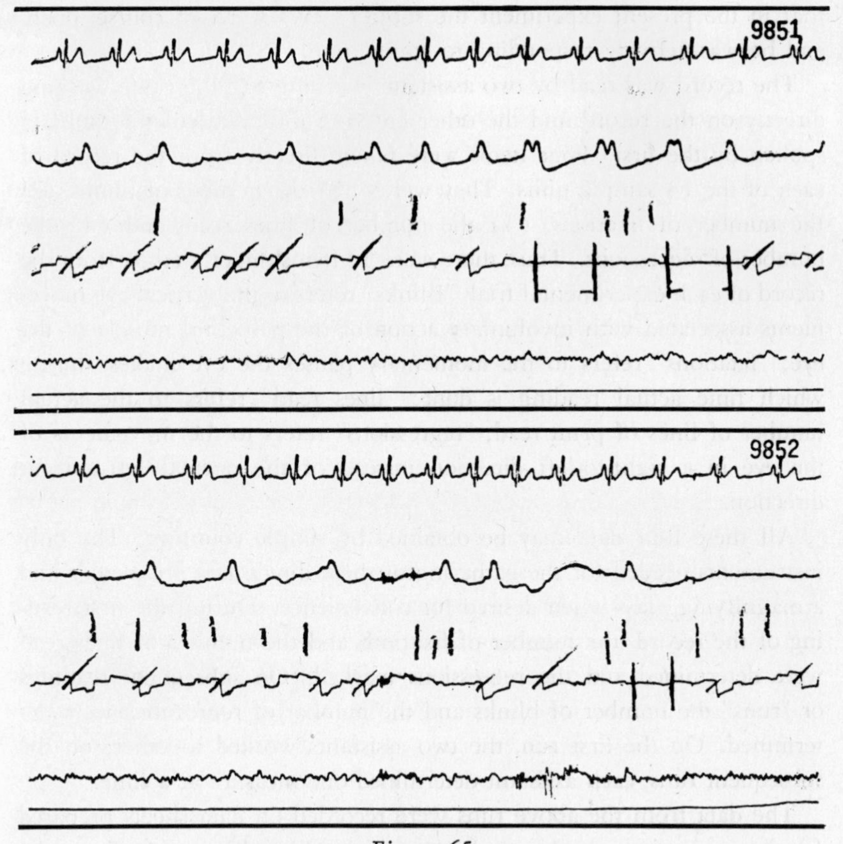

Figure 65

SAMPLE OF AN EDITED RECORD

third and fourth record lines marks the occurrence of regressive movements; these lines merely indicate the presence of a regression but are not necessarily beside the regressions they are to indicate. The fourth line on the page records the blinks of the subject. The fifth and last record line is the characteristic PRT wave of the electrocardiogram.

The records of the heart beat and the brain waves as recorded in this experiment have not yet been fully studied; reference to these records will be made only incidentally in this report (see Appendix). As mentioned previously, the electroencephalogram did not show itself during the six-hour period in the form typical of records made when the subject has his eyes closed in the dark, as is customary. This is due to the fact that in the present experiment the subject's eyes were, of course, open, and he was actively responding to stimulation.

The record was read by two assistants working together, one working directly on the record and the other entering into a calculator the data spoken by the first. Four items were taken directly from the record of each of the 13 sample units. They were: (1) the number of blinks, (2) the number of fixations, (3) the number of lines read, and (4) the number of regressions. Thus, there were 52 items directly taken from the record of each experimental trial. "Blinks" refers to the vertical eye movements associated with involuntary action of the palpebral muscle of the eye; "fixations" refers to the momentary pauses the eye makes, during which time actual reading is done; "lines read" refers to the actual number of lines of print read; "regressions" refers to the movements of the eye in a right-to-left direction instead of the normal left-to-right direction.

All these four data may be obtained by simple counting. The only instruments needed for the gathering of these direct data are pencils and a magnifying glass when desired for convenience. During the first reading of the record, the number of fixations and the number of lines read were determined and the regressions marked. On subsequent readings or "runs" the number of blinks and the number of regressions were determined. On the first run, the two assistants worked together; on the subsequent runs, each assistant determined one measure at a time.

The data from the above runs were recorded on data sheets prepared for these experiments. A sample sheet is shown in Figure 66. From the direct data, derived data were computed. The number of fixations per line was determined by dividing the number of fixations made in a sample period by the number of lines read during that period. The fixation sigma score (the standard deviation of the number of fixations per line) was computed using the fixations per line as the mean and the number of lines read as N. The number of regressions per line was determined by dividing the total number of regressions made during a five-minute period by the number of lines read in that period of time.

It has been found that individual differences in the above data were so great as to make graphic representation of the actual scores difficult and time-consuming. Percentage scores of several of the data were, therefore, derived for purposes of immediate graphic representation. The percentage scores were computed for each subject by adding the data of the 13

Code Number ______ ______ Pages read ______

5 ' Sample ___ ___ ___ ___ ___ ___ ___ ___ ___ ___ ___ ___ ___

Blinking

Number ______ ______ ______ ______ ______ ______ ______

% Score ______ ______ ______ ______ ______ ______ ______

Fixations

Number ______ ______ ______ ______ ______ ______ ______

% Score ______ ______ ______ ______ ______ ______ ______

X^2 ______ ______ ______ ______ ______ ______ ______

No./L ______ ______ ______ ______ ______ ______ ______

% Score ______ ______ ______ ______ ______ ______ ______

Sigma ______ ______ ______ ______ ______ ______ ______

Lines Read

Number ______ ______ ______ ______ ______ ______ ______

% Score ______ ______ ______ ______ ______ ______ ______

Regressions

Number ______ ______ ______ ______ ______ ______ ______

% Score ______ ______ ______ ______ ______ ______ ______

No./L ______ ______ ______ ______ ______ ______ ______

% Score ______ ______ ______ ______ ______ ______ ______

Figure 66

SAMPLE DATA SHEET

sample periods of any particular measure and then expressing the raw score of each sample as a percentage of the total. Percentage scores were derived for the number of blinks, number of fixations, number of fixations per line, number of lines read, number of regressions, and number of regressions per line. Graphs will be shown later of the number of blinks, number of fixations, number of lines read, and number of regressions made during each sample of the six-hour period. As an example, the entire data for the reading of Adam Smith by the seventh subject of the Grant Study Group (normal reading) are shown in Table 8.[3]

All the above computations were performed by two assistants working together, since this arrangement was found to reduce both time and errors. On the average, 14 hours were required to prepare the data sheet for a single record, during 12 of which two assistants were necessary.

After the reading of the eye-movement record, seven measures were available for statistical analysis of the reading behavior. These seven were: Blinking Number, Fixations Number, Fixations per Line, Fixation Sigma Score, Lines Read Number, Regressions Number, and Regressions per Line.

The 40 subjects of the experiment, however, were equally divided into four experimental situations during each of which two experimental books were read. For the first analysis, then, of *each* of the seven measures, there were available eight sets of data, each set comprising 13 sample periods. The statistical analysis performed for one of these eight sets of a particular type of measure may be described as typical of all the others. Take, for example, the blinking number data for the reading of Lorna Doone by each of the 10 subjects in the Grant Study group (normal reading).

For each of the 13 sample periods, the mean performance of the 10 subjects was computed. This figure represents the average number of blinks made by the 10 subjects during each sample period. Variations in the magnitude of the mean performance from sample to sample would indicate changes in blinking performance as the reading period progressed. For the same sample periods, the standard deviation (or sigma) of the distributions of 10 scores was computed. This statistic is a measure of how much the subjects varied among themselves in blinking performance during a particular sample period. Variation in the magnitude of the standard deviation from sample period to sample period would

[3] See Appendix.

indicate that the subjects varied more or less, as the case might be, among themselves as the reading continued. For example, if the magnitude of the sigmas became smaller, the indication would be that the blinking performance of the subjects of the G.S. group became more alike as the reading continued. The mean performance and the standard deviation of the distribution of performance of each sample period are measures which were used to compare the eye-movement performance in the four experimental situations and during the reading of the two books.

Also computed were the Pearson product-moment coefficients of correlation between the 10 scores of the first sample period and the corresponding 10 scores of each of the subsequent 12 sample periods. This statistic would show not so much whether the subjects varied among themselves in number of blinks made during the sample period as whether the subjects tended to maintain their same relative positions in their own experimental group from sample period to sample period. If the order or relative position of the subjects in the initial series of measures (that is, the first sample period, Ia) is considered as the base, a correlation of 1.00 between this series and the distribution of scores at another sample period would indicate perfect agreement. The top-ranking subject in the first series would be top ranking in the subsequent distributions, the lowest would again be lowest, and those subjects in between would have the same position relative to each other in the subsequent distributions as they held during the first sample period. As the correlations with subsequent sample periods approach zero, however, there would be less and less agreement in relative position. Thus it could be concluded that the subjects tended to shift their positions during subsequent sample periods more and more. The correlation statistic, then, is a measure of the variation in individual differences occurring during prolonged reading. It may be said that the sigma score shows whether the subjects' blinking performances dispersed more or became more alike from sample to sample; the coefficient of correlation indicates whether each of the subjects varied or maintained his level of performance as compared with that of the other subjects.

Differences between the mean performance of sample period Ia and any subsequent sample period might be used to indicate trends in performance, as might also a comparison of standard deviations. However, these differences must be more rigorously analyzed to determine whether they may be due simply to chance fluctuation, or whether they may be regarded as representing some actual change in performance which can be explained as due to some specific feature or features of the experimental situation. In short, the significance of a difference must be determined before observed changes in performance can be properly evaluated.

We may consider the analysis of mean performance as a typical example of a procedure for determining the significance of differences. If the same experiment had been performed an infinite number of times (replicated) and the mean performance computed in each case, as has been done for the present experiment, there would be available (for each of the 13 sample periods of one experimental group for one eye-movement measure for the reading of one of the books) a distribution of mean scores. This distribution, according to statistical logic, would be a normal curve which showed the number of times (ordinate) a mean score of each magnitude (base line) could be found by chance alone. Now, if performance described by one such distribution were observed in one set of repeated experimental conditions and if a second distribution were obtained in another and different set of replicated experimental conditions, it may be that, in the first place, the grand-mean (really, mean of the mean performances) of the one distribution would be different in magnitude from the grand-mean of the other distribution of means, and, secondly, that the magnitudes of the chance variations (the base line) in those two distributions of mean performances would not overlap; that is, they would be two separate distributions. In other words, the standard deviation of each distribution of means is small enough so that the two distributions do not at all appreciably overlap on the same base line. If in two other sets of experimental conditions, the two distributions of mean performances (derived again from an infinite number of replications of the two experiments) did overlap, that is, if the magnitude of the grand-mean of one distribution was within the range of variation (standard deviation) of the other distribution, then it is reasonable to assume that both distributions are alike. Therefore, significant effect of the experimental conditions either did not exist or was not demonstrated; chance variation could explain the differences.

The mean and standard deviation of a normal curve may be used to determine when two distributions, such as have been described above, may be regarded as overlapping and when they may not. Three times the value (or magnitude) of the standard deviation plus and minus the value of the mean of a normal curve will include the majority of the scores plotted in the curve — in fact, about 99.7 per cent of them. Three times the value of the standard deviation (sigma) then becomes a so-called criterion value. To return to the example in the preceding paragraph: if most of the means in one distribution are within a range of plus or minus three sigma from their grand-mean and the grand-mean of the other distribution is not found within that range of chance variation, then the conclusion may be drawn that the two distributions are not the same but represent experimental conditions which have significantly different effects. In short, they result from significant difference in data, and therefore it may be said that an experimental effect has been established.

It would be more than inconvenient to have to determine mean performances in a large number, let alone an infinite number, of repetitions of an experiment in order to determine whether or not the difference in two particular means was significant, that is, represented differential experimental influences. However, a much more convenient statistical method, based on the same reasoning and achieving the same end, may be used. This involves the use of the standard *error* statistic. This value is computed from knowledge of the standard deviation of an observed distribution of performance scores and the number of the scores in that distribution. In the present example, the value of the standard error of an observed blinking mean estimates the value of the standard deviation of a distribution of the infinite number of means derived as described above without having to make the infinite number of replications. The standard error of an observed statistic estimates the standard deviation of an infinite number of such statistics similarly derived.

The values of the standard errors of two means can then be used to determine whether or not the difference between means is due to chance or to other operative factors. If two observed statistics are not within the range of three times each others' standard errors, then the two statistics may not be regarded as two scores from the same distribution, but rather as scores from two different distributions — the significance of the difference between them, has, in other words, been established.

The standard error of a difference depends on the standard errors of the two opposed statistics. The so-called critical-ratio technique, used in the present experiment to evaluate differences, then, simply computes the ratio between an observed difference and the standard error of that difference. If the value of the ratio is greater than three, the difference is regarded as significant; from which finding it is concluded that experimental factors, in addition to chance, were operating to produce the difference. The statistical procedure, of course, does not define the nature of those factors or even what they are; it simply evaluates an observed difference.

The precision with which the critical-ratio technique can be applied to the evaluation of observed differences unfortunately depends not so much on the observed measures of performance as on the exact knowledge of the distribution of the total population of which only samples have been drawn. Also, the procedure for interpreting even an observed standard deviation requires that the observed distribution of scores be relatively normal. Because of the necessity for sampling, these prerequisites are lacking and only estimations of the exact measures are available. However, though any particular estimation may not be valid when a number of estimations (and the analysis dependent on them) are considered together, it is highly probable that statistical errors in estimations (too high or too low) will cancel out each other. In the present experiments, then, trends in the significance of difference are certainly to be taken as more important than isolated instances.

The measure of performance during the first sample period (Ia) is used here as the criterion of comparison in computing differences. In the typical example, the differences between the mean blinking performance of the first sample and the means of subsequent samples were evaluated by the critical-ratio technique. Similar analysis was made of the differences between the standard deviation of blinking performance during period Ia and during subsequent periods. Similar reasoning can be followed in evaluating the magnitude of an observed coefficient of correlation. If a coefficient that is zero in absolute magnitude is within the range of three times the value of the standard error of an observed coefficient minus the absolute magnitude of that observed coefficient, then that observed coefficient may be regarded as not significantly different from zero and hence indicative of no relationship between the two distributions being compared.

H. E. Garrett (113), E. F. Lindquist (189), H. Sorenson (321), and others have discussed the sampling problems briefly reviewed above, and have described the formulae and procedures necessary for the computation of critical ratios and their interpretation.

The analysis just outlined was made of the seven eye-movement measures for each of the four experimental situations in which the subjects read each of the two books. Some of these data may be used to compare those four experimental situations and the two books. To compare the two books, the distribution of each eye-movement measure during the reading of one of the books in each of the experimental situations was correlated with the corresponding distribution during the reading of the other book. The Pearson product-moment coefficient indicates whether relative position in performance for the reading of one book was the same as for the reading of the other book or whether the material being read differentially affected the position of the subjects reading it. In other words, the value of the correlation coefficient determines with what efficiency the position of a subject could be predicted in a second distribution if his relative position in the first were known. To determine further the possible differential effect of the two types of reading material, critical ratios were computed evaluating the differences in mean performance and in standard deviation of performance for each sample period of reading the two books in each of the four experimental situations.

Mean performance and standard deviation of performance were compared among the four experimental situations for the several eye-movement measures during the reading of the two books. Differences were here also evaluated by the critical-ratio technique. Mean performances were compared to determine whether or not the experimental situation affected average performance; standard deviations were compared to determine the possible differential effect of the situations upon the variability among the subjects whether or not the average performance was affected.

In the next chapter we turn to a detailed consideration of the eye-movement records of the subjects of the present experiments. The methods of analyzing the data as described in this chapter will then be used in providing answers to some of the basic questions concerning the changes which take place in the performance of the eyes during long periods of work.

Chapter 8

The Electro-Oculogram

TO THE casual observer, the subject in the reading chamber of the present experiments would no doubt be the center of primary interest. But the objectives of the present research focused the attention of the experimenter on the miles of paper on which were recorded the eye movements of the reading. It is, therefore, these records or electro-oculograms [1] which will be given first consideration. From them have been derived the data, as described above, the analysis of which will be presented in this chapter.

The pattern of the present study was such that eight sets of 10 electro-oculograms each were made during the course of the experiments. The fact that there were eight sets is due to the use of four experimental situations in which reading was done from two books, which were each read for six hours in each situation. Figure 67 presents samples of the records taken from each of the eight sets. The most pertinent sample of the eye-movement records to show the reader would, of course, include the passage of time as the most significant variable by presenting sample pages taken at several points during the six-hour reading of each set. The limitations of space, however, make such a pictorial presentation

[1] The term electro-oculogram in this book is used to apply to the records traced in ink upon the recording paper used in the experiment. These records are made, as indicated above, by an ink-writing oscillograph which is actuated by amplified currents originating in electrodes placed about the orbits of the eyes.

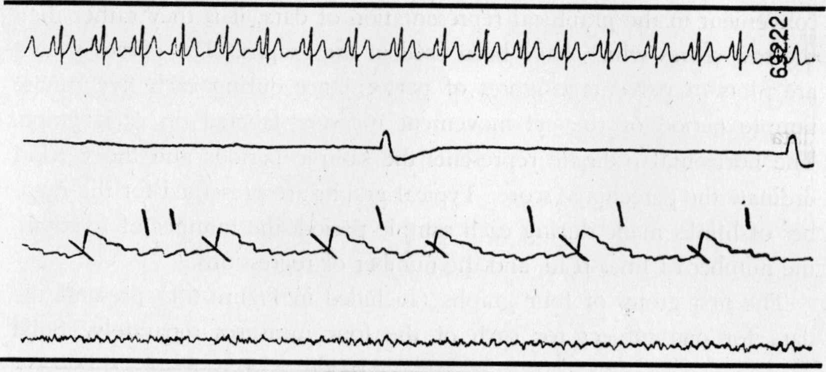

LORNA DOONE

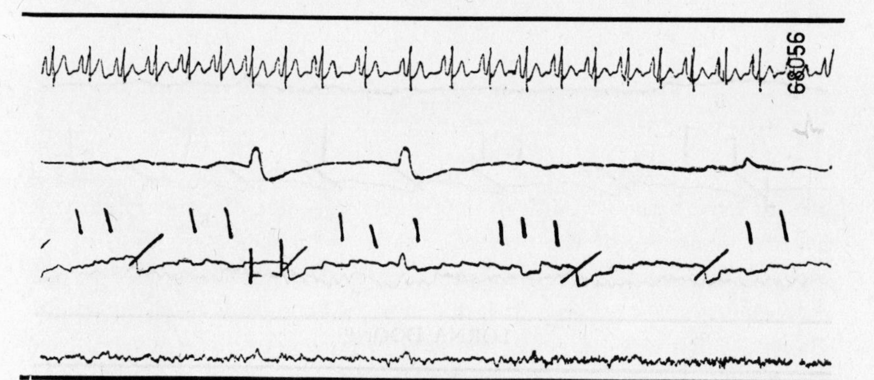

ADAM SMITH

Figure 67

SAMPLE RECORDS TAKEN IN PRESENT STUDY

Grant Study Subjects (normal reading)

difficult. In its stead, sample graphs of the data will be presented. The sample pages shown, however, may be of interest as instances of what the records themselves look like and as the basis of some comparison between the several conditions of the present experiment. These conditions will be compared in detail in the following chapter. Here are presented the changes which may be found to occur in the eye-movement data themselves as a function of time.

Since percentage scores achieve the same purpose and are much more convenient in the graphical representation of data, it is they rather than the raw scores which have been used in the graphs. The curves shown are plots of percentage scores of performance during each five-minute sample period of the eye-movement measure labeled on each graph. The horizontal ordinate represents the sample periods and the vertical ordinate the percentage score. Typical graphs are presented for the number of blinks made during each sample period, the number of fixations, the number of lines read, and the number of regressions.

The first group of four graphs (included in Figure 68) presents the data for one subject for each of the four measures separately. Solid

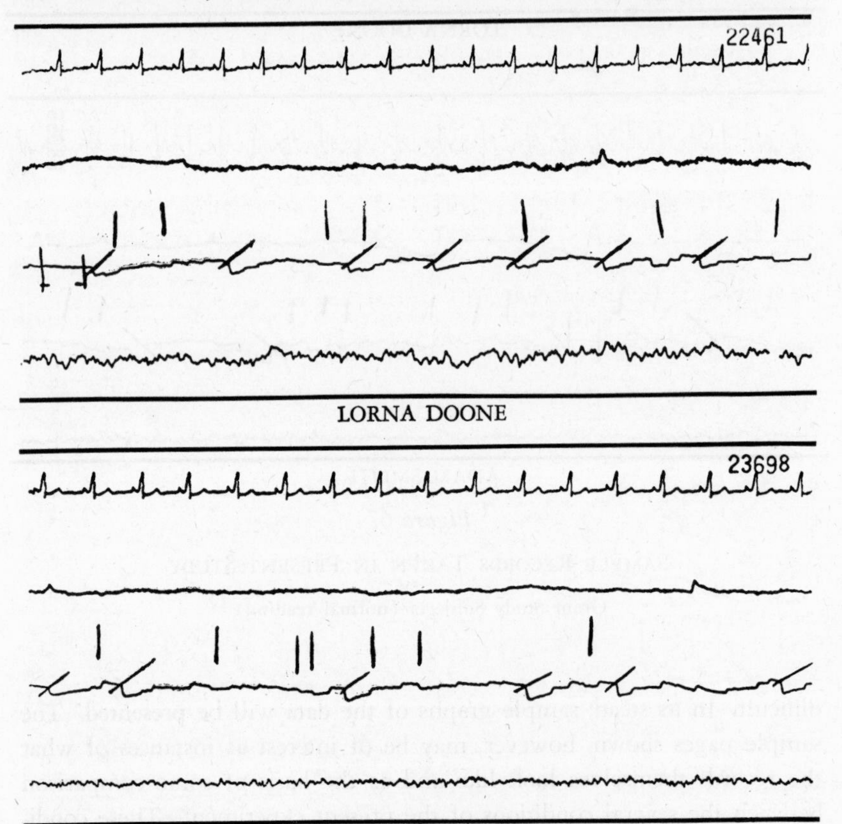

Figure 67 (continued)

Sample Records Taken in Present Study

High School Subjects (normal reading)

lines have been used to present the data for the book Lorna Doone, and broken lines for the data gathered for Adam Smith. Then follow four groups (Figures 69, 70, 71, and 72) of two graphs each. Each group presents the data for a single subject. The first graph in each group presents the data for all four measures for the reading of Lorna Doone; the second presents the data for the reading of Adam Smith.

Two conclusions may be drawn from a review of all the graphs for the present experiment, of which typical examples have just been presented. The first is the general tendency for the curves to be oriented horizontally in the graphical space. This suggests that performance did not

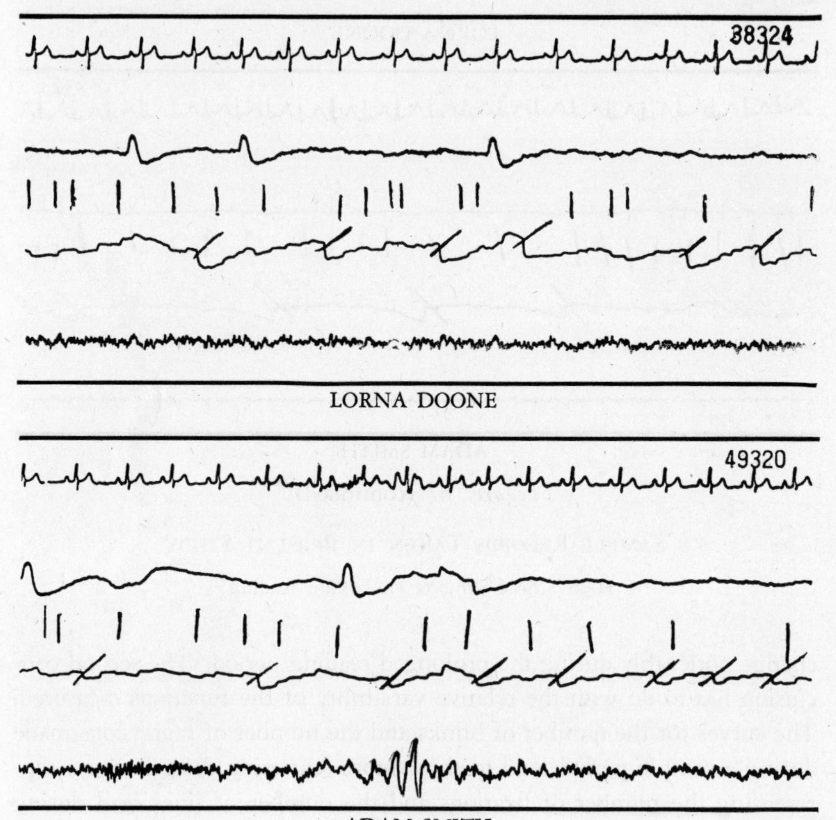

Figure 67 (continued)

SAMPLE RECORDS TAKEN IN PRESENT STUDY

Grant Study Subjects (microfilm reading)

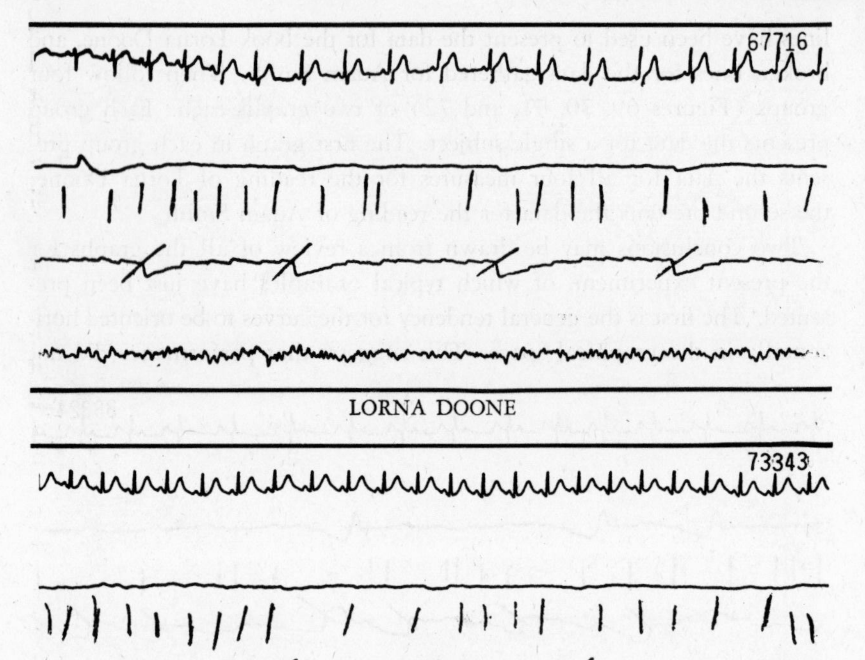

Figure 67 (continued)

SAMPLE RECORDS TAKEN IN PRESENT STUDY

High School Subjects (microfilm reading)

change noticeably during the prolonged reading period. The second conclusion has to do with the relative variability of the functions measured. The curves for the number of blinks and the number of regressions made during a sample period tend to show more scattering than do those representing the number of fixations and the number of lines read during the same sample period. It is to be remembered, however, that regressions and blinks are more or less "discrete" or relatively discontinuous phenomena, whereas fixations and lines read are an intimate and integral part of the total eye-movement pattern. A five-minute sample might be

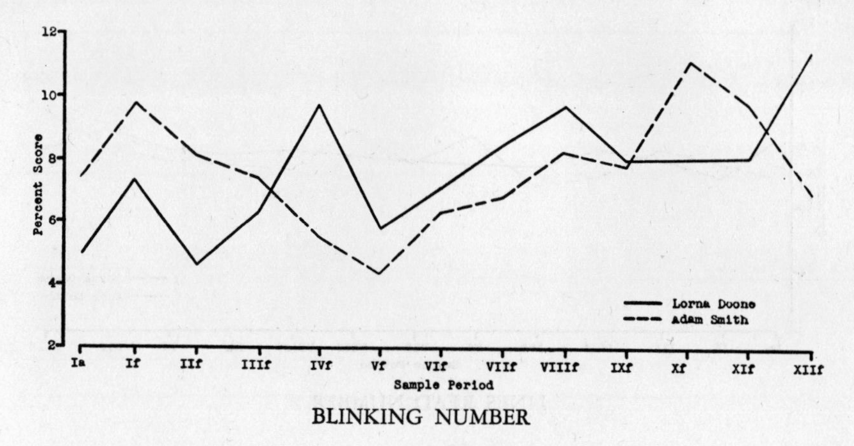

BLINKING NUMBER

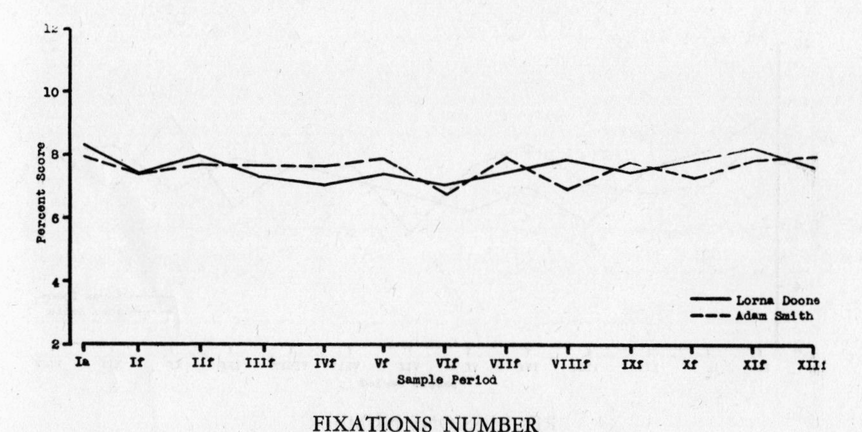

FIXATIONS NUMBER

Figure 68

SUMMARY GRAPHS FOR SUBJECT G.S. 1

expected to show more stable results in the case of phenomena which appear more often. It may be that this second observation has more statistical importance than real significance; for example, the absolute magnitude of the change in rate of blinking must be greater than the absolute magnitude of the change in number of fixations in order to be significantly affected by the prolonged reading activity as determined by statistical methods. After the presentation of the statistical analysis of the raw data of this experiment, the above graphs can, of course, be more fully interpreted.

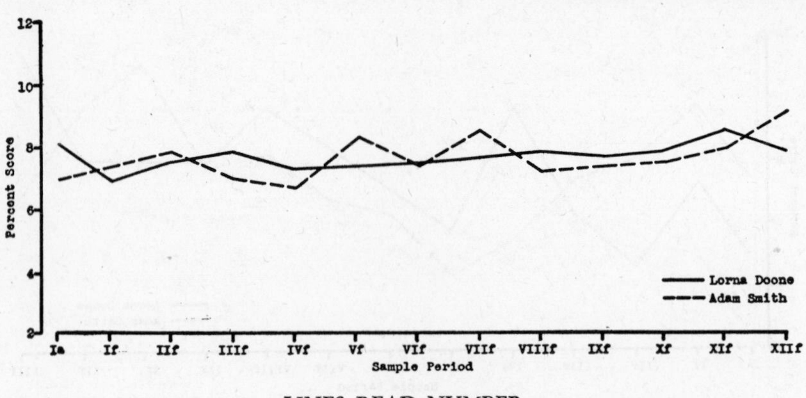

LINES READ NUMBER

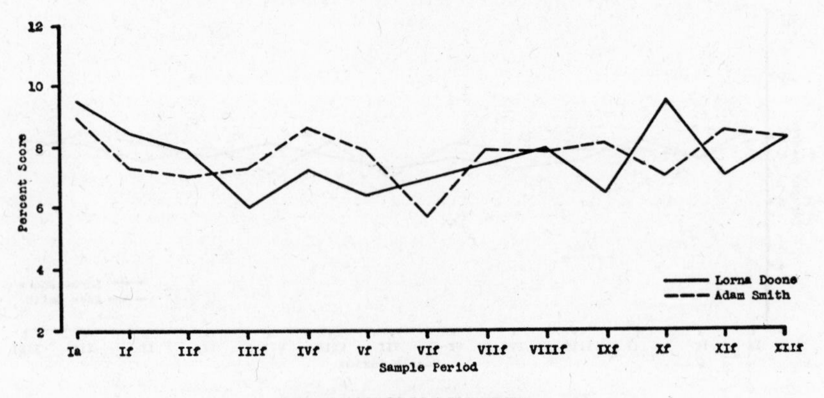

REGRESSIONS NUMBER

Figure 68 (continued)

SUMMARY GRAPHS FOR SUBJECT G.S. 1

The analysis of the data of the eye-movement measures will be presented in 28 individual tables, one for each of the seven measures used in each of the four experimental situations of the present study.[2]

The first group of seven tables (Tables 9 to 15) is for the college subjects previously included in the Grant Study who read the printed pages of the books used under relatively normal circumstances. These tables are each headed *Grant Study Subjects (normal reading).* The second group of seven, headed *High School Subjects (normal reading),* presents

[2] These tables are presented in the Appendix.

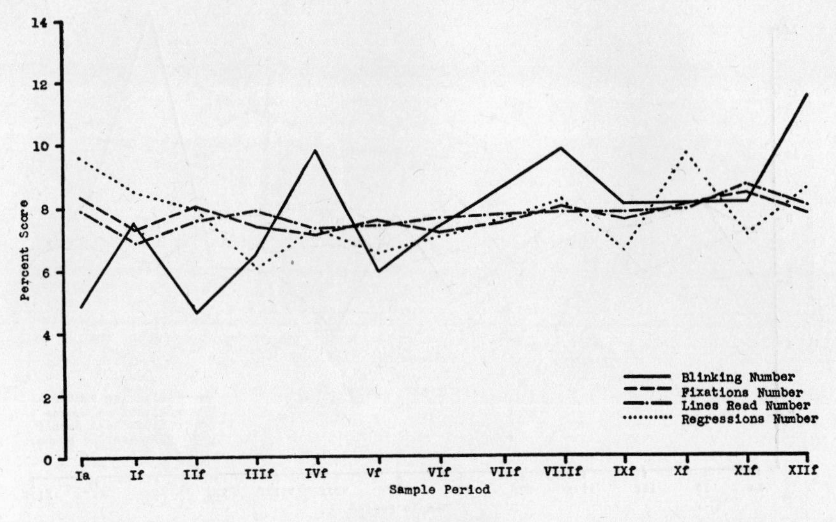

LORNA DOONE

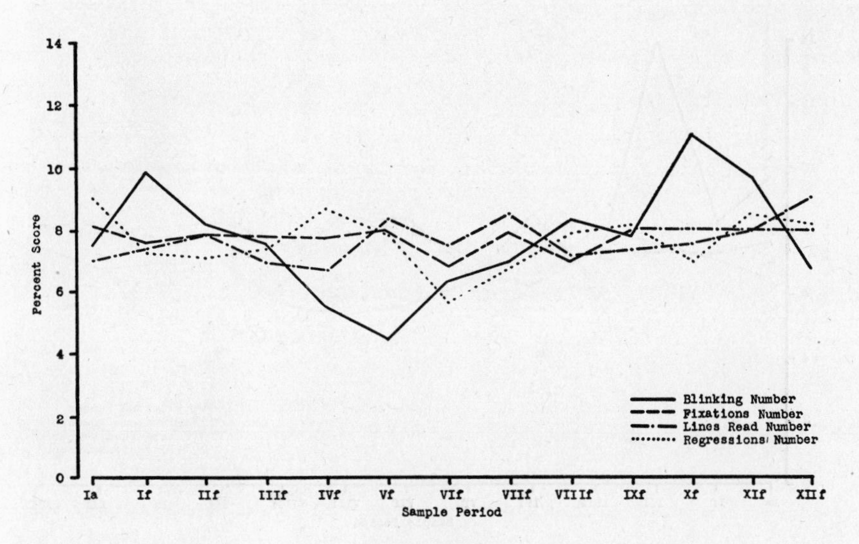

ADAM SMITH

Figure 69

SAMPLE SUMMARY GRAPHS OF EYE-MOVEMENT MEASURES

Grant Study Subject (normal reading) — G.S. 1

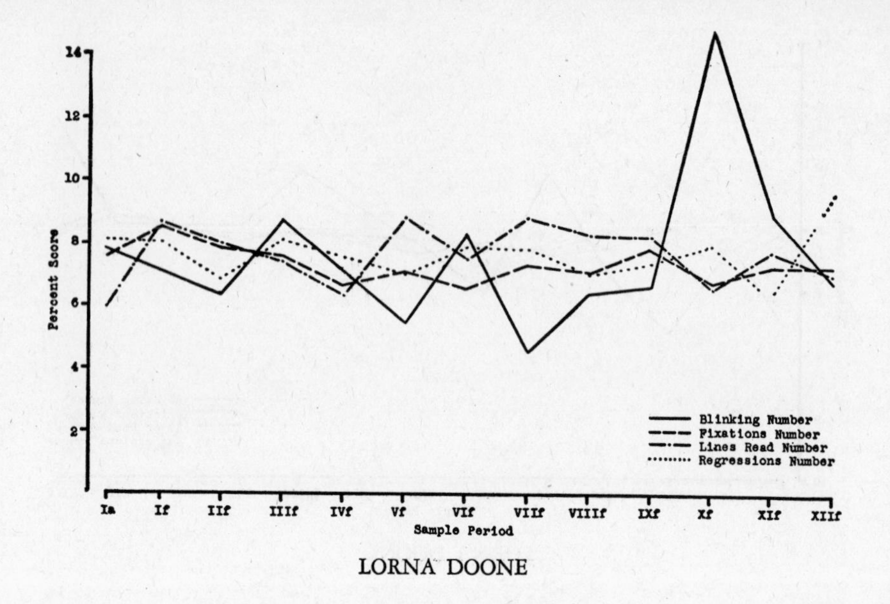

LORNA DOONE

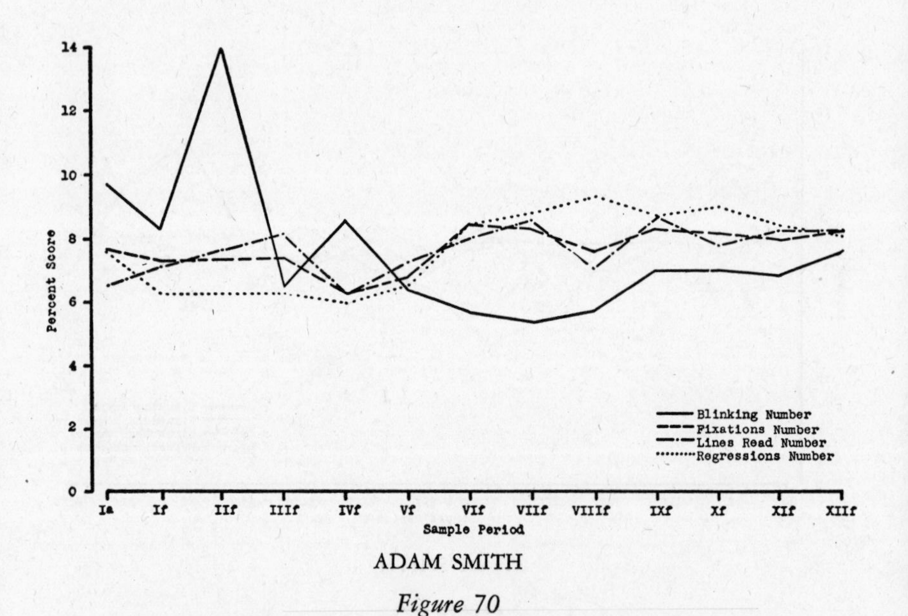

ADAM SMITH

Figure 70

SAMPLE SUMMARY GRAPHS OF EYE-MOVEMENT MEASURES

High School Subject (normal reading) — H.S. 1

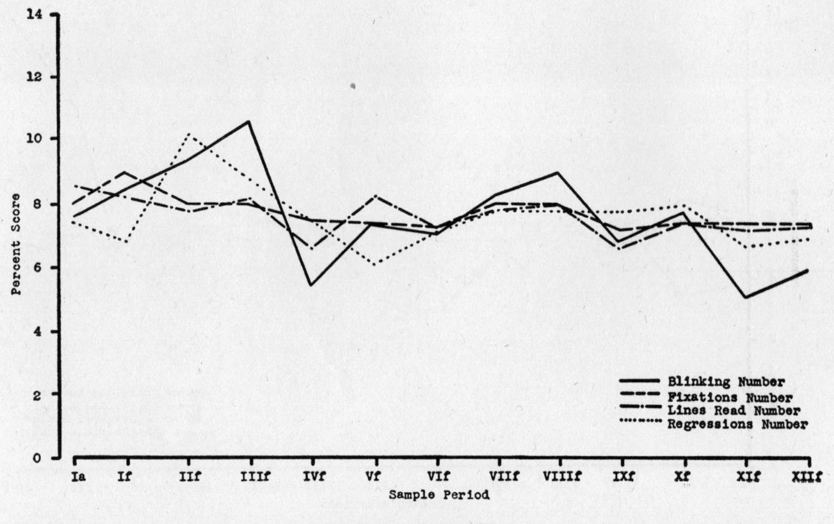

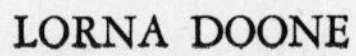
LORNA DOONE

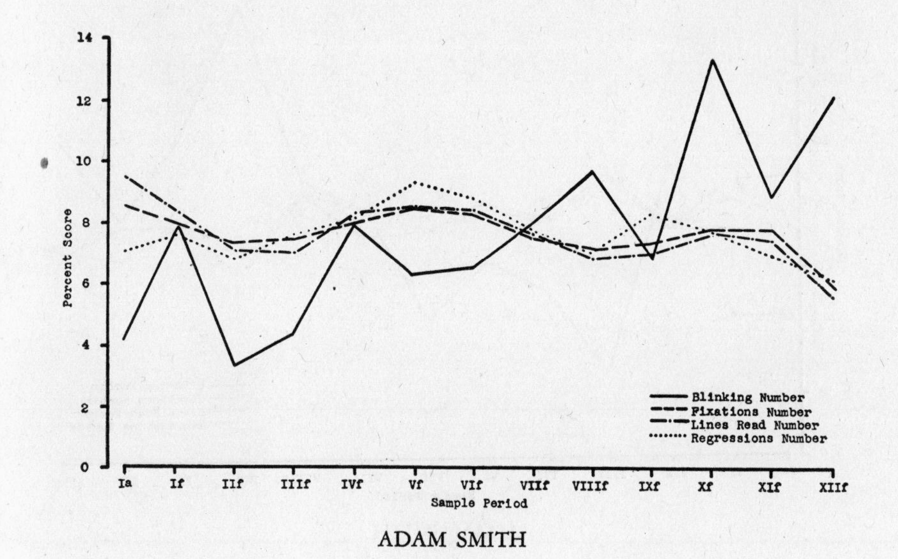

ADAM SMITH

Figure 71

SAMPLE SUMMARY GRAPHS OF EYE-MOVEMENT MEASURES

Grant Study Subject (microfilm reading) — G.S.M. 1

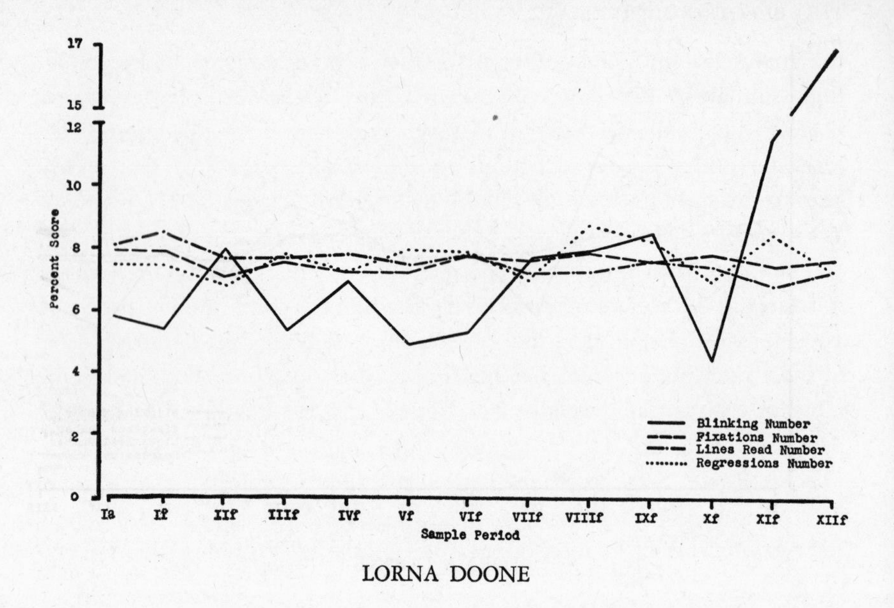

LORNA DOONE

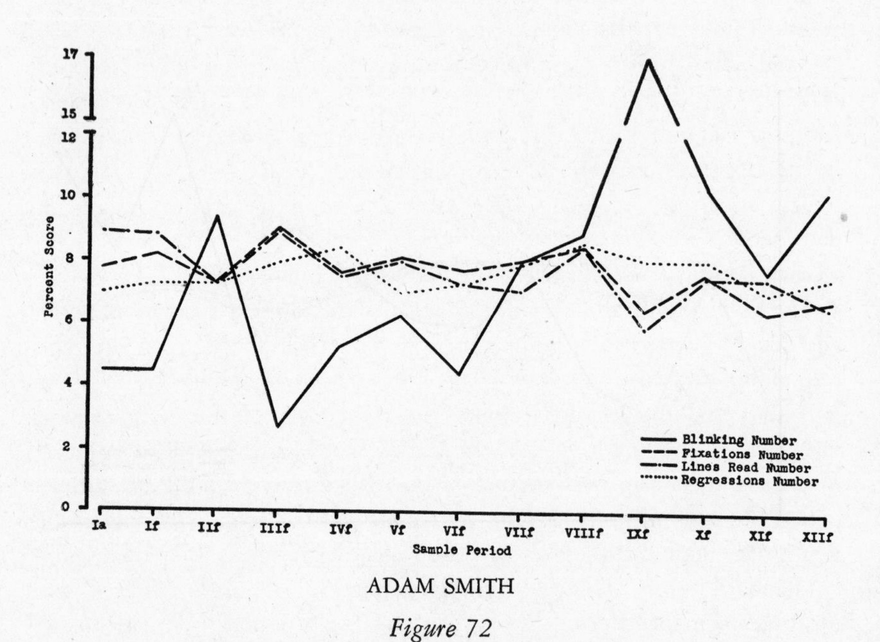

ADAM SMITH

Figure 72

SAMPLE SUMMARY GRAPHS OF EYE-MOVEMENT MEASURES

High School Subject (microfilm reading) — H.S.M. 1

the analysis of the data gathered for high school students under conditions similar to the above situation. *Grant Study Subjects (microfilm reading)* heads the next group of seven tables for college subjects who read the microfilm reproductions of the books used. The tables presenting similar data for high school students are designated *High School Subjects (microfilm reading)*.

The tables of a group will consider each of the seven eye-movement measures in the following order: The first table in each group (Tables 9, 16, 23, and 30) considers the total number of blinks made during each of the 13 sample periods. The heading is *Blinking Number.* The second table in each group presents the data for the total number of fixation pauses made during the five-minute sample periods—*Fixations Number* (Tables 10, 17, 24, and 31). *Fixations per Line* (Tables 11, 18, 25, and 32) refers to the number of fixations made per line, derived by dividing the total number of fixations made during a sample period by the number of lines read during the same sample period. The standard deviation of the number of fixation pauses made per line is the *Fixation Sigma Score* (Tables 12, 19, 26, and 33). *Lines Read Number* (Tables 13, 20, 27, and 34) is, in the case of each sample period, the number of lines read. *Regressions Number* (Tables 14, 21, 28, and 35) and *Regressions per Line* (Tables 15, 22, 29, and 36) are scores derived for regressions in the same way as were those for fixations.

The upper half of each table *(Lorna Doone)* presents the analysis of data derived for the subjects' reading of Lorna Doone. The lower half of each table is the analysis for the reading of Adam Smith.

The first column of each table *(Sample)* designates by Roman numeral and letter the particular sample period for which the data in the corresponding row are presented. The first five-minute period of the first half-hour and the last five-minute period of each of the 12 half-hour intervals of the total experimental trial were sampled. The column *Mean* lists the mean performance of the 10 subjects during each sample period for the measure in the particular experimental situation with which the table in question is concerned. Each mean is quoted with its standard error. Thus, for the quotation 58.6 ± 17.05, 58.6 is the mean performance during the particular sample period indicated in the first column and 17.05 is the standard error of the mean. The *Sigma* column lists the standard deviation of the distribution of the 10 scores for each sample period. Each standard deviation is followed by its standard error. Pearson product-moment coefficients of correlation between the 10 scores of the first sample period and the corresponding 10 scores of each of the subsequent sample periods are listed in column *r.* Each correlation is followed by its standard error. *C.R. S* lists the critical ratios of the differences between the standard deviation of the distribution at the first sample period, Ia, and the standard deviation of each of the following sample periods. A critical ratio of 3.00 or larger is taken in this study, as is customary, as being requisite to establish a statistically significant difference. The last column, *C.R. M,* lists the critical ratios of the differences between the mean of the distribution of 10 scores for the first sample period and the mean of each of the subsequent sample periods. A critical ratio of 3.00 or larger is again regarded as requisite to establish a statistically significant difference.

For convenience of presentation, the discussion of each table in each group will be headed by the eye-movement measure considered in the table.

The first set of seven tables presents the eye-movement data for the 10 college subjects who read under relatively normal conditions.

Blinking Number — Table 9.

The means of the sample periods for Lorna Doone show slight evidence of an increase in the number of blinks made — the last three means are as high as or higher than the first three, but the largest mean performance tends to be during the middle of the experimental trial. The increase in the case of Adam Smith is a little more definite. It will be noted that the mean performances during the reading of Adam Smith are higher than during the reading of Lorna Doone. In the case of both Lorna Doone and Adam Smith, the change in degree of variability of performance (Sigma) is not regular and indicates no trend. The correlation data for D indicate that the relative position of the subjects in the distribution at Ia changes more or less regularly during the first seven sample periods; thereafter, there is an irregular tendency to return to the relative position held during Ia. The correlation data for Adam Smith indicate a more rapid fluctuation in relative position — sample periods of greatest change in relative position are IIIf, VIIf, and XIf. The critical-ratio columns indicate that none of the changes in mean performance or variability among subjects is significant, nor is there any indication of a trend toward a significant change.

It must be concluded, therefore, that in the case of the present group of subjects there is no sure indication of a change in the rate of blinking. According to these findings, this motor phenomenon may not, therefore, be taken as indicating any "work decrement" under the conditions of the present experiments.

Fixations Number—Table 10.

The mean performance for the reading of Lorna Doone decreases until VIf and tends to increase thereafter. For the reading of Adam Smith, the mean number of fixations made decreases regularly until IIIf; another low point appears during VIIIf; and thereafter, the performance is sporadic. For D the degree of variability of performance decreases until Vf; thereafter, there is indication of an increase. For S the variability decreases irregularly until VIf and is sporadic thereafter. The correlation data for D show that the relative position at Ia changes markedly until VIIf, and thereafter the change persists; and later, there is a tendency to return to the relative position held at Ia. For S the change in relative position is marked at IVf and especially marked during sample periods VIIIf to Xf. The critical ratios indicate that the change in degree of variability is not significant for the reading of either book. The critical ratios for mean performance, however, indicate that mean differences are significant at several sample periods—especially IIIf, VIf, and Xf for the reading of D; and IIf, Vf, and VIIf for the reading of S. It will be noted, however, that in the case of both D and S the mean performance during Ia is considerably higher than during any of the subsequent sample periods. High critical ratios would, therefore, be expected in the last column of the table.

What is important is that these critical ratios do not increase in magnitude and do not show any regular trend during subsequent sample periods, and that the change in mean performance that has occurred after Ia is a decrease in the number of fixations made rather than an increase which might indicate a decrement in efficiency. It is concluded, therefore, that no sure decrement is indicated by this measure of the reading work.

Fixations per Line—Table 11.

The mean performance for D decreases until VIf and is sporadic thereafter; for S some decrease in mean performance is suggested by the data, but any such trend is irregular. The degree of variability tends to remain the same with some indication of a decrease in the case of S and a sporadic increase at IIf in the case of D. The C.R. S column shows, however, that there is no significant change in degree of variability. In the case of D, the subjects tended to maintain their relative position held at Ia throughout the experimental trial. In the case of S, changes in relative position increase (as indicated by the decrease, though irregular, in the magnitude of r). In the case of S, none of the changes in mean performance is significant; in the case of D, however, mean performance in number of fixations per line is significantly different from what it was during Ia.

These differences do not indicate a trend, however, after sample periods IIIf or Vf; nor is the change that has occurred a decrement in efficiency, but rather an improvement represented by making fewer fixations per line during the subsequent sample periods. Here again there is no evidence of change in performance as a result of prolonged activity which justifies the assumption of a work decrement.

Fixation Sigma Score—Table 12.

The mean performance in the case of both D and S would not indicate a trend except for the fact that the values in the last half of the experimental period are in some cases larger than in the first half. In the case of D, the data on degree of variability in performance do not indicate a regular trend; in the case of S, the sigma values are larger and there is some suggestion of an increase in degree of variability. The correlation data for both books show that the subjects did not maintain their relative position held during Ia. These values of the coefficients are the lowest for this experimental group. In the case of D, the coefficient values are lowest at VIf and XIf-XIIf. In the case of S, the values are lowest at IVf and XIf. The degree of variability does not change significantly (C.R. S); nor is there any indication of significant change in mean performance (C.R. M).

This measure, therefore, does not show any work changes which are consistent enough to demonstrate a decrement in the functional efficiency of the visual mechanism resulting from the prolonged reading.

Lines Read Number—Table 13.

The data on mean performance for D show an increase in the number of lines read. This trend is evident, however, only after the middle of the experimental period. The C.R. M data show that this trend is not significant. The mean performance for S tends to be the same during the experimental period with no significant changes. The degree of variability in both cases is also rather steady — with a slight increase in the case of D at the end of the experimental period. Any observed changes in degree of variability, however, are not significant. The correlation data for D show that the subjects tended to maintain the relative position they held during Ia. The coefficient values are lowest at Vf and VIIIf, with the trend toward Vf being a regular decrease (interpreted as an increase in the variability of relative position). In the case of S, variability in maintaining relative position increases in a steady, though not unbroken, trend.

This measure, as is true of those previously considered, does not provide any index of consistent change in the mechanism of the eye as a function of visual work done during six hours of reading activity.

Regressions Number — Table 14.

The mean performance in the case of both D and S tends to show a decrease in number of regressions made until the middle sample periods of the experimental trial, and an increase thereafter until the mean performance during the last periods is about the same as during the first periods. None of these changes, however, is significant. The degree of variability in the case of D remains about the same during the experimental period; in the case of S there is a suggestion of an irregular decrease in degree of variability if the first values of sigma are compared with the last values. The C.R. S data show that none of the changes in degree of variability, however, is significant. In the case of both books, relative position of the subjects remains rather steady except for a short trend toward increased shifting ending at the Xf and XIf sample periods.

Regressions Number, which *a priori* might well be assumed to serve as an index of fatigue, has not been found here to show any consistent changes. This measure, therefore, cannot be taken as an indication of work decrement during the six hours of reading.

Regressions per Line — Table 15.

The number of regressions made per line tended to remain quite steady in the case of both books. None of the changes that did appear is significant. Though none of the trends is significant, the data on degree of variability of performance show an increase up to IXf in the case of D and a decrease in the case of S. The subjects tended to change their relative positions more and more as the experimental period progressed in the case of both books. This trend is most pronounced in the case of S. Here again, there is no clear or consistent indication of a work decrement.

The seven tables next to be considered present the eye-movement data for the 10 high school subjects who read the two experimental books under normal reading conditions.

Blinking Number — Table 16.

The mean number of blinks made during the reading of both books tends to increase irregularly during the experimental period. This increase, however, is not significant. The differences in the case of D tend to be greater than in the case of S. If any trend is indicated in the degree of variability of performance, it is toward an increase, which changes in some instances approach significance. The correlation data indicate a trend, more pronounced in the case of S than of D, toward returning to the relative position held during Ia — the lowest values are found in the first half of the experimental period rather than in the latter half.

It may be argued that this evidence does suggest some change during the reading work. Careful interpretation, however, shows that the observed changes are usually not significant. Here again, therefore, it must be concluded that blink rate does not provide a clear index of change under the conditions of the present experiments.

Fixations Number — Table 17.

The mean performance during the reading of D tends to decrease irregularly, with low points at VIIf and XIIf. In the case of S, the decrease reaches its lowest point at Xf. In the case of both books, the mean data at XIIf are of interest with reference to the correlation data at the same sample point. In both cases relative position seems to have reversed itself (negative correlation). In the case of D, the coefficient is not significantly different from zero, and the influence of this reversal does not seem to have materially affected the trend in mean performance. In the case of S, however, the reversal in relative position is quite definite and seems to have had a marked effect on the mean performance, making it the highest of all the sample periods in contradistinction to the trend up to that point. A sporadic increase in the degree of variability is suggested by the sigma data in the case of both books. The correlation data for D show that relative position is not significantly maintained after IIIf. In the case of S, relative position changes more and more until about the tenth sample period, but thereafter it tends to become more like that held during Ia. The changes in degree of variability and in mean performance are not significant.

It will be noted that the observed changes are as often as not in the direction of increased visual efficiency, and, further, they are not usually significant. No clear-cut indication of work decrement, therefore, is demonstrated by this measure.

Fixations per Line — Table 18.

If any trend is indicated in the mean performance in the case of both books, it is toward a decrease. Changes in the degree of variability are too sporadic to indicate a trend, and the changes observed are not significant. The correlation data for both books indicate a trend toward increasing variability in the maintenance of relative position. The changes in mean performance in the case of S are not significant (C.R. M), but in the case of D the changes are sporadically significant.

It will be noted in the case of D that the mean performance during Ia is the highest for the sample periods and that the degree of variability for that sample period is the lowest. Since the critical ratio (of differences between means) is based on the observed difference between two means *and* on the standard deviations of the distributions which the means represent, Ia may not have been a valid criterion with which to compare the subsequent sample periods of this measure. The significant changes that are noted in the data of this measure are not, however, in the direction of decreased efficiency and so do not indicate a work decrement.

Fixation Sigma Score — Table 19.

Mean performance tends to remain rather steady with no significant changes in the fixation sigma scores. The data on degree of variability in performance show an increase during the experimental period. Thus, though mean performance did not change much, the subjects varied more among themselves as the experimental period progressed. The same fact is indicated by the correlation data, which show that relative position is less well maintained as the reading is prolonged. Relative position is most variable during the middle sample periods of the experimental trial. Except possibly for the change in relative position, however, this measure shows no significant change as a function of the prolonged reading.

Lines Read Number — Table 20.

Except for the datum at Ia in the case of D, mean performance tends to remain rather steady during the experimental period, with lower values in the case of S (that is, fewer lines read per sample period). The degree of variability in the case of D tends to remain the same (with the exception of Ia); in the case of S, an increase in variability is indicated. In general, the trend in maintaining relative position is toward greater variability (r). The critical ratio columns (C.R.S and C.R.M) in the case of Adam Smith show that changes in variability and in mean performance are generally not significant; however, the trend toward increased variability (sigma) approaches significance and is significant at XIf. The C.R. columns in the case of Lorna Doone include high values. Sporadically significant changes in degree of variability are indicated, but few or no significant changes in mean performance are indicated.

As was noted previously in connection with other measures showing similar changes, this sporadic significance may be due only to chance error at Ia — the mean and sigma at Ia are the lowest of all the sample periods. At any rate the change that has occurred represents essentially an improvement (since more lines were read per sample period during If to XIIf than during Ia) and certainly not a work decrement of any clear-cut nature, at least as far as mean performance is concerned.

Regressions Number — Table 21.

The mean performance in the reading of D shows a very slight decrease in number of regressions made during the middle of the experimental period, but is otherwise quite steady. The mean performance for S is steady throughout the experimental period. The degree of variability tends to decrease in the case of D; the decrease is not so pronounced in the case of S. The subjects tend to change their relative position more while reading D than while reading S—in the case of the latter, the correlation data are quite steady. The C.R. columns for both books indicate no significant changes in degree of variability or in mean performance. No work decrement, therefore, is demonstrated by this measure of the prolonged reading.

Regressions per Line—Table 22.

In the reading of Lorna Doone, the mean performance decreases, if any trend is indicated. The mean performance for the reading of S is fairly steady, with a slight increase during the middle sample periods. The degree of variability shows only sporadic changes, none of which is significant. The correlation data are less steady in the case of D than of S—in D an increase in variability of relative position is indicated after IXf. Changes in mean performance are not significant in the case of S and only once (IXf) in the case of D. Here again, no clear-cut evidence of a work decrement is found.

Data for the 10 college students of the Grant Study group who read the microfilm reproductions of the books used will be considered in the following seven sections.

Blinking Number—Table 23.

Mean performance during the reading of D is fairly steady; during the reading of S, an irregular increase is indicated. The changes in mean performance are not significant, though the critical ratios for Adam Smith tend to be larger than those for Lorna Doone. The degree of variability for D wavers in magnitude during the experimental period; for S it increases somewhat. None of these changes is significant. The magnitude of the correlation coefficients is unsteady in the case of both books, but no particular trend is noticeable.

It may be concluded that again this measure demonstrates no significant change in the visual performance of these 10 subjects.

Fixations Number—Table 24.

The mean performance in the case of D decreases to IIIf, rises suddenly, and decreases again at VIf and at XIf. Similar phenomena occur during the reading of S. Changes at these sample points tend to be significant. The degree of variability during the reading of D is sporadic;

during the reading of S, it tends to increase in wavering fashion, with high values of sigma associated with low values of mean (that is, the subjects tended to vary among themselves most when the group mean was lowest). None of the changes in degree of variability is significant. A similar periodicity in variability may be noted in the maintenance of relative position. At some sample periods of S, relative position tends to reverse itself from what it was at Ia.

Again, as in the case of other Fixations Number tables which have been reviewed, the mean at Ia is high in comparison with the means of other sample periods. The results of this measure suggest a fairly sharp decline in the number of fixations made during the very first of the experimental period and no similar change thereafter. This finding, again, does not support in any clear-cut fashion the assumption of a progressive work decrement.

Fixations per Line — Table 25.

Mean scores tend to maintain a similar value in the case of both books when decimal values are minimized, and none of the changes in these is significant. The same is true of the degree of variability, with the values in the case of D being more sporadic than in the case of S. The maintenance of relative position also remains fairly steady. In the case of S, XIIf data are interesting for their divergence from the data of the other sample periods — the mean and sigma are high, and the correlation coefficient low — suggesting a sudden decrement in over-all performance. The changes observed, however, are so few and insignificant that the conclusion that a work decrement has occurred is not warranted.

Fixation Sigma Score — Table 26.

Mean scores are high in the case of D at IIIf, VIf, and IXf-XIf, but none of these trends is significant, though they in some instances approach a significant level. It will be remembered that the Fixation Sigma Score is essentially a measure of variability; hence a high value here would suggest decremental effects of prolonged reading. The trends in mean performance in the case of S tend to be similar to those for D, but they occur earlier in the experimental period and in a less pronounced fashion. Degree of variability in the case of both books decreases, but not significantly. The changes in relative position are too sporadic to indicate a general trend.

The lack of over-all trends and the general insignificance of the changes in this measure suggest that little or no effect of prolonged reading has been demonstrated.

Lines Read Number — Table 27.

Mean performance shows a slight decrease in the case of D and tends to remain about the same in the case of S. None of the changes is significant in the case of S, and only at VIf and from VIIIf to Xf are they significant in the case of D. At these sample periods, the lowest means of the table are opposed to the highest mean, which in this case is the criterion mean (Ia). In the case of D, the sigma values for the first periods tend to be higher than for the last periods; the reverse is true for S. None of these changes is significant. In the case of D corresponding to the lowest mean, XIf is the lowest correlation value; this suggests that during that sample period the subjects changed relative position very markedly. The other correlation values are fairly steady. In the case of Adam Smith, the subjects tended to change their relative position more and more during the experimental period.

There is evidence for a work decrement in this measure, but it is so restricted and inconsistent as not to warrant general conclusions regarding the appearance of a true work decrement or "fatigue."

Regressions Number — Table 28.

No regular trend is indicated in the data of mean performance in the reading of either book. What changes occur are not significant. The degree of variability in the case of both books tends to decrease during the middle periods and then increase toward the end of the experimental period but not to so high a value as during the first sample periods. These changes, however, are also not significant. The same is true of the change in relative position, which is more pronounced during the middle of the experimental period than at the beginning or end. This shift in relative position occurs earlier in the case of S than D. It is concluded that no significant decrement is demonstrated by this measure.

Regressions per Line — Table 29.

Mean performance tends to waver in the case of both books, with the periodicity more pronounced for D. The changes represented by the high points or peaks of the periodicity tend to be significant only in the case of D. Similar fluctuations may be noted in the degree of variability during the reading of both books; only one of these changes, however, is significant. Relative position tends to remain quite steady during the reading of both books.

The sporadic nature of the only five instances of significant change noted in the table for this measure minimizes their importance as far as establishing the presence of a work decrement is concerned.

The seven tables next to be considered present the eye-movement data for the 10 high school subjects who read the microfilm reproductions of the books used.

Blinking Number — Table 30.

The trend in mean performance in the case of both books is toward an increase in the number of blinks made; however, as has been true in several instances previously, the trend is not apparent until the later sample periods. The sigma values in the last half of the experimental period tend to be larger than those during the first half, suggesting an increase in degree of variability. The maintenance of relative position is very unsteady in the case of both books. This is especially pronounced in the reading of Lorna Doone. In the case of S, increased variability in relative position would be indicated were it not for the high correlation values at the last sample periods. In the case of Lorna Doone, the changes in mean performance and in degree of variability are not significant. In the case of S, they are sporadically so.

It will be noted that in the case of Adam Smith, the mean performance and the sigma value at Ia are considerably smaller than the other values in the column. Thus, it is doubtful if significant differences would have been indicated if If had instead been used as the criterion value in each case.

Fixations Number — Table 31.

The mean performance data suggest, if anything, a decrease in the number of fixations made in the case of D, with a slight rise toward the end of the experimental period. In the case of S, an irregular decrease in number of fixations made is more evident than in the case of D. The degree of variability in the case of D shows no trend, but the values are higher toward the end of the experimental period. In the case of S, the sigma values tend to decrease. None of these changes is significant. The subjects while reading D tended to shift their relative position more toward that held at Ia as the experimental period progresses; the opposite is true in the case of S.

The changes in mean performance in the case of S are not significant; in the case of D, the changes are significant for the middle sample periods. Such findings do not support the conclusion that a general work decrement occurred in this measure during the six-hour reading period.

Fixations per Line — Table 32.

Mean performance in the case of both books tends to remain rather steady, none of the changes that do occur being significant. The degree of variability changes sporadically but not significantly. In the case of D, smaller values of sigma are found in the latter half of the experimental period. In the case of D, relative position is maintained fairly well until sample period IXf; thereafter, there is a tendency for shifts in relative position to occur. In the case of S, there is a suggestion in the data of more and more shifting in relative position as the experimental period progresses. It is concluded that this measure shows little or no significant change during the prolonged reading.

Fixation Sigma Score — Table 33.

In the case of D, the mean performance does not show any very definite trend; the changes that do occur are not significant. In the case of S, the mean values change sporadically, with more of the high values found toward the end of the experimental period. Many of these changes are significant, an effect heightened by the fact that the mean at Ia is low in comparison with the other means. The degree of variability tends to decrease in the case of D after the first periods of the experimental trial; this trend is less regular in the case of S. None of these changes is significant. Relative position tends to shift radically in the case of D, and also, but less regularly, in the case of S. Again, the correlation values found for this measure are the lowest of the group.

It will be remembered that tests of variability are being made of this measure, which is itself a measure of variability. The scatter and irregularity of the data presented in the table for this experimental situation, then, may be given some consideration. But it will be noted that very little of the evidence for scatter is oriented toward a work decrement or a "fatigue trend."

Lines Read Number—Table 34.

The correlation data in the case of both books waver. In the case of D, the subjects shifted their relative position more and more during the first sample periods, then tended to return to their original positions, shifted slightly again, and then went back toward the original positions. The wavering in the case of S is toward a greater shift in relative position. The number of lines read of Lorna Doone tended to decrease until the middle sample periods and to increase somewhat thereafter. The mean performance in the case of S remains fairly steady. None of the changes which appear is significant. The degree of variability in the case of both books does not show any trend, and none of the sporadic changes which do appear is significant. Again, there is no clear-cut evidence of a work decrement.

Regressions Number—Table 35.

A slight decrease is suggested in the mean performance during the reading of D and an increase in number of regressions during the reading of S. None of these trends is significant. In the case of D, the degree of variability changes sporadically at first and then decreases during the last sample periods. No trend is indicated in the degree of variability during the reading of S. The degree of variability does not change significantly. No regular trend is indicated in the correlation data for D. The data for S suggest a shift in relative position toward that held during Ia as the experimental trial progresses. What evidence for change is present in this measure is contrary to what would be expected if a work decrement had occurred.

Regressions per Line—Table 36.

Changes in mean performance are too sporadic to indicate a trend. The changes that do occur are not significant. For the reading of Lorna Doone, the degree of variability tends to decrease if any trend is indicated in the data. In the case of S, the degree of variability tends to increase sporadically. None of these changes, however, is significant. The relative position of the subjects remains rather steady, with some suggestion of increased shifting in the case of S. Again, there is little or no clear-cut evidence of a decrease in functional efficiency of the visual mechanism as reading was prolonged.

For purposes of comparison, it is of interest to note the total number of pages read by each group, as shown in Table 37.

The findings which have just been reviewed in detail will be summarized with reference to the eye-movement measures, leaving for later consideration (Chapter 9) differences of phenomena observed when the experimental books or the experimental situations are compared.

Even though the subjects of the present experiments read for six continuous hours, the eye-movement measures investigated show surprisingly few instances of significant change. Inasmuch as seven ocular measures were analyzed for differences both in mean performance and in degree of variability in each of four experimental situations during the reading of each of two books, there were 112 distributions in which work decrements, or changes in efficiency, could have appeared. And yet in only 14 instances (13 per cent) were significant changes demonstrated for more than one sample period of a data column. For convenience of discussion, these 14 instances are listed in Table 38. (The number in parentheses following each item refers to the number of critical ratios for the 13 sample periods of that eye-movement measure which are greater than 3.00.)

The statistical procedures used to analyze differences in performance are designed to test the so-called null hypothesis — that is, that in this case, no change in performance occurred during the six hours of reading. The table shows that only 13 per cent of the tests of that hypothesis demonstrated evidence for disproving it. The present evidence, then, indicates that the hypothesis of no change is still acceptable. From this finding alone, it may be generally concluded that significant changes in eye-movement performance do not occur during a six-hour reading period under any of the conditions of the present experiment.

The importance of even the few instances of significant change may be minimized when other factors are considered, especially in relation to the further stipulation that when changes occur they are in the direction of a work decrement or a decrease in visual efficiency. When significant changes were found to occur in mean performance (right-hand column of the chart), they were in most instances sporadic and usually of brief duration. Instead of a progressive change of one sort or another, so that at some point during the experimental trial a measure significantly changes and remains changed, the critical ratio is significant at one or two sample periods, decidedly not at the next sample period, significant again a few samples later, and so on. Such irregularity suggests chance errors or discrepancies of the sort which are to be expected in any sampling procedure rather than the measurable effect of reading as a function of the passage of time. Further support is given this impression by the fact that in some instances the change represents an increment in performance, while in others a decrement is indicated.

If the instances of significant differences were real phenomena and not sampling artifacts, one would expect significant changes to be generally present in the data for one measure, for one book, or for one experimental situation. The scattered appearance of the 11 instances of change in mean performance does not enable one to make any such general conclusion. It will be noted that the 11 instances are not peculiar to one of the seven measures of the experiment nor to one of the experimental situations. It may be that the number of fixations is the most generally affected (5 of the 11 instances), but even this measure does not display any consistent trend in significant change.

Somewhat more difficult to interpret is the fact that in most of the instances of significant change, the mean or sigma criterion values (data at Ia) have been unusual when compared with the data of the other sample periods. The criterion values have been much higher or much lower than similar data for the rest of the experimental period. The question, then, arises as to the reality or validity of these criterion values in these special instances. One interpretation would be that these were statistical artifacts in that more variation in the mean or sigma had occurred than is usually present. In this case the significance of the changes dependent on these "artifacts" is minimized.

It may be, however, that these special values are definite instances of trends suggested by a review of all the data. In some instances the trend was relatively rapid at first and leveled off during the experimental trial. This seems to mean that initial changes appeared rapidly or that the subjects early found a level of performance at which they could continue for some time. As suggested in the final chapter, this may mean that the working organism achieved a new "steady state." Other experimenters have drawn this conclusion from "fatigue" studies involving manual tasks.

Assuming for the moment that these significant changes, when they do occur, are real effects, the changes still may not be of great enough magnitude to justify characterizing them as indications of "fatigue." The word "significant" may be interpreted in two ways, both of which may apply to the present experiments. One meaning of the word is statistical (the meaning used previously). The differences in the data between sampling periods of the several measures may or may not be due to factors of chance fluctuation. Where statistically significant differences have been demonstrated, they are interpreted as due to experimental factors other than chance. The second meaning of the word significant represents what might be called the layman's view: Does the change make any difference? Are the changes great enough to interfere with or otherwise influence the functioning of the organism with a manifest or practical result?

In the case of the number of blinks, the significant change found in the data represents about 11 blinks out of the 30 made on the average during a sample period. Changes in the number of fixations represent 100 fixations in one experimental group (G.S.M.) and 50 or less in another (H.S.M.); the average number made in a sample period was 1100 and 1000 fixations respectively. The significant change in the case of Fixation Sigma Score represented about one fixation per line; in the case of the number of lines read, 15 lines when the average was about 138 lines read in a sample period; in the case of Regressions per Line, about 0.4 out of an average of 2.3 regressions per line made during a sample period. Considering the magnitude of these changes from the point of view of the second meaning of the word significant, the significance of these changes with reference to the subjects' behavior is on the whole minimized.

The conclusions to be drawn from the sigma data and the critical ratios (C.R. S) of the differences that occur in the degree of variability are similar to those just drawn from the C.R. M data.

It may therefore be generally concluded that *significant changes or trends in the degree of variability do not occur when reading is prolonged under the conditions of the present experiments.* In only three instances (left-hand column of Table 38) out of 56 data columns are significant critical ratios found for the change in degree of variability, and these are sporadically distributed. More often than not, no trends appear in the sigma data. Where progressive changes in the degree of variability are suggested, they are not definite enough nor consistently enough in the same direction to warrant any general conclusion. The possibility, however, that a trend may be either toward decreased variability among the subjects or toward increased variability gives rise to two not necessarily opposed hypotheses. When variability among subjects has decreased, it would suggest that the prolonged reading has reduced individual differences or that "fatigue" has affected the subjects regardless of their personal differences — the prolonged task itself is primarily operative. When variability among subjects has increased, it may be that "fatigue" has differentially affected the subjects, causing a greater spread — the influence of the prolonged task has been dominated by individual differences. The three instances of significant change noted in the sigma data show, if any trend is indicated, a tendency toward increase. This would suggest that the latter may be more likely to happen when fatigue effects appear — subjects may "fatigue" at their own individual rates.

If any trend is indicated in the correlation data (*r*), it is toward a decrease in the magnitude of the correlation coefficients. If, as has been pointed out before, the magnitude of the coefficients gradually approaches zero, it could be concluded that the subjects tended to shift their positions during subsequent sample periods more and more. There is some evidence for this type of shift in the data of this experiment. The paucity of instances in which such a shift may be assumed to occur, of course, mimimizes the importance of this conclusion. The instances that do occur might support the hypothesis just previously ventured, that the effects of prolonged activity are manifest in individual differences, since it is they which affect the magnitude of the coefficient of correlation.

Although it is concluded that the changes occurring in the number of blinks made from sample period to sample period are not significant, it may be interesting to note that if any trend is present, it is toward an increase. If tension is produced by the prolongation of reading, this finding would suggest, according to the tension theory of blinking previously reviewed, that the reading itself was not a sufficient "outlet" for the tension. The tenuousness of this supporting evidence, however, is obvious.

In the data for several of the measures, regular fluctuations seem to have occurred. To this phenomenon the name "periodicity" might be given. (The data on number of fixations show perhaps most definitely of all the measures this periodicity. The significant changes in this measure occur only at the "inflection" points of the fluctuations.) For the reading of Lorna Doone, this periodicity appears rather regularly at sample periods IIIf, VIf, and IXf or Xf. In the case of Adam Smith, this periodicity is not so regular, tends to appear earlier, and after one or two fluctuations ends in sporadic changes. At the sample periods named, the magnitude of several statistics for some of the measures is especially low or high (in some cases significantly so) in relation to the same statistics for the other sample periods of the same measure.

Considering these periodic changes, the hypothesis may be worth entertaining that superimposed on the prolonged activity of the peripheral mechanism (eye muscles, and so forth) is a periodic breakdown or alteration in the control or determination of the ocular functions which is mediated primarily by the brain's neural mechanisms. This hypothesis of "fatigue" is, of course, related to the more psychological definitions of fatigue. It may be that these periodic changes are related in some way to the finding by L. H. Sharp (315) that residual tension in the resting arm, after two minutes of ergographic work, does not gradually fade but tends to show diminution of a cyclic character.

It will be noted from the chart that the number of regressions did not significantly change during the experimental period. In fact, more often than not the number tended to remain fairly steady without even a trend toward change. It may be proposed that this does not necessarily mean that prolonged reading has no effects on the number of regressions made. Some experimenters have suggested that regressions may be related to the ability to comprehend what is being read, on the grounds that a regressive movement would not be made unless the material had not been comprehended during the earlier fixation pause. It would, then, be argued further that more difficult material or material read in difficult circumstances (for example, prolonged task) would make greater demands on comprehension, and thereby increase the number of regressions. But if it is assumed that one book was more difficult to read than the other and that a later sample period was a greater strain than an earlier one and still the number of regressions did not significantly increase at all, it is as likely that the subjects were not paying much "attention" to what they were reading as it is that prolonged reading had little or no effect on regressive behavior. In this case, of course, the subject's not paying attention may be the fatigue effect rather than any change in the number of regressions.

In three instances the critical ratios evaluating differences in the per line measures (Fixations per Line and Regressions per Line) were significant. It is difficult to interpret changes in a per line measure because the fact that they are derived measures raises special problems.

The measure Fixations per Line is derived by dividing the number of fixations made during a sample period by the number of lines read during that sample period. The measure Regressions per Line is derived similarly by dividing the number of regressions made by the number of lines read. These measures are often regarded as measures of the efficiency of reading; that is, as reading is continued, they make it possible to answer questions concerning what change there is in the number of fixations required to read a line of print, or what change there is in the number of regressive movements made in reading a line.

From the very logic of their derivation, per line measures may be statistical artifacts. It is conceivable that in and of themselves they could not indicate changes during prolonged activity. For example, assume that during a sample period it was found that the subjects on the average made a particular number of fixations per line as derived from a certain number of fixations and a certain number of lines read. If during that sample period a larger number of fixations or a smaller number of fixations had been made, and a proportionally larger or smaller number of lines read respectively, the number of fixations per line would be the same in all three cases. Therefore, if for several sample periods the number of fixations per line tends to remain the same (as the data of this experiment show they do), all that can be concluded is that either the number of fixations and the number of lines read remained the same or the number of fixations and the number of lines read varied proportionally. The data of this experiment are not definite enough to determine just which of these alternatives has occurred. A similar statement, of course, could be made regarding regressions per line.

The general conclusion of the present experiments that significant changes in eye movements do not occur during six hours of continuous reading still requires interpretation. Taken at its face value, this conclusion would mean that college and high school students may read for six hours without any demonstrable work decrement. With no objective evidence to the contrary, the corollary assumption would be that this continuous reading could be done without deleterious effects to the subject or, more specifically, to his visual functions. It may also be suggested that a physiological mechanism which does not show a work change during the period of exercise should not be expected at a later time to reveal some "hidden" injury to the systems concerned. It is to be remembered that the experimental period was considerably longer than the usual study periods of these subjects.

In the reading experiment by Hoffman previously referred to (142), subjects were required to read for *four hours* continuously *without* comprehension checks or examinations inserted during the reading period. The 30 Harvard College students who served as subjects read a light, historical, prose selection. These subjects were paid $2.50 (50 cents an hour for five hours, four of which were spent in reading) for the experimental session. The same eye-movement functions as in the present experiment were recorded and measured. The data were analyzed by means of Fisher's analysis of variance technique—a procedure serving more precisely the same purpose as the more usual critical-ratio technique used in the present experiments. In this connection it may be said that the application of the variance technique to the data on college subjects in the present experiments showed the same results as the critical-ratio technique reported in this chapter.

Both experiments found periodicity in the data having inflection points at certain sample periods during the experimental trial. The sample periods at which these fluctuations occurred tended to be the same for the four-hour study and for Lorna Doone in the present experiments. In both experiments, changes in degree of variability are regarded as not significant. In the four-hour study, the degree of variability tended to increase; in the present experiments, an increase is suggested in some instances, but this is balanced by others showing a tendency to decrease. Changes in relative position tended to be the same in both studies but are more definite in the four-hour experiment.

As noted above, in the present experiments the general conclusion is drawn that significant changes did not occur during the six-hour reading period. However, under the conditions of the four-hour experiment, statistically significant changes in eye-movement behavior were found to occur rather generally and in progressive order. The number of blinks increased and was significantly different after one hour of reading (IIf). The number of fixations decreased and the number of lines read decreased during the prolonged reading and were significantly different after one-half hour of reading (If). The fixation sigma score had significantly increased at the second-hour sample period IVf. The number of regressions changed sporadically.

The difference in the general conclusions to be drawn from the statistical findings of the two experiments is obvious. But are the conclusions necessarily in apposition to each other? The subjects in the present experiments were required to read for six hours; in the other study, they were required to read for only four hours. But the significant differences were found in the four-hour study; had the situation been reversed, it could be said that the reading was not sufficiently prolonged in the experiment in which decrements were not found. In the six-hour study, subjects read light material and a formal treatise. If anything, the reading material in the four-hour research was easier and lighter. It will be noted from the chart (Figure 38) that eight instances of significant change were found in the reading of Lorna Doone and six in the reading of Adam Smith. It is doubtful, however, whether the difference in reading matter was great enough to account for the difference in results.

By far the most striking difference in the design of the two experiments was the full continuity of reading without interpolated "motivating" tests in the four-hour study as opposed to the lack of continuity resulting from the insertion of comprehension checks during the reading period of the six-hour experiment. It may be that even the slight change in reading material occurring periodically during the six hours is important in explaining the difference in results. But there is probably a deeper reason. It has been suggested in the statements by the subjects and from the reading of the records that the interspersed comprehension exercises seem to improve the morale and efficiency of the subject by the very fact that they offered a new working task from the point of view of the reader. One reads in a different way if he expects to be examined in detail upon his reading than if he is merely "reading for pleasure." The attitude or intent of the reading may have introduced differences in the recorded changes of the reading pattern. Besides this basic change in attitude, it is important also to note that the insertion of comprehension checks produced a significant interruption in the routine of reading. The task thus became less homogeneous, although the eye muscles continued to work. In a very real sense, it is the reader who keeps himself at any task of reading, be it for a few moments or for the four- or six-hour periods under discussion. It is well known that the more immediate and real the goal or motivation, the greater is its effect on present behavior, whether the human organism is aware of this effect or not. In the four-hour experiment, the goal may be assumed to have been the finishing in four hours, in relatively confined circumstances, of a relatively homogeneous task. Judging from the reports given by the subjects themselves, the goal in the six-hour experiments also may be assumed to have been the finishing of a prolonged task. In addition, the subjects of both sets of these experiments were school and college students, and most satisfactory school and college students have learned almost as second nature to take examinations seriously. Each interpolated test in the six-hour series, it is likely, functioned as a real goal to the subject. These goals were lacking in the four-hour experiment, in which indeed the subjects were not asked to set for themselves any especially high self-motivated level of aspiration.

If it is deemed reasonable to make the above assumptions, then the differences in objective results of the four- and six-hour experiments represent differences in homogeneity of task and, in general, self-accepted motivating conditions. If this be true, it seems fortunate in retrospect that the two studies can be so well compared, because this comparison points to the motivation of the subjects as an all-important variable. It may be concluded from the results of the eye-movement measures of the study of the subjects who read for six hours that readers can be motivated in such a way that they maintain their visual efficiency without significant change when required to read for a long period. It should also be pointed out that in a study of a less well self-motivated group of subjects, definite changes in reading took place in a shorter work period. It should be noted that this motivation does not seem to have been of the sort characterized as "conscious effort." The individual has probably no more control over the regressive movements of his eyes — to select but a single measure — than he has over his heart rate. Finally, it may be observed that the most important fact about reading for long periods as shown by the laborious recording and statistical techniques of these experiments is not a specific change in the physiological mechanism. It is not a change in eye muscles, for example. Rather, the basic variable which seems to determine the presence or absence of changes during work done in long periods of time and which can be described as "fatigue" is a general characteristic of the subject's whole attitude toward his task. Fatigue of this sort may be seen as related to the organism's changing motivation. To put this in another way, the social conditioning of the subjects during educational experience, and their general desire to excel in a difficult academic task are important in evaluating such objective scores as blinking rate in the four-hour and six-hour experiments which have just been compared.

In a most general sense, the findings of this chapter show how impossible it is to separate "physiology," "physiological psychology," and "social psychology" in a study of even the most concrete pattern of behavior of the normal adult human subject. Reading, like every other learned adaptive act of man, is to be understood only in a full biosocial setting.

Chapter 9

Books and Reading Groups

THE CONDITIONS of the present study of reading for six hours allowed comparisons of certain aspects of the reading materials used, such as fiction or nonfiction, the educational age of the subjects, and printed books *versus* microfilm. Some of these variables as shown in the eye-movement data of the subjects themselves will be considered in this chapter.

Each of the 10 subjects in each experimental situation read for six hours both Lorna Doone and Adam Smith. Therefore in each experimental situation there is available for each of the eye-movement measures a performance score at each sample period for the reading of both books. In effect, the experimental procedure at any one sample period held constant the reading situation, the eye-movement measure, and the subjects, but varied the books being read. Comparison of the two books, therefore, can be made using each eye-movement measure in each of the four experimental situations.

Four sets of graphs (Figures 73, 74, 75, and 76) are presented, one set for each experimental situation as indicated on each graph. The four individual graphs in each set compare the two books with regard to mean performance in number of blinks, number of fixations, number of lines read, and number of regressions made. Percentage scores (derived for the sample mean scores in the same way as was previously done for

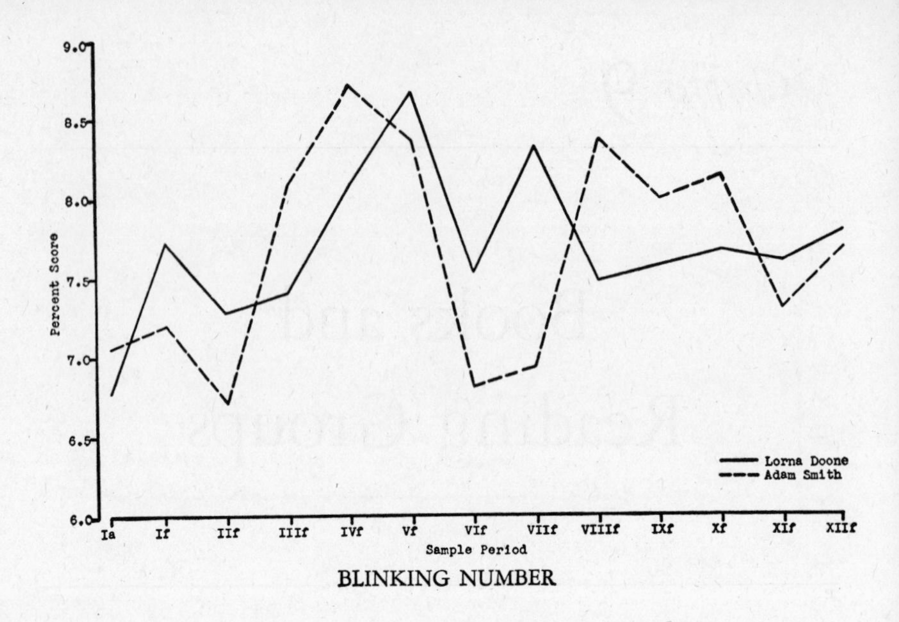

BLINKING NUMBER

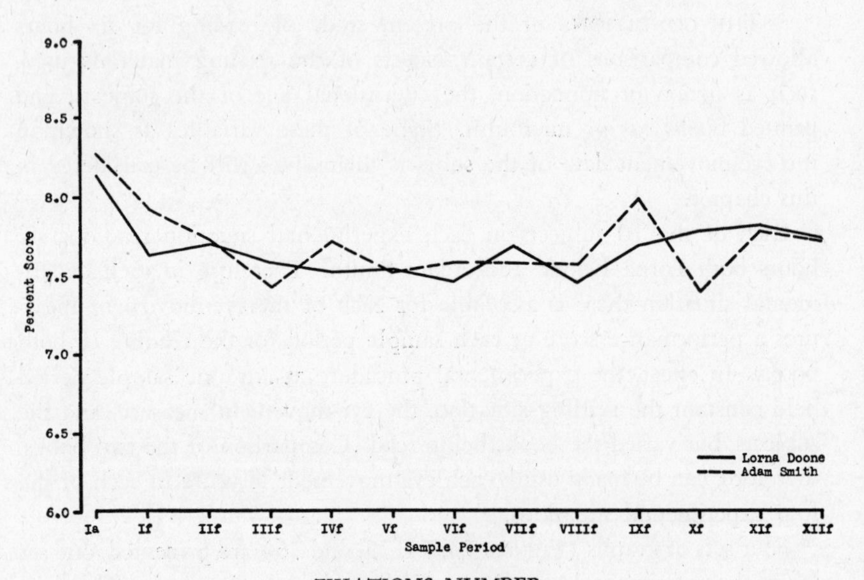

FIXATIONS NUMBER

Figure 73

GRAPHICAL COMPARISON OF THE EXPERIMENTAL BOOKS

Grant Study Subjects (normal reading)

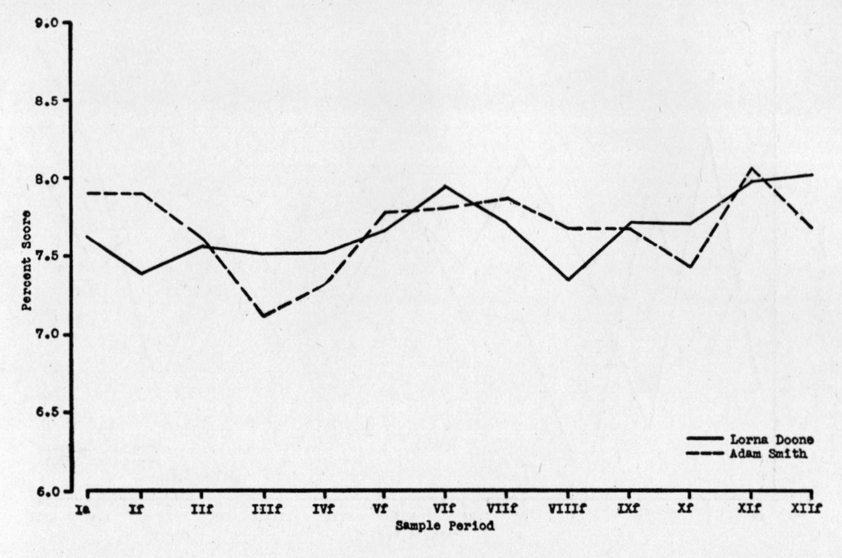

LINES READ NUMBER

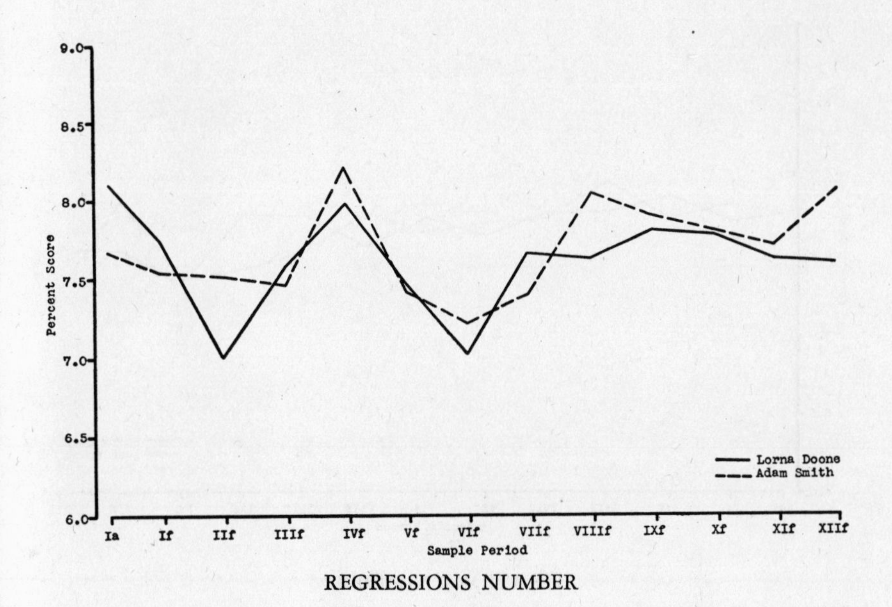

REGRESSIONS NUMBER

Figure 73 (continued)

GRAPHICAL COMPARISON OF THE EXPERIMENTAL BOOKS

Grant Study Subjects (normal reading)

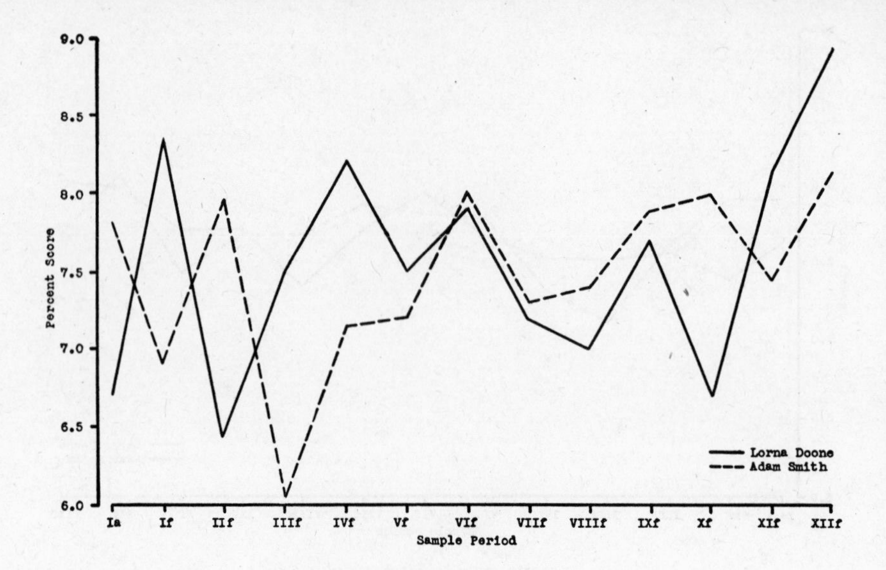

BLINKING NUMBER

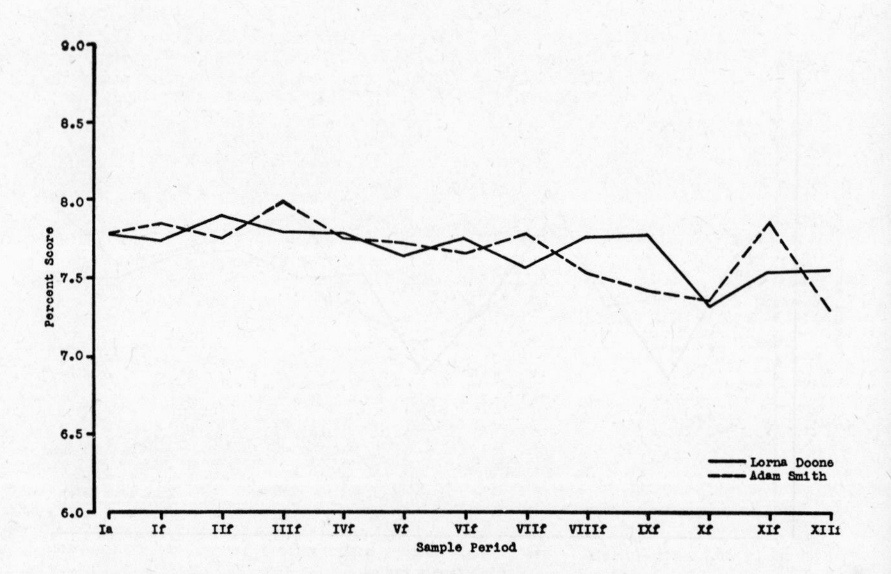

FIXATIONS NUMBER

Figure 74

GRAPHICAL COMPARISON OF THE EXPERIMENTAL BOOKS

High School Subjects (normal reading)

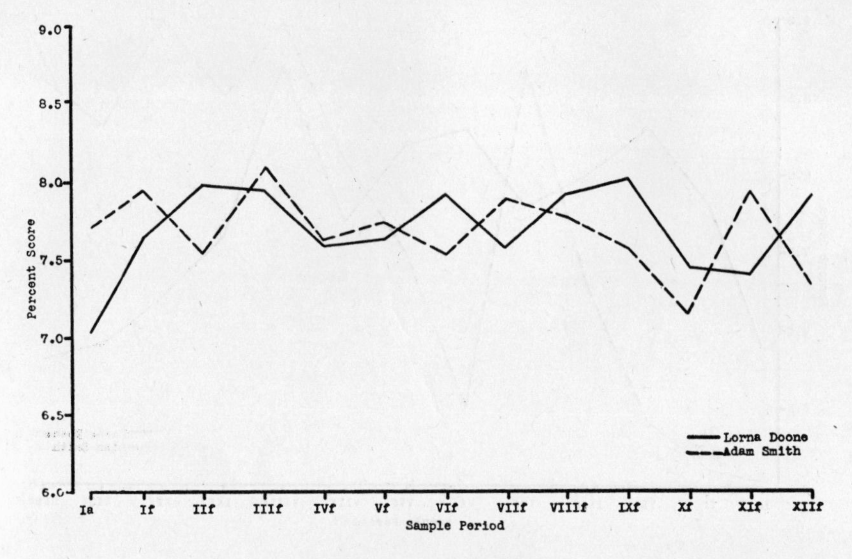

LINES READ NUMBER

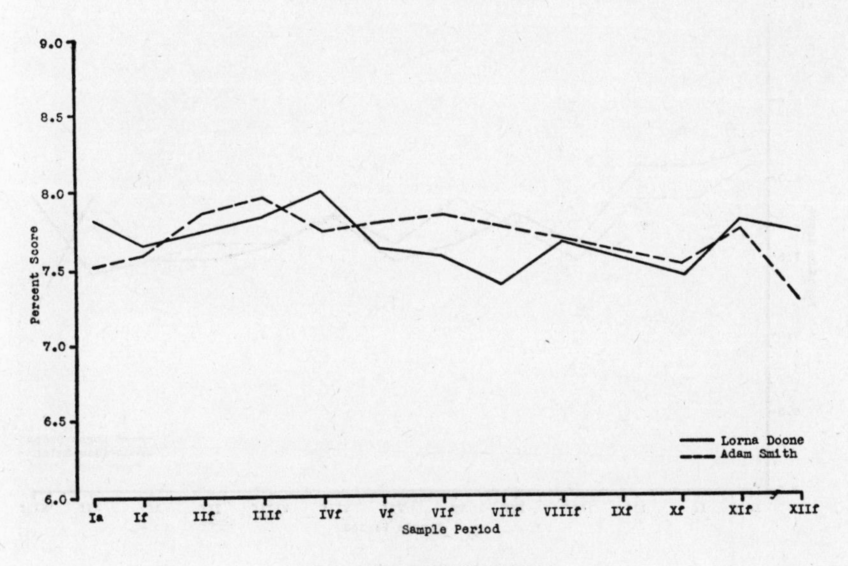

REGRESSIONS NUMBER

Figure 74 (continued)

GRAPHICAL COMPARISON OF THE EXPERIMENTAL BOOKS

High School Subjects (normal reading)

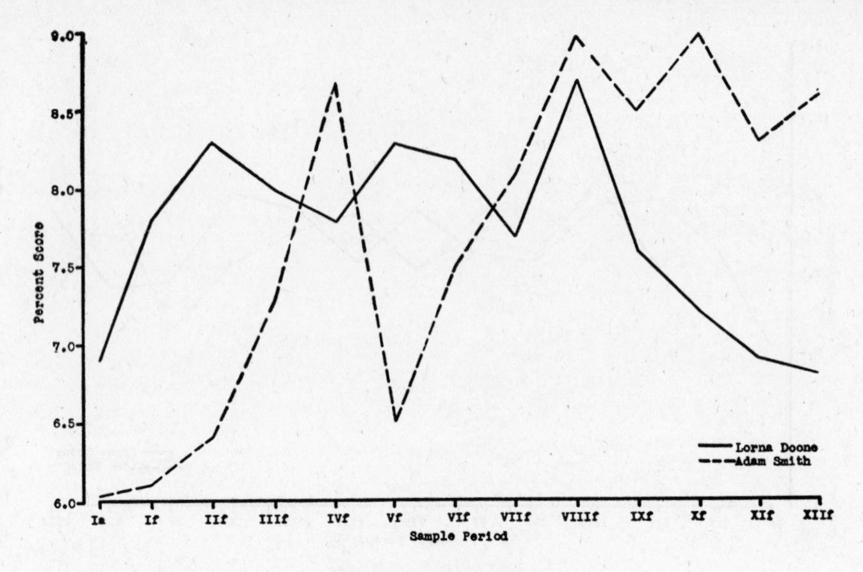

BLINKING NUMBER

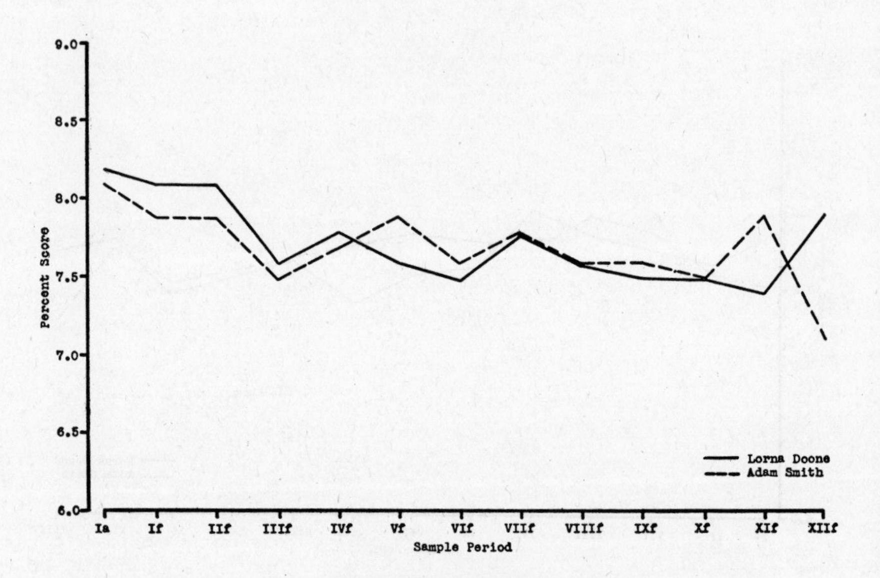

FIXATIONS NUMBER

Figure 75

GRAPHICAL COMPARISON OF THE EXPERIMENTAL BOOKS

Grant Study Subjects (microfilm reading)

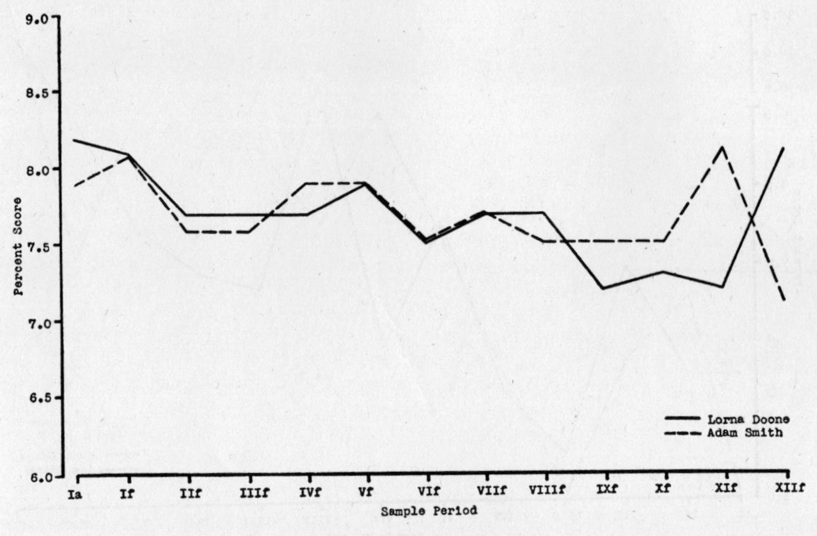

LINES READ NUMBER

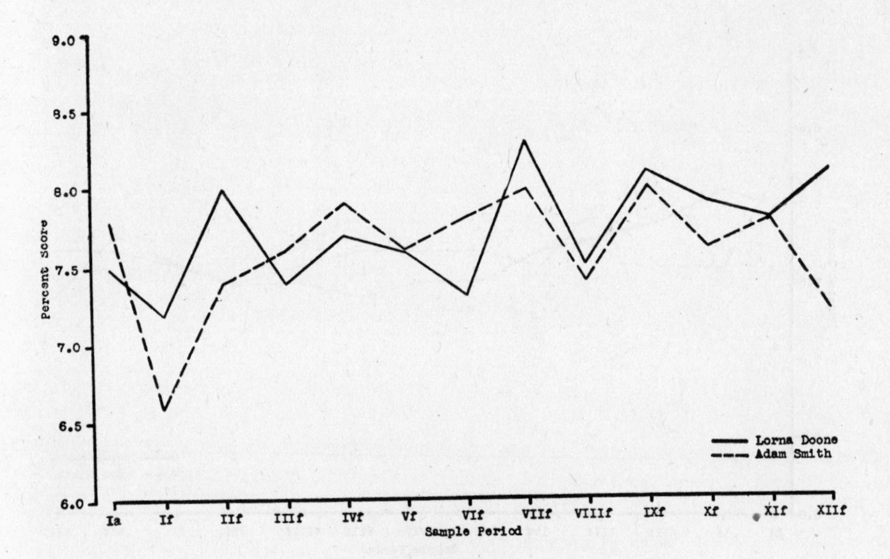

REGRESSIONS NUMBER

Figure 75 (continued)

GRAPHICAL COMPARISON OF THE EXPERIMENTAL BOOKS

Grant Study Subjects (microfilm reading)

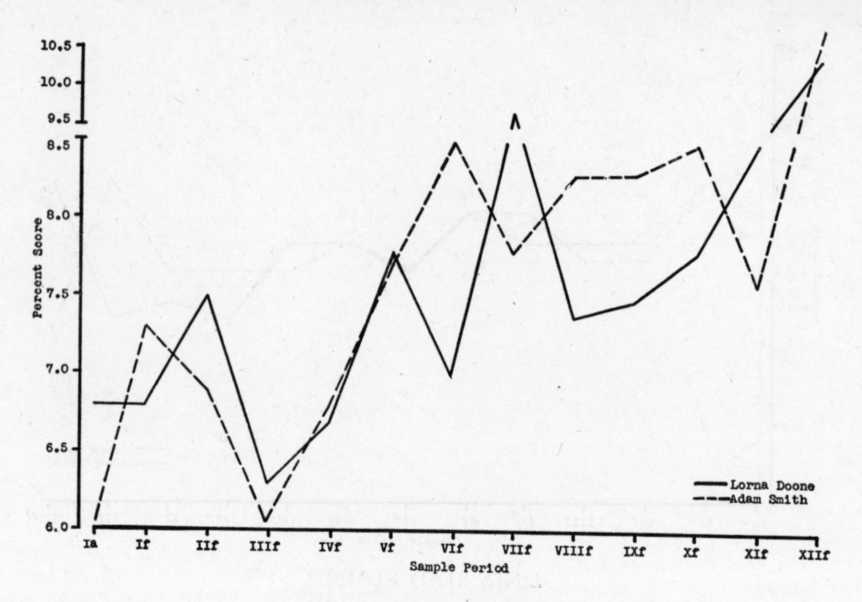

BLINKING NUMBER

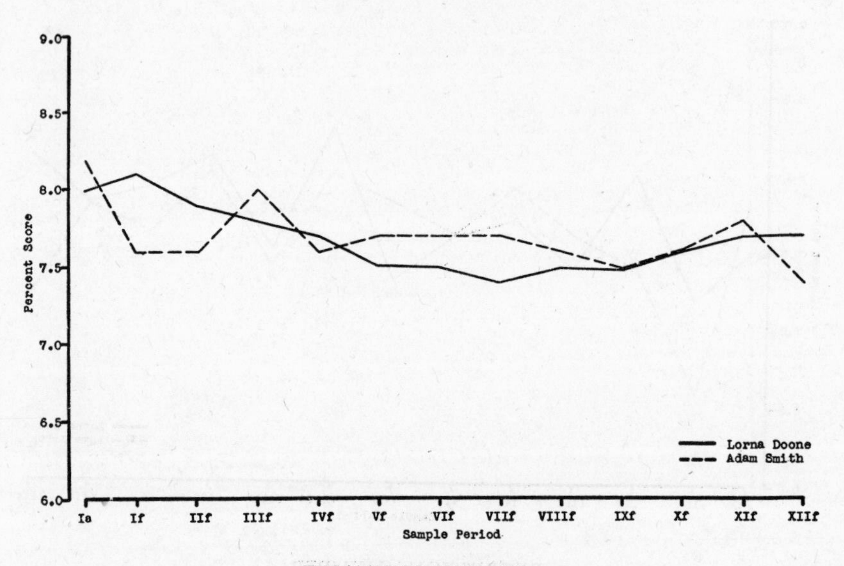

FIXATIONS NUMBER

Figure 76

GRAPHICAL COMPARISON OF THE EXPERIMENTAL BOOKS

High School Subjects (microfilm reading)

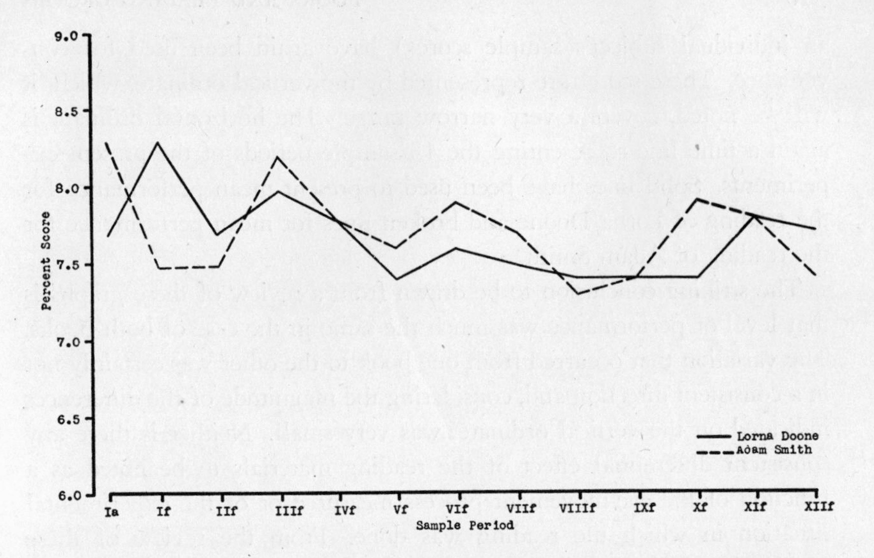

LINES READ NUMBER

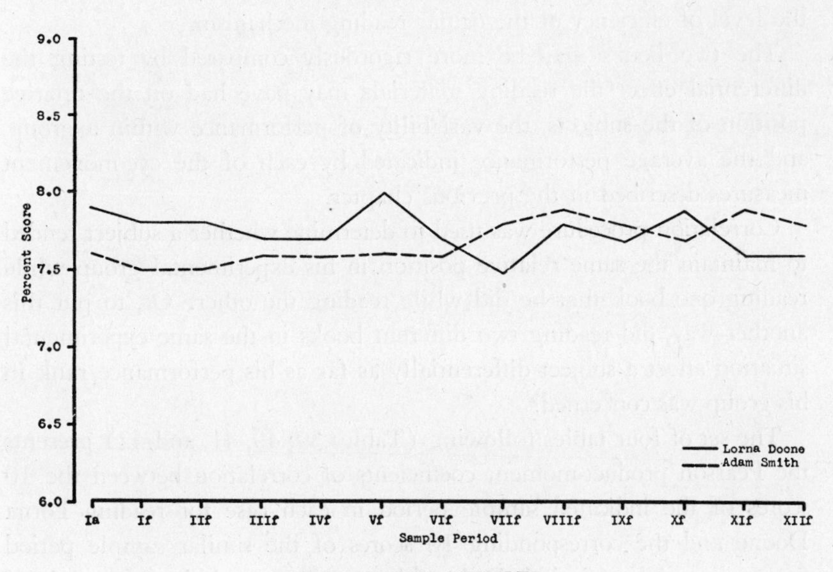

REGRESSIONS NUMBER

Figure 76 (continued)

GRAPHICAL COMPARISON OF THE EXPERIMENTAL BOOKS

High School Subjects (microfilm reading)

an individual subject's sample scores) have again been used for convenience. These scores are represented by the vertical ordinate, which, it will be noted, covers a very narrow range. The horizontal ordinate is again a time line representing the 13 sample periods of the present experiments. Solid lines have been used to present mean performance for the reading of Lorna Doone and broken lines for mean performance for the reading of Adam Smith.

The striking conclusion to be drawn from a review of these graphs is that level of performance was much the same in the case of both books. The variation that occurred from one book to the other was certainly not in a consistent direction and, considering the magnitude of the differences indicated on the vertical ordinate, was very small. Neither is there any consistent differential effect of the reading materials to be noted as a function of the eye-movement process measured or of the experimental situation in which the reading was done. From the review of these graphs, it may be concluded that the "interest" or attractiveness of the reading materials of the present experiments did not noticeably affect the level of efficiency of the ocular reading mechanism.

The two books may be more rigorously compared by testing the differential effect the reading materials may have had on the relative position of the subjects, the variability of performance within a group, and the average performance indicated by each of the eye-movement measures described in the previous chapter.

Correlation procedure was used to determine whether a subject tended to maintain the same relative position in his experimental group while reading one book that he did while reading the other. Or, to put this another way, did reading two different books in the same experimental situation affect a subject differentially as far as his performance rank in his group was concerned?

The set of four tables following (Tables 39, 40, 41, and 42) presents the Pearson product-moment coefficients of correlation between the 10 scores of the indicated sample period in each case for reading Lorna Doone and the corresponding 10 scores of the similar sample period for reading Adam Smith. Each table presents correlations for each of the 13 sample periods of each of the seven measures derived from one of the four experimental situations. These correlations are of interest both for the trends which may appear in them as reading is prolonged and for the differential effects on performance rank they show.

Grant Study Subjects (normal reading) — Table 39.[1]

Trends are suggested only in the case of Fixations Number and Regressions per Line. In the former, relative position changes more and more toward the middle sample periods; thereafter, the subjects tend to maintain the same relative position while reading both books. In the case of Regressions per Line, although the correlations are relatively low throughout the 13 sample periods, relative position during the reading of both books does tend to become more alike as the experimental period progresses.

In the case of Blinking Number, Fixations Number, Lines Read Number, and Fixations per Line, knowing the relative position during the reading of one book would more or less make possible a prediction of relative position during the reading of the other book — the correlation coefficients are fairly high in these instances. Correlation coefficients are low in the case of Fixation Sigma Score, Regressions Number, and Regressions per Line, indicating in these measures a differential effect on relative position.

High School Subjects (normal reading) — Table 40.

The Fixation Sigma Score suggests that the subjects maintained more and more their same relative position while reading both books as the experimental period progressed. During the latter half of the experimental trial, the subjects tended to shift relative position more and more in the case of Regressions Number.

The subjects tended to have similar relative positions in the case of Fixations per Line and Lines Read Number. Relative positions are not quite so similar in the case of Blinking Number, Fixation Sigma Score, and Regressions per Line. Relative position during the reading of one book bears little or no relation to position during the reading of the other book in the case of Fixations Number and Regressions Number.

That there are marked differences between the college and the high school students should also be noted, although the significance of the differences is not clear. The college students, as noted, maintained their relative position as between the two books in the number of fixations; the high school students did not; whereas the high school students were very consistent as regards the number of regressions and the regressions per line, and the college students were quite the opposite.

[1] See Appendix for all tables referred to in this chapter.

Grant Study Subjects (microfilm reading)—Table 41.

In the case of number of blinks made and number of lines read, there is some suggestion of more shifting in relative position at the end of the experimental period. Prediction of relative position is good in the case of Fixations per Line and Regressions per Line. It is low in the case of Fixations Number and of Fixation Sigma Score. Relative position is fairly well maintained in the case of the other measures.

High School Subjects (microfilm reading)—Table 42.

There was a tendency in the case of both Fixations per Line and Number of Lines Read for the subjects to maintain more and more their same relative position while reading both books as the experimental period progressed.

In general, relative position during the reading of both books is not very well maintained in this experimental group. Prediction from the distribution for the reading of one book to the distribution for the reading of the other is especially low in the case of Fixations Number, Fixation Sigma Score, and Regressions Number.

The differential effects noted in the data of these tables may be summarized as shown in Table 43. In the left-hand column of the table, instances of eye-movement measures which suggest a change in the maintenance of relative position as reading was prolonged have been listed for each experimental situation. The direction of the change or trend is indicated by a plus or a minus sign, the former for trends toward maintaining the same relative position during the reading of the two books, the minus sign to indicate a gradual shift in relative position. It will be noted from the chart that very few of the seven measures are affected in any one experimental situation and that the same measures have not been affected in all the experimental situations—for example, Fixations Number score was affected in the Grant Study Subjects (normal reading) but not in any of the other situations, and so forth. Of more importance is the finding that the direction of trend is not the same for all measures listed. All the above would suggest that the trends which do appear are to be regarded as sporadic instances of chance fluctuation rather than as general indications of a differential effect of the reading material on measured characteristics of eye behavior after prolonged reading.

Another purpose of the tables just reviewed, however, was to compare the two books simply as reading materials and not necessarily as factors in the prolongation of reading. The right-hand column of Table 43 lists the eye-movement measures differentially affected by the two books (as indicated by coefficients generally low in magnitude). According to the summary, relative position was differentially affected rather consistently in the case of Fixations Number, Regressions Number, and Fixation Sigma Score. Correlation coefficients were lowest for these measures, indicating that relative position of the subjects is not the same during the reading of the two books. The fact, however, that these three measures and not all seven indicate differential effects warrants consideration. If it were the reading materials themselves which were entirely responsible for the differential results, general indications in all measures would be expected. These results suggest, therefore, that something in the nature of the measures themselves, perhaps in conjunction with the reading materials, is also a responsible agent. But before the conclusion is drawn that the books may or may not have differentially affected eye-movement results, other tests of the reading materials should be reviewed.

The significance of differences in performance during the reading of each of the two books will be considered with reference again to four tables (Tables 44, 45, 46, and 47), one for each experimental group. The upper half of each of the four individual tables presents the critical ratios of the difference between the mean of the indicated sample period in each case for reading Lorna Doone and the mean of the similar sample period for reading Adam Smith. Each of these four tables presents the critical ratios for each of the 13 sample periods of each of the seven measures derived from one of the four experimental situations. The lower half of each table presents the critical ratios of the difference between the standard deviation of the distribution of 10 scores at the indicated sample period in each case during the reading of D, and the standard deviation of the distribution of the 10 scores at the similar sample period for the reading of S. A critical ratio of 3.00 or larger is regarded as indicating a statistically significant difference.

Review of all four tables shows that no trends are apparent. The appearance of significant changes is sporadic. Thus, the tables will be discussed only with reference to the appearance or nonappearance of a critical ratio establishing a significant difference in any particular case.

G.S.—Table 44.

For the 13 sample periods, significant critical ratios of mean differences appear only three times in the case of Fixations Number and five times in the case of Fixations per Line. Only in the case of Regressions per Line is there a significant difference in standard deviations during the reading of the two books.

H.S.—Table 45.

There are instances of significant differences in mean scores during the reading of the two books in the case of all the measures except Blinking Number and Regressions Number.

There is an instance of significant difference in standard deviations in each case for Blinking Number, Fixation Sigma Score, and Lines Read Number.

G.S.M.—Table 46.

Instances of significant differences occur only in the case of Fixations Number, Fixations per Line, and Lines Read Number.

The only instance of significant differences in standard deviations is in the case of Blinking Number.

H.S.M.—Table 47.

Instances of significant differences in mean scores appear in the case of Fixations per Line, Fixation Sigma Score, Lines Read Number, and Regressions per Line.

None of the differences in standard deviations during the reading of the two books is significant.

Instances of significant critical ratios in these tables are summarized in Table 48: the right-hand column lists the measures which showed greater than 3.00 critical ratios evaluating differences in mean performance; the left-hand column lists the measures which showed greater than 3.00 critical ratios evaluating differences in degree of variability during the reading of the two books. The numbers in parentheses after each measure indicate the number of critical ratios in the distribution of 13 which were greater than 3.00. With seven measures in each of four experimental situations, there are 28 distributions of 13 critical ratios each for both mean differences and standard deviation differences with which to test the hypothesis that significant differences did not occur. In the case of sigma differences (left-hand column), there are only five instances of measures disproving the hypothesis, and in each of these there was only one critical ratio in the distribution which may be regarded as significant. In the case of mean differences, there are 14 instances out of 28 which might disprove the hypothesis, but in these instances only from one to six of the critical ratios in each distribution of 13 may be regarded as significant. The general conclusion to be drawn is that significant differences in mean performance and in degree of variability during the reading of the two books are not consistently demonstrated by the present findings.

The two books of the present experiments have just been compared with respect to their possible differential effect on eye-movement performance as it was prolonged during the six-hour period from sample period to sample period. A test was also made of the maintenance of relative position, of the stability of mean performance, and of degree of variability at each sample period. Some instances of trends were found in the correlation data, which, however, were not consistent or general. No noticeable trends were found in the critical-ratio data. From these findings it may be concluded that reading materials differing as do those used in the present experiments do not appreciably affect eye-movement performance even when reading is prolonged for six hours. To put this in another way, it may be that the motivational effectiveness of the total situation, as discussed in Chapter 8, is such as to transcend any intrinsic motivational factors in the "interest" of the subject matter of the two books.

The correlation data show that in the case of the number of fixations made, the number of regressions, and the fixation sigma score, relative position tends to change from book to book, but the critical-ratio data show that this variation is not such as to affect consistently mean performance or degree of variability. There is some evidence, then, for differential effect; the majority of the results, however, support the general conclusion that eye-movement performance was not significantly affected by the reading materials used in the present experiment.

The presentation of eye-movement data up to this point has been for the purpose of discussing experimental variables which could be considered within any specific situation without particular regard for the circumstances of that experimental situation. It will be recalled, however, that in each of the four experimental situations, the same reading materials were used and the same seven eye-movement measures tested. The eye-movement data gathered for the reading of either book may, therefore, be used to compare performance as it may have been affected by the variables of the experimental situation.

It will be remembered that in the present experiments, groups of 20 college students and 20 high school students were each divided into two subgroups of 10 each. The first group of each educational age read the printed pages of the books themselves. The second group read microfilm reproductions of the books. The four groups so arranged are referred to as follows:

Grant Study Subjects (normal reading)
High School Subjects (normal reading)
Grant Study Subjects (microfilm reading)
High School Subjects (microfilm reading)

As noted previously, with these four groups six combinations of eye-movement data can be made for purposes of comparing the situation variables:

1. Grant Study Subjects (normal reading) *vs.* Grant Study Subjects (microfilm reading)
2. High School Subjects (normal reading) *vs.* High School Subjects (microfilm reading)
3. Grant Study Subjects (normal reading) *vs.* High School Subjects (normal reading)
4. Grant Study Subjects (microfilm reading) *vs.* High School Subjects (microfilm reading)
5. Grant Study Subjects (normal reading) *vs.* High School Subjects (microfilm reading)
6. Grant Study Subjects (microfilm reading) *vs.* High School Subjects (normal reading)

Since in comparisons 1 and 2 above, educational age was held fairly constant—both college or both high school subjects—but the type of reading varied, these two comparisons may be used to test differences arising in the experimental period when normal reading is opposed to microfilm reading. Since in comparisons 3 and 4 above, type of reading was held constant—both normal or both microfilm reading—and the subjects varied, these two comparisons may be used to test differences arising in the experimental period when subjects of one educational level are opposed to subjects of another. Comparisons 5 and 6 may be used to verify or support the findings from the first four comparisons. Assuming that performance is more efficient when the readers are of a higher educational age or the circumstances of the reading are relatively normal (as opposed to readers of a lower educational age or the reading of microfilm reproductions), comparison 5 opposes situations which may be regarded as most diverse, and comparison 6 opposes situations which may be assumed to show the least differences in efficiency of performance. In comparison 5, a high educational age and normal reading situation is opposed to a lower educational age and microfilm reading situation. In comparison 6, a high educational age but microfilm reading situation is opposed to a lower educational age but normal reading situation. The hypothesis to be tested by analysis of the eye-movement data in each of these cases is whether or not there are any significant differences in eye-movement performance which may be attributable to educational age or to the distinction between normal reading and microfilm reading. If such differences as do exist are found to be significant, then it can be further questioned whether high school educational level or microfilm reading is more demonstrably effective during prolonged activity than either college educational level or normal reading.

A cursory comparison can be made of the experimental situations in graph form by plotting the percentage scores for the measures of eye movements derived in the four experimental situations during the reading of the two books of the experiments. Four groups of two graphs each are presented in Figures 77, 78, 79, and 80. Each group presents the per cent mean data for an eye-movement measure — Blinking Number, Fixations Number, Lines Read Number, and Regressions Number. The two graphs in each group are one for Lorna Doone and the other for Adam Smith. The experimental situation represented by each curve on each graph is indicated by the legend on the graph. The horizontal ordinate represents the sample periods; the vertical scale represents percentage score.

In reviewing these graphs, a modifying factor must be kept in mind. The ordinate scale representing percentage score shows that the range of scores is very small — usually no more than 1.5 per cent units. This fact minimizes in interpretation any trends of progressive change the graphs may show, since the range of the change represented is so small. By the same token, differences between the situations shown by these

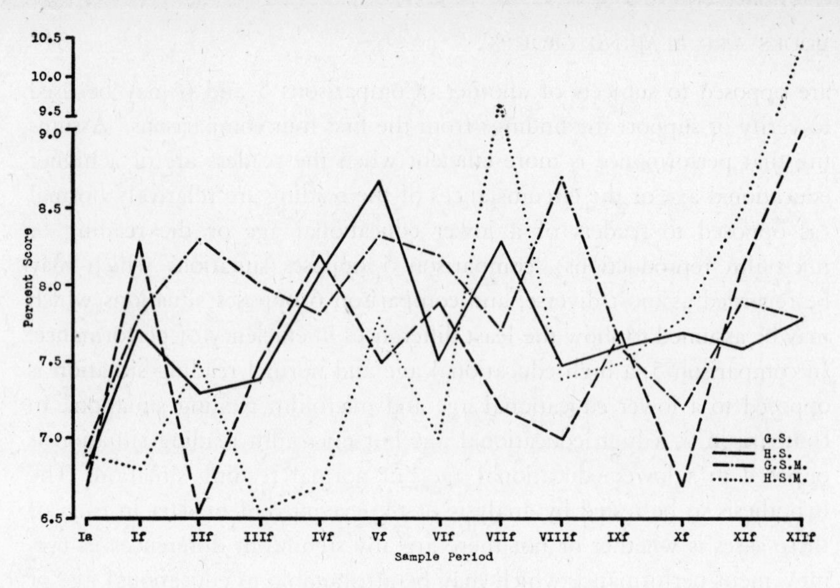

LORNA DOONE

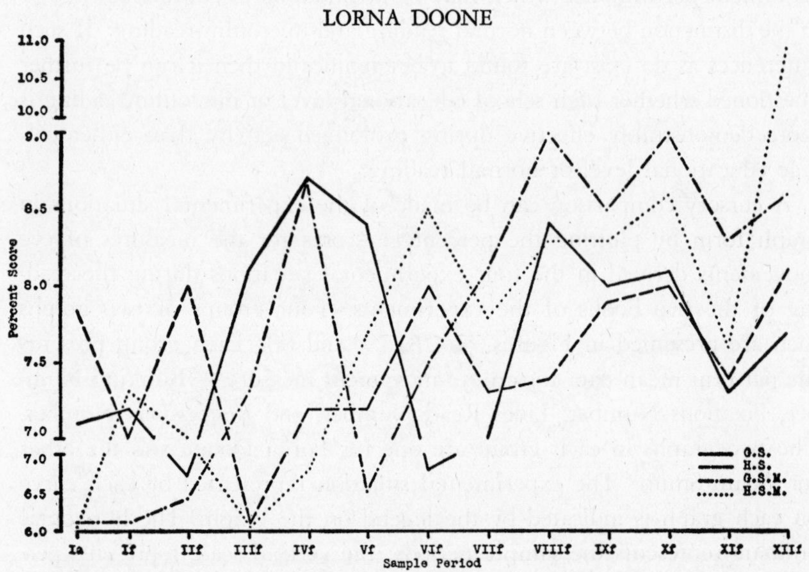

ADAM SMITH

BLINKING NUMBER

Figure 77

GRAPHICAL COMPARISON OF THE EXPERIMENTAL SITUATIONS

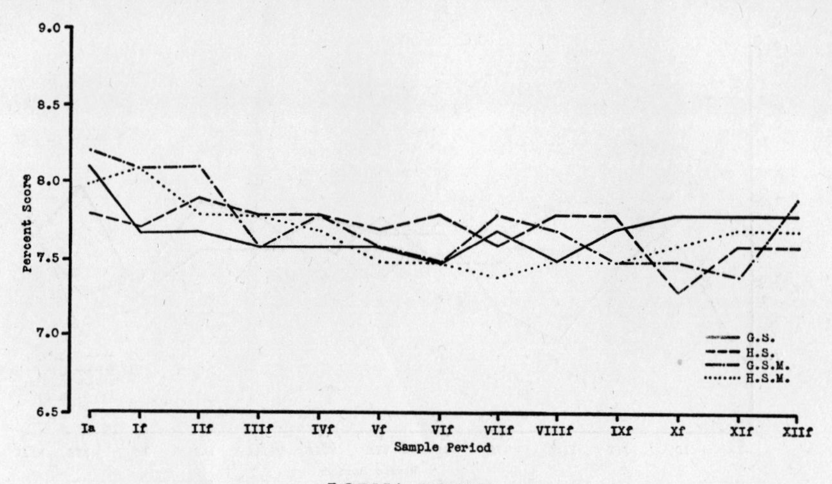

LORNA DOONE

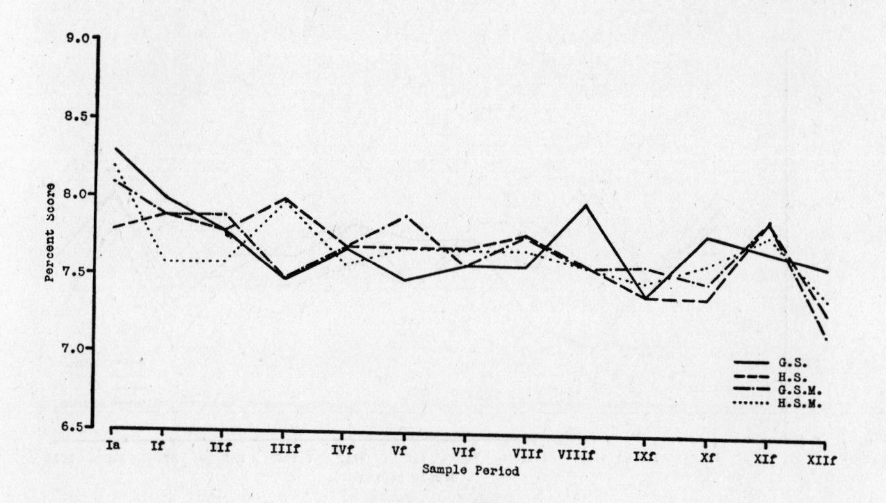

ADAM SMITH

FIXATIONS NUMBER

Figure 78

GRAPHICAL COMPARISON OF THE EXPERIMENTAL SITUATIONS

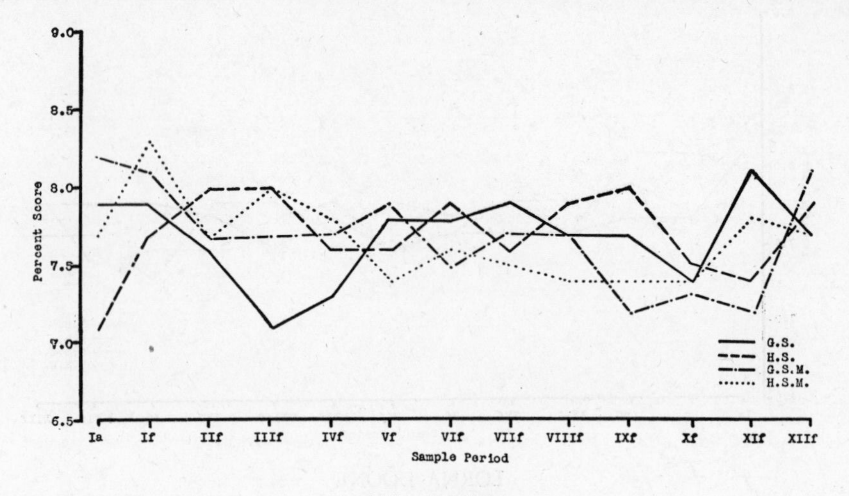

LORNA DOONE

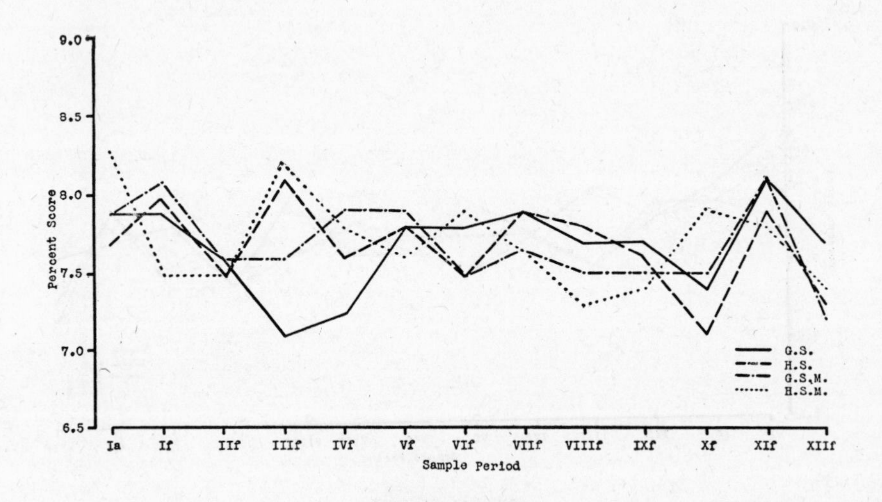

ADAM SMITH

LINES READ NUMBER

Figure 79

GRAPHICAL COMPARISON OF THE EXPERIMENTAL SITUATIONS

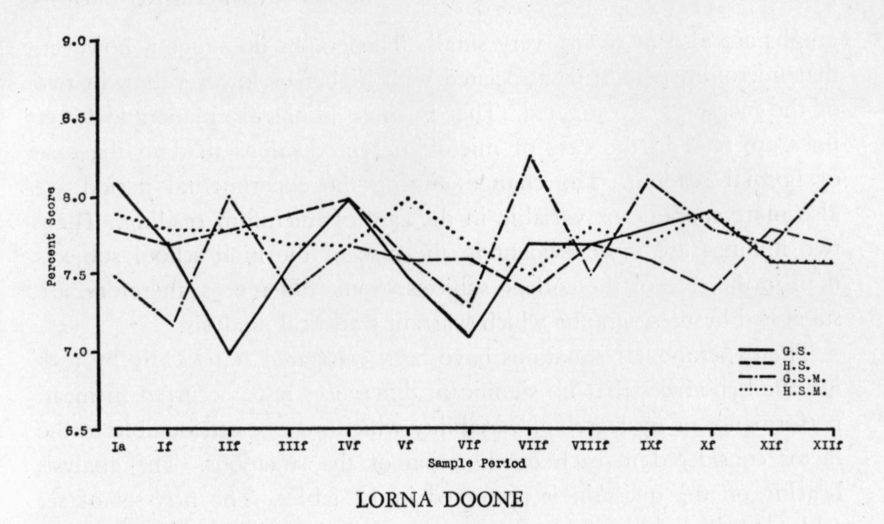

LORNA DOONE

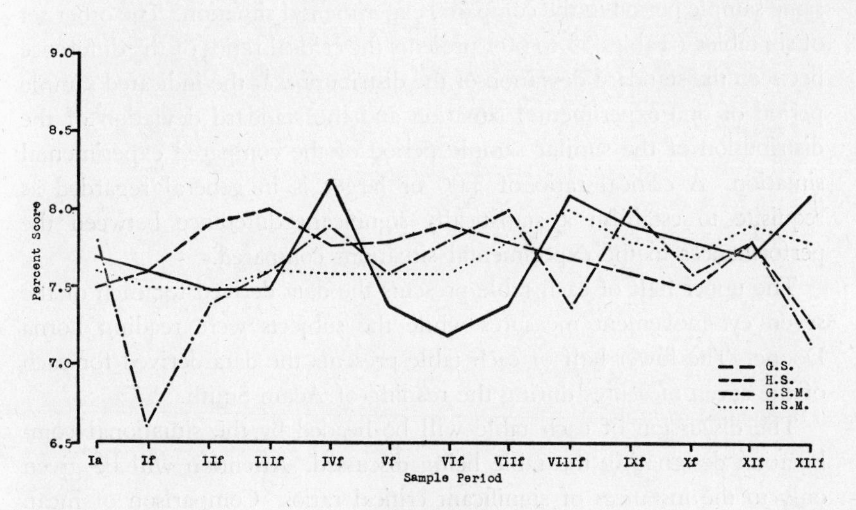

ADAM SMITH

REGRESSIONS NUMBER

Figure 80

GRAPHICAL COMPARISON OF THE EXPERIMENTAL SITUATIONS

graphs are also in reality very small. The graphs do suggest, however, that microfilm reading is associated with higher or lower values in two of the measures investigated. That is, more blinks are made and fewer lines are read in the case of microfilm reproductions than in the case of normal reading. The changes during the experimental period are also more sporadic or variable in the case of microfilm reading. These two findings are more evident in the case of the high school subjects than in the case of the college subjects. Some differences, therefore, are suggested by these graphs which warrant statistical analysis.

The experimental situations have been compared statistically by testing the hypothesis that no significant differences have occurred in mean performance or in degree of variability which may be attributable to the factor considered in each combination of the situations. The analysis bearing on the question is presented in 12 tables. The first set of six tables (Tables 49 to 54) presents the critical ratios of the differences between the mean performance in one experimental situation (for the measure indicated by the column caption, and during the sample period indicated in the left-hand column) and the mean performance during the same sample period in the compared experimental situation. The other set of six tables (Tables 55 to 60) presents the critical ratios of the difference between the standard deviation of the distribution at the indicated sample period of one experimental situation and the standard deviation of the distribution of the similar sample period of the compared experimental situation. A critical ratio of 3.00 or larger is in general regarded as requisite to establish a statistically significant difference between the performances in the experimental situations compared.

The upper half of each table presents the data derived for each of the seven eye-movement measures while the subjects were reading Lorna Doone. The lower half of each table presents the data derived for each of the seven measures during the reading of Adam Smith.

The discussion of each table will be headed by the situational combination designating the table being discussed. Attention will be given only to the instances of significant critical ratios. Comparison of mean performance will be considered first.

G.S. vs. *G.S.M.*—Table 49.

No significant critical ratios are found in this table. It will be noted, however, that the highest critical ratios tend to be found for Blinking Number and Regressions Number in the reading of Adam Smith.

H.S. vs. *H.S.M.* — Table 50.

In the case of Lorna Doone, the Fixations Number measure shows only one significant critical ratio, and Blinking Number, only a few. Critical ratios for all the other measures, however, are significant. In the case of Adam Smith, only Blinking Number, Fixations Number, and Fixation Sigma Score show few or no significant critical ratios.

G.S. vs. *H.S.* — Table 51.

Significant critical ratios are found in the case of Fixations per Line in the reading of both books. Some are found in the case of Regressions Number in the reading of Adam Smith.

G.S.M. vs. *H.S.M.* — Table 52.

No significant critical ratios are found for Blinking Number and Fixations Number. Some are found in the Fixation Sigma Score measure. The critical ratios for all the other measures are significant.

G.S. vs. *H.S.M.* — Table 53.

Blinking Number and Fixations Number show few or no significant critical ratios. Only four of the critical ratios for Lines Read Number are significant for the reading of Lorna Doone. The critical ratios of the rest of the table are significant.

G.S.M. vs. *H.S.* — Table 54.

Only one significant critical ratio is found in the whole table — Fixations Number, Lorna Doone, XIIf.

The previous set of tables compared the situations with regard to mean performance; the set of tables to follow compares the degree of variability in the several situations.

G.S. vs. *G.S.M.* — Table 55.

There are no significant critical ratios in this comparison. The critical ratios tend to be highest for Fixation Sigma Score in the case of D and for Regressions Number in the case of S.

H.S. vs. *H.S.M.* — Table 56.

There are no significant critical ratios in this comparison, nor is there a preponderance of high critical ratios in the case of either book.

G.S. vs. *H.S.* — Table 57.

There are only two significant critical ratios in this comparison (Blinking Number, D, Ia, and S, If). Some of these critical ratios are higher than those found in the two previous comparisons.

G.S.M. vs. *H.S.M.* — Table 58.

There is only one significant critical ratio (Blinking Number, S, Ia) in this comparison.

G.S. vs. *H.S.M.* — Table 59.

The only significant critical ratios in this comparison are found for Blinking Number (only a few in the case of both D and S) and for Regressions Number during the reading of S.

G.S.M. vs. *H.S.* — Table 60.

There are no significant critical ratios in this comparison. These critical ratios tend to be the smallest in this set of comparisons.

These tables show, as have the analyses in all previous considerations, that the degree of variability among the subjects (standard deviation data) does not significantly change. It does not seem to be differentially affected to a significant degree by prolonged activity, by the reading material used, or by the situation in which the reading was done. Also, what is found for the reading of one book tends to be found in the present comparisons for the reading of the other book. This supports the conclusion previously drawn when comparing the two experimental books directly: *per se* the books were not significantly effective variables.

Instances of measures showing significant differences in *mean* performance in the present comparison of experimental situations are summarized for convenience in Table 61. The measures listed are those whose distributions of 13 critical ratios were generally or all significant. The analysis of the *progressive* changes in eye-movement performance allowed the conclusion that mean performance did not change significantly during the experimental period in a single experimental situation. The table, however, shows that when the various conditions at each sample period ("cross-section" point of view) are compared, the results in the four experimental situations show in some instances significant differences.

But the significant critical ratios actually found suggest that no single factor — educational age or type of material — is itself and by itself consistently associated with significant differences in performance. In the attempt to justify this last statement, it is all too easy to use the language of causality — to imply, for example, that this factor caused that effect. However, such implications are not always to be made. What we present as findings here are simply the best assumptions that can be made at present. All the analysis shows is that significant variations occur in eye-movement performance in combinations of situations which have been *given* various names. The assigning of causal relationships is not necessarily determined by the data at hand; the problem should be kept open until the nature of the experimental factors is better understood or determined rather than merely subjectively defined. But in the meantime, the language of causal relationships will be used tentatively for convenience of discussion.

There were no significant differences between the reading of microfilm by Grant Study college students and the reading of printed books by the same students. That is, microfilm reading did not result in significant differences in the comparison G.S. *vs.* G.S.M. Educational age alone was not differentially effective in the comparison G.S. *vs.* H.S., unless it be in the efficiency of reading (Fixations per Line) — an interpretation sometimes made of this measure. Combining educational age and microfilm reading in the comparison G.S.M. *vs.* H.S. (comparison 6 above) showed no significant differences, suggesting that neither factor (age or type of reading) was able to offset the other. This supports the *a priori* assumption that relatively difficult material for a high educational level might be read in a manner similar to the reading of easier material by subjects of a relatively lower educational level.

It may be that one of the two factors (educational age and type of reading — microfilm or normal) is predominantly effective. The present data do not show which one. Significant differences are found in H.S. *vs.* H.S.M., but not in G.S. *vs.* G.S.M. (microfilm is not effective in *both* instances); in G.S.M. *vs.* H.S.M. but not in G.S. *vs.* H.S. (age is not effective in *both* instances); in G.S. *vs.* H.S.M. but not in G.S.M. *vs.* H.S. This would suggest — reviewing again the above — that high school students' normal reading is different from high school students' microfilm reading, but microfilm does not seem to have a differential effect if college students' normal reading is compared to college students' microfilm reading. College students' microfilm reading seems to be a different performance from high school students' microfilm reading, but educational level does not seem to have the same importance when normal reading is done by the two groups. The two latter comparisons (G.S. *vs.* H.S.M. and G.S.M. *vs.* H.S.) support both the contradictory findings just reviewed and the hypothesis that two factors acting together may be effective, for college-level normal reading seems different from high school-level microfilm reading, but college-level microfilm reading is not different from high school-level normal reading.

The conclusion, then, is that significant differences are due to a combination of these two factors — educational age level and type of reading — under certain conditions of combination. H.S.M. is significantly different from H.S., G.S., and G.S.M., but these latter three are not significantly different from each other. High school students' microfilm reading is, therefore, an important experimental situation. It will be noted that this significant difference is not shown in the case of Blinking Number and Fixations Number. Whether these two measures can vary independently of experimental conditions and only with the nature of the task imposed (all reading in the present experiment), or whether the present experimental conditions were not effective cannot be answered by the present data.

It is concluded that the mean performance of *high school subjects reading microfilm reproductions* is significantly different from performance in the other experimental situations investigated in these experiments. This difference is not striking, and it is certainly not such as to suggest that high school students should not read microfilm even for long periods of time. The fact that this is the only positive conclusion of this whole series of comparisons seems to give strong emphasis to the basic conclusion of the experiments reported here: The high school or college student can read an ordinary book or a microfilm of such a book for the long period of six hours and still not suffer any ill effects from the experience.

Chapter 10

Changes in Comprehension and Related Processes

THE foregoing findings resulting from the statistical analysis of the electro-oculograms might possibly have been anticipated if the reports of the readers as to their feelings and physical condition during the period of prolonged reading had first been examined and carefully appraised. At any rate these subjective judgments must be taken account of in the final analysis. The electro-oculograms have the scientific advantages of objective measurement of phenomena and quantifiable treatment of results. Conclusions drawn from data so gathered are more valid than conclusions drawn from data gathered by less objective procedures of measurement. To overlook the personality of each reader, however, simply for lack of precise methods of studying it is to give an incomplete and inadequate picture of the reading process. The importance of this fact is made all the more clear when we remember the importance of the motivation of the subjects which was emphasized in Chapter 8.

Because in the present experiment the gathering of data on feeling-tone and comprehension has depended more on the report of the subjects than on relatively objective measurement by the experimenter, the results now to be considered are referred to as subjective. The validity of conclusions drawn from these subjective results is, of course, recognized as in large measure dependent upon factors, personal and experimental, which the present experimenters may not have been able to control adequately under the conditions of the present experiment. Subjective results are presented in this chapter, however, for the clues they give as to the effect of prolonged reading on the subjective feeling-tone of the reader and on the comprehension of the material read during the six-hour period.

After the experimental reading period the subjects were asked to answer question Number 20 of the questionnaire: "Briefly describe below the subjective feelings that you noticed during the period in which you were reading in the experimental room." The statements made by the subjects offer at least a preliminary approach to the problem of subjective feeling during prolonged activity which orients itself in the larger problem of motivation. Sample responses are presented below according to the book read and the experimental group in which the reading was done.

Since the difference in the type of literature read was obvious to the readers in the present experiment, the major division in presenting the protocols will be according to the book read. The subjective reports for the reading of Lorna Doone will be considered first.

After reading Lorna Doone, the Grant Study subjects who read under the above described relatively normal conditions reported:

> After about two hours I got very sleepy and lost all concentration. Fifteen minutes' rest ended that.[1]
>
> Desire to sleep after first hour or so, then settling down.
>
> After the first hour my eyes would seem to give a blurred image until I had taken them from the print for a moment. The most noticeable feeling was that of cramped muscles and a desire to exercise.
>
> The time seemed to pass much faster in reading Lorna Doone than in reading Adam Smith's book. I did not seem to get as tired as last time.
>
> I had quite a bit of trouble with my eyes watering. I was always in a quite strained position and did not slump much for fear of loosening the electrodes. I got quite interested in the story and did not mind the passing of time.

High school subjects who read Lorna Doone under similar conditions (High School Subjects — normal reading) reported:

> Trouble concentrating towards latter period. When plot became more exciting, I was inclined to skim.

[1] Authors' note: Reading continued during what the subject called his "rest" period.

At first the time dragged and I wished I had a watch, but at the end it went pretty fast. The book was very interesting and that helped to pass the time.

There were a few times when I felt uncomfortable. On the whole I enjoyed and was interested in what I read. I did feel a little eyestrain.

I enjoyed what I was reading but found that toward the end the light on the book bothered me. There was little or no tired feeling.

The time seemed to pass very quickly; my only weariness was from being in one position so long.

After reading the microfilm reproductions of Lorna Doone, the Grant Study subjects made the following sample reports:

Frustration at blurred and indistinct lines and words; annoyance at dropping pencils and at reaching for page corners instead of for lever; numerous aches caused by unnatural position in uncomfortable chair and also feeling of general lassitude, etc.

Stiffness due to uncomfortable seat. Time passed — seemed to pass — more slowly later in the period because I had apparently underestimated my rate of reading. Reading easier and much more interesting than Adam Smith.

Continual interest in the reading, but fatigue more from lack of body movement than anything else.

Back got extremely tired after a couple of hours and was quite painful thereafter. Occasionally feel like about to need to rest for few minutes. Didn't mind reading after got used to it.

Increasing interest in book. Second hour the period of most restlessness, because I had not gotten "into spirit" of story. Time went surprisingly fast.

High school subjects who read the microfilm reproductions of Lorna Doone reported:

My legs were getting tired. My back began to hurt some. Getting a little tired.

I found no noticeable fatigue before I had read about one hundred pages, then I found a tendency to be uneasy and restless. I was not too comfortable during the latter period.

I became more accustomed to the print after about fifty pages. I wondered what time it was and slowly became hungry. I wanted a cigarette.

Neck got tired. Back tired.

The first hour, it was very difficult to concentrate; after that I had little trouble. I could have continued reading if necessary as my eyes felt all right.

Sample responses are presented below regarding the reading of Adam Smith.

After reading Adam Smith from the book, the Grant Study subjects reported:

> I couldn't seem to concentrate until about half the time had elapsed. Even then, I kept counting the pages and guessing at the time. Got sleepy after about one and one-half hours, but that passed away rapidly.
>
> I felt as if I might have done better work had there been less silence — at times I also seemed to lose consciousness of everything except the printed words and had to awaken my mind as it were to the fact that I must keep alert in order to follow the thought of the book.
>
> About halfway through the period I felt dizzy for a short time. There was also muscular stiffness and a desire to exercise.
>
> I grew fairly tired after several hours and got a little bored with the material.
>
> I had more trouble at first than later in the test, in getting adjusted. At first I was quite tense, then gradually I relaxed and began to enjoy the reading. I also seemed to understand what I was reading much better toward the end.

High school subjects who read Adam Smith under similar conditions (High School Subjects — normal reading) reported:

> Almost went to sleep. Had to concentrate on parts I didn't understand.
>
> The book was very dry. That was what made me think I was in there sixteen instead of six hours.
>
> The time passed away faster than I expected. I felt a bit tired at times while reading. However, while reading I didn't have a great feeling of interest for the book.
>
> It seems to me that time passed as though someone had gone off and forgotten that I was there. After one hundred pages the facts seemed very jumbled.
>
> I was as comfortable as possible, my only discomfort coming from being in a rather cramped position for several hours.

After reading the microfilm reproduction of Adam Smith, the Grant Study subjects made the following sample reports:

> Time seemed longer — chief annoyance caused by three miniscule insects which flew around and carefully eluded attempts to snare them. Wondering why the book had to be so abysmally dull.
>
> Intense back pain from chair.
>
> Boredom during the first chapter; interest and quite a bit of pleasure thereafter; fatigue and restlessness during the last hour.
>
> Toward end mind kept wandering and I felt slightly dizzy. Back very uncomfortable. Did not feel hungry.
>
> Spotty interest in reading matter. Not much fatigue or physical restlessness.

High school subjects who read the microfilm reproduction of Adam Smith reported:

> My eyes got very tired. I had sort of a headache. My feet were cramped.
>
> My general feeling was one of complete boredom. This resulted in a nervous tension and a complete lack of confidence in myself and the book.
>
> I lost all track of time. After a boring first fifty pages I really enjoyed the book because of its historical significance. I was very tired when I finished, but not as tired as when I read Lorna Doone. I am pretty hungry.
>
> Quite tired at first; not so much later.
>
> The time passed quite rapidly as long as it was quiet. My eyes didn't feel tired. There was very little strain on my eyes that I felt.

These reports suggest that the subjects reacted more to the necessity of being restricted to a sitting position and to being confined to one surrounding than they did to the prolongation of the particular task. It will also be noted that in the majority of instances the changes in feeling-tone are generally or vaguely expressed. These readers were, of course, not trained in what psychologists have called introspective report, but their statements seem clear. On the other hand, these reports bear out, on the whole, the expectations of the present experimenters: The reading of Adam Smith was found to be more tiring and boring than that of Lorna Doone, and the reading of the microfilm projection — chiefly because of the more restricted and less natural position — was found to be much more irksome and subjectively fatiguing than ordinary reading. That these feelings were not registered in the records of ocular performance would seem surprising except for a fact brought out by another question.

Following the reading period, the subjects also answered another question, Number 19 of the questionnaire presented in Chapter 7:

> Following the experience that I have just had in prolonged reading in one position I feel that
>
> (*a*) After a half hour's rest and some food I could do an evening's studying without inconvenience. ....
>
> (*b*) I could do some studying, although with reluctance. ....
>
> (*c*) I could study and read effectively if required to do so. ....
>
> (*d*) I doubt my ability to do any further reading or studying. ....
>
> (*e*) I would absolutely refuse to use my eyes again until after a night's sleep. ....

The number of responses to each part of this question are presented in Table 62.[2] They are arranged according to the book read and the

[2] See Appendix for tables referred to in this chapter.

experimental group that did the reading.

It will be noted from a review of Table 62 that in 60 out of the 80 instances, the subjects reported that they could continue study (parts *a* and *b* above). This would suggest that the degree of "fatigue" noted in feeling-tone was neither very intense nor very long lasting. This subjective finding agrees in general with the objective conclusion that significant changes did not occur in eye-movement performance. But with regard to other considerations, all the subjective data do not seem to be well related to the objective results. Though the subjects preferred Lorna Doone to Adam Smith and seemed to be more "tired" after reading Adam Smith than after reading Lorna Doone, these two books were not found to have had differential effects on the eye-movement functions measured. The responses in the situation *High School Subjects (microfilm reading)* do suggest the objective results which show this situation to be somewhat retarding when compared with the others; but in general the differences noted in the eye-movement data are not reflected in these subjective reports of the experimental groups concerning the "intrinsic interest" of the books.

Judging from the literature on fatigue available, a discrepancy between the objective measures of output and the subjective report of feeling-tone is not at all a novel finding (290). It seems that the human organism may continue to work satisfactorily even though it may not "wish" to do so. Some of the factors which underlie the ordinary motivations of life may be affected by prolonged reading long before exhaustion of the visual mechanism occurs. The present findings indicate that even though the readers could have continued reading satisfactorily, they would have preferred to stop. Further, despite possible changes in feeling-tone, the present experimental conditions sufficiently motivated the subjects to continue reading effectively. This finding has a most important pedagogical implication. It suggests that if the student teaches himself to disregard transient sleepiness or body-muscle strain and a general attitude of "I want to stop all this," he can effectively go on reading without danger.

Another approach to the determination of the psychological changes that may occur during continuous activity can be made by measuring how much of the material read is comprehended by a subject as reading is continued for long periods. It will be recalled that in the present experiments comprehension checks were inserted at periodic intervals during the reading. A final comprehension examination was also administered at the conclusion of the experimental period.

The data sheets shown in Tables 63 to 70 present the *raw* comprehension scores made by each subject while reading both books in the four experimental situations. There is one table for each book in each experimental situation. The figures at the top of each column of scores in each table refer to the number of pages covered by each interspersed comprehension check and hence the number of questions included in each such test. The raw final comprehension score is reported on these sheets in the far right-hand column. This score on the final comprehension exercises is expressed here as a fraction—the number correct over the number of questions attempted. Because of the varying number of questions in each interspersed test and the varying number attempted on each final exercise, all the raw scores shown in the tables have been transmuted to percentage-correct scores. It is this percentage-correct score, referred to below as the comprehension score, which has been used in the present experiments. These tables of raw scores have been presented, however, should the reader prefer another treatment of the data.

An average interspersed score was derived for each subject simply by averaging the percentage-correct scores he earned on each of the interspersed comprehension checks which he completed. There were available for study, therefore, 80 average interspersed comprehension scores corresponding to the 80 final comprehension scores. An analysis of the difference between the mean of the distribution of the 80 average interspersed scores and of the distribution of the 80 final comprehension scores resulted in a t-ratio (critical-ratio technique applied to small samples) of 7.579. This value indicates a significant difference. From this finding, it could be concluded that the average interspersed score is a measure essentially different from the final comprehension score. This supports the subjective assumption that two types of comprehension questions were used. The interspersed comprehension questions were subjectively designed to measure comprehension of details; the final comprehension questions were arranged according to thought units. The Pearson product-moment coefficient of correlation between the distributions of average interspersed scores and of the final comprehension scores is 0.725. From this finding, the present experimenters conclude that, even though the two scores may represent different psychological processes, a subject tended to maintain the same relative position in both distributions. It is recognized, of course, that this correlation may be spuriously high, since the scores of two age groups were simultaneously correlated.

In Table 71, the average interspersed comprehension scores are presented. In Table 72, the final comprehension scores for each subject in each of the four experimental situations for the reading of each book are presented. In interpreting these tables, it is to be remembered that the exercises themselves have not been standardized. The comparative difficulty of the two sets of exercises (for Lorna Doone and for Adam Smith) is not known, nor is the relative difficulty of the exercises of one set established. Also, a comprehension-exercise score involves not only the material being read, the conditions under which it is read, and the nature of the questions asked, but also the intelligence of the subjects and their reading ability.

The data in these tables suggest that the comprehension of Adam Smith was in every case poorer than the comprehension of the material read in Lorna Doone. Comprehension on the part of the high school students was poorer than that of the college students. Microfilm reproductions of the reading materials seem to have affected adversely the high school students but not necessarily the college students. Some of the above observations are suggested by the subjective reports reviewed in the preceding section. The objective data on eye-movement performance, however, are in several instances at variance with the present data, supporting only the conclusion that high school students were less efficient while reading microfilm than while reading the original printed material.

The present experiments are, of course, primarily concerned with the changes in comprehension ability which may occur during prolonged reading. The number of pages read during the six hours of the experimental period suggests itself as a measure of the amount of visual exercise. This statement implies the assumption that the greater the number of pages read, the greater the amount of work demanded of the subject. The correlation between the number of pages read and the final comprehension scores is 0.121; between the number of pages read and the average interspersed comprehension score, 0.170. Neither of these coefficients indicates a significant relationship between the variables named. Following the assumption made above, it might be concluded that comprehension was not significantly affected by the amount of reading.

All the subjects, however, read for the same length of time. It is possible that prolongation of working time during the experimental period might affect comprehension even though final output (number of pages read) may not show that effect. It is difficult, however, to analyze the present comprehension data with reference to the above time variable. A glance at the original data sheets shows that the subjects did not all take the same number of comprehension checks — some took as few as four, others as many as 12. Simply computing the average score on one comprehension check and comparing this score with the averages of the other checks would obviously be a spurious technique, since the score contributed by one subject would not necessarily have been earned at the same time during the reading period as the score contributed by some other subjects. Allocating a portion of the raw score to a particular unit of time in the case of each subject would be equally spurious, since the numerical values so assigned would lose their meaning.

It was decided to apportion the data for each subject on a percentage basis. The eye-movement data were sampled in 13 units; this sample unit suggested itself in the present case. Since a question was asked per page, all the questions answered by a subject might be thought of as constituting a series from the beginning of the reading period to the end. This series was divided, in the case of each subject, into 13 samples, and for each sample a percentage-correct score was derived. Thus, the percentage scores earned by the subjects for the first sample could be compared with the percentage scores earned for the second sample, and so on. The statistical disadvantages of this treatment are, of course, recognized — especially the unreliability of percentage scores derived from samples of such varying sizes. The technique has the practical advantage, however, of satisfying a pragmatic interest in what the data will show when time is the principal variable. The finding that the original average interspersed score is highly correlated ($r = .973$) with the average of these new interspersed scores supports this pragmatism by suggesting that both treatments of the data will show essentially the same results.

In the graphs shown in Figures 81 to 98 the 13 sample scores of each subject in each experimental situation are plotted. Each graph presents the data for each subject in one of the four experimental situations during the reading of one of the books. The base line shows the 13

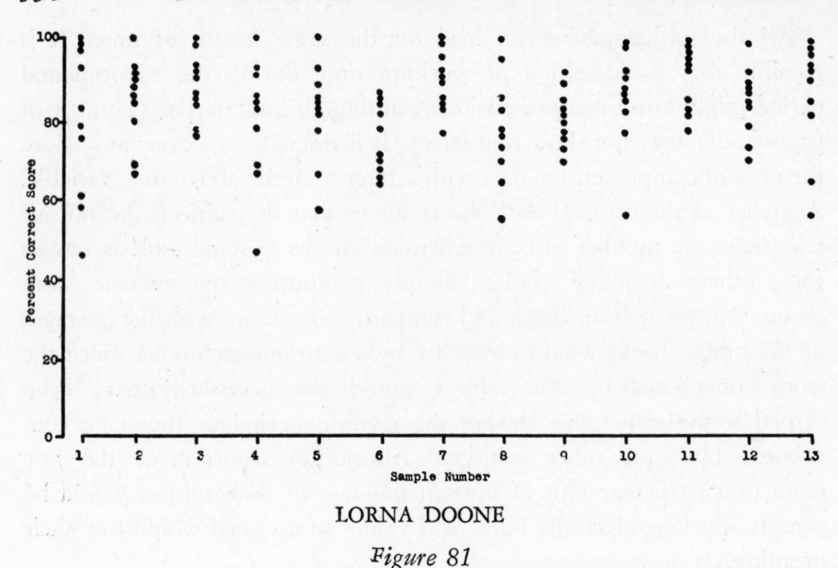

LORNA DOONE

Figure 81

INDIVIDUAL SCORES ON INTERSPERSED COMPREHENSION CHECKS

Grant Study Subjects (normal reading)

sample numbers. The ordinate represents the percentage score; the same unit has been used in each graph so that they maye be directly compared.

These graphs show that the subjects tended to vary much more among themselves while reading Adam Smith than while reading Lorna Doone. In general the high school students tended to vary more among themselves than did the college students. Microfilm reading tended to increase the variability of the high school subjects, but it does not seem to have affected noticeably the reading by college students. The general position of the lines on the graph page suggests that level of performance was about the same for college students reading Lorna Doone, either in the original or in microfilm reproduction, and for high school students reading Lorna Doone in the original. Level of comprehension seems to be lower for college students reading Adam Smith, either in the original or in microfilm reproduction, and for high school students reading Lorna Doone in microfilm reproduction. Level of performance seems to be lower still for high school students reading Adam Smith, either in the original or in microfilm reproduction.

Certain features of these graphs may be more conveniently compared by summarizing these data with reference to particular variables (Figures 89 to 93). (On the several graphs to follow, the unit representing a

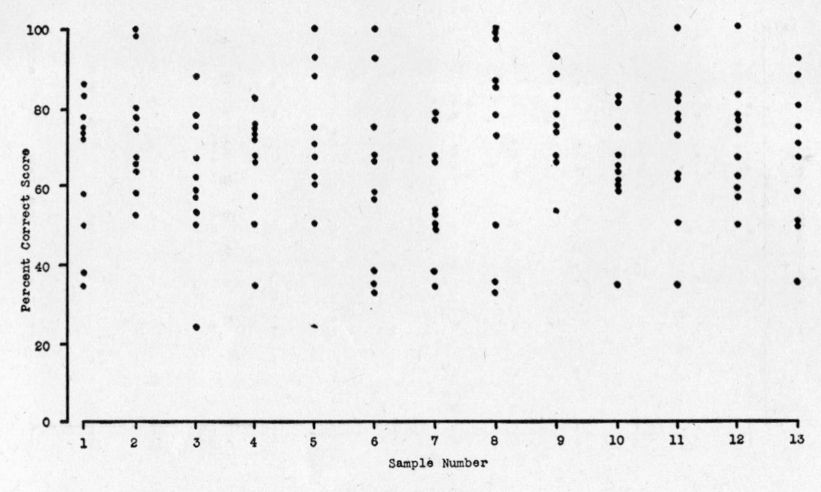

ADAM SMITH

Figure 82

INDIVIDUAL SCORES ON INTERSPERSED COMPREHENSION CHECKS

Grant Study Subjects (normal reading)

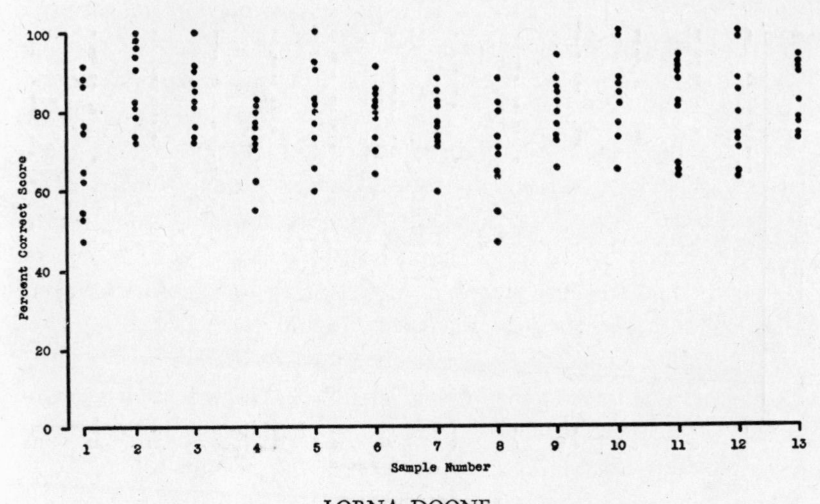

LORNA DOONE

Figure 83

INDIVIDUAL SCORES ON INTERSPERSED COMPREHENSION CHECKS

High School Subjects (normal reading)

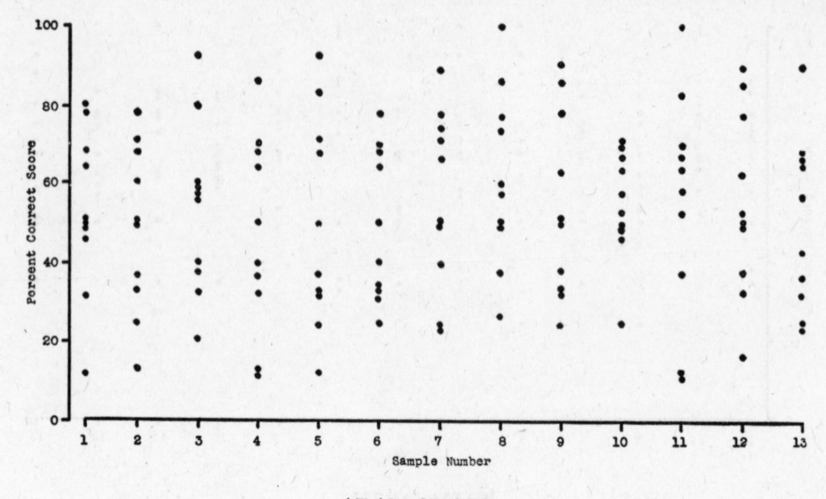

ADAM SMITH

Figure 84

INDIVIDUAL SCORES ON INTERSPERSED COMPREHENSION CHECKS

High School Subjects (normal reading)

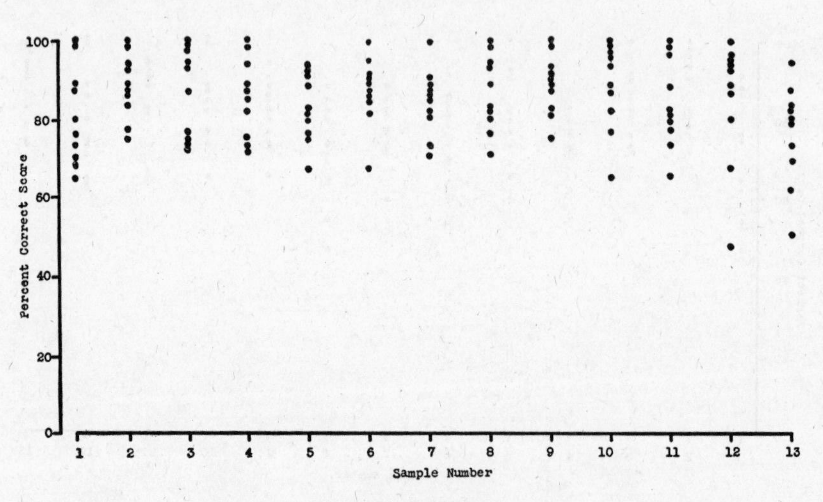

LORNA DOONE

Figure 85

INDIVIDUAL SCORES ON INTERSPERSED COMPREHENSION CHECKS

Grant Study Subjects (microfilm reading)

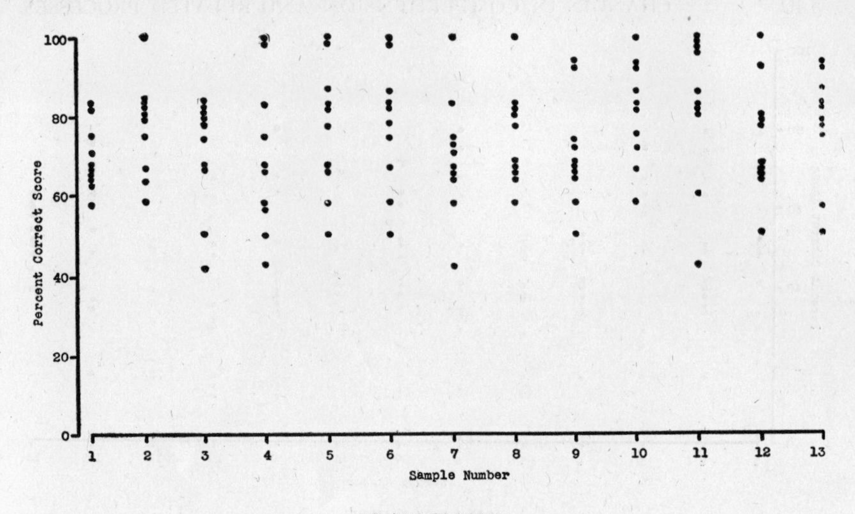

ADAM SMITH

Figure 86

INDIVIDUAL SCORES ON INTERSPERSED COMPREHENSION CHECKS

Grant Study Subjects (microfilm reading)

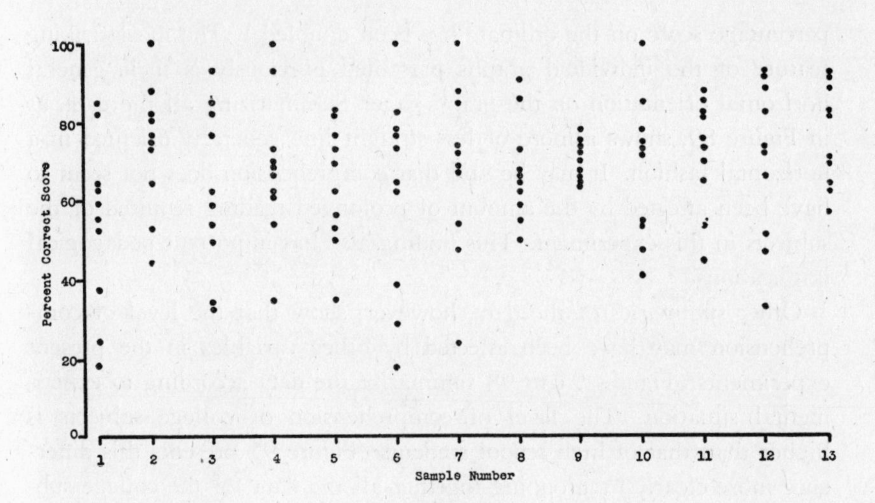

LORNA DOONE

Figure 87

INDIVIDUAL SCORES ON INTERSPERSED COMPREHENSION CHECKS

High School Subjects (microfilm reading)

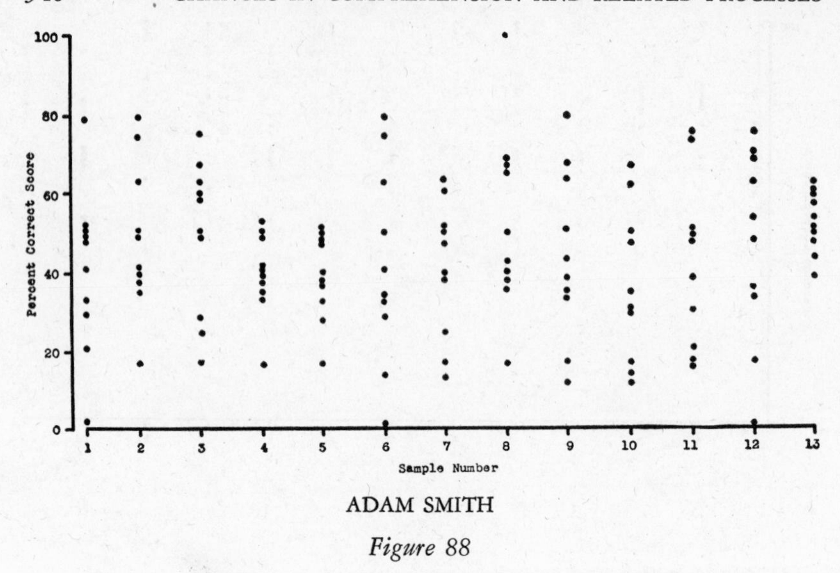

ADAM SMITH

Figure 88

INDIVIDUAL SCORES ON INTERSPERSED COMPREHENSION CHECKS

High School Subjects (microfilm reading)

percentage score on the ordinate has been doubled.) The most striking feature of the individual graphs presented previously is their general horizontal orientation on the graph page. Summarizing all the data, as in Figure 89, shows a more or less straight line generally oriented in a horizontal fashion. It may be said that comprehension does not seem to have been affected by the amount of prolonged reading required of the subjects in this experiment. This finding also has important pedagogical implications.

Other summaries of the data, however, show that the level of comprehension may have been affected by other variables in the present experiments. Figures 94 to 98 summarize the data according to experimental situation. The level of comprehension of college subjects is higher than that of high school students. Figure 95 presents this difference more clearly by grouping together all the data for the college subjects and comparing them with all the data for the high school subjects. Figure 96 summarizes the data according to reading material. The level of comprehension for the reading of Lorna Doone was higher than for the reading of Adam Smith. Figure 97 shows this difference more clearly by grouping together all the data for one book and comparing them with

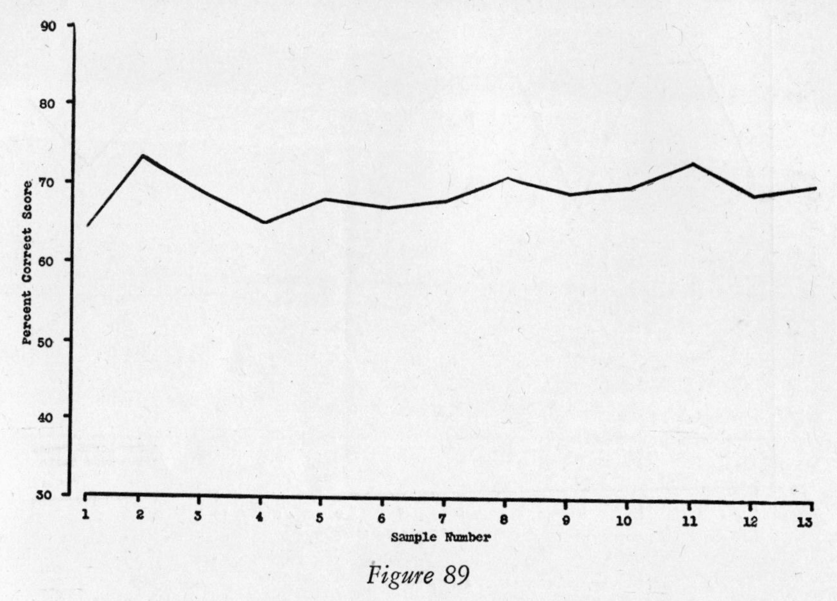

Figure 89

AVERAGE INTERSPERSED COMPREHENSION SCORE

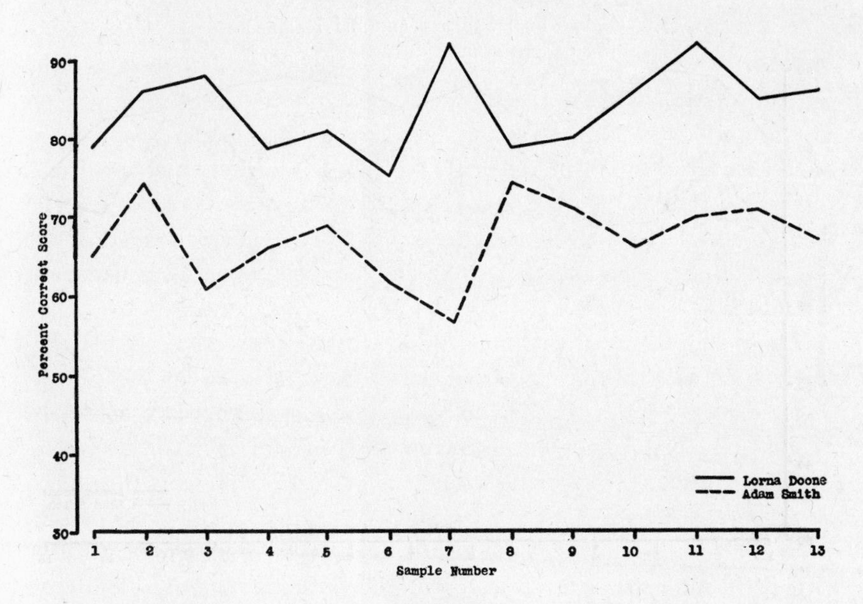

Figure 90

COMPREHENSION SCORES IN EACH EXPERIMENTAL SITUATION

Grant Study Subjects (normal reading)

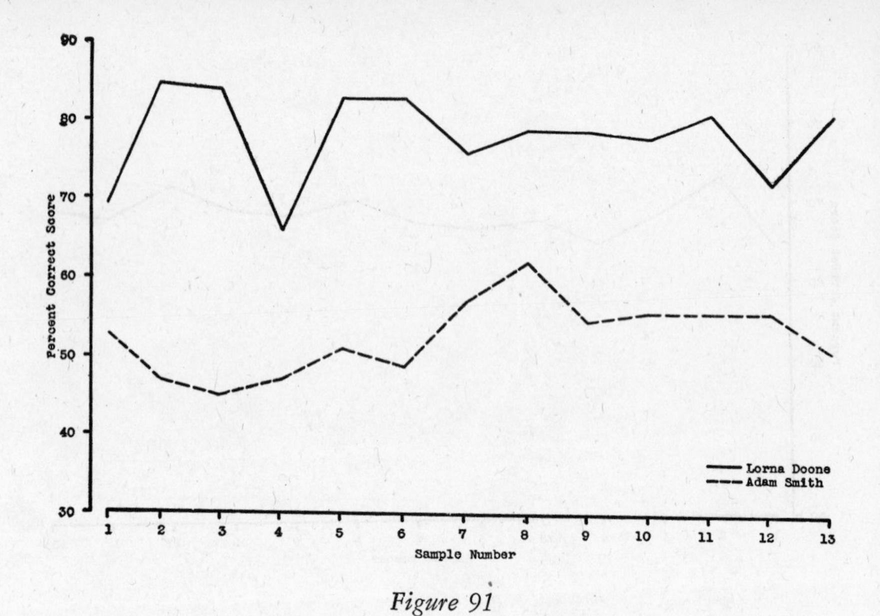

Figure 91

COMPREHENSION SCORES IN EACH EXPERIMENTAL SITUATION

High School Subjects (normal reading)

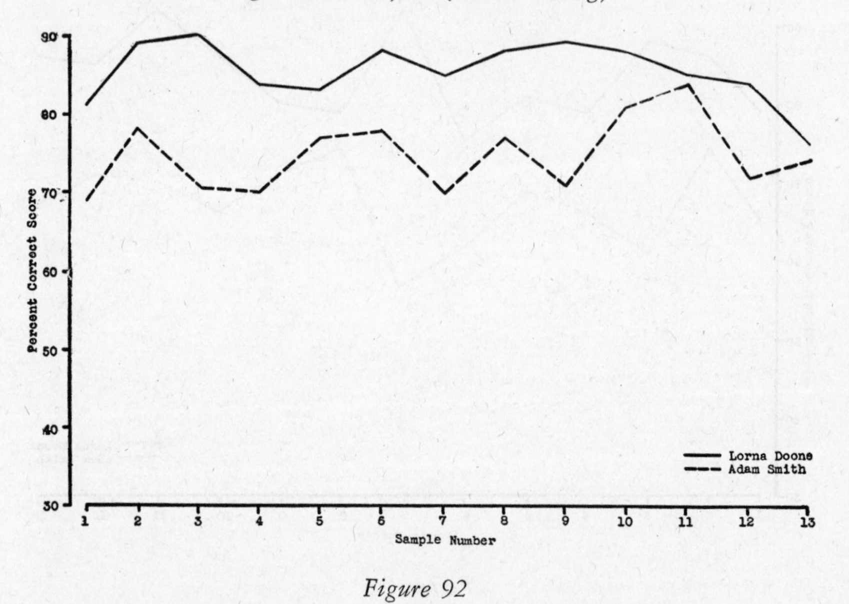

Figure 92

COMPREHENSION SCORES IN EACH EXPERIMENTAL SITUATION

Grant Study Subjects (microfilm reading)

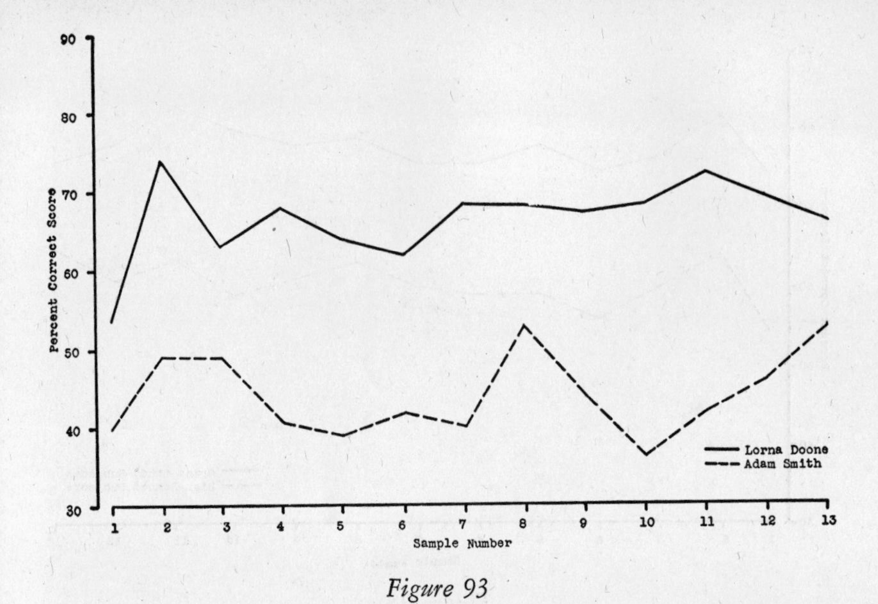

Figure 93

COMPREHENSION SCORES IN EACH EXPERIMENTAL SITUATION

High School Subjects (microfilm reading)

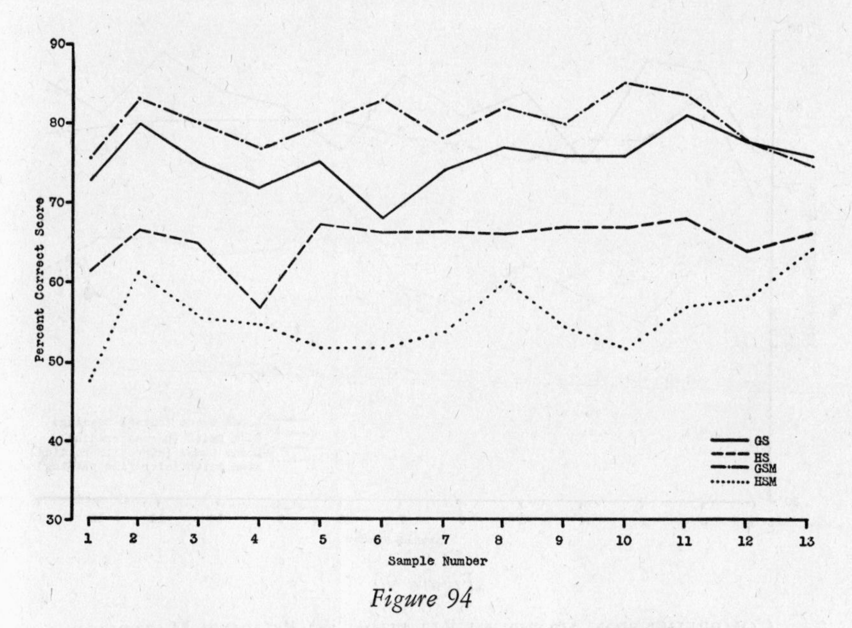

Figure 94

SUMMARY GRAPH — EXPERIMENTAL SITUATIONS

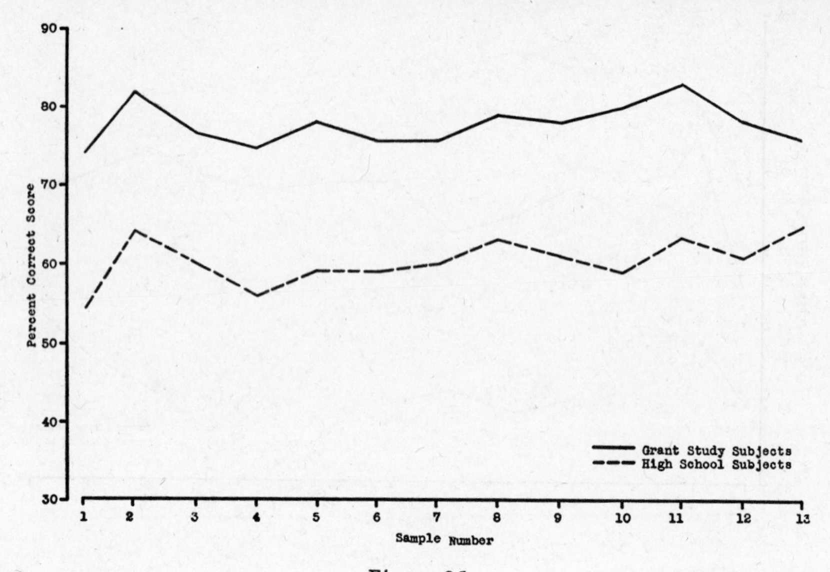

Figure 95

SUMMARY GRAPH — EDUCATIONAL AGE

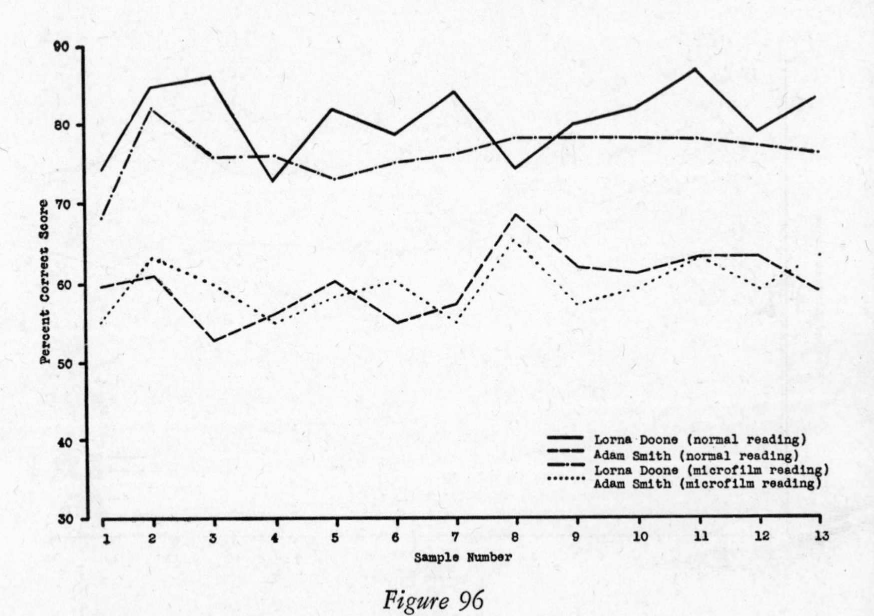

Figure 96

COMPREHENSION SCORES IN RELATION TO READING MATERIALS

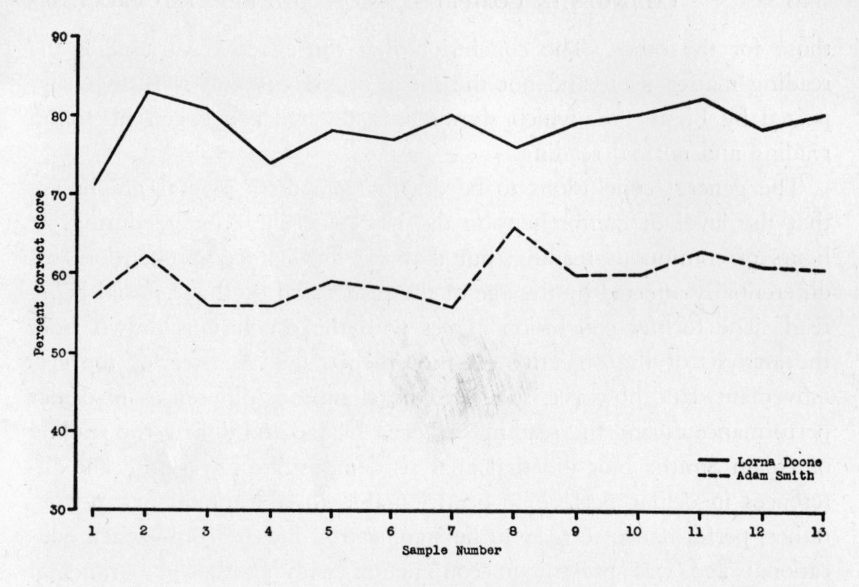

Figure 97

SUMMARY GRAPH — EXPERIMENTAL BOOKS

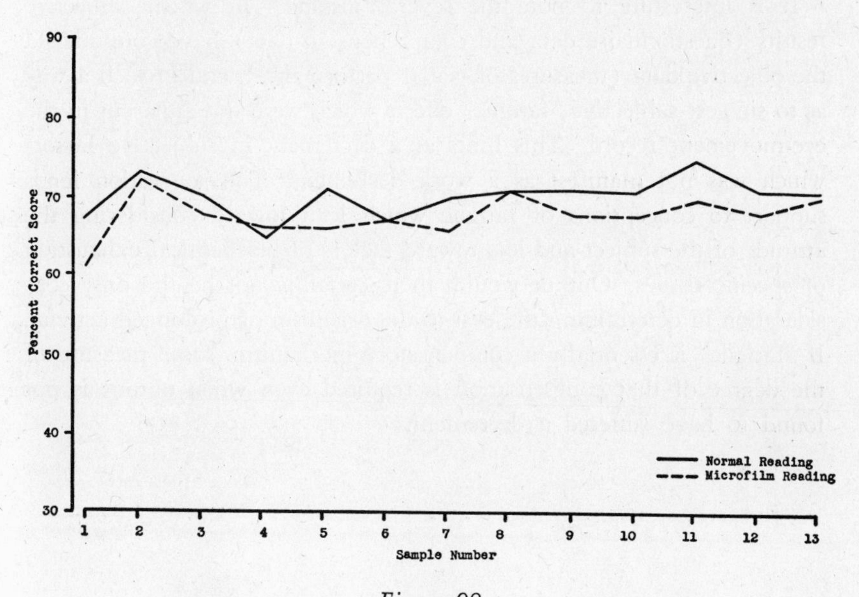

Figure 98

SUMMARY GRAPH — MODE OF PRESENTATION

those for the other. The conclusion that the effective variable is the reading matter itself and not the mode of presentation is further supported by Figure 98, which shows little difference between microfilm reading and normal reading.

The general conclusions to be drawn from these several graphs are that the level of comprehension did not noticeably change during six hours of continuous reading, but that the level of comprehension was differentially affected by the age of the reader and by the material being read. The former conclusion agrees with the conclusions drawn from the analysis of the objective eye-movement data. Analysis of the eye-movement data, however, suggested no significant differences in ocular performance during the reading of Lorna Doone and during the reading of Adam Smith. Nor did that analysis demonstrate any significant differences in ocular performance attributable to educational age *per se*; rather, performance seemed to be significantly lowered only when educational age was present in conjunction with another experimental variable—and that variable was not the reading matter but the microfilm reproduction.

It is interesting to note the several instances in which subjective results (questionnaire data and comprehension data) have contradicted the objective data (measures of ocular performance), and in such a way as to suggest subjective "fatigue" effects which were not apparent in the eye-movement record. This hints at a decrement in subjective factors which was not manifest as a work decrement. The suggestion lends support to conceptions of fatigue which lean toward considering the attitude of the subject and less toward factors of biochemical exhaustion of specific tissues. Output would, then, certainly not be the only consideration in determining the cost to the organism of prolonged activity. If "fatigue" is essentially a compensatory mechanism, some measure of the degree of that compensation is required even when output is not found to have suffered a decrement.

Chapter 11

Discussion and Interpretation of the Results of These Experiments

AS HAS BEEN amply set forth in the preceding chapters, it is now generally recognized alike by the layman and the scientist — with a few notable exceptions — that there are different manifestations of fatigue. Thus, to speak of just being fatigued is, to a degree, like saying that one is sick without specifying the kind of sickness. However, any such clear-cut delineation of differing conditions of fatigue as has been accomplished with disease entities in the field of medicine is so far from being in sufficient prospect as to make this comparison seem "ambitious," if, indeed, it is not an instance of wishful thinking. Certain groupings of types of fatigue are nevertheless commonly recognized: First, there is what is ordinarily spoken of as "physical" fatigue, in which there is evidence of impairment in efficiency or of work decrement or loss of form or precision of performance, or in which there is some overt evidence of nervousness, tenseness, jumpiness, or irritability, as in the usually composed combat officer who "bawls out" his men. This last variety is sometimes spoken of as "nervous" fatigue, which, when its manifestations are not overt, may be expressed in feelings of frustration, tension, or discomfort. When none of these manifestations is in evidence, even though an individual has undergone excessive conditions of stress, a change in the organism, describable as fatigue, may be suspected inasmuch as greater than usual stimulation or motivation may be required to maintain normal response. Then there is what, for lack of a better name, is spoken of as one sort of "mental" fatigue — the feelings of boredom, ennui, or unpleasantness in action, and a desire to quit the task or to have a change, to do something else, or to rest, such states as have been described in the last chapter.

In the present experimental study, except for a few mild expressions of discomfort or willingness to quit, some feelings of stiffness, the desire to have a chance to stretch and stir around a bit, on the part of some of the subjects, and the fact that one of the subjects fell asleep momentarily, *there was no evidence of fatigue at all.* In fact, many of the subjects said that after a little change and a bite to eat, and so forth, they could have gone on reading perfectly well. As for the more overt signs of fatigue, there was no work decrement or impairment, there was no permanent change in the pattern of eye movements, and there were no signs of nervousness or of irritability in the case of either the ordinary reading of a novel or of an eighteenth century treatise on economics, or of microfilm projections of the same books.

The reason or reasons for this outcome may be appreciated if a brief comparison is made with three other experiments in which evidence of fatigue has been found.

Let us first review the preliminary experiment by Hoffman (142) which has been described in Chapter 8. In this experiment there were no interpolated examination questions, the pay was somewhat less, the importance of the students' contribution to science was not emphasized, the subjects read for but four hours, the materials read were "easy and light," and there was no reading of projected microfilm. Yet, under these conditions, there was evidence of impairment or work decrement: there were, as time went on, more blinkings and more variability in the number of fixations per line. The number of lines read and (since there was no change in the number of fixations per line) the number of fixations made during the experimental period decreased significantly.

With this comparison in mind, the statement of the conclusion of the present or six-hour experiments might read: Subjects of good intelligence and adequate vision can be motivated to maintain their visual efficiency without significant change for at least six hours of continuous reading. However, the matter requires further consideration. If it is agreed that subjects may be stimulated or self-motivated or may simply learn from hard and long work how to work harder and longer, a question may then be asked concerning the effect of this different motivation. Is there some danger that subjects may force themselves to read well for too long a time? Are the changes in personality, which in the recent war were named combat or operational fatigue, instances in which individuals who have been stimulated or forced by conditions to prolonged exertions under circumstances such that the ordinary danger signals in the subjective feelings of fatigue have not so much been disregarded as not been given a change to operate?

It is not proposed in this discussion to answer the latter question, but only through it to suggest the importance of the subjective feelings of fatigue and the possible hazard of motivational conditions or situations by which they may be masked. In fact, one active investigator in this field, S. H. Bartley (16), after a very circumspect review of the literature with respect to the definition of fatigue, has come out with the contentions (1) that the subject's report of fatigue is its *sine qua non*—"One is not tired until he knows it" and "Prior to this one is only impaired"; (2) that fatigue *is* the desire to quit a given activity as a result of impairment or discomfort; and (3) that the basis of fatigue is conflict and frustration.

Bartley (16) designed two series of experiments in which two sets of eye muscles—one set involving the pupillary mechanism, the other the extrinsic eye muscles—were brought into conflict. There was a work decrement, and there was discomfort of which the subjects were very much aware. It should be noted that under conditions of conflict, the work decrement may be more prompt and the feelings of discomfort more acute than under ordinary circumstances. But does all fatigue involve conflict? There are certainly good grounds—and Bartley has himself reviewed some of them—as well as experimental evidence for asserting (1) that under some conditions, the individual does not know when he is tired; (2) that, just as the sensations of hunger and thirst may on occasion belie the actual nutritional state of the organism, so the feeling of fatigue may be perverted and the individual feel tired when he is not; and (3) that fatigue is associated with conditions other than conflict and frustration.

As is well known, common eye defects may cause just such conflicts as Bartley has produced experimentally. Normally convergence and accommodation of the eyes go hand in hand, but in farsightedness, as previously noted on page 39, accommodation of the lens must be effected without convergence, which may result in feelings of eyestrain. Also, as there noted, the visual condition described as aniseikonia — a lack of equality or a difference in size of the images in the two eyes — may interfere especially with the peripheral view of the line of print. The incongruent images on the peripheries of the eyes may thus present different space cues for the movements of the eyes as they move from one fixation to the next. Thus, there is again conflict. In the cases of both extreme farsightedness and of aniseikonia, a dislike of reading and a work decrement are common findings. Again, as above noted, the inability to persevere and the fact that, after relatively brief periods of reading, the subjects find themselves perusing pages mechanically without adequate recollection of the materials covered are common complaints. A. Ames and his associates at the Dartmouth Eye Institute have explored these important phenomena in detail.

On the other hand, especially in the case of the reading of some school children (and also in the case of some adult "nonreaders"), the outcome may not be describable as fatigue at all — certainly not in the commonly accepted usage of the word. As a result of the sensations of strain in the one case and possibly of peripheral blurring in the other, the children may not read enough to be fatigued. There may well be mild discomfort, mild annoyance, the desire to quit, and what Bartley calls anticipation-fatigue — the desire to quit before they have started — but that such subjective feelings and attitudes in and of themselves constitute fatigue is questionable. The pupils may indeed look at their books and perhaps follow along as others read or look at the pictures and figure out, with the recognition of a word or two here and there, what has been written, but there is no prior impairment or work decrement because, for one thing, there is really no prior performance. However they may act or feel, it can hardly be said that they are fatigued from reading.

Finally, a third study in which evidence of fatigue was found and in which, incidentally, there was no evidence of conflict or frustration, may, by comparison, aid in the interpretation of the results of the present experiments. It is an experiment made by the United States Public Health

Service on the fatigue and hours of service of interstate truck drivers (323). The point to be brought out is that, although there may be neither subjective feelings nor evidence of impairment or of work decrement during the performance of a task, such evidence may be obtainable directly after the completion of the task. There were no means, such as were employed in the present experiments, for recording changes in performance *during* the long periods of driving (it is, however, a reasonable assumption that no easily detected changes would have been observable during the driving), but immediately afterwards a series of psychomotor tests and one visual test of the ability to distinguish flicker in the visual field demonstrated that men who had driven over 10 hours had the lowest average efficiency; those who had driven up to 10 hours, the next lowest; and a control group of men who had not driven at all after a night of sleep had the highest efficiency. That the fatigue resulting from such long periods of truck driving may have been more severe than the fatigue shown in this experiment in prolonged reading is indicated by the fact that the findings held consistently for all seven of the above-noted series of tests and less consistently on three other tests, including one on the speed of the saccadic movements of the eyes. In this finding concerning eye movements, which is of particular interest for comparison with the performance of the eyes in the present experiments, the subjects looked back and forth at two alternately lighted disks, five inches apart and at about the usual "reading" distance (13 inches). Both groups of men who had driven had, on the average, significantly slower eye movements than those who had not driven.

The following interpretation of these findings in relation to the present experiments in prolonged reading is suggested. In 2½ minutes (the length of time of the experiment) of a monotonous and unmotivated task of looking back and forth at alternating lights, the subjects "let down" the tension to which they were keyed (motivated or stimulated) while driving to reveal a loss of efficiency describable as fatigue. That the truck drivers may not have been so well motivated by the test procedures as were the reading subjects is indicated by the fact that there was objection on the part of the former to repeating some of the tests, while the latter were ready to a man for any further ordeals which were in store for them.

The fact that those who had driven the longer, and thus were presumably the more fatigued, did not show any more "letdown" than those who had driven less parallels the finding (see Appendix) in this experiment of an actual increase of visual acuity on the part of some subjects after six hours of reading. As will be noted later on, something like "momentum" may account for this increase and may have masked possible fatigue effects.

Although the "after" tests employed in the present experiments produced no more evidence of fatigue than was observable in the actual performance of the eyes (and of "mental processes," as revealed in the tests of comprehension), there is one final aspect of the matter to which we return, namely, the so-called subjective results as presented in Chapter 10. Again a finding of the experiment with interstate truck drivers is of interest as given in the statement that: "The subjective judgment of the drivers . . . agreed remarkably well with the estimate of fatigue obtained from the scores" (of the tests). On the whole, this was also the finding in the present experiments. In reviewing the responses to the inquiry in regard to the willingness to continue the reading and study after the six-hour period, one must conclude that what fatigue was noted in feeling-tone was neither very intense nor long lasting. This subjective finding also agrees with the objective conclusion that significant changes did not occur in eye-movement performance. Taken together with the finding that comprehension did not seem to have been affected by the amount of prolonged reading required of the subjects in this experiment, it would seem safe to conclude that evidences of fatigue, such as were indicated by both objective and subjective means or measures in the experiment with truck drivers (and this experiment has been singled out for comment simply because of this clear-cut contrast), have not been demonstrated by either objective measures or subjective reports in the case of the present experiments. This, then, is the conclusion reached as to the effects or the lack of effects of six hours of continuous reading of both "light" and "heavy" books as well as of six hours of continuous reading of microfilm projections of the same books.

Two supplementary statements find support in the experimental data: First, in the case of high school students, the results of the tests and the subjective reports are so far in agreement as to warrant the statement that the reading of microfilm reproductions, under the conditions of these experiments, brings these younger and presumably less practiced readers closer to the critical point of fatigue than does ordinary reading. Second, the feelings of tiredness and boredom with the need for change and of "nervous" tension and irritability; the sensations of smarting or watering eyes, of blurred images, of headaches, and of cramped muscles; and other reactions of the subject to the task in hand, although they may be masked in periods of unusual stimulation or motivation and although they do not, as we must hold, in and of themselves constitute fatigue, are important as indices or signals of fatigue or of its approach and of the possible depleting of energy reserves. In fact, they may be the only indications of the onset of fatigue on which we can count prior to the actual impairment of performance or reduction of output.

Since the characterization of what is accomplished by an action or a process sometimes assists in the description, if not in the real scientific understanding, of that process, an analogy may clarify or point to the significance of the phenomenon just noted. It is possible to think of a subject's feelings of fatigue and his general attitude of boredom as similar to warning signals activated by a thermostat to indicate that a continuously running motor is becoming overheated. Such a thermostat may be so set that it throws a switch and turns off the motor before the number of revolutions per minute or the efficiency of the motor has been in any way impaired. A motor may turn on and off frequently when it is at the critical temperature, but when it is running at all, it may run with full speed and with full efficiency. In the main experiments reported in this book, the complex and subjectively known warning signals of "feelings of fatigue" and of "boredom" characteristically appeared before any loss in efficiency in the total responding mechanism of eye movements could be detected in the objective records of such movements made in this study.

It is important to recognize that the fact just stated does not mean that as time passed the subjects of our experiments just tried harder and harder and so compensated by greater "effort" for gradually increasing fatigue. That this is almost certainly not the case can be demonstrated. In the chapter on the nature of eye movements, it was pointed out that the normal reader cannot "voluntarily" control the number of his fixation pauses, regressive movements, or the other regular actions of his eyes as he reads. It is possible by very specific training to change the frequency and character of such movements, but this is not accomplished merely by "consciously trying" to do so. It was not possible, that is, for any subject with whom we have worked to change his eye movements merely by resolving to himself, "I will now fixate less frequently than

I have done in the past and make fewer regressive movements while I carefully read for comprehension this printed page." The normal subject of course has no direct knowledge of the number of fixation pauses or regressive movements that his eyes make as he reads.

It is, therefore, of especial significance to note that it was just these quantitative measures of the special eye movements of regression and fixation which did not show any statistically significant change during the six-hour reading period. All our objective evidence indicates that during the period of reading in these experiments, the eye mechanism was essentially working as well at the end of the experimental period as at its beginning. The performance of the eyes after six hours of reading was not therefore held up to its initial performance level by a voluntary increase in eye movements induced by increased motivation on the part of the subject to compensate for his feelings of fatigue.

This observation seems to confirm the view that the total normal sensory-neuromuscular eye mechanism is remarkably resistant to fatigue in an operation such as normal reading. It must be emphasized, however, that this does not mean that fatigue of the eye mechanism cannot be brought about by abnormal means. The insertion of suitable distorting lenses in front of one or both eyes or the use of apparatus which induces abnormal vision or other phenomena may well fatigue the mechanism in a longer or shorter time. The experiments reported here do not deal with this problem.

Further, as above noted, it is most likely that "fatigue" in the visual system, when it does develop in the normal movements required in reading, is first seen in the subject's own desire to discontinue the work upon which he is engaged. There must be a physiological basis for all changes in "motivation." Similarly, the phenomena discussed above as "blocking" and as "boredom" must have a physiological cause. It is indeed these complex and little understood physiological mechanisms which first become "fatigued" by the continuous reading of normal subjects. The fact that these processes are probably in part determined by socially directed learning shows how complex must be their final analysis.

Some boys and girls and even men and women who have not had much experience in reading continuously for a number of hours may feel a desire to stop reading before it is wise or necessary for them to cease work. If such a student is to learn to master long assigned reading tasks in meeting educational, business, or professional requirements, he must probably learn to disregard the first signs of discomfort in reading. Knowledge of the results reported in this study may help such individuals to motivate themselves to accomplish long periods of necessary reading by relieving them of the fear that they are "hurting their eyes" by such work. It may be said that as long as a reader is willing to disregard his own feelings of fatigue and his desire to sleep, there is little evidence, if he has a normal visual mechanism, that he is harmed by reading for long periods if the reading matter is printed in satisfactory type and if proper illumination is provided. To put the matter most simply, nature seems certain to turn off the desire to continue work so that the subject really stops before the reading mechanism itself is injured.

As has just been noted, the study by Hoffman (142) gives a clue to reading fatigue. The subjects in these experiments were not given interpolated examinations, and other stimuli which proved so effective in the present experiments in motivating the wish to continue regular reading during the full experimental period were missing. This less highly motivated reading gave in one sense a better clue to the ordinary operation of the warning signs of fatigue than do the experiments reported in this book. Study of the records of the four-hour reading period of the less highly motivated subjects shows that drowsiness and what we have here called the warning signs of motivational change, including feelings of unpleasantness, are effective "stop" signals. If contrary motivation is not present, as in the six-hour experiments, the eyes interrupt their continuous work for shorter or longer periods as the reading period progresses. Such a poorly motivated reader tends to close his eyes or look about. He often skims over a page or two and then suddenly starts good, well ordered, and rapid reading with effective eye movements. The reading which he does when he starts once more has not been shown to be inferior in respect to the quality or quantity of eye movements to the same subject's reading when he is in a nonfatigued state.

The continuous electrical recording of every eye movement in both of these experiments is calculated to show these subtle starting and stopping effects very well. In one of the rare cases in the second or "highly motivated" experiments in which a subject became drowsy, one can see in the record a most interesting picture of some of the changes in the organism as well as in the reading pattern which result from a momentary lapse into drowsiness. Part of this record is shown in Figure 99. In looking at this record, the reader will note that the individual

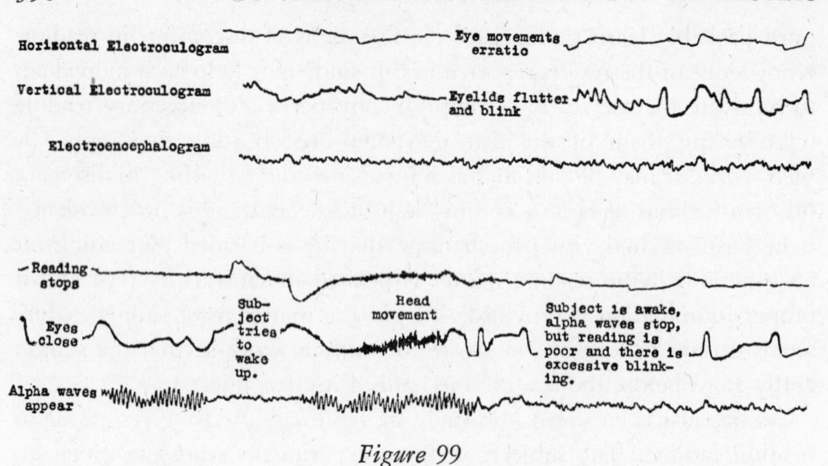

Figure 99

SAMPLE FROM THE RECORD OF A SUBJECT WHO DOZED DURING THE EXPERIMENTAL PERIOD

stopped reading, his eyes winked and then closed, his electrical brain rhythms changed, and then again he opened his eyes and began to read once more. If the part of the record reproduced were longer, it would show that after a few moments the subject's reading record was just as good as it had been before the momentary lapse recorded in the part of the record which has been reproduced.

If the description of the onset of visual fatigue as appearing first in motivation is correct, and it seems that both the results of the present experiments and those of Hoffman's earlier experiment support it, there is every reason to understand why the experiments in which *all* eye movements for four or six hours were recorded should show certain "starting and stopping" phenomena of fatigue, while most earlier experiments have not noted these phenomena. An experiment in which the eyes were photographed for brief samples of time in the course of a long period of reading would almost certainly miss these long-term fluctuations, temporary blockings, or "on and off" responses. The very clamping of the subject's head in the photographic apparatus preceding the making of a brief record of his eye movements would affect the subject's interest in his work. The novelty and zest induced by the recording situation might well determine that reading would rise to a typical level, even if it had become somewhat intermittent immediately before the photographing began.

The studies reported in this book, therefore, indicate that subjects who have really learned to read satisfactorily are so constituted that warning signs of fatigue and a disinclination to work will in general inhibit the continuous operation of the visual mechanism before physiological harm comes to this mechanism from too long continued reading. Previous studies of visual work other than reading show that such tasks may be fatiguing. Six hours of reading from a closely printed page or from microfilm, however, was not too long a period of reading for any of our subjects. According to all the criteria of measurement that we used, they read as well at the end of this period as they did in the first few minutes. Therefore, we conclude that the visual mechanism can be exhausted, but that normal reading, even for very long continued periods, does not necessarily produce visual fatigue.

Chapter 12

Summary and Conclusions

AS POINTED out in the first chapter, this book has been written for those interested in the eyes in use. Those so concerned include all readers in regard to their own eyes, parents of school children, teachers, school and college administrators, librarians, industrialists charged with supervision of workers, office managers, military leaders, and indeed those who are responsible in any way for the use of the eyes in vocation or recreation.

Especially in its detailed reporting of new experiments, this book has suggested problems for further scientific study to certain readers. It is hoped that the techniques developed in connection with the experiments described here and the other older techniques reviewed will be of value to other investigators in related visual science. The conclusion that a book can be read by a normal subject continuously for six hours without undue signs of fatigue is important in planning for many types of visual work.

Similarly, the conclusion that microfilm reading can be carried on for six hours without unduly fatiguing the normal subject is important. This fact should assist in the determination of the part that this new supplement to the printed paper page may play in specialized publication and in planning for future libraries.

By summarizing existing scientific literature and new experiments here reported for the first time, the earlier chapters of this book have attempted to answer the fundamental problems just mentioned and a number of other questions about the effect upon the living human organism of prolonged use of the eyes in reading. The literature reviewed includes that which bears in a significant way on the definition of fatigue, on the makeup of the visual mechanism, and on the specific fatigue of the visual system. The development of experimental procedures used in the accurate study of the movements of the eyes has also been reviewed in some detail.

The findings of the new experiments reported in this book are valid in the strictest sense only under the conditions in which they were secured. This statement should not be interpreted so rigorously, however, as to limit too greatly the use of knowledge gained in these studies. When these experiments are considered in relation to previously reported studies on the nature of fatigue and on the functions of the eyes in reading, they seem so consistent with what is already known as to allow the formulation of some really general conclusions. These conclusions may then with reasonable assurance be applied to the guidance of policy concerning the use of the eyes in everyday reading.

The first conclusion, as just noted, is that significant changes were not found in the various measured aspects of the eyes' behavior in reading during an experimental six-hour period. This held true for both high school and college students reading books and microfilm. Exceptions to this statement took place under very specific circumstances, as previously noted. One subgroup of our experimental subjects, the group made up of high school boys, read the microfilm reproduction of the books used in the experiment less well than they did the regularly printed books. This was true in regard to measures of eye movements and also to tests of understanding or comprehension. This subgroup showed on the average the lowest general academic aptitude as measured by "intelligence tests." There is very little indication, however, that even in this group of subjects, the reading of microfilm itself produced any definite and continuous decreases in effectiveness as a result of the six-hour reading period.

No single factor that we have isolated as delimiting the experimental situation in the present investigations produced special differences in ability to read for six hours. The two specific educational ages, that is, college or high school levels, did not show such a distinction. The form of reproduction of reading material, book or microfilm, was not clearly differentiated in producing "fatigue." The so-called intrinsic interest of the material, such as that found in an eighteenth-century treatise on economics and a novel, was not found to be associated with significant differences in fatigue or in the capacity to read with understanding for six hours.

No fully significant differences in total performance were found consistently when any single factor which we isolated for experimental or statistical purposes was varied in the experiments in relation to other factors. Again, it may be noted, however, that the purely statistical combination of the records of high school subjects and the reading of microfilm is associated with the lowest general level of "performance" as evaluated in these experiments. In the previous sentence, the single word performance is intended to include both certain characteristics of eye movements themselves and comprehension or "understanding what is read" as measured by tests.

The subjective reports given by the readers who participated in the experiments also provided general results. Six hours' reading in a sound-resistant chamber, in a relatively stiff and uncomfortable straight-backed wooden chair, and reading so that answers could be given to specific and detailed questions, was for many, but not for all, of the subjects increasingly unpleasant as the time of the experiments passed. This unpleasantness, the tendency of the subject to say to himself, "I wish this were over," in various vigorous ways has been taken, as indicated in a previous chapter, following the published reports of Thorndike and others, as indicative of "feelings of fatigue." Thus, even though the objective level of performance was maintained in most instances throughout the experiments by all typical subjects, these same individuals found that their own attitude toward the experiments changed in many cases as the hours of continuous reading passed.

This suggests that prolonged visual work of the sort required of the subjects in reading under the conditions of the present experiments does not bring about any detectable and consistent physical alteration in the visual mechanism which changes the ability of this mechanism to perform in an effective and normal way. It must be, however, that reading for six hours in a relatively fixed posture does in some way affect the total organism. The initiating and maintaining of the muscular tensions of the body necessary to hold the required sitting posture, as well as the use of the eyes in reading, produce changes which were related to the over-all "feeling-tone" of the subjects, who were in general glad when the reading time was over and they could stretch, talk, eat, and move about freely. Interestingly enough, however, many subjects said that after a little change, they would be glad to go on reading.

Again, however, we must return to the basic objective results of the present experiments, which indicate that no alteration that was statistically reliable took place in any aspect of the record of eye movements measured during long periods of reading. It should be remembered that type of format, lighting, and other conditions were essentially optimal according to present standards in these experiments. On the basis of this resistance to fatigue, one seems forced to assume that the total visual mechanism, including the sensory cells and related structures of the retina, the motor mechanism, and all connecting neural links, central and peripheral, is able to function approximately as effectively at the end of a long period of continuous activity as at the onset of that activity.

This finding does not mean that the visual mechanism is tireless. With work long extended beyond six hours, all other conditions remaining the same, it is possible that a true work decrement of some type might develop. Twelve or 24 hours might be required, but eventually a combination of "local" and "general" fatigue would almost certainly produce a change in the objective record. It is reasonable to expect, however, on the basis of some work not reported here, that sleep deprivation rather than any specific effects of prolonged reading itself might first show in the records of some subjects.

The present results indicate that the task of reading for six hours is such that, at least for normal subjects, a new "steady state" of some sort may be established during continuous work by the visual receptor-neuromuscular mechanism. It is hard otherwise to explain why no consistent decrement in performance is apparent in our results. In this connection it may be interesting to compare the activity of the eyes when reading apparently "fatiguelessly" for long periods with the activity of the heart. Heart muscle, as is well known, is able to recuperate in the short time intervals between its contractions. This continues during the whole of normal life in such a manner that each succeeding contraction is not reduced as a result of any products of metabolism resulting from preceding normal action. In the case of the heart, it has also been demonstrated that when special demands are made upon it requiring unusual circulation of the blood, the heart or the whole circulatory mechanism is often able to rise to a *new level of activity.* Again in this new "steady state," the circulatory mechanism continues its operations without showing any specific work decrement. Proper athletic training assists in conditioning for these new work loads. The use of the eyes may under certain conditions also be a "physical conditioner" for later eye use. It has been pointed out above that the total eye mechanism may be said to be a most effectively "engineered" one in the biological sense. The factor of safety in its construction is great. It will be remembered that the muscles which activate and control the movement of the eyes are larger and stronger than seems at all necessary to start and stop and move the eyeballs as they shift in their smooth orbits.

Except for some subjective reports of mild discomfort on the part of a few of the participants in these experiments, we have not found that reading taking place during this long period of time was done at any "cost" to the organism. The authors are not aware of any scientific evidence which indicates that there is any activity carried out by an organism which does not lead to a measurable change in the organism when it is active, which later causes a subtle deterioration or cost to the organism. The concept of "hidden fatigue" or "hidden cost" resulting from continuous eye work but not showing itself in any measurable change in eye-muscle action or in intellectual comprehension has not had scientific or medical proof so far as the present writers are aware. It may even be suggested that activity of this sort will itself lead to a real strengthening of the neuromuscular mechanism of the eye as a result of helpful and advantageous physical exercise. Ophthalmological exercises are under specific conditions prescribed by physicians to improve the strength of weak eye muscles. Regular exercise in a rowing machine in a gymnasium unquestionably strengthens muscles. This is true even when the exercise is accompanied by a temporary and often easily measurable work decrement or "fatigue." There is no evidence known to the authors which indicates that it is not at least possible that exercise of eye muscles such as that given in prolonged reading may not strengthen rather than harm the total visual mechanism.

The conclusions of these experiments, it is true, are based upon the study of typical groups of normal secondary school and college students. There is little evidence in other experimental studies which would make us believe that the employment of older subjects or of subjects selected in some other way, provided they were really able to read easily, would alter the present results in any marked manner. Conclusions similar to those of this book might well not be found in experiments with groups of individuals with definite eye pathology. It should be noted, however, that in the case of the subjects of the present experiments whose eyes required refractive correction by the wearing of eyeglasses, no special disadvantageous effects of long periods of work were discovered.

One very practical educational inference that seems justified from the present study is that there seems to be no basis for the belief that requiring long periods of reading on the part of secondary school or college students may be injurious to the visual mechanisms of such students if they have reasonably satisfactory eyes to begin with. The very experimental situation of the present investigation seems on the contrary to point to an interesting conclusion concerning the amount of reading that may wisely be required in a given number of days of any normal student, at least so far as vision is concerned. In this connection it may be noted that R. G. Simpson (317) has shown that there is only a very low correlation between eye-movement measures and the weekly amount of reading reported by freshmen. This seems to indicate that the amount of free reading does not markedly influence the student's control of his eye movements; and also that those who have good eye movements do not seem to read much more than those who have more faulty reading habits.

In making any generalization about reading, it is well not to forget that the tables given in the study reported in this book indicate that there is great variability in the amount of material read and comprehended by different college students as well as by different high school students. This points again to an old but often neglected truism of education: All students, even of the same age and, in certain respects, of similar academic ability, do not work or study at the same rate or with the same effectiveness.

In general it is the belief of the present writers that more reading for real comprehension was carried out by the present subjects during the experimental sessions than is often expected in a given six hours of assigned study in college or school. It is possible that more extensive requirements of assigned reading for given class recitations or for a given number of days of study might be required of students than is now commonly considered to be wise. In such assignments, individual differences in ability to read rapidly and to comprehend clearly should not be overlooked.

If reading materials in school or college could be made comparable to the reading materials developed in the present experiment, it might be that learning from the printed page would be more rapid. Such an hypothesis is worthy of later full experimentation in any case. The principal factor making for this increase in reading efficiency in the present experiments is the provision of objective tests on which the subject must examine himself at the end of approximately each 25 pages. By the use of these tests, the subject is helped in judging whether or not his understanding of the material that he has just read is satisfactory. Incidental observations made during the present experiments suggest that the level of comprehension might be noticeably raised over that now secured in regular school and college reading by the introduction of this simple device. This conclusion is largely grounded on a comparison between the experiment by Hoffman summarized above (142) and the more complete new experiments described in the present book. The reader will recall that in the earlier experiment a visual work decrement was sometimes secured after four hours of unaided reading and that in this earlier study there were no interpolated examinations. In these preliminary experiments, as the hours passed the subjects became careless, "skipped" words and lines, and let their eyes wander over the page and off the book. This behavior was much less common in the present examination-controlled reading even though two extra hours were added to the required reading period.

It may be valuable to compare the results of the present experiments with certain well known experiments of Thorndike and others upon the relationship between "mental" and "physical" fatigue. Thorndike's various experiments (339) show that the alteration of the conditions of his experiments in certain instances demonstrated fatigue from long continued "mental" work. In other cases, possibly analogous in some respects at least to the present experiments, no such effect was noticed. In one experiment using R. S. Woodworth as a subject, Thorndike showed that there was no demonstrated loss of efficiency in continuous mental work for three to eight hours. The task required was to mark every word containing both e and i in 151 pages of a book. At the end of each minute a bell sounded and the subject made a mark. The work continued from 10:15 A.M. to 6:20 P.M. The subject was experi-

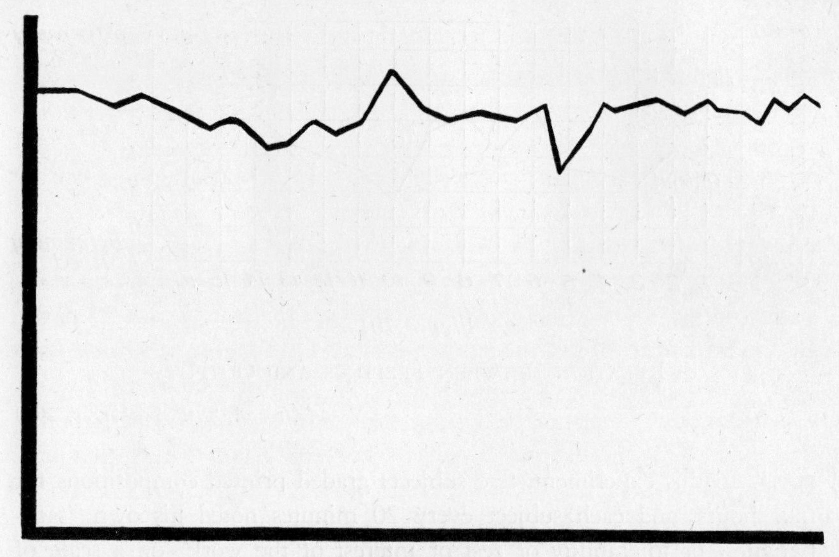

Figure 100

A CURVE OF MENTAL WORK

(After E. L. Thorndike, 339)

enced in this type of work and was not "learning" during the experiment. The lack of change in work during eight hours' continuous work is shown in Figure 100.

The terms "mental" and "physical" as applied to work are not satisfactory for the reasons pointed out in the first chapter of this book. Nevertheless, it is almost certain that the visual mechanism as studied here by an objective method shows much less change during prolonged reading than was shown by the reports of the subjects concerning their own feelings or their motivation towards the task. That is, as the long period of continuous required reading went on, a number of subjects reported after the experiment that they had experienced at least slight "feelings of fatigue" during the experiment. Such feelings were reported when their eye movements, as accurately measured, and their ability in comprehension of the meaning of the material read showed no statistically significant loss. This conclusion suggests another well known experiment on mental and physical fatigue. Figure 101 shows comparable curves from a graph made by A. T. Poffenberger (291) from data of an experiment by Thorndike (338) on the curve of work and the curve of "satisfying-

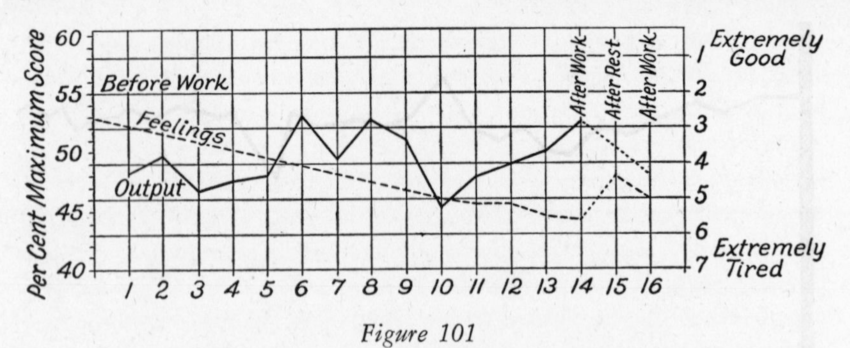

Figure 101

Relation Between Feelings and Output

(After A. T. Poffenberger, 291)

ness." In this experiment, five subjects graded printed compositions for four hours, and each subject every 20 minutes noted his own "satisfyingness or tolerability or zest or interest of the work" on a scale of 0 to 10. As the graph shows, the errors and time required showed no constant decrement, but the "satisfyingness" fell off sharply.

The present experiments do not allow the plotting of a "feeling of fatigue" curve for each subject during the six hours of his reading, but a comparison of our subjects' recorded feelings in relation to objective recording of eye movements and of comprehension seems to be similar to Poffenberger's curves of satisfyingness and of accomplishment. In the present six-hour period, satisfyingness decreased but accomplishment remained constant. It is probable that great individual differences would have appeared as noted in the chapter on subjective results if such data had been collected so that they could be plotted. Some subjects seemed able to read for six hours and show no work decrement in measured performance and also to like the long continued work of reading. Some also showed no objective decrement but did not like the task.

There is some suggestion in comparing our subjects that this "liking" or "not liking" of the work required in the long period of reading is a function of educational age. A school which requires its students to read for long periods during the years when study habits are being established may well produce students who at a later time *can* read for long periods without subjective feelings of fatigue or annoyance. At first, long required reading assignments may seem difficult to the young student, but soon, in many cases, such a requirement may make these very students able to study effectively for long hours and even *like* to study for long hours or at least find no difficulty in such study. It is hard to prove the soundness of the observation just made, but the evidence of the present experiments seems to favor the idea that long periods of reading may be carried out without fatigue or annoyance if the subject has trained himself to read in this way. This point of view is mentioned here as a stimulus to a reconsideration of the limits on study time now accepted. Certainly in the experiments reported here, subjects who did not report unpleasantness in the required situation of the prolonged reading were subjects with a good deal of previous experience in long periods of required concentrated study. It may be suggested that one pedagogical gain from demanding relatively long periods of concentrated detailed study on the part of school and college students of generally good eyesight and good academic ability is that the subject who proves able to do such work soon becomes able to study without feeling uncomfortable.

The question may now be raised as to the light which the present experiments throw upon the general theory of "mental" and "physical" fatigue. After a review of the various meanings of fatigue in the first chapter, it was pointed out that the word fatigue would be used in these pages as a descriptive term. Thus we have tried to limit the use of the word fatigue to descriptions of decreased ability of all sorts resulting from prolonged activity or work. The changes that take place as a result of work and which, using the definition accepted here, may be marshaled under this heading are, as already noted, many and varied. In the second world war, the terms "combat fatigue" or "operational fatigue" were commonly employed to describe a rather wide range of personality changes in military and naval men who had had prolonged duty. Fatigue in this sense is characterized by such different symptoms in different individuals that the use of the term has been questioned by some medical authorities. In general, such fatigue is marked by a lessening of effectiveness in the performance of duties, an alteration in motivation such as a loss in desire for action, and a change in the general subtle attitudes which are summarized under the name "morale."

The term "chronic fatigue" also appears occasionally in technical writings as characterizing a condition in an individual of "staleness" or various states of lassitude. An individual characterized as suffering from chronic fatigue is sometimes "lazy" and shows a lack of zest, enthusiasm, and ability in the performance of tasks which at one time in the individual's career would have been undertaken and carried through to completion without difficulty.

The term "general fatigue" is applied to tiredness ordinarily resulting from specific action of a known character carried on for a known time which nevertheless seems to affect quite generally the entire organism. Thus, as a result of a taxing athletic performance, such as that required in a cross-country race or in the competitive rowing of intercollegiate crews, a final state of fatigue may result which temporarily renders the total organism and any member or muscle of that organism less effective than normally.

Besides general fatigue, one may use the word fatigue to summarize changes in individual organs, muscle groups, or other special systems of the living organism. So far as the intact organism is concerned, the study of the change of the hand and arm muscles involved in experiments with the finger ergograph demonstrates the work decrement of such isolated groups of muscles. To fatigue the neuromuscular mechanism involved in lifting a weight by the index finger of the right hand until the mechanism has been brought to a point of almost complete exhaustion in a given motivational setting may not necessarily affect in any easily measurable way the similar ability of the same finger on the other hand to produce another complete work curve. In other words, there is a specificity of fatigue of such systems which has, so far as crude measurement at any rate shows, very little transfer to other comparable mechanisms.

The word fatigue also may be applied in a descriptive way to changes that take place in a nerve and muscle preparation excised from the organism and studied in the physiological laboratory. By manipulating the stimulation of such preparations, it is possible to determine the part played in the work decrement by the neural and by the muscle cell elements of this isolated system. It is also possible in this way to investigate the part played in work decrement by changes at the junction between the nerve and muscle. Experiments of this sort, as well as experiments upon intact laboratory animals required to exercise continuously until exhaustion is brought about, make possible the study of the chemical and even physical changes that take place in living systems during prolonged activity.

Thus, from a very general description of personality alteration in combat fatigue to a precise characterization of alterations in the physical and chemical makeup of the body fluids and of cellular masses, the word fatigue may be used to describe changes resulting from more or less prolonged activity. It is clear that in explaining these changes, the special terms useful in describing alterations at each level must be employed in making clear the underlying mechanisms which bring about the changes interpreted as fatigue. In the case of combat or operational fatigue, the alterations that are first to be described are changes in the total personality of the individual concerned. Such alterations often show themselves in subtle differences in social reactions. On the other hand, alterations of the protoplasm of muscle cells and the electrolytes of living protoplasm resulting from excessive activity are also to be characterized as fatigue but described in the regular terms of chemistry and of physics.

In the special study of visual fatigue, therefore, it is clear that we must recognize the complexity of the problem in the light of all the facts just summarized. From one point of view, changes in the visual system following prolonged work may include an alteration on the part of the subject in his attitudes toward further work and in his description of his own feeling state. On the other hand, it may be that ultimate investigation will show, if a real work decrement can be demonstrated in the continued activity of the visual mechanism, that these alterations are related to basic changes in the chemistry and physics of muscles and nerves brought about by prolonged activity.

In considering the basic contribution of the present experiments to an understanding of visual fatigue, it is first important to compare again the results of the preliminary experiment referred to several times above and the experiments reported in this book. It will be remembered that in the preliminary experiment, subjects were asked only to read from a book for four hours. The task assigned to them was a simple one; they were merely requested to seat themselves in an experimental chamber and continue reading until told by the experimenter that the period required had elapsed. Under these conditions, with the use of various measures of the recorded eye movements, definite work decrement was discovered. This decrement, as above noted, was especially noticeable in the loss of effectiveness as shown in the tendency of subjects to stop reading for a few seconds or to allow the eyes to roam over the pages without reading. Some subjects in these early experiments began to skip sentences and paragraphs as the period of reading progressed and in other ways to indicate the breaking down of the regular, fully motivated pattern of careful and continuous reading. In popular terms, it was perfectly proper therefore to say that in four hours' reading of the sort just described, certain objective signs which could be thought of as "fatigue" had begun to appear. These symptoms were characterized by a differentiation in the basic pattern and the breaking up of ordered responses as time passed.

There was no indication whatever in these earlier experiments to show that if the subject had been induced to turn back to the book and read carefully and with a real desire to find out what the ideas in the book were, he could not have done so with maximum effectiveness. In the new experiments reported in this book, it will be remembered that by the introduction of tests at approximately every 25 pages and by certain other devices calculated to render the performance more constant, the motivation and general attitude of the subject were controlled in a way that they had not been in the preliminary experiments. The result of this apparently small change in experimental conditions was to demonstrate the virtual absence of work decrement or fatigue on the part of all the subjects, regardless of age or educational level, so far as objective records of the eyes' behavior were concerned. It should be remembered that in the six-hour reading period required of the subjects in the present experiments some individuals reported annoyance or a feeling that they would prefer not to continue throughout the entire time, but they were able to overcome these feelings because they "tried" to do so. In the earlier experiments, the subjects had little reason to try to continue reading and hence the signs of a breakup of the reading pattern that have been described appeared. The motivation provided by promised payment, the desire of most normal school and college students to perform well on any printed examination, and our urgent request to help in a scientific study were sufficient to maintain efficiency at a high level in spite of subjective alterations in attitude in the experiments reported in this book.

A conclusion which can be drawn from a comparison of these two experiments in regard to the basic nature of visual fatigue in reading and which also finds support in the literature of related experimentation as reviewed in this chapter is summed up in the following statement: In the use of a mechanism as well protected against the deleterious effects of the prolonged work of normal reading as is the visual mechanism, the first index of fatigue seems to come in the alterations of the *general* attitudes and *general* feelings of the subject, not in a breakdown of the sensory-neuromuscular mechanism which actually performs the task.

At the same time, it should be recalled that this experimental investigation has also demonstrated a further and more objective characteristic of the oncoming of fatigue, namely, the so-described starting and stopping phenomenon of temporary blockings, fluctuations, or the on and off effects in the performance of reading, the observation of which was made possible through the continuous records of the entire experimental period. Finally, the most constructive aspect of this experiment may well be the demonstration of the ease with which well-considered alterations of the motivational pattern — in this instance through the introduction of regularly interspersed tests of comprehension — may forestall these first phases of fatigue and enable the individual to maintain for hours a high level of efficiency in reading.

Appendix

Supplementary Observations

THE primary experimental emphasis of the present study was on the eye-movement functions of the subject and his comprehension of the material read. The other functions measured or recorded were, therefore, not so widely treated; they may perhaps be more conveniently considered here. The measures of these functions included the electrocardiogram, the electroencephalogram, the Keystone Test of Visual Acuity, the Keystone Test of Stereoscopic Acuity, and the Zeiss Test of Stereoscopic Acuity.

The elecrical changes of the heart beat and of the so-called brain waves were recorded simultaneously with the eye-movement record throughout the six-hour period of reading. Neither the electrocardiogram nor the electroencephalogram was so closely interpreted as were the eye-movement records. There were instances noted, however, when the time between the P-wave and the T-wave of the electrocardiogram was shorter than usual, indicating simply a faster heart beat. This quickening of the heart beat was not found to be regular or rhythmic or to bear any immediately observable relationship to the various conditions of the experiment.

The electroencephalogram is of particular interest in the case of the subject who went to sleep and in whose record alpha rhythms appeared briefly. Figure 99 shows samples of the electroencephalogram when the subject was thought to have dozed for a moment. The bursts of alpha rhythms appeared for only a short time, and no particular trends in their appearance were easily noticeable. One subject in whose record alpha cycles had occurred was tested further at the end of his experimental reading period. The electroencephalogram was taken when the subject was reading, and when he sat with his eyes closed in the dark and with his eyes closed in the light. Table 73 shows the number of cycles which appeared at any one time, the length of the record occupied by the cycles (a millimeter is equal to 1/15 of a second), and the rate at which the cycles occurred. It will be noted that the cycles were slightly slower when they appeared during reading than when the subject's eyes were closed.

If a more formal analysis of the encephalograms were made and if it were found that periods of alpha rhythms or periods of sleep rhythms occurred with some degree of regularity or periodicity, then the encephalogram might suggest itself as an excellent tool for further study of fatigue as a compensatory mechanism. The present study, however, is not an adequate basis for such a conclusion. The periods of sleep or even the alpha cycles observed during the new experiments reported in this volume might have been instances of brief recuperation on the part of the subject which enabled him to continue the prolonged task. That the subjects were not or may not have been "conscious" of these periods of sleep or inattention to the reading matter makes the encephalogram all the more an objective instrument useful in fatigue studies. In the present study, the encephalograms provided an excellent "check" on momentary lapses into sleep or rest with closed eyes, at least in certain subjects.

The Keystone Test of Visual Acuity was administered before and again after each experimental reading period. The scores obtained indicated little or no change in acuity as measured by this test. In some instances the acuity score at the end of the reading period was a little higher than it had been for the first test. This did not occur frequently or consistently enough to constitute a significant finding, but it is interesting to speculate whether or not these slight increases would have occurred if the subject had not been tested immediately after finishing the reading period. It has been suggested that an activity in progress is more easily continued, even by a "fatigued" subject, than a new activity is started. Something like "momentum," then, might account for the few instances of increases in acuity as measured in these experiments. It is equally likely that the momentum may have masked possible fatigue effects.

The Keystone Test of Stereoscopic Acuity and the Zeiss Test of Stereoscopic Acuity were also given before and again after each six-hour reading period. The same subjects, it will be recalled, read for two trial periods, one for each experimental book. Four scores were available, therefore, for each subject on each of the two tests of stereoscopic acuity. (Data on all 40 subjects of the experiments are not complete because of irremediable scoring errors.) Test Number 1 will refer to the first time each subject took these tests, Test Number 2 will refer to the test taken after the first experimental reading period, Test Number 3, to the retest before the second experimental period, and Test Number 4 to the retest taken after the second reading period.

Figure 102 shows the average Keystone stereopsis scores for each of the four test trials. Figure 103 shows the average Zeiss stereopsis scores for each

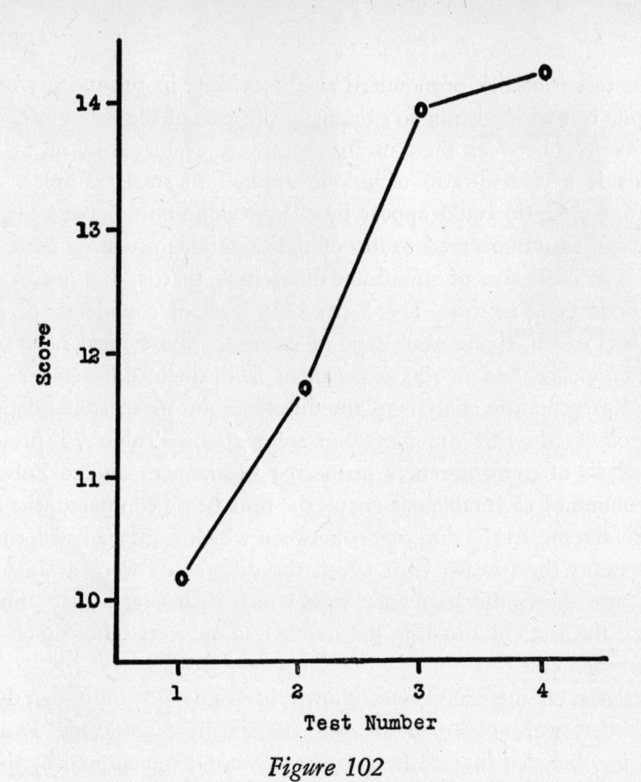

Figure 102

AVERAGE KEYSTONE STEREOPSIS SCORES

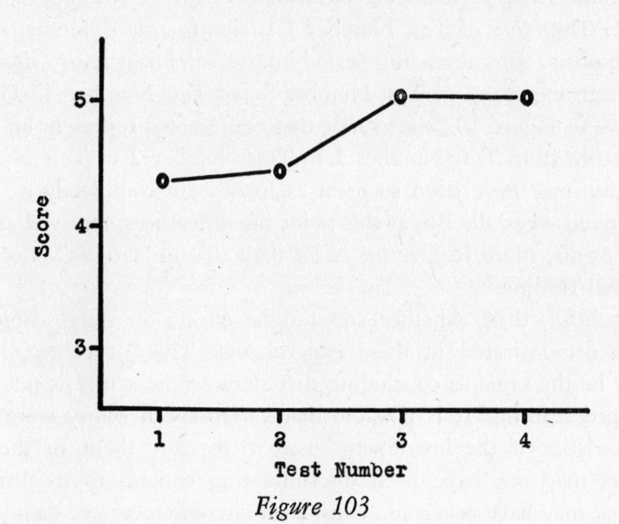

Figure 103

AVERAGE ZEISS STEREOPSIS SCORES

of the four test trials. A pronounced rise is evident in the mean scores for the Keystone test which is not so evident in the case of the Zeiss test.

The differences between these mean scores were evaluated by means of the t-test. This is a critical-ratio technique applied to small samples. If the magnitude of a t-ratio could appear by chance alone only 5 per cent of the time or less, then an observed t-ratio of the same magnitude or more might be regarded as indicative of significant differences, that is, due not to chance but to experimental factors. The 5 per cent level of confidence or significance, as it is called, is the same type of criterion as a critical ratio of 3.00 or more previously used in this experiment to evaluate differences.

Table 74 presents the analysis of the differences in mean stereoscopic performance observed with the Keystone stereograms. Table 75 presents a similar analysis of the differences in mean performances on the Zeiss slide. The first column of each table designates the tests being compared, the second column lists the means the differences between which were analyzed, the third column presents the t-ratios with which the differences were evaluated, the fourth column shows the frequency with which each t-ratio may appear by chance, and the last column lists the number of subjects whose scores were involved in each case.

The analysis of the Zeiss data shown in Table 75 indicates that the differences that were observed are not statistically significant. From this finding, it is concluded that no fatigue effects were demonstrated by this test. For the Keystone data, all the differences may be regarded as significant except the difference between the mean scores of Test Number 3 and Test Number 4. The score of Test Number 1 is significantly different from that of Test Number 2 after a reading period intervened, but it is *also* significantly different from the scores of Test Number 3 and Test Number 4. The shape of the curve in Figure 102 shows that these differences represent an increase in acuity score from Test Number 1 to Test Number 2 to Test Number 3. This increase may have been so great as to obscure completely a "fatigue" factor, if it existed at all. But at this point the differences observed are better explained as due more to practice effect than to any "fatigue" effect of the experimental reading.

It is doubtful, then, whether any fatigue effects on stereoscopic acuity have been demonstrated in these experiments. This, of course, may not necessarily be the same as concluding that stereoscopic acuity is not affected by prolonged reading. It is possible that variations in acuity were masked by characteristics of the instruments used to measure them, or the testing instruments may not have been discriminating enough to measure small changes that may have occurred. Until such circumstances are demonstrated, however, the conclusion above may be accepted.

List of Tables in Appendix

Summary of Data According to Eye-Movement Measure

Grant Study Subjects (normal reading)

High School Subjects (normal reading)

Grant Study Subjects (microfilm reading)

High School Subjects (microfilm reading)

COMPARISON OF EXPERIMENTAL BOOKS

Pearson Product-Moment Correlation between sample of D and corresponding sample of S

COMPARISON OF EXPERIMENTAL BOOKS

Critical Ratios

COMPARISON OF EXPERIMENTAL SITUATIONS

Critical Ratios of Mean Scores

COMPARISON OF EXPERIMENTAL SITUATIONS

Critical Ratios of Standard Deviations

Comprehension Scores

Table 7

PSYCHOMETRIC DATA ON THE TWENTY COLLEGE SUBJECTS

Subject code number	Psychometric Data							Diagnostic Sheet			Snellen Test	
	Sat	Mat	A-v	A-n	M-d	M-i	Voc.	Adjust.	Emot.	Matur.	Right	Left
G.S. 1	B-	B	C	C	B+	B+	B	bor.	sta.	bor.	20/30	20/25
G.S. 2	D	D+	C	B	C-	E	E	adj.	sta.	mat.	20/20	20/20
G.S. 3	C+	A	C-	A	B+	C+	C	adj.	uns.	mat.	20/15	20/15
G.S. 4	C+	C-	C+	B+	B+	B+	C+	adj.	sta.	mat.	20/20	20/20
G.S. 5	D-	C+	C	D	A-	B-	D-	adj.	sta.	mat.	20/25	20/20
G.S. 6	C	A	A-	B	B+	B-	D+	bor.	sta.	bor.	20/20	20/20
G.S. 7	C-	D-	B	C	E	B-	C-	non.	bor.	imm.	20/40	20/40
G.S. 8	D+	C	C	C+	B-	C	C+	bor.	uns.	mat.	20/13	20/20
G.S. 9	D+	--	C	C+	B-	C-	E+	adj.	bor.	bor.	20/20	20/20
G.S. 10	C-	C+	B-	A	C-	E	C-	non.	uns.	imm.	20/30	20/30
G.S.M. 1	B+	C	A	B	B	B	B+	bor.	bor.	bor.	20/25	20/25
G.S.M. 2	B	--	A	C+	B	A-	B	adj.	sta.	bor.	20/15	20/15
G.S.M. 3	A-	A	B	B	B	C	B	bor.	bor.	bor.	20/30	20/40
G.S.M. 4	B	C	B	C	A-	B	B-	bor.	uns.	imm.	20/25	20/20
G.S.M. 5	C+	D	B-	C	B	D-	B	adj.	sta.	mat.	20/25	20/20
G.S.M. 6	C+	B-	C+	C	C+	C	C+	bor.	bor.	imm.	20/20	20/20
G.S.M. 7	B-	B	B	C	B-	C+	B	adj.	sta.	mat.	20/15	20/20
G.S.M. 8	B-	--	C	A	B-	B	C+	adj.	sta.	imm.	20/15	20/15
G.S.M. 9	B+	C	--	--	--	--	B+	adj.	bor.	mat.	20/25	---
G.S.M. 10	B-	B+	C	C	B+	C+	C	adj.	sta.	mat.	20/20	20/20

Key for headings under 'Psychometric Data':
- Sat - Scholastic Aptitude Test
- Mat - Mathematical Aptitude Test
- A-v - Alpha verbal
- A-n - Alpha number
- M-d - Manual dexterity
- M-i - Manipulative insight
- Voc. - Vocabulary

Key for headings under 'Diagnostic Sheet':
- Adjust. - Adjustment
- Emot. - Emotional stability
- Matur. - Maturity

The letter grades are in terms of sigma-units: $.25\sigma$ = one grade step.
A = 1.5σ above the mean (C); E = not less than 1.5σ below the mean

Level of Adjustment is based on a nonadjusted-borderline-adjustment rating

Emotional stability is based on an unstable- borderline- stable rating

Level of Maturity is based on an immature-borderline-mature rating

Table 8

DATA SHEET FOR SUBJECT #G.S. 7S

Code Number G.S. 7S Pages read 188

5' Sample	Ia	If/IIf	IIIf/IVf	Vf/VIf	VIIf/VIIIf	IXf/Xf	XIf/XIIf
Blinking							
Number	192	194	199	204	188	178	181
		203	200	197	196	167	170
% Score	7.8	7.9	8.1	8.3	7.6	7.2	7.3
		8.2	8.1	8.0	7.9	6.8	6.9
Fixations							
Number	1239	1324	1246	1233	1106	1167	1183
		1196	1325	1191	1183	1163	1215
% Score	7.9	8.4	7.9	7.8	7.0	7.4	7.5
		7.6	8.4	7.6	7.5	7.4	7.7
X^2	10621	9944	9814	8619	8274	7849	8517
		9748	9303	8785	8757	8557	8525
No./Line	7.5	6.7	6.8	6.2	6.4	6.0	6.1
		7.0	6.3	6.4	6.5	6.4	6.3
% Score	8.9	7.9	8.0	7.3	7.6	7.1	7.2
		8.3	7.4	7.6	7.7	7.6	7.4
Sigma	2.8	2.2	2.7	2.2	2.7	2.2	2.6
		2.8	2.2	2.4	2.5	2.5	2.1
Lines Read							
Number	165	199	183	200	172	193	193
		171	210	187	181	182	194
% Score	6.8	8.2	7.5	8.2	7.1	7.9	7.9
		7.0	8.6	7.7	7.4	7.5	8.0
Regressions							
Number	295	291	290	293	291	291	255
		318	300	306	291	288	290
% Score	7.8	7.7	7.6	7.7	7.7	7.7	6.7
		8.4	7.9	8.0	7.7	7.6	7.6
No./Line	1.79	1.46	1.58	1.46	1.70	1.51	1.32
		1.86	1.43	1.64	1.61	1.58	1.49
% Score	8.8	7.2	7.7	7.2	8.3	7.4	6.5
		9.1	7.0	8.0	7.9	7.7	7.3

Table 9

SUMMARY OF DATA ACCORDING TO EYE-MOVEMENT MEASURE

Blinking Number

Grant Study Subjects (normal reading)

Sample	Mean		Sigma		r		C.R. S	C.R. M
			LORNA DOONE					
Ia	58.6±	17.05	53.9±	12.04				
If	66.0	15.43	48.8	10.91	.911±	.054	0.75	1.05
IIf	61.8	14.39	45.5	10.16	.912	.053	1.25	0.45
IIIf	61.9	12.08	38.2	8.54	.805	.111	1.70	0.32
IVf	70.4	15.30	48.4	10.82	.751	.138	0.51	1.02
Vf	76.1	18.52	58.6	13.09	.628	.192	0.34	1.14
VIf	63.6	15.00	47.4	10.58	.663	.177	0.54	0.38
VIIf	70.8	15.71	49.7	11.10	.542	.223	0.30	0.78
VIIIf	65.0	13.78	43.6	9.75	.714	.155	0.94	0.53
IXf	67.1	17.23	54.5	12.18	.617	.196	0.04	0.57
Xf	67.0	14.24	45.0	10.07	.844	.091	1.03	0.92
XIf	66.4	14.65	46.3	10.36	.846	.090	0.88	0.86
XIIf	69.3	15.74	49.8	11.13	.720	.152	0.36	0.87
			ADAM SMITH					
Ia	73.4±	17.06	54.0±	12.08				
If	70.3	15.16	47.9	10.72	.938±	.038	1.07	0.52
IIf	73.6	17.92	56.7	12.69	.891	.065	0.34	0.02
IIIf	83.0	18.74	59.3	13.26	.708	.158	0.42	0.70
IVf	88.5	18.03	57.0	12.75	.829	.099	0.30	1.46
Vf	87.0	18.78	59.4	13.27	.835	.096	0.54	1.30
VIf	73.4	16.97	53.6	12.00	.938	.038	0.07	0.00
VIIf	75.9	19.10	60.4	13.50	.704	.160	0.50	0.18
VIIIf	83.1	17.41	55.1	12.30	.901	.060	0.15	1.26
IXf	85.2	17.77	56.2	12.56	.811	.108	0.22	1.10
Xf	85.9	15.90	50.3	11.24	.852	.087	0.43	1.38
XIf	76.7	17.52	55.4	12.39	.709	.157	0.11	0.25
XIIf	81.0	16.89	53.4	11.95	.796	.116	0.06	0.70

Table 10

SUMMARY OF DATA ACCORDING TO EYE-MOVEMENT MEASURE

Fixations Number

Grant Study Subjects (normal reading)

Sample	Mean		Sigma		r		C.R. S	C.R. M
				LORNA DOONE				
Ia	1128.2	±32.49	102.7	±22.97				
If	1063.8	32.35	102.3	22.88	.748	±.139	0.02	2.80
IIf	1071.3	27.86	88.1	19.70	.834	.096	0.86	3.17
IIIf	1052.6	27.57	87.2	19.49	.868	.078	1.02	4.68
IVf	1046.3	24.17	76.4	17.09	.826	.100	1.56	4.43
Vf	1044.0	23.13	73.1	16.35	.456	.250	1.17	2.80
VIf	1034.5	28.99	91.7	20.49	.788	.120	0.58	4.62
VIIf	1067.0	26.32	83.3	18.62	.254	.296	0.68	1.69
VIIIf	1036.3	38.74	122.5	27.39	.576	.211	0.68	2.76
IXf	1065.5	25.77	81.5	18.22	.520	.231	0.84	2.15
Xf	1078.3	26.53	83.9	18.76	.956	.027	1.96	4.73
XIf	1084.3	36.00	113.8	25.46	.817	.105	0.56	2.09
XIIf	1073.1	34.79	110.0	24.60	.865	.080	0.43	3.13
				ADAM SMITH				
Ia	1091.2	±39.99	126.5	±28.27				
If	1048.4	36.06	114.1	25.50	.790	±.119	0.53	1.72
IIf	1023.0	33.83	107.0	23.92	.867	.078	1.03	3.42
IIIf	981.4	44.57	140.9	31.51	.621	.194	0.43	2.96
IVf	1021.8	41.99	132.8	29.70	.373	.272	0.16	1.51
Vf	1000.0	38.92	123.1	27.52	.703	.160	0.12	3.00
VIf	1000.1	26.18	82.8	18.51	.527	.228	1.50	2.65
VIIf	1002.1	28.55	90.3	20.18	.776	.126	1.59	3.52
VIIIf	997.5	29.67	93.9	20.99	.154	.309	0.94	2.04
IXf	1010.4	37.42	118.3	26.46	-.166	.308	0.21	1.47
Xf	976.6	31.36	99.2	22.18	.164	.308	0.77	2.46
XIf	1031.4	42.77	135.2	30.24	.754	.136	0.32	2.05
XIIf	1016.8	39.64	125.4	28.04	.668	.175	0.04	2.29

Table II

SUMMARY OF DATA ACCORDING TO EYE-MOVEMENT MEASURE

Fixations per Line

Grant Study Subjects (normal reading)

Sample	Mean		Sigma		r		C.R. S	C.R. M
			LORNA DOONE					
Ia	9.22±	.372	1.17±	.263				
If	8.96	.400	1.26	.283	.912±	.053	0.57	1.60
IIf	8.83	.462	1.46	.326	.945	.034	2.57	2.41
IIIf	8.71	.415	1.31	.293	.917	.050	0.88	3.11
IVf	8.67	.405	1.28	.286	.848	.089	0.53	2.55
Vf	8.48	.358	1.13	.253	.866	.079	0.22	3.94
VIf	8.13	.402	1.27	.285	.929	.043	0.69	7.32
VIIf	8.57	.395	1.25	.279	.944	.034	0.63	5.04
VIIIf	8.81	.385	1.22	.272	.844	.091	0.25	1.95
IXf	8.58	.422	1.33	.298	.954	.028	1.29	5.00
Xf	8.65	.392	1.24	.278	.817	.105	0.32	2.46
XIf	8.42	.365	1.15	.257	.881	.071	0.12	4.49
XIIf	8.31	.365	1.15	.257	.896	.062	0.12	5.48
			ADAM SMITH					
Ia	8.37±	.464	1.47±	.327				
If	8.00	.397	1.26	.281	.837±	.095	0.88	1.46
IIf	8.13	.428	1.35	.302	.910	.054	2.70	1.26
IIIf	8.34	.474	1.50	.335	.914	.052	0.16	0.15
IVf	8.46	.529	1.67	.374	.845	.090	0.74	0.32
Vf	7.75	.412	1.30	.292	.863	.081	0.76	2.65
VIf	7.69	.329	1.04	.232	.827	.100	1.80	2.56
VIIf	7.68	.351	1.11	.247	.769	.129	1.34	2.33
VIIIf	7.70	.352	1.11	.249	.631	.190	1.11	1.84
IXf	7.91	.349	1.10	.247	.792	.118	1.43	1.62
Xf	7.92	.308	0.97	.217	.671	.174	1.67	1.31
XIf	7.74	.401	1.27	.293	.653	.181	0.61	1.73
XIIf	7.96	.338	1.07	.239	.639	.187	1.26	1.14

Table 12

SUMMARY OF DATA ACCORDING TO EYE-MOVEMENT MEASURE

Fixation Sigma Score

Grant Study Subjects (normal reading)

Sample	Mean		Sigma		r		C.R. S	C.R. M
				LORNA DOONE				
Ia	2.76±	.140	.44±	.099				
If	2.85	.167	.53	.118	.613±	.197	0.74	0.66
IIf	2.84	.138	.44	.097	.613	.197	0.00	0.66
IIIf	2.84	.143	.45	.101	.897	.062	0.16	1.21
IVf	2.95	.123	.39	.087	.667	.176	0.51	1.74
Vf	2.80	.126	.40	.089	.614	.197	0.38	0.34
VIf	2.61	.108	.34	.076	.584	.208	0.98	1.28
VIIf	2.92	.107	.34	.075	.714	.155	1.12	1.63
VIIIf	3.00	.173	.55	.122	.665	.176	0.93	1.83
IXf	2.93	.177	.56	.125	.821	.103	1.29	1.70
Xf	2.94	.136	.43	.096	.637	.188	0.09	1.52
XIf	2.82	.135	.43	.095	.274	.292	0.08	0.36
XIIf	2.77	.121	.38	.085	.142	.310	0.46	0.06
				ADAM SMITH				
Ia	2.78±	.159	.50±	.112				
If	2.77	.128	.40	.090	.277±	.292	0.72	0.06
IIf	2.82	.131	.41	.093	.719	.153	0.88	0.36
IIIf	2.78	.171	.54	.121	.461	.249	0.27	0.00
IVf	3.02	.171	.54	.121	.172	.307	0.25	1.13
Vf	2.72	.155	.49	.110	.593	.205	0.08	0.42
VIf	2.89	.163	.52	.115	.622	.194	0.16	0.78
VIIf	2.63	.117	.37	.083	.592	.205	1.14	1.15
VIIIf	2.80	.121	.38	.085	.368	.273	0.91	0.12
IXf	2.96	.118	.38	.084	.385	.269	0.92	1.15
Xf	2.81	.125	.40	.088	.266	.294	0.72	0.17
XIf	2.78	.179	.57	.127	.164	.308	0.42	0.00
XIIf	2.69	.181	.57	.128	.066	.315	0.41	0.39

Table 13

SUMMARY OF DATA ACCORDING TO EYE-MOVEMENT MEASURE

Lines Read Number

Grant Study Subjects (normal reading)

Sample	Mean		Sigma		r		C.R. S	C.R. M
			LORNA DOONE					
Ia	125.5±	8.19	25.9±	5.79				
If	122.3	9.03	28.6	6.39	.865±	.080	0.62	0.70
IIf	125.0	8.24	26.0	5.83	.971	.018	0.05	0.26
IIIf	125.0	9.76	30.8	6.90	.948	.032	1.61	0.15
IVf	124.2	8.13	25.7	5.75	.868	.078	0.05	0.31
Vf	125.7	7.19	22.7	5.09	.726	.150	0.60	0.03
VIf	131.6	9.93	31.4	7.02	.902	.059	1.35	1.40
VIIf	127.9	8.62	27.2	6.10	.931	.042	0.42	0.76
VIIIf	121.2	9.83	31.1	6.95	.734	.146	0.84	0.64
IXf	128.1	8.91	28.2	6.30	.885	.068	0.57	0.62
Xf	128.1	8.33	26.3	5.89	.879	.072	0.10	0.64
XIf	132.8	10.02	31.7	7.09	.876	.074	1.27	1.50
XIIf	133.5	10.76	34.0	7.61	.894	.063	1.77	1.59
			ADAM SMITH					
Ia	135.5±	11.27	35.6±	7.97				
If	136.2	11.27	35.6	7.97	.870±	.077	0.00	0.12
IIf	130.6	10.01	31.6	7.08	.922	.047	0.96	1.09
IIIf	122.4	10.26	32.5	7.26	.804	.112	0.48	1.92
IVf	126.9	11.72	37.1	8.29	.628	.192	0.17	0.87
Vf	133.8	10.20	32.2	7.21	.733	.146	0.46	0.22
VIf	133.1	8.18	25.9	5.78	.810	.109	1.60	0.36
VIIf	133.5	7.83	24.7	5.53	.773	.127	1.69	0.28
VIIIf	129.8	6.90	21.8	4.88	.454	.251	1.64	0.56
IXf	129.7	7.52	23.8	5.32	.131	.311	1.24	0.46
Xf	125.6	7.14	22.6	5.05	.301	.288	1.44	0.87
XIf	138.6	11.42	36.1	8.08	.631	.190	0.06	0.32
XIIf	131.2	9.47	29.9	6.70	.546	.222	0.65	0.43

Table 14

SUMMARY OF DATA ACCORDING TO EYE-MOVEMENT MEASURE

Regressions Number

Grant Study Subjects (normal reading)

Sample	Mean		Sigma		r		C.R. S	C.R. M
				LORNA DOONE				
Ia	275.8±	17.07	54.0±	12.07				
If	261.9	16.86	53.3	11.92	.750±	.138	0.06	1.16
IIf	261.8	16.41	51.9	11.60	.821	.103	0.22	1.40
IIIf	260.8	19.67	62.2	13.91	.788	.120	0.72	1.23
IVf	274.3	18.64	58.9	13.18	.820	.104	0.48	0.14
Vf	257.1	19.21	60.7	13.58	.728	.149	0.54	1.38
VIf	242.8	16.66	52.7	11.78	.794	.117	0.13	3.05
VIIf	263.5	18.94	59.9	13.39	.798	.115	0.54	1.04
VIIIf	261.8	18.75	59.3	13.26	.694	.164	0.41	0.99
IXf	270.2	21.90	69.3	15.49	.684	.168	1.05	0.35
Xf	264.0	16.78	53.1	11.87	.490	.240	0.06	0.69
XIf	261.3	17.45	55.2	12.34	.743	.142	0.10	1.17
XIIf	258.5	13.25	41.9	9.37	.755	.136	1.18	1.55
				ADAM SMITH				
Ia	236.2±	16.75	53.0±	11.85				
If	230.2	11.46	36.2	8.10	.823±	.102	1.93	0.61
IIf	230.6	14.68	46.4	10.38	.728	.149	0.61	0.48
IIIf	230.2	17.20	54.4	12.16	.825	.101	0.14	0.60
IVf	249.8	11.08	35.0	7.83	.861	.082	2.25	1.40
Vf	229.6	16.76	53.0	11.85	.872	.076	0.00	0.78
VIf	223.3	19.31	61.1	13.66	.785	.121	0.72	1.07
VIIf	226.0	11.80	37.3	8.35	.832	.097	1.84	1.07
VIIIf	244.4	10.42	32.9	7.37	.725	.150	1.98	0.70
IXf	241.2	12.90	40.8	9.12	.753	.137	1.21	0.45
Xf	237.3	10.33	32.7	7.31	.626	.192	1.81	0.08
XIf	234.2	11.25	35.6	7.96	.560	.217	1.45	0.14
XIIf	246.0	11.60	36.7	8.20	.656	.180	1.46	0.77

Table 15

SUMMARY OF DATA ACCORDING TO EYE-MOVEMENT MEASURE

Regressions per Line

Grant Study Subjects (normal reading)

Sample	Mean		Sigma		r		C.R. S	C.R. M
			LORNA DOONE					
Ia	2.206±	.2482	.785±	.1755				
If	2.141	.2379	.753	.1682	.878±	.072	0.27	0.54
IIf	2.138	.2480	.784	.1752	.938	.038	0.01	0.78
IIIf	2.198	.2256	.713	.1594	.856	.084	0.58	0.06
IVf	2.258	.2617	.828	.1849	.814	.107	0.29	0.33
Vf	2.118	.2433	.769	.1720	.829	.099	0.12	0.61
VIf	1.913	.2193	.694	.1549	.826	.100	0.68	2.08
VIIf	2.125	.2642	.835	.1868	.838	.094	0.36	0.55
VIIIf	2.265	.2895	.916	.2447	.824	.102	0.84	0.36
IXf	2.247	.2898	.916	.2049	.819	.104	0.84	0.24
Xf	2.081	.2610	.825	.1844	.699	.162	0.22	0.63
XIf	2.087	.2398	.758	.1694	.800	.114	0.18	0.77
XIIf	2.003	.2387	.755	.1688	.837	.095	0.22	1.46
			ADAM SMITH					
Ia	1.861±	.2022	.640±	.1428				
If	1.790	.1581	.500	.1118	.710±	.157	1.08	0.50
IIf	1.862	.1778	.562	.1257	.788	.120	0.66	0.01
IIIf	2.014	.2276	.720	.1609	.823	.102	0.65	1.17
IVf	2.131	.2170	.686	.1533	.722	.151	0.32	1.72
Vf	1.807	.1868	.591	.1319	.770	.129	0.39	0.41
VIf	1.738	.1825	.577	.1288	.677	.171	0.44	0.79
VIIf	1.737	.1204	.381	.0848	.719	.153	2.11	0.87
VIIIf	1.923	.1113	.352	.0787	.490	.240	1.98	0.35
IXf	1.884	.0954	.302	.0671	.622	.194	2.55	0.14
Xf	1.929	.1100	.348	.0775	.362	.275	1.90	0.35
XIf	1.802	.1643	.520	.1162	.326	.283	0.69	0.27
XIIf	1.965	.1578	.499	.1113	.516	.232	0.90	0.57

Table 16

SUMMARY OF DATA ACCORDING TO EYE-MOVEMENT MEASURE

Blinking Number

High School Subjects (normal reading)

Sample	Mean	Sigma	r	C.R. S	C.R. M
		LORNA DOONE			
Ia	43.1± 4.62	14.6±3.27			
If	52.3 6.98	22.1 4.94	.626±.192	1.58	1.69
IIf	41.8 5.03	15.9 3.56	.716 .154	0.38	0.36
IIIf	47.5 5.23	16.5 3.70	.378 .271	0.42	0.80
IVf	56.3 8.53	26.9 6.03	.806 .111	2.66	2.39
Vf	53.4 10.30	32.6 7.29	.722 .151	2.88	1.34
VIf	52.6 7.44	23.5 5.26	.584 .208	1.72	1.57
VIIf	48.8 7.04	22.3 4.98	.811 .108	2.05	1.34
VIIIf	47.2 7.24	22.9 5.12	.701 .161	1.84	0.79
IXf	51.0 6.64	21.0 4.70	.729 .148	1.58	1.74
Xf	54.4 5.29	16.7 3.74	.446 .250	0.47	2.15
XIf	57.1 11.34	35.9 8.02	.730 .148	3.10	1.63
XIIf	60.0 8.68	27.4 6.14	.700 .161	2.39	2.65
		ADAM SMITH			
Ia	54.3± 7.94	25.1± 5.62			
If	45.3 4.37	13.8 3.09	.648±.183	2.19	1.48
IIf	54.2 8.26	26.1 5.84	.259 .295	0.13	0.01
IIIf	43.0 6.91	21.8 4.89	.859 .083	0.86	2.78
IVf	53.3 10.94	34.6 7.74	.913 .053	2.18	0.20
Vf	50.8 8.09	25.6 5.72	.712 .156	0.09	0.57
VIf	56.9 9.61	30.4 6.80	.792 .118	0.97	0.44
VIIf	51.8 6.68	21.1 4.72	.859 .083	1.04	0.62
VIIIf	59.9 14.58	46.1 10.30	.932 .042	3.44	0.72
IXf	60.3 11.74	37.1 8.30	.946 .033	2.92	1.21
Xf	61.8 12.96	41.0 9.17	.908 .253	2.88	1.13
XIf	56.2 11.54	36.5 8.17	.920 .048	2.52	0.36
XIIf	61.2 11.99	37.9 8.47	.884 0.69	2.38	1.11

Table 17

SUMMARY OF DATA ACCORDING TO EYE-MOVEMENT MEASURE

Fixations Number

High School Subjects (normal reading)

Sample	Mean		Sigma		r		C.R. S	C.R. M
			LORNA DOONE					
Ia	1062.3±	32.17	101.7±	22.75				
If	1057.1	29.06	91.9	20.55	.637±	.188	0.41	0.20
IIf	1078.5	31.28	98.9	22.12	.716	.154	0.13	0.68
IIIf	1066.7	25.77	81.5	18.22	.746	.140	1.02	0.20
IVf	1061.9	33.39	105.6	23.60	.521	.230	0.14	0.01
Vf	1045.5	28.04	88.7	19.83	.472	.246	0.49	0.54
VIf	1059.0	15.88	50.2	11.23	.248	.297	2.08	0.10
VIIf	1034.9	34.20	108.2	24.19	.090	.314	0.20	0.61
VIIIf	1062.9	22.12	70.0	15.64	.398	.266	1.24	0.02
IXf	1058.9	29.88	94.5	21.13	.206	.303	0.24	0.09
Xf	1002.7	31.01	98.1	21.93	.306	.287	0.12	1.60
XIf	1033.5	33.35	105.5	23.58	.245	.297	0.12	0.72
XIIf	903.9	40.02	126.6	28.29	-.294	.289	0.72	2.79
			ADAM SMITH					
Ia	1040.0±	29.28	92.6±	20.70				
If	1032.9	35.33	111.7	24.98	.790±	.119	0.95	0.33
IIf	1024.5	35.15	111.2	24.83	.747	.140	0.86	0.66
IIIf	1051.7	29.69	93.9	20.99	.847	.089	0.08	0.72
IVf	1023.9	48.60	153.7	34.36	.792	.118	2.28	0.52
Vf	1022.1	38.90	122.9	27.49	.780	.124	1.37	0.74
VIf	1016.6	46.67	147.6	33.00	.823	.102	2.26	0.83
VIIf	1027.1	26.87	85.0	19.00	.584	.208	0.33	0.50
VIIIf	1000.1	46.51	147.1	32.89	.636	.188	1.76	1.11
IXf	983.8	41.06	129.8	29.03	.597	.204	1.28	1.69
Xf	969.8	36.94	116.8	26.12	.574	.212	0.88	2.24
XIf	1041.4	41.50	131.2	29.34	.804	.112	1.72	0.06
XIIf	1099.9	29.82	94.3	21.08	-.861	.082	0.11	1.05

Table 18

SUMMARY OF DATA ACCORDING TO EYE-MOVEMENT MEASURE

Fixations per Line

High School Subjects (normal reading)

Sample	Mean		Sigma		r		C.R. S	C.R. M
			LORNA DOONE					
Ia	8.62±	.455	1.44±	.321				
If	8.00	.620	1.96	.438	.918±	.050	2.16	2.28
IIf	7.75	.532	1.68	.376	.909	.055	1.14	3.90
IIIf	7.68	.456	1.44	.323	.800	.114	0.00	3.26
IVf	8.08	.595	1.88	.421	.892	.065	1.72	1.94
Vf	7.90	.524	1.66	.370	.870	.077	0.90	2.78
VIf	7.69	.555	1.75	.392	.776	.126	0.95	2.65
VIIf	7.95	.547	1.73	.386	.755	.136	0.87	1.86
VIIIf	7.71	.538	1.70	.379	.868	.078	1.03	3.42
IXf	7.62	.463	1.46	.327	.780	.124	0.07	3.29
Xf	7.74	.547	1.73	.386	.787	.120	0.92	2.60
XIf	8.08	.580	1.83	.410	.818	.105	1.27	1.62
XIIf	7.55	.491	1.55	.346	.831	.098	0.42	3.86
			ADAM SMITH					
Ia	8.56±	.527	1.67±	.373				
If	8.25	.490	1.55	.346	.946±	.033	0.72	1.81
IIf	8.61	.505	1.60	.356	.763	.132	0.21	0.14
IIIf	8.24	.515	1.63	.363	.902	.059	0.18	1.38
IVf	8.60	.709	2.24	.501	.957	.027	2.61	0.16
Vf	8.35	.533	1.68	.377	.893	.064	0.04	0.85
VIf	8.61	.670	2.12	.473	.856	.084	1.39	0.14
VIIf	8.30	.578	1.83	.409	.826	.100	0.51	0.79
VIIIf	8.14	.411	1.30	.290	.788	.120	1.24	1.29
IXf	8.24	.435	1.37	.307	.645	.185	0.81	0.77
Xf	8.65	.588	1.86	.416	.903	.058	0.78	0.35
XIf	8.38	.632	2.00	.447	.855	.085	1.15	0.52
XIIf	8.31	.584	1.85	.412	.811	.108	0.55	0.72

Table 19

SUMMARY OF DATA ACCORDING TO EYE-MOVEMENT MEASURE

Fixation Sigma Score

High School Subjects (normal reading)

Sample	Mean		Sigma		r		C.R. S	C.R. M
			LORNA DOONE					
Ia	3.02±	.161	.51±	.114				
If	2.85	.215	.68	.152	.718±	.153	1.27	1.14
IIf	3.00	.222	.70	.157	.353	.277	1.04	0.09
IIIf	2.95	.207	.66	.147	.760	.134	1.23	0.52
IVf	3.15	.237	.75	.167	.633	.190	1.50	0.71
Vf	2.95	.241	.76	.170	.771	.128	1.82	0.45
VIf	2.84	.161	.51	.114	.497	.238	0.00	1.12
VIIf	3.07	.262	.83	.185	.772	.128	2.15	0.29
VIIIf	2.95	.208	.66	.147	.487	.241	0.92	0.37
IXf	2.96	.195	.62	.138	.682	.169	0.83	0.41
Xf	2.97	.220	.69	.155	.701	.161	1.28	0.32
XIf	3.28	.249	.79	.176	.641	.186	1.69	1.36
XIIf	3.08	.224	.71	.158	.559	.217	1.23	0.32
			ADAM SMITH					
Ia	3.04±	.190	.60±	.134				
If	3.13	.208	.66	.147	.744±	.141	0.45	0.62
IIf	3.35	.206	.65	.146	.626	.192	0.32	1.79
IIIf	3.38	.237	.75	.167	.686	.167	0.95	1.95
IVf	3.39	.238	.76	.168	.606	.200	0.92	1.78
Vf	3.37	.264	.84	.187	.766	.131	1.56	1.93
VIf	3.44	.321	1.02	.227	.494	.239	1.79	1.42
VIIf	3.36	.232	.73	.164	.469	.247	0.69	1.45
VIIIf	3.42	.136	.43	.096	.632	.190	1.31	2.57
IXf	3.43	.220	.69	.155	.345	.278	0.47	1.65
Xf	3.46	.310	.98	.220	.834	.096	2.39	2.27
XIf	3.34	.215	.68	.156	.677	.171	0.53	1.82
XIIf	3.27	.277	.88	.196	.481	.243	1.33	0.92

Table 20

SUMMARY OF DATA ACCORDING TO EYE-MOVEMENT MEASURE

Lines Read Number

High School Subjects (normal reading)

Sample	Mean		Sigma		r		C.R. S	C.R. M
			LORNA DOONE					
Ia	125.9±	6.18	19.5±	4.37				
If	141.2	13.04	41.2	9.22	.870±	.077	3.30	1.85
IIf	146.1	11.35	35.9	8.03	.845	.090	2.83	2.89
IIIf	145.0	10.55	33.4	7.46	.568	.214	1.90	2.20
IVf	137.5	9.00	28.5	6.36	.833	.097	1.96	2.25
Vf	140.2	12.59	39.8	8.91	.827	.100	3.02	1.73
VIf	145.0	11.10	35.1	7.85	.876	.074	2.94	2.97
VIIf	139.3	14.26	45.1	10.09	.662	.178	2.82	1.20
VIIIf	145.5	11.97	37.8	8.46	.891	.065	3.23	2.78
IXf	145.2	11.22	35.5	7.93	.731	.147	2.38	2.44
Xf	136.7	10.51	33.2	7.43	.851	.087	2.62	1.75
XIf	135.7	12.21	38.6	8.64	.718	.153	2.58	1.10
XIIf	143.1	11.53	36.5	8.15	.784	.122	2.63	2.23
			ADAM SMITH					
Ia	124.6±	6.11	19.3±	4.32				
If	128.2	6.48	20.5	4.58	.875±	.074	0.39	1.14
IIf	122.9	7.77	24.6	5.49	.752	.137	1.13	0.33
IIIf	131.8	7.88	24.9	5.57	.785	.122	1.25	1.47
IVf	124.9	9.09	28.7	6.42	.832	.097	2.02	0.06
Vf	126.4	7.60	24.0	5.37	.779	.124	1.07	0.38
VIf	125.3	10.84	34.3	7.67	.752	.137	2.37	0.09
VIIf	130.0	10.11	32.0	7.15	.832	.097	2.44	0.89
VIIIf	126.5	9.13	28.9	6.45	.539	.224	1.44	0.24
IXf	127.0	11.58	36.6	8.19	.642	.186	2.30	0.27
Xf	118.8	11.09	35.1	7.84	.847	.089	2.81	0.86
XIf	131.8	10.98	34.7	7.77	.891	.065	3.04	1.16
XIIf	123.3	11.30	35.7	7.99	.692	.165	2.33	0.16

Table 21

SUMMARY OF DATA ACCORDING TO EYE-MOVEMENT MEASURE

Regressions Number

High School Subjects (normal reading)

Sample	Mean		Sigma		r		C.R. S	C.R. M
			LORNA DOONE					
Ia	306.4±	24.90	78.7±	17.61				
If	301.5	27.79	87.9	19.66	.907±	.056	0.82	0.42
IIf	307.3	28.64	90.6	20.25	.970	.019	1.70	0.12
IIIf	305.6	24.34	77.0	16.92	.913	.053	0.17	0.08
IVf	313.7	24.99	79.0	17.67	.921	.048	0.03	0.74
Vf	299.1	23.61	74.7	16.69	.846	.090	0.31	0.54
VIf	294.5	21.18	67.0	14.98	.814	.107	0.86	0.82
VIIf	285.6	17.57	55.6	12.42	.718	.153	1.50	1.20
VIIIf	297.2	17.45	55.2	12.34	.762	.133	1.62	0.57
IXf	295.4	20.28	64.1	14.34	.798	.115	1.05	0.73
Xf	287.7	18.23	57.6	12.99	.862	.081	1.79	1.44
XIf	303.6	20.59	65.1	14.56	.813	.107	1.00	0.19
XIIf	297.0	21.04	66.5	14.87	.773	.127	0.82	0.59
			ADAM SMITH					
Ia	318.1±	29.82	94.3±	21.09				
If	323.3	32.36	102.3	22.88	.938±	.038	0.73	0.46
IIf	332.9	31.32	99.0	22.15	.896	.062	0.34	1.06
IIIf	336.5	32.30	102.1	22.84	.958	.026	0.86	1.97
IVf	327.9	32.78	103.7	23.18	.892	.065	0.66	0.66
Vf	326.7	26.49	83.8	18.73	.946	.033	1.11	0.87
VIf	327.7	27.98	88.5	19.79	.953	.029	0.66	1.06
VIIf	325.9	26.60	84.1	18.81	.911	.054	0.86	0.63
VIIIf	323.3	28.78	91.0	20.35	.912	.053	0.27	0.42
IXf	315.3	22.43	70.9	15.86	.947	.033	2.38	0.25
Xf	313.8	25.96	82.1	18.36	.895	.063	0.96	0.32
XIf	326.9	30.50	96.4	21.56	.917	.050	0.17	0.71
XIIf	305.6	27.11	85.7	19.17	.964	.022	1.10	1.54

Table 22

SUMMARY OF DATA ACCORDING TO EYE-MOVEMENT MEASURE

Regressions per Line

High School Subjects (normal reading)

Sample	Mean		Sigma		r		C.R. S	C.R. M
				LORNA DOONE				
Ia	2.511±	.2456	.777±	.1735				
If	2.385	.3558	1.125	.2516	.952±	.030	2.91	0.88
IIf	2.274	.2888	.913	.2042	.962	.024	1.73	2.79
IIIf	2.253	.2567	.812	.1814	.871	.076	0.28	2.01
IVf	2.450	.3344	1.057	.2364	.870	.077	1.81	0.36
Vf	2.354	.3072	.972	.2172	.910	.054	1.60	1.19
VIf	2.228	.3003	.950	.2124	.847	.089	1.16	1.77
VIIf	2.301	.2828	.894	.2000	.905	.057	1.02	1.74
VIIIf	2.248	.2713	.858	.1918	.859	.083	0.61	1.89
IXf	2.185	.2360	.746	.1667	.907	.056	0.30	3.14
Xf	2.315	.3084	.975	.2179	.828	.099	1.23	1.13
XIf	2.477	.2988	.945	.2112	.808	.110	1.03	0.19
XIIf	2.238	.2504	.792	.1769	.723	.151	0.09	1.48
				ADAM SMITH				
Ia	2.681±	.3329	1.053±	.2354				
If	2.630	.3172	1.003	.2243	.961±	.024	0.55	0.56
IIf	2.862	.3408	1.077	.2408	.881	.071	0.15	1.10
IIIf	2.689	.3217	1.017	.2274	.942	.036	0.33	0.07
IVf	2.826	.3965	1.254	.2804	.942	.036	1.55	1.04
Vf	2.728	.3058	.967	.2161	.898	.061	0.61	0.32
VIf	2.864	.3697	1.169	.2613	.840	.093	0.60	0.91
VIIf	2.720	.3500	1.107	.2474	.950	.031	0.50	0.36
VIIIf	2.612	.2328	.736	.1646	.935	.040	2.61	0.49
IXf	2.670	.2296	.726	.1622	.822	.102	1.88	0.06
Xf	2.889	.3567	1.128	.2522	.923	.047	0.56	1.52
XIf	2.688	.3325	1.052	.2349	.923	.047	0.01	0.05
XIIf	2.692	.3341	1.056	.2362	.881	.071	0.02	0.07

Table 23

SUMMARY OF DATA ACCORDING TO EYE-MOVEMENT MEASURE

Blinking Number

Grant Study Subjects (microfilm reading)

Sample	Mean		Sigma		r		C.R. S	C.R. M
			LORNA DOONE					
Ia	43.0±	11.51	36.4±	8.14				
If	45.0	9.83	31.1	6.95	.705±	.159	0.69	0.24
IIf	46.3	8.92	28.2	6.31	.799	.114	1.29	0.48
IIIf	44.0	7.91	25.0	5.59	.642	.186	1.47	0.11
IVf	42.8	7.95	25.1	5.62	.870	.077	2.12	0.03
Vf	47.3	10.70	33.8	7.56	.947	.033	0.72	1.16
VIf	47.5	9.95	31.4	7.03	.931	.042	1.23	1.05
VIIf	44.3	10.43	33.0	7.37	.978	.014	1.41	0.52
VIIIf	46.1	8.65	27.3	6.12	.810	.109	1.47	0.46
IXf	43.9	9.57	30.2	6.77	.949	.031	1.74	0.23
Xf	42.8	8.76	27.7	6.19	.898	.061	1.80	0.04
XIf	39.9	9.14	28.9	6.46	.966	.021	2.39	0.87
XIIf	41.7	8.95	28.3	6.33	.869	.077	1.52	0.22
			ADAM SMITH					
Ia	43.7±	12.31	38.9±	8.71				
If	41.5	10.75	34.0	7.61	.881±	.071	0.88	0.38
IIf	40.9	10.03	31.7	7.09	.895	.063	1.38	0.60
IIIf	45.2	10.39	32.9	7.35	.938	.038	1.44	0.34
IVf	51.5	10.68	33.8	7.55	.950	.031	1.35	1.95
Vf	43.5	8.59	27.1	6.07	.886	.068	2.16	0.03
VIf	51.1	11.05	34.9	7.82	.898	.061	0.77	1.36
VIIf	59.3	15.81	50.0	11.18	.878	.072	2.39	2.02
VIIIf	60.4	11.89	37.6	8.42	.875	.074	0.22	2.74
IXf	52.7	11.72	37.1	8.29	.967	.020	0.62	2.83
Xf	63.2	13.42	42.4	9.49	.722	.151	0.39	2.02
XIf	57.7	13.41	42.4	9.48	.820	.104	0.47	1.79
XIIf	59.7	13.67	43.2	9.67	.753	.137	0.50	1.74

Table 24

SUMMARY OF DATA ACCORDING TO EYE-MOVEMENT MEASURE

Fixations Number

Grant Study Subjects (microfilm reading)

Sample	Mean	Sigma	r	C.R. S	C.R. M
		LORNA DOONE			
Ia	1183.5±30.57	96.7±21.62			
If	1150.3 28.32	89.6 20.02	.937±.039	0.69	3.11
IIf	1119.4 32.81	103.7 23.19	.769 .129	0.34	2.96
IIIf	1095.3 36.57	115.6 25.85	.685 .168	0.76	3.24
IVf	1126.3 46.05	145.6 32.56	.895 .063	2.45	2.47
Vf	1104.2 36.13	114.3 25.54	.783 .122	0.84	3.51
VIf	1084.2 40.50	128.1 28.65	.719 .153	1.33	3.52
VIIf	1132.8 34.08	107.8 24.09	.567 .214	0.42	1.68
VIIIf	1103.2 42.48	134.3 30.04	.777 .125	1.55	2.99
IXf	1084.3 27.04	85.5 19.12	.519 .231	0.45	3.49
Xf	1090.1 34.83	110.1 24.62	.774 .127	0.64	4.18
XIf	1063.2 30.08	95.1 21.27	.107 .313	0.05	2.97
XIIf	1144.8 33.30	105.3 23.54	.770 .129	0.42	1.78
		ADAM SMITH			
Ia	1116.9±23.71	75.0±16.76			
If	1083.5 21.56	68.2 15.25	.600±.202	0.37	1.64
IIf	1045.2 26.93	85.2 19.04	.618 .195	0.51	3.21
IIIf	1031.2 29.54	93.4 20.89	.316 .285	0.72	2.72
IVf	1057.9 28.18	89.1 19.92	.342 .279	0.58	1.97
Vf	1090.0 27.75	87.8 19.62	.225 .300	0.51	0.81
VIf	1033.2 19.55	61.8 13.83	-.034 .316	0.61	2.68
VIIf	1072.6 21.22	67.1 15.01	-.628 .192	0.45	1.09
VIIIf	1038.2 25.95	82.1 18.36	.474 .245	0.32	3.08
IXf	1049.4 30.54	96.6 21.59	-.162 .308	0.80	1.62
Xf	1036.3 22.02	69.6 15.57	.507 .235	0.27	3.54
XIf	1084.6 24.47	77.4 17.30	.510 .234	0.12	1.35
XIIf	993.1 32.42	102.5 22.92	-.429 .258	1.07	2.60

Table 25

SUMMARY OF DATA ACCORDING TO EYE-MOVEMENT MEASURE

Fixations per Line

Grant Study Subjects (microfilm reading)

Sample	Mean		Sigma		r		C.R. S	C.R. M
				LORNA DOONE				
Ia	8.43±	.625	1.97±	.442				
If	8.43	.673	2.13	.475	.982±	.011	1.26	0.00
IIf	8.47	.572	1.81	.404	.979	.013	1.28	0.31
IIIf	8.42	.722	2.28	.511	.988	.008	2.54	0.07
IVf	8.68	.684	2.16	.484	.968	.020	1.13	1.44
Vf	8.21	.591	1.87	.417	.942	.036	0.49	1.06
VIf	8.39	.529	1.67	.374	.976	.015	2.11	0.25
VIIf	8.60	.649	2.05	.458	.994	.004	1.13	2.50
VIIIf	8.47	.662	2.09	.468	.978	.014	0.89	0.29
IXf	8.89	.619	1.96	.437	.944	.044	0.05	2.23
Xf	8.71	.520	1.64	.367	.966	.021	2.00	1.56
XIf	8.77	.603	1.90	.425	.959	.025	0.40	1.95
XIIf	8.29	.580	1.83	.410	.982	.011	1.21	1.19
				ADAM SMITH				
Ia	8.37±	.584	1.85±	.412				
If	8.04	.600	1.90	.424	.943±	.035	0.25	1.65
IIf	8.16	.512	1.62	.362	.896	.062	0.93	0.81
IIIf	8.12	.581	1.84	.411	.900	.060	0.04	0.96
IVf	8.05	.610	1.93	.431	.912	.053	0.33	1.31
Vf	8.19	.584	1.85	.412	.884	.069	0.00	0.64
VIf	8.17	.581	1.84	.410	.896	.062	0.04	0.76
VIIf	8.25	.563	1.78	.397	.941	.036	0.36	0.61
VIIIf	8.18	.502	1.59	.355	.942	.036	1.36	0.94
IXf	8.30	.448	1.42	.316	.942	.036	2.18	0.32
Xf	8.26	.587	1.86	.415	.934	.040	0.05	0.51
XIf	8.09	.670	2.12	.473	.919	.049	1.06	1.05
XIIf	8.60	.699	2.21	.494	.796	.116	0.91	0.54

Table 26

SUMMARY OF DATA ACCORDING TO EYE-MOVEMENT MEASURE

Fixation Sigma Score

Grant Study Subjects (microfilm reading)

Sample	Mean		Sigma		r		C.R. S	C.R. M
			LORNA DOONE					
Ia	2.84±	.248	.78±	.175				
If	3.01	.227	.72	.160	.888±	.067	0.54	0.99
IIf	2.95	.249	.79	.176	.871	.076	0.08	0.87
IIIf	3.03	.267	.84	.189	.952	.030	0.75	2.32
IVf	2.95	.274	.87	.194	.928	.044	0.91	1.07
Vf	2.83	.213	.67	.150	.899	.061	1.05	0.09
VIf	3.02	.219	.69	.155	.907	.056	0.89	1.71
VIIf	3.19	.218	.69	.154	.876	.074	0.79	2.92
VIIIf	2.96	.201	.64	.142	.844	.091	1.12	0.90
IXf	3.17	.149	.47	.105	.582	.209	1.81	1.63
Xf	3.06	.277	.88	.196	.935	.040	1.05	2.24
XIf	3.26	.240	.76	.170	.767	.130	0.13	2.51
XIIf	2.93	.198	.63	.140	.870	.077	1.30	0.72
			ADAM SMITH					
Ia	2.92±	.253	.80±	.179				
If	2.88	.224	.71	.158	.710±	.157	0.53	0.22
IIf	3.02	.258	.82	.182	.670	.174	0.10	0.48
IIIf	2.85	.193	.61	.136	.471	.246	0.95	0.30
IVf	3.04	.275	.87	.194	.808	.110	0.45	0.73
Vf	2.84	.217	.69	.154	.614	.197	0.59	0.38
VIf	2.94	.146	.46	.103	.653	.181	2.07	0.10
VIIf	3.00	.250	.79	.177	.756	.136	0.06	0.45
VIIIf	2.89	.188	.60	.133	.557	.218	1.07	0.14
IXf	3.06	.223	.71	.158	.644	.185	0.49	0.69
Xf	2.97	.173	.55	.122	.701	.161	1.56	0.28
XIf	3.09	.245	.78	.173	.622	.194	0.10	0.77
XIIf	2.89	.182	.58	.128	.819	.104	1.65	0.20

Table 27

SUMMARY OF DATA ACCORDING TO EYE-MOVEMENT MEASURE

Lines Read Number

Grant Study Subjects (microfilm reading)

Sample	Mean		Sigma		r		C.R. S	C.R. M
				LORNA DOONE				
Ia	147.1±	11.01	34.8±	7.78				
If	143.8	10.19	32.2	7.20	.949±	.031	0.76	0.95
IIf	137.3	9.30	29.4	6.58	.955	.028	1.67	2.80
IIIf	138.5	10.96	34.6	7.75	.918	.050	0.04	1.93
IVf	138.3	12.74	40.3	9.01	.955	.028	1.47	2.23
Vf	141.5	10.85	34.3	7.67	.958	.026	0.16	1.76
VIf	135.0	10.82	34.2	7.65	.943	.035	0.16	3.29
VIIf	138.4	9.90	31.3	7.00	.911	.054	0.80	1.91
VIIIf	138.8	12.28	38.8	8.68	.984	.010	1.75	3.44
IXf	127.3	8.29	26.2	5.86	.900	.060	1.87	3.91
Xf	131.4	10.17	32.2	7.19	.983	.011	1.27	7.37
XIf	126.4	8.11	25.6	5.73	.591	.206	1.17	2.29
XIIf	144.0	9.23	29.2	6.53	.928	.044	1.41	0.73
				ADAM SMITH				
Ia	138.6±	8.41	26.6±	5.95				
If	140.9	8.70	27.5	6.15	.829±	.099	0.19	0.46
IIf	132.8	8.02	25.4	5.67	.774	.127	0.23	1.05
IIIf	132.7	8.78	27.8	6.21	.823	.099	0.24	1.15
IVf	138.8	9.81	31.0	6.93	.834	.096	0.86	0.04
Vf	137.9	8.76	27.7	6.19	.829	.099	0.23	0.14
VIf	131.7	7.75	24.5	5.48	.917	.050	0.65	2.06
VIIf	134.6	7.84	24.8	5.54	.801	.113	0.37	0.78
VIIIf	131.1	7.65	24.2	5.41	.686	.167	0.41	1.17
IXf	129.4	6.93	21.9	4.90	.660	.178	0.81	1.42
Xf	131.4	8.59	27.2	6.07	.862	.081	0.14	1.61
XIf	141.4	9.43	29.8	6.67	.760	.134	0.55	0.45
XIIf	125.3	9.48	30.0	6.71	.526	.229	0.44	1.52

Table 28

SUMMARY OF DATA ACCORDING TO EYE-MOVEMENT MEASURE

Regressions Number

Grant Study Subjects (microfilm reading)

Sample	Mean		Sigma		r		C. R. S	C. R. M
			LORNA DOONE					
Ia	294.8±	30.07	95.1±	21.26				
If	285.7	28.85	91.2	20.40	.943±	.035	0.40	0.91
IIf	314.3	29.86	94.4	21.11	.861	.082	0.04	1.23
IIIf	292.8	27.07	85.6	19.14	.903	.058	0.76	0.16
IVf	299.7	25.31	80.1	17.90	.912	.053	1.27	0.39
Vf	291.6	21.38	67.6	15.12	.768	.130	1.58	0.16
VIf	284.6	21.63	68.4	15.30	.862	.081	1.88	0.64
VIIf	319.5	21.90	69.2	15.48	.842	.092	1.72	1.49
VIIIf	291.1	23.08	73.0	16.32	.870	.077	1.59	0.24
IXf	309.0	19.04	60.2	13.46	.776	.126	2.06	0.73
Xf	306.0	24.15	76.4	17.08	.826	.100	1.19	0.66
XIf	300.3	25.27	79.9	17.87	.854	.086	1.03	0.35
XIIf	316.8	26.52	83.9	18.75	.838	.094	0.72	1.34
			ADAM SMITH					
Ia	284.7±	28.90	91.4±	20.43				
If	268.2	23.06	72.9	16.30	.911±	.054	1.62	1.34
IIf	264.4	21.17	66.9	14.97	.873	.075	1.85	1.38
IIIf	270.8	20.34	64.3	14.39	.577	.211	1.31	0.58
IVf	282.3	23.93	75.7	16.92	.656	.180	0.78	0.11
Vf	289.2	19.88	62.9	13.70	.466	.248	1.30	0.17
VIf	283.4	22.68	71.7	16.04	.638	.188	0.98	0.06
VIIf	289.5	25.65	81.1	18.14	.860	.082	0.73	0.32
VIIIf	266.3	20.58	65.1	14.55	.905	.057	2.20	1.36
IXf	288.3	22.60	71.5	15.98	.768	.130	1.17	0.19
Xf	271.1	16.20	51.2	11.46	.779	.124	2.47	0.71
XIf	281.8	24.83	78.5	17.56	.805	.111	0.80	0.17
XIIf	260.1	23.94	75.7	16.93	.831	.098	1.04	1.53

Table 29

SUMMARY OF DATA ACCORDING TO EYE-MOVEMENT MEASURE

Regressions per Line

Grant Study Subjects (microfilm reading)

Sample	Mean		Sigma		r		C.R. S	C.R. M
				LORNA DOONE				
Ia	2.243±	.4200	1.328±	.2970				
If	2.233	.4229	1.337	.2990	.979±	.013	0.10	0.12
IIf	2.490	.3998	1.264	.2818	.962	.024	0.57	2.15
IIIf	2.451	.4855	1.535	.3433	.990	.006	2.65	2.27
IVf	2.460	.4282	1.353	.3026	.993	.004	0.49	4.43
Vf	2.277	.3643	1.152	.2577	.916	.051	1.09	0.20
VIf	2.308	.3211	1.015	.2269	.958	.026	2.47	0.45
VIIf	2.556	.3923	1.240	.2773	.986	.009	1.24	4.26
VIIIf	2.411	.4373	1.383	.3092	.970	.019	0.52	1.58
IXf	2.626	.3500	1.106	.2474	.970	.019	2.11	3.27
Xf	2.553	.3846	1.216	.2718	.954	.028	0.91	2.44
XIf	2.608	.4182	1.322	.2956	.964	.022	0.05	3.25
XIIf	2.371	.3441	1.088	.2433	.977	.014	2.47	1.15
				ADAM SMITH				
Ia	2.269±	.3968	1.254±	.2805				
If	2.114	.3715	1.175	.2627	.950±	.031	0.65	1.18
IIf	2.169	.3405	1.076	.2406	.922	.047	1.20	0.64
IIIf	2.271	.3688	1.166	.2608	.896	.062	0.51	0.01
IVf	2.321	.4404	1.392	.3113	.900	.060	0.75	0.27
Vf	2.268	.3320	1.050	.2347	.848	.089	1.03	0.00
VIf	2.343	.3608	1.141	.2551	.886	.068	0.64	0.40
VIIf	2.351	.3773	1.193	.2666	.971	.018	0.65	0.86
VIIIf	2.202	.3237	1.024	.2289	.962	.024	2.07	0.54
IXf	2.253	.2362	.747	.1670	.950	.031	3.42	0.08
Xf	2.264	.3271	1.034	.2313	.932	.042	1.58	0.03
XIf	2.247	.4009	1.268	.2834	.928	.044	0.09	0.14
XIIf	2.355	.4212	1.332	.2978	.946	.033	0.58	0.63

Table 30

SUMMARY OF DATA ACCORDING TO EYE-MOVEMENT MEASURE

Blinking Number

High School Subjects (microfilm reading)

Sample	Mean	Sigma	r	C.R. S	C.R. M
		LORNA DOONE			
Ia	23.0±5.19	16.4±3.67			
If	23.1 4.44	14.0 3.14	.744±.141	0.74	0.03
IIf	24.2 4.17	13.2 2.95	.839 .094	1.22	0.42
IIIf	20.4 3.69	11.7 2.61	.778 .125	1.60	0.80
IVf	21.1 3.38	10.7 2.38	.413 .262	1.42	0.39
Vf	25.9 4.30	13.6 3.04	.663 .177	0.78	0.73
VIf	24.1 4.55	14.4 3.22	.434 .257	0.45	0.21
VIIf	32.7 6.58	20.8 4.66	.834 .096	1.31	2.66
VIIIf	23.5 3.56	11.2 2.51	.520 .231	1.35	0.11
IXf	24.0 3.63	11.5 2.56	.527 .228	1.27	0.22
Xf	25.0 5.12	16.2 3.62	.620 .195	0.05	0.44
XIf	29.2 6.28	19.9 4.44	.775 .126	0.95	1.56
XIIf	34.6 8.75	27.7 6.19	.057 .315	1.57	1.17
		ADAM SMITH			
Ia	21.9±3.08	9.7±2.18			
If	28.9 5.58	17.6 3.94	.999±.001	4.44	2.79
IIf	27.6 6.51	20.6 4.60	.780 .124	2.94	1.26
IIIf	25.9 7.94	25.1 5.61	.804 .112	3.41	0.69
IVf	26.2 4.73	14.9 3.35	.866 .079	2.33	1.67
Vf	27.8 3.79	12.0 2.68	.853 .086	1.24	2.96
VIf	33.3 6.61	20.9 4.67	.874 .075	3.37	2.72
VIIf	28.2 5.37	17.0 3.80	.722 .151	2.25	1.66
VIIIf	31.9 5.90	18.6 4.17	.779 .124	2.67	2.50
IXf	30.7 7.09	22.4 5.02	.639 .187	2.77	1.56
Xf	33.8 6.38	20.2 4.51	.876 .074	3.32	3.00
XIf	32.4 9.29	29.4 6.57	.765 .131	3.53	1.46
XIIf	43.8 8.54	27.0 6.04	.993 .004	4.44	3.99

Table 31

SUMMARY OF DATA ACCORDING TO EYE-MOVEMENT MEASURE

Fixations Number

High School Subjects (microfilm reading)

Sample	Mean		Sigma		r		C.R. S	C.R. M
				LORNA DOONE				
Ia	1144.5±	24.29	76.8±	17.18				
If	1157.1	32.88	104.0	23.25	.439±	.255	1.04	0.40
IIf	1126.5	36.78	116.3	26.01	.735	.145	1.79	0.72
IIIf	1115.1	30.10	95.2	21.29	.332	.281	0.71	0.92
IVf	1104.9	34.42	108.8	24.33	.810	.109	1.74	1.93
Vf	1070.8	33.99	107.5	24.03	.796	.116	1.64	3.55
VIf	1067.2	23.05	72.9	16.29	.554	.219	0.20	3.45
VIIf	1064.9	29.05	91.9	20.54	.909	.055	1.31	6.48
VIIIf	1075.2	19.88	62.9	14.06	.791	.118	1.01	4.66
IXf	1066.9	24.18	76.5	17.10	.359	.275	0.01	2.83
Xf	1083.9	27.86	88.1	19.70	.725	.150	0.62	3.09
XIf	1103.9	45.44	143.7	32.13	.855	.085	2.93	1.47
XIIf	1107.3	38.99	123.3	27.57	.874	.075	2.55	1.74
				ADAM SMITH				
Ia	1135.1±	36.88	116.5±	26.06				
If	1063.0	42.24	133.6	29.87	.617±	.196	0.55	2.06
IIf	1063.1	52.61	166.3	37.20	.753	.137	1.60	2.08
IIIf	1116.8	47.14	149.2	33.34	.704	.160	1.07	0.54
IVf	1058.9	50.79	160.6	35.91	.703	.160	1.36	2.11
Vf	1081.5	53.68	169.8	37.96	.548	.221	1.36	1.18
VIf	1082.1	40.75	128.9	28.81	.483	.242	0.36	1.34
VIIf	1066.9	41.21	130.3	29.14	.484	.242	0.40	1.71
VIIIf	1056.2	45.64	144.3	32.27	.432	.257	0.74	1.77
IXf	1041.0	40.66	128.6	28.75	.632	.190	0.40	2.82
Xf	1066.0	46.79	147.9	33.09	.610	.198	0.93	1.82
XIf	1084.1	40.69	128.7	28.77	.377	.271	0.34	1.18
XIIf	1024.4	34.40	108.7	24.32	.303	.287	0.23	2.63

Table 32

SUMMARY OF DATA ACCORDING TO EYE-MOVEMENT MEASURE

Fixations per Line

High School Subjects (microfilm reading)

Sample	Mean	Sigma	r	C.R. S	C.R. M
		LORNA DOONE			
Ia	11.89±.630	1.99±.445			
If	11.42 .538	1.70 .379	.955±.028	1.57	2.40
IIf	11.98 .637	2.01 .451	.866 .079	0.06	0.27
IIIf	11.49 .663	2.10 .469	.912 .053	0.41	1.46
IVf	11.62 .677	2.14 .479	.815 .106	0.40	0.68
Vf	11.80 .561	1.77 .396	.791 .118	0.60	0.23
VIf	11.62 .532	1.68 .376	.854 .086	1.01	0.82
VIIf	11.74 .720	2.28 .509	.802 .113	0.71	0.35
VIIIf	12.01 .723	2.29 .511	.961 .024	1.52	0.57
IXf	11.88 .582	1.84 .411	.971 .018	1.01	0.06
Xf	11.86 .504	1.59 .356	.899 .061	1.53	0.11
XIf	11.47 .523	1.65 .369	.758 .134	0.89	1.02
XIIf	11.66 .533	1.68 .377	.758 .134	0.81	0.47
		ADAM SMITH			
Ia	12.16±.549	1.73±.387			
If	12.71 .677	2.14 .479	.606±.200	0.83	0.99
IIf	12.53 .598	1.89 .423	.806 .111	0.47	1.03
IIIf	12.13 .640	2.02 .453	.771 .128	0.76	0.07
IVf	12.10 .711	2.25 .502	.742 .142	1.20	0.13
Vf	12.68 .755	2.39 .534	.524 .229	1.16	0.79
VIf	12.19 .642	2.03 .454	.481 .243	0.57	0.05
VIIf	12.26 .617	1.95 .436	.490 .240	0.43	0.17
VIIIf	12.79 .662	2.09 .468	.585 .208	0.73	1.12
IXf	12.60 .662	2.09 .468	.528 .228	0.69	0.74
Xf	11.84 .608	1.92 .430	.531 .227	0.39	0.57
XIf	12.45 .644	2.04 .455	.486 .242	0.59	0.48
XIIf	12.63 .607	1.92 .429	.570 .213	0.40	0.87

Table 33

SUMMARY OF DATA ACCORDING TO EYE-MOVEMENT MEASURE

Fixation Sigma Score

High School Subjects (microfilm reading)

Sample	Mean		Sigma		r		C.R. S	C.R. M
				LORNA DOONE				
Ia	3.76±	.136	.43±	.096				
If	3.70	.123	.39	.087	.614±	.197	0.39	0.53
IIf	3.80	.154	.49	.109	.603	.201	0.52	0.31
IIIf	3.84	.139	.44	.093	.616	.196	0.10	0.67
IVf	3.50	.218	.69	.154	.401	.265	1.55	1.26
Vf	3.94	.142	.45	.100	.292	.289	0.15	1.09
VIf	4.15	.230	.73	.163	.459	.250	1.76	1.88
VIIf	3.84	.141	.44	.099	.482	.243	0.08	0.57
VIIIf	3.83	.172	.54	.122	.518	.231	0.83	0.45
IXf	3.84	.147	.46	.104	.402	.265	0.23	0.52
Xf	3.86	.124	.39	.088	.247	.297	0.32	0.62
XIf	3.97	.133	.42	.094	-.051	.315	0.07	1.08
XIIf	3.86	.101	.32	.071	.548	.221	1.09	0.86
				ADAM SMITH				
Ia	3.40±	.173	.55±	.122				
If	4.11	.191	.60	.135	.554±	.219	0.33	4.13
IIf	3.98	.205	.65	.145	.764	.132	0.81	4.36
IIIf	3.82	.183	.58	.130	.514	.233	0.20	2.40
IVf	3.98	.164	.52	.116	.297	.288	0.19	2.91
Vf	3.93	.195	.62	.138	.572	.213	0.46	3.10
VIf	3.87	.177	.56	.125	.468	.247	0.06	2.61
VIIf	4.01	.119	.38	.084	.588	.207	1.39	4.36
VIIIf	4.03	.139	.44	.098	.475	.245	0.80	3.89
IXf	4.40	.079	.25	.056	.167	.307	2.26	5.65
Xf	3.82	.188	.59	.133	-.083	.314	0.22	1.58
XIf	3.95	.166	.52	.117	.944	.034	0.54	10.00
XIIf	4.12	.106	.33	.075	.281	.291	1.59	4.11

Table 34

SUMMARY OF DATA ACCORDING TO EYE-MOVEMENT MEASURE

Lines Read Number

High School Subjects (microfilm reading)

Sample	Mean		Sigma		r		C.R. S	C.R. M
			LORNA DOONE					
Ia	99.4±	6.38	20.2±	4.51				
If	102.9	5.12	16.2	3.62	.770±	.129	1.06	0.86
IIf	96.6	6.22	19.7	4.40	.763	.132	0.13	0.64
IIIf	100.4	6.98	22.1	4.94	.684	.168	0.39	0.19
IVf	98.5	6.61	20.9	4.67	.634	.189	0.14	0.16
Vf	92.7	5.51	17.4	3.90	.636	.188	0.61	1.30
VIf	94.1	5.36	17.0	3.79	.820	.104	0.93	1.44
VIIf	95.1	7.59	24.0	5.36	.854	.086	1.02	1.09
VIIIf	93.7	7.31	23.1	5.17	.955	.028	1.36	2.53
IXf	91.8	4.93	15.6	3.49	.844	.091	1.45	2.20
Xf	93.1	5.40	17.1	3.82	.757	.135	0.79	1.49
XIf	99.0	7.08	22.4	5.01	.822	.102	0.57	0.10
XIIf	97.3	6.29	19.9	4.33	.857	.084	0.09	0.62
			ADAM SMITH					
Ia	95.3±	7.84	24.8±	5.54				
If	86.1	6.27	19.8	4.43	.567±	.214	0.85	1.37
IIf	87.2	6.91	21.9	4.89	.809	.109	0.66	1.74
IIIf	94.8	6.81	21.5	4.82	.822	.102	0.78	0.11
IVf	91.5	7.96	25.2	5.63	.825	.101	0.09	0.81
Vf	89.0	7.60	24.0	5.37	.553	.220	0.12	0.86
VIf	91.3	6.12	19.4	4.33	.528	.228	0.90	0.59
VIIf	89.1	6.26	19.8	4.43	.583	.209	0.86	0.94
VIIIf	85.4	6.46	20.4	4.57	.644	.185	0.80	1.60
IXf	84.8	5.70	18.0	4.03	.634	.189	1.26	1.72
Xf	91.6	7.03	22.2	4.97	.645	.185	0.46	0.59
XIf	89.1	5.71	18.1	4.04	.415	.262	1.07	0.82
XIIf	83.3	5.61	17.7	3.97	.476	.244	1.18	1.68

Table 35

SUMMARY OF DATA ACCORDING TO EYE-MOVEMENT MEASURE

Regressions Number

High School Subjects (microfilm reading)

Sample	Mean		Sigma		r		C.R. S	C.R. M
			LORNA DOONE					
Ia	485.9±	19.91	63.0±	14.08				
If	481.4	25.16	79.6	17.79	.856±	.084	1.36	0.34
IIf	480.3	24.95	78.9	17.64	.921	.048	1.70	0.55
IIIf	472.7	20.88	66.0	14.76	.852	.087	0.28	1.18
IVf	475.4	24.69	78.1	17.46	.861	.082	1.28	0.83
Vf	489.5	20.72	65.5	14.65	.906	.057	0.29	0.41
VIf	474.4	22.08	69.8	15.62	.898	.061	0.73	1.18
VIIf	461.0	20.21	63.9	14.29	.816	.106	0.08	2.05
VIIIf	476.7	18.32	57.9	12.95	.726	.150	0.39	0.65
IXf	474.5	22.75	71.9	16.09	.744	.141	0.62	0.74
Xf	481.4	19.39	61.3	13.71	.926	.045	0.23	0.59
XIf	465.0	15.90	50.3	11.24	.526	.229	0.82	1.18
XIIf	465.8	16.47	52.1	11.64	.811	.108	1.00	1.72
			ADAM SMITH					
Ia	512.4±	22.92	72.5±	16.21				
If	505.0	27.05	85.5	19.13	.884±	.069	1.08	0.58
IIf	509.3	31.16	98.5	22.03	.948	.032	2.52	0.26
IIIf	515.4	25.39	80.3	17.95	.923	.047	0.83	0.31
IVf	513.7	27.37	86.5	19.35	.874	.075	1.11	0.10
Vf	515.1	27.18	85.9	19.22	.925	.046	1.35	0.26
VIf	516.6	27.04	85.5	19.12	.922	.047	1.29	0.39
VIIf	527.4	31.53	99.7	22.29	.903	.058	2.08	1.02
VIIIf	538.1	27.83	88.0	19.68	.898	.061	1.33	2.07
IXf	529.3	31.07	98.3	21.97	.924	.046	2.20	1.28
Xf	522.3	26.05	82.4	18.42	.944	.034	1.18	1.13
XIf	530.1	30.50	96.4	21.56	.919	.049	2.04	1.36
XIIf	527.0	24.04	76.0	17.00	.968	.020	0.59	2.41

Table 36

SUMMARY OF DATA ACCORDING TO EYE-MOVEMENT MEASURE

Regressions per Line

High School Subjects (microfilm reading)

Sample	Mean		Sigma		r		C.R. S	C.R. M
				LORNA DOONE				
Ia	5.148±	.4781	1.512±	.3381				
If	4.811	.3945	1.248	.2789	.960±	.025	1.95	2.27
IIf	5.217	.5083	1.607	.3594	.985	.009	1.08	0.76
IIIf	4.967	.4596	1.453	.3250	.902	.059	0.29	0.87
IVf	5.122	.5609	1.774	.3966	.888	.067	1.07	0.10
Vf	5.538	.5662	1.790	.4004	.886	.068	1.12	1.48
VIf	5.236	.4279	1.353	.3025	.937	.038	0.98	0.52
VIIf	5.268	.5914	1.870	.4181	.897	.062	1.44	0.45
VIIIf	5.460	.5215	1.649	.3688	.934	.040	0.76	1.67
IXf	5.353	.4239	1.340	.2997	.910	.054	0.90	1.03
Xf	5.351	.4073	1.288	.2879	.946	.033	1.48	1.26
XIf	5.001	.4673	1.478	.3305	.838	.094	0.13	0.54
XIIf	5.026	.4214	1.333	.2980	.897	.062	0.88	0.57
				ADAM SMITH				
Ia	5.793±	.6435	2.035±	.4550				
If	6.209	.6657	2.105	.4708	.893±	.064	0.24	1.37
IIf	6.163	.5110	1.616	.3612	.869	.077	1.40	1.15
IIIf	5.717	.5263	1.664	.3722	.873	.075	1.26	0.25
IVf	6.222	.9046	2.860	.6396	.862	.081	1.92	0.90
Vf	6.280	.7726	2.443	.5463	.760	.134	0.87	0.96
VIf	5.883	.5258	1.662	.3718	.745	.141	0.94	0.21
VIIf	6.266	.6837	2.162	.4834	.739	.144	0.28	0.98
VIIIf	6.927	1.0118	3.200	.7154	.786	.121	2.07	1.76
IXf	6.609	.7241	2.290	.5120	.657	.180	0.49	1.43
Xf	6.067	.6316	1.997	.4465	.789	.119	0.10	0.66
XIf	6.280	.6822	2.157	.4823	.698	.162	0.26	0.94
XIIf	6.733	.7560	2.390	.5345	.751	.138	0.76	1.86

Table 37

NUMBER OF PAGES READ

Grant Study Subjects (normal reading)	D	S	High School Subjects (normal reading)	D	S
G.S.1	150	170	H.S.1	400	248
G.S.2	194	218	H.S.2	428	250
G.S.3	120	100	H.S.3	155	130
G.S.4	178	130	H.S.4	211	197
G.S.5	140	111	H.S.5	170	93
G.S.6	255	188	H.S.6	166	137
G.S.7	152	184	H.S.7	240	219
G.S.8	180	137	H.S.8	250	184
G.S.9	243	230	H.S.9	196	142
G.S.10	167	138	H.S.10	176	120

Grant Study Subjects (microfilm reading)	D	S	High School Subjects (microfilm reading)	D	S
G.S.M.1	151	110	H.S.M.1	119	96
G.S.M.2	278	161	H.S.M.2	248	203
G.S.M.3	234	192	H.S.M.3	225	228
G.S.M.4	249	166	H.S.M.4	200	143
G.S.M.5	219	180	H.S.M.5	114	88
G.S.M.6	122	106	H.S.M.6	128	124
G.S.M.7	241	180	H.S.M.7	165	147
G.S.M.8	124	208	H.S.M.8	169	108
G.S.M.9	209	182	H.S.M.9	328	260
G.S.M.10	128	112	H.S.M.10	170	116

Table 38

SUMMARY CHART OF EYE-MOVEMENT MEASURES
SHOWING SIGNIFICANT CHANGES

	Sigma	Mean
Lorna Doone G. S.		Fixations Number (6) Table 10 Fixations per Line (7) Table 11
H. S.	Lines Read Number (4) Table 20	Fixations per Line (5) Table 18
G. S. M.		Fixations Number (9) Table 24 Lines Read Number (4) Table 27 Regressions per Line (4) Table 29
H. S. M.		Fixations Number (5) Table 31
Adam Smith G. S.		Fixations Number (4) Table 10
H. S.	Blinking Number (2) Table 16	
G. S. M.		Fixations Number (3) Table 24
H. S. M.	Blinking Number (7) Table 30	Blinking Number (3) Table 30 Fixation Sigma Score (9) Table 33

Table 39

COMPARISON OF EXPERIMENTAL BOOKS--Pearson Product-Moment Correlation between sample of D and corresponding sample of S

Grant Study Subjects (normal reading)

	Blinking Number	Fixations Number	Fixations per Line	Fixation Sigma Sc.	Lines Read Number	Regressions Number	Regressions per Line
Ia	.871±.076	.768±.130	.634±.189	.383±.270	.820±.104	-.259±.295	.127±.311
If	.968 .020	.741 .142	.702 .160	.097 .313	.850 .088	-.439 .255	.219 .301
IIf	.950 .031	.764 .132	.875 .074	.738 .144	.903 .058	-.042 .316	.523 .230
IIIf	.860 .082	.901 .060	.735 .145	.040 .316	.953 .029	.108 .312	.405 .264
IVf	.872 .076	.720 .152	.697 .163	.498 .238	.817 .105	-.125 .311	.302 .287
Vf	.909 .055	.450 .252	.769 .129	.520 .231	.788 .120	.004 .316	.310 .286
VIf	.789 .119	.483 .242	.723 .151	.753 .137	.898 .061	-.241 .298	.204 .303
VIIf	.915 .051	.614 .197	.721 .152	.361 .275	.708 .158	-.326 .283	.228 .300
VIIIf	.834 .096	.721 .152	.561 .217	.560 .217	.740 .143	-.039 .316	.438 .256
IXf	.848 .089	.071 .315	.848 .089	.419 .261	.412 .262	.108 .312	.445 .254
Xf	.903 .058	.445 .254	.719 .153	.259 .295	.688 .166	-.160 .308	.399 .266
XIf	.922 .047	.858 .083	.849 .088	.650 .183	.883 .070	.029 .316	.584 .208
XIIf	.921 .048	.882 .070	.699 .162	.128 .311	.881 .071	-.097 .313	.585 .208

Table 40

COMPARISON OF EXPERIMENTAL BOOKS--Pearson Product-Moment Correlation between sample of D and corresponding sample of Ŝ

High School Subjects (normal reading)

	Blinking Number	Fixations Number	Fixations per Line	Fixation Sigma Sc.	Lines Read Number	Regressions Number	Regressions per Line
Ia	.772±.127	-.199±.304	.568±.214	.376±.272	.848±.089	.615±.197	.710±.157
If	.327 .282	.064 .315	.926 .045	.756 .136	.831 .098	.726 .150	.885 .068
IIf	.199 .304	-.150 .309	.902 .059	.719 .153	.718 .153	.688 .166	.933 .041
IIIf	.593 .205	.130 .311	.824 .102	.592 .205	.759 .134	.779 .124	.858 .083
IVf	.804 .112	.367 .274	.718 .153	.762 .133	.813 .107	.639 .187	.720 .152
Vf	.884 .069	.188 .305	.963 .023	.890 .066	.871 .076	.879 .072	.951 .030
VIf	.793 .117	.265 .294	.902 .059	.758 .134	.766 .131	.668 .175	.808 .110
VIIf	.799 .114	.493 .239	.818 .105	.473 .245	.801 .113	.843 .092	.819 .104
VIIIf	.914 .052	-.038 .316	.912 .053	.944 .034	.765 .131	.512 .233	.867 .078
IXf	.582 .209	.104 .313	.830 .098	.823 .102	.837 .095	.652 .182	.890 .066
Xf	.328 .282	.457 .250	.873 .075	.847 .089	.890 .066	.566 .215	.749 .139
XIf	.550 .220	.664 .177	.907 .056	.813 .107	.906 .057	.488 .241	.738 .144
XIIf	.737 .144	.030 .316	.884 .069	.878 .072	.884 .069	.550 .220	.787 .120

Table 41

COMPARISON OF EXPERIMENTAL BOOKS--Pearson Product-Moment Correlation between sample of D and corresponding sample of S

Grant Study Subjects (microfilm reading)

	Blinking Number	Fixations Number	Fixations per Line	Fixation Sigma Sc.	Lines Read Number	Regressions Number	Regressions per Line
Ia	.850±.088	.525±.229	.875±.074	.627±.192	.695±.163	.840±.093	.918±.050
If	.928 .044	.215 .302	.696 .163	.871 .076	.830 .098	.857 .084	.977 .014
IIf	.829 .099	.282 .291	.941 .036	.747 .140	.838 .094	.650 .183	.918 .050
IIIf	.725 .150	.624 .193	.972 .017	.649 .183	.923 .047	.742 .142	.968 .020
IVf	.874 .075	.389 .268	.961 .024	.846 .090	.727 .149	.764 .132	.795 .116
Vf	.753 .137	.653 .181	.916 .051	.577 .211	.830 .098	.545 .222	.822 .102
VIf	.888 .067	.111 .312	.911 .054	.747 .140	.645 .185	.612 .198	.919 .049
VIIf	.946 .033	-.047 .316	.934 .040	.780 .124	.752 .137	.744 .141	.945 .034
VIIIf	.756 .136	.123 .311	.925 .046	.796 .116	.698 .162	.767 .130	.968 .020
IXf	.847 .089	-.357 .276	.823 .102	.482 .243	.321 .284	.603 .201	.878 .072
Xf	.801 .113	.406 .264	.918 .050	.737 .144	.744 .141	.737 .144	.913 .053
XIf	.533 .226	.054 .315	.951 .030	.662 .178	.859 .082	.650 .183	.924 .046
XIIf	.602 .202	-.079 .314	.854 .086	.472 .246	.561 .217	.656 .180	.877 .073

Table 42

COMPARISON OF EXPERIMENTAL BOOKS--Pearson Product-Moment Correlation between sample of D and corresponding sample of S

High School Subjects (microfilm reading)

	Blinking Number	Fixations Number	Fixations per Line	Fixation Sigma Sc.	Lines Read Number	Regressions Number	Regressions per Line
Ia	.576±.211	.309±.286	.624±.193	.507±.235	.656±.180	.417±.261	.788±.120
If	.482 .243	.262 .294	.632 .190	.620 .195	.395 .267	.279 .292	.718 .153
IIf	.012 .316	.082 .314	.755 .136	.732 .147	.779 .124	.252 .296	.795 .116
IIIf	.166 .308	-.089 .314	.759 .134	.420 .260	.597 .204	.267 .294	.789 .119
IVf	.446 .253	.320 .284	.807 .110	-.309 .286	.785 .121	.138 .310	.868 .078
Vf	.822 .102	.268 .294	.714 .155	-.115 .312	.547 .222	.534 .226	.896 .062
VIf	.799 .114	.362 .275	.698 .162	.404 .265	.799 .114	.462 .460	.807 .110
VIIf	.446 .253	.192 .304	.762 .133	.338 .280	.706 .159	.410 .263	.800 .114
VIIIf	.608 .199	.540 .224	.850 .088	-.399 .266	.791 .118	.519 .231	.818 .105
IXf	.590 .206	-.013 .316	.703 .160	-.209 .302	.718 .153	.378 .271	.702 .160
Xf	.662 .178	.308 .286	.868 .078	.486 .242	.720 .152	.190 .305	.768 .130
XIf	.438 .256	.641 .186	.679 .170	-.094 .313	.714 .155	.615 .197	.847 .089
XIIf	.836 .095	.704 .160	.893 .064	.121 .312	.884 .069	.307 .286	.869 .077

Table 43

SUMMARY CHART OF EYE-MOVEMENT MEASURES SHOWING DIFFERENTIAL EFFECTS OF THE READING MATERIALS ON RELATIVE POSITION

	Trends	Low Coefficients
G. S. Table 39	Fixations Number (-) Regressions per Line (+)	Fixation Sigma Score Regressions Number Regressions per Line
H. S. Table 40	Fixation Sigma Score (+) Regressions Number (-)	Fixations Number Regressions Number
G. S. M. Table 41	Blinking Number (-) Lines Read Number (-)	Fixations Number Fixation Sigma Score
H. S. M. Table 42	Fixations per Line (+) Lines Read Number (+)	Fixations Number Fixation Sigma Score Regressions Number

Table 44

COMPARISON OF EXPERIMENTAL BOOKS--Critical Ratios

Grant Study Subjects (normal reading)

	Blinking Number	Fixations Number	Fixations per Line	Fixation Sigma Sc.	Lines Read Number	Regressions Number	Regressions per Line
Difference between MEAN SCORES							
Ia	1.70	1.44	2.32	0.12	1.53	1.48	1.15
If	1.09	0.62	3.12	0.40	2.33	1.31	1.38
IIf	1.90	2.20	3.12	0.21	1.28	1.39	1.27
IIIf	2.03	3.09	1.13	0.27	0.83	1.24	0.74
IVf	2.05	0.82	0.55	0.46	0.39	1.07	0.44
Vf	1.37	1.25	2.73	0.57	1.28	1.08	1.21
VIf	0.93	1.22	1.56	2.57	0.34	0.69	0.69
VIIf	0.64	2.68	3.17	2.28	0.89	1.48	1.47
VIIIf	1.88	1.44	3.21	1.38	1.30	0.80	1.31
IXf	1.87	1.26	2.99	0.18	0.18	1.20	1.39
Xf	2.76	3.30	2.66	0.81	0.40	1.27	0.63
XIf	1.48	2.41	3.19	0.29	1.08	1.32	1.45
XIIf	1.78	3.01	1.28	0.39	0.45	0.68	0.20
Difference between STANDARD DEVIATIONS							
Ia	0.01	1.00	0.92	0.43	1.64	0.06	0.64
If	0.23	0.51	0.00	0.88	1.26	1.31	1.28
IIf	2.00	1.07	0.51	0.33	1.37	0.35	1.20
IIIf	2.34	2.77	0.63	0.57	0.56	0.42	0.03
IVf	1.03	2.22	1.13	1.15	1.85	1.57	0.62
Vf	0.10	1.72	0.68	0.74	1.67	0.43	0.86
VIf	0.62	0.37	0.89	1.88	1.32	0.48	0.59
VIIf	1.44	0.32	0.54	0.28	0.43	1.50	2.26
VIIIf	1.29	1.17	0.36	1.36	1.57	1.74	2.76
IXf	0.18	1.15	1.10	1.31	0.58	1.58	3.03
Xf	0.80	0.59	1.09	0.24	0.65	1.48	2.54
XIf	1.39	1.03	0.59	1.15	0.86	1.34	1.40
XIIf	0.56	0.86	0.32	1.24	0.84	0.42	1.53

Table 45

COMPARISON OF EXPERIMENTAL BOOKS--Critical Ratios

High School Subjects (normal reading)

	Blinking Number	Fixations Number	Fixations per Line	Fixation Sigma Sc.	Lines Read Number	Regressions Number	Regressions per Line
Difference between MEAN SCORES							
Ia	2.13	0.47	0.13	0.10	0.38	0.48	0.72
If	1.01	0.55	1.00	1.89	1.54	0.96	1.48
IIf	1.51	1.07	3.72	2.16	2.93	1.08	4.69
IIIf	0.79	0.41	1.91	2.13	1.92	1.52	2.62
IVf	0.46	0.79	1.04	1.46	2.28	0.56	1.34
Vf	0.53	0.54	3.10	3.50	1.96	2.18	3.90
VIf	0.73	0.94	3.13	2.65	2.62	1.58	2.92
VIIf	0.69	0.25	1.03	1.14	1.08	2.66	2.08
VIIIf	1.49	1.20	1.84	5.11	2.47	1.05	2.69
IXf	0.97	1.56	2.37	3.73	2.79	1.11	4.43
Xf	0.60	0.92	3.15	2.88	3.52	1.20	2.39
XIf	0.08	0.25	1.16	0.41	0.75	0.86	0.92
XIIf	0.15	3.98	2.77	1.41	3.59	0.37	2.20
Difference between STANDARD DEVIATIONS							
Ia	2.33	0.30	0.57	0.55	0.06	0.72	1.31
If	1.50	0.61	1.80	0.14	3.00	0.69	0.77
IIf	1.52	0.37	0.36	0.34	1.61	0.38	1.38
IIIf	1.06	0.45	0.68	0.50	1.36	1.36	1.33
IVf	1.28	1.23	0.78	0.06	0.04	1.09	0.77
Vf	1.54	1.03	0.14	0.69	2.65	0.75	0.05
VIf	1.28	2.86	1.34	2.73	0.11	1.15	1.08
VIIf	0.29	0.86	1.08	0.46	1.68	2.15	1.14
VIIIf	3.48	2.12	1.88	3.07	1.27	1.72	0.95
IXf	2.00	0.99	1.00	0.59	0.18	0.42	0.19
Xf	2.55	0.62	0.47	1.90	0.38	1.31	0.69
XIf	0.06	0.90	0.66	0.80	0.78	1.36	0.50
XIIf	1.44	0.92	1.16	1.35	0.15	0.94	1.40

Table 46

COMPARISON OF EXPERIMENTAL BOOKS--Critical Ratios

Grant Study Subjects (microfilm reading)

	Blinking Number	Fixations Number	Fixations per Line	Fixation Sigma Sc.	Lines Read Number	Regressions Number	Regressions per Line
Difference between MEAN SCORES							
Ia	0.11	2.46	0.20	0.37	1.07	0.60	0.16
If	0.87	2.11	0.78	1.14	0.51	1.17	1.20
IIf	0.96	2.06	1.60	0.39	0.88	2.19	2.00
IIIf	0.17	2.18	1.42	0.88	1.31	1.21	1.14
IVf	1.62	1.57	3.28	0.59	0.06	1.02	0.50
Vf	0.54	0.48	0.08	0.05	0.59	0.12	0.04
VIf	0.71	1.19	0.92	0.54	0.40	0.06	0.24
VIIf	2.19	1.47	1.49	1.20	0.58	1.73	1.60
VIIIf	1.83	1.38	1.06	0.56	0.87	1.64	1.41
IXf	1.41	0.74	1.65	0.55	0.24	1.10	2.05
Xf	2.46	1.64	1.92	0.47	0.00	2.13	1.82
XIf	1.54	0.57	3.25	0.85	3.11	0.88	2.25
XIIf	1.65	3.14	0.85	0.20	2.13	2.69	0.08
Difference between STANDARD DEVIATIONS							
Ia	0.40	0.93	0.41	0.10	1.14	0.23	0.45
If	0.75	0.86	0.50	0.09	0.88	1.32	1.77
IIf	0.65	0.64	1.02	0.18	0.83	1.22	1.24
IIIf	1.22	0.85	2.42	1.28	1.67	1.32	2.75
IVf	1.78	1.59	1.24	0.00	1.17	0.28	0.15
Vf	1.03	1.07	0.08	0.11	1.17	0.27	0.51
VIf	0.72	2.09	0.74	1.77	1.32	0.19	0.92
VIIf	3.01	1.44	1.20	0.68	1.08	0.74	0.37
VIIIf	1.47	1.49	2.03	0.34	1.90	0.56	2.89
IXf	1.18	0.41	1.68	1.43	0.59	0.68	2.25
Xf	2.02	1.51	0.98	2.00	0.79	1.74	1.21
XIf	1.37	0.65	1.08	0.11	0.92	0.07	0.34
XIIf	1.58	0.08	1.11	0.30	0.10	0.43	1.28

Table 47

COMPARISON OF EXPERIMENTAL BOOKS--Critical Ratios

High School Subjects (microfilm reading)

	Blinking Number	Fixations Number	Fixations per Line	Fixation Sigma Sc.	Lines Read Number	Regressions Number	Regressions per Line
Difference between MEAN SCORES							
Ia	0.26	0.25	0.52	2.31	0.68	1.14	1.62
If	1.12	2.04	2.41	2.73	2.65	0.75	2.97
IIf	0.44	1.03	1.27	1.28	2.13	0.84	2.90
IIIf	0.67	0.03	1.41	0.11	0.90	1.51	2.29
IVf	1.15	0.89	1.11	1.55	1.42	1.12	2.19
Vf	0.77	0.19	1.66	0.04	0.57	1.08	2.03
VIf	2.28	0.38	1.22	1.23	0.75	1.63	2.08
VIIf	0.71	0.04	1.11	1.13	1.10	2.24	2.42
VIIIf	1.79	0.49	2.03	0.77	1.84	2.55	2.23
IXf	1.16	0.54	1.48	3.11	1.72	1.78	2.40
Xf	1.81	0.38	0.07	0.24	0.31	1.39	1.74
XIf	0.37	0.54	2.04	0.09	1.98	2.69	3.37
XIIf	1.86	2.90	3.57	1.90	4.76	2.48	3.86
Difference between STANDARD DEVIATIONS							
Ia	1.87	1.33	0.56	0.90	0.84	0.49	1.45
If	0.81	0.81	0.92	1.62	0.68	0.24	2.12
IIf	1.35	1.10	0.30	1.27	0.53	0.72	0.03
IIIf	2.19	1.37	0.19	0.96	0.11	0.64	0.69
IVf	1.14	1.25	0.27	0.92	0.94	0.32	2.53
Vf	0.69	1.43	1.39	1.00	1.17	0.99	1.99
VIf	1.80	1.80	0.82	0.90	0.69	0.72	1.07
VIIf	0.70	1.10	0.76	0.49	0.84	1.47	0.75
VIIIf	1.85	2.61	0.54	0.69	0.64	1.47	2.86
IXf	2.28	1.56	0.56	1.81	0.64	1.04	2.12
Xf	0.91	1.62	1.16	1.42	1.15	0.94	1.96
XIf	1.32	0.45	0.90	0.67	0.94	2.28	2.02
XIIf	0.15	0.56	0.92	0.10	0.80	1.21	2.89

Table 48

SUMMARY CHART OF EYE-MOVEMENT MEASURES
SHOWING DIFFERENTIAL EFFECTS OF THE
READING MATERIALS ON MEAN PERFORMANCE
AND DEGREE OF VARIABILITY

	Sigma	Mean
G. S. Table 44	Regressions per Line (1)	Fixations Number (3) Fixations per Line (6)
H. S. Table 45	Blinking Number (1) Fixation Sigma Score (1) Lines Read Number (1)	Fixations Number (1) Fixations per Line (4) Fixation Sigma Score (3) Lines Read Number (3) Regressions per Line (4)
G. S. M. Table 46	Blinking Number (1)	Fixations Number (1) Fixations per Line (2) Lines Read Number (1)
H. S. M. Table 47		Fixations per Line (1) Fixation Sigma Score (1) Lines Read Number (1) Regressions per Line (4)

Table 49

COMPARISON OF EXPERIMENTAL SITUATIONS--Critical Ratios of Mean Scores
Grant Study Subjects (normal reading) vs. Grant Study Subjects (microfilm reading)

	Blinking Number	Fixations Number	Fixations per Line	Fixation Sigma Sc.	Lines Read Number	Regressions Number	Regressions per Line
LORNA DOONE							
Ia	0.76	1.24	1.09	0.28	1.57	0.55	0.08
If	1.15	2.01	0.68	0.57	1.58	0.71	0.19
IIf	0.92	1.12	0.49	0.38	0.99	1.54	0.75
IIIf	1.24	0.93	0.35	0.63	0.92	0.96	0.47
IVf	1.60	1.54	0.01	0.00	0.93	0.81	0.40
Vf	1.35	1.40	0.39	0.12	1.21	1.20	0.36
VIf	0.90	1.00	0.39	1.68	0.23	1.53	1.02
VIIf	1.40	1.53	0.04	1.11	0.80	1.93	0.91
VIIIf	1.16	1.16	0.44	0.15	1.12	0.98	0.28
IXf	1.18	0.50	0.14	1.04	0.06	1.34	0.83
Xf	1.45	0.27	0.09	0.39	0.25	1.43	1.02
XIf	1.53	0.45	0.50	1.60	0.50	1.27	1.08
XIIf	1.52	1.49	0.03	0.69	0.74	1.97	0.88
ADAM SMITH							
Ia	1.41	0.55	0.00	0.47	0.22	1.45	0.92
If	1.55	0.84	0.06	0.43	0.33	1.48	0.80
IIf	1.59	0.51	0.04	0.69	0.17	1.31	0.80
IIIf	1.76	0.93	0.16	0.27	0.76	1.52	0.59
IVf	1.76	0.71	0.52	0.06	0.78	1.23	0.39
Vf	2.11	1.90	0.62	0.55	0.30	2.29	1.21
VIf	1.10	1.01	0.72	0.23	0.12	2.02	1.50
VIIf	0.67	1.98	0.86	1.34	0.10	2.25	1.55
VIIIf	1.08	1.03	0.78	0.40	0.13	0.95	0.81
IXf	1.53	0.81	0.69	0.40	0.03	1.80	1.45
Xf	1.09	1.56	0.51	0.75	0.52	1.76	0.97
XIf	0.86	1.08	0.45	1.02	0.19	1.75	1.03
XIIf	0.98	0.46	0.82	0.78	0.44	0.53	0.87

Table 50

COMPARISON OF EXPERIMENTAL SITUATIONS--Critical Ratios of Mean Scores
High School Subjects (normal reading) vs. High School Subjects (microfilm reading)

	Blinking Number	Fixations Number	Fixations per Line	Fixation Sigma Sc.	Lines Read Number	Regressions Number	Regressions per Line
LORNA DOONE							
Ia	2.90	2.04	4.21	3.52	2.98	5.63	4.91
If	3.53	2.28	4.16	3.43	2.73	4.80	4.47
IIf	2.60	0.99	5.10	2.96	3.82	4.56	5.03
IIIf	4.23	1.22	4.73	3.56	3.53	5.21	5.16
IVf	3.84	0.90	3.93	1.09	3.49	4.60	4.09
Vf	2.46	0.57	5.08	3.54	3.45	6.06	4.94
VIf	3.27	0.29	5.11	4.66	4.13	5.88	5.75
VIIf	1.67	0.67	4.19	2.58	2.74	6.55	4.52
VIIIf	2.94	0.41	4.77	3.26	3.62	7.09	5.46
IXf	3.57	0.21	5.72	3.61	4.36	5.88	6.53
Xf	3.99	1.95	5.54	3.53	3.69	7.28	5.94
XIf	2.15	1.25	4.34	2.44	2.60	6.20	4.55
XIIf	2.06	3.64	5.67	3.17	3.48	6.32	5.69
ADAM SMITH							
Ia	3.80	2.02	4.73	1.40	2.95	5.17	4.30
If	2.31	0.55	5.33	3.46	4.67	4.31	4.85
IIf	2.53	0.61	5.01	2.16	3.43	3.99	5.37
IIIf	1.62	1.17	4.73	1.47	3.55	4.35	4.90
IVf	2.27	0.50	3.49	2.04	2.77	4.35	3.44
Vf	2.57	0.90	4.69	1.71	3.48	4.96	4.27
VIf	2.02	1.06	3.86	1.17	2.73	4.85	4.70
VIIf	2.75	0.81	4.69	2.50	3.44	4.88	4.62
VIIIf	1.78	0.86	5.97	3.14	3.68	5.36	4.16
IXf	2.16	0.99	5.50	4.16	3.27	5.88	5.18
Xf	1.94	1.61	3.77	0.99	2.07	5.67	4.38
XIf	1.60	0.73	4.50	2.24	3.45	4.71	4.73
XIIf	1.18	1.66	5.13	2.86	3.17	6.11	4.89

Table 51

COMPARISION OF EXPERIMENTAL SITUATIONS--Critical Ratios of Mean Scores

Grant Study Subjects (normal reading) vs. High School Subjects (normal reading)

	Blinking Number	Fixations Number	Fixations per Line	Fixation Sigma Sc.	Lines Read Number	Regressions Number	Regressions per Line
LORNA DOONE							
Ia	0.88	1.44	10.20	1.22	0.04	1.01	0.87
If	0.81	0.15	13.01	0.00	1.19	1.22	0.57
IIf	1.31	0.17	15.34	0.61	1.50	1.38	0.36
IIIf	1.10	0.37	16.69	0.44	1.39	1.43	0.16
IVf	0.80	0.38	8.19	0.75	1.10	1.26	0.45
Vf	1.07	0.04	9.13	0.55	1.00	1.38	0.60
VIf	0.66	0.74	6.41	1.18	0.90	1.92	0.85
VIIf	1.28	0.74	9.18	0.53	0.68	0.86	0.45
VIIIf	1.14	0.60	16.64	0.18	1.57	1.38	0.04
IXf	0.87	0.17	15.34	0.11	1.19	0.84	0.16
Xf	0.83	1.85	13.52	0.12	0.64	0.96	0.58
XIf	0.50	1.04	4.96	1.62	0.18	1.57	1.02
XIIf	0.52	3.19	12.42	1.22	0.61	1.55	0.68
ADAM SMITH							
Ia	1.01	1.03	2.71	1.05	0.85	2.39	2.10
If	1.58	0.31	3.96	1.48	0.62	2.71	2.37
IIf	0.98	0.03	7.25	2.17	0.61	2.96	2.60
IIIf	2.00	1.31	1.43	2.05	0.73	2.90	1.71
IVf	1.67	0.03	1.58	1.26	0.13	2.26	1.54
Vf	1.77	0.40	8.90	2.12	0.58	3.10	2.57
VIf	0.85	0.31	12.76	1.52	0.57	3.07	2.73
VIIf	1.19	0.64	9.17	2.81	0.27	3.43	2.66
VIIIf	1.02	0.05	8.13	3.41	0.29	2.58	2.67
IXf	1.17	0.48	5.91	1.89	0.20	2.86	3.16
Xf	1.17	0.14	10.70	1.94	0.52	2.74	2.57
XIf	0.98	0.17	8.68	2.00	0.43	2.85	2.39
XIIf	0.96	1.68	5.18	1.75	0.54	2.02	1.97

Table 52

COMPARISON OF EXPERIMENTAL SITUATIONS--Critical Ratios of Mean Scores
Grant Study Subjects (microfilm reading) vs. High School Subjects (microfilm reading)

	Blinking Number	Fixations Number	Fixations per Line	Fixation Sigma Sc.	Lines Read Number	Regressions Number	Regressions per Line
LORNA DOONE							
Ia	1.58	0.96	3.90	3.25	3.75	5.30	4.56
If	2.03	0.15	3.47	2.67	3.59	5.11	4.46
IIf	2.24	0.15	4.10	2.90	3.64	4.27	4.22
IIIf	2.70	0.48	3.13	2.69	2.93	5.26	3.76
IVf	2.51	0.51	3.06	1.57	2.77	4.97	3.77
Vf	1.86	0.81	4.40	4.34	4.01	6.65	4.84
VIf	2.14	0.46	4.31	3.55	3.39	6.14	5.47
VIIf	0.94	1.73	3.24	2.51	3.47	4.75	3.82
VIIIf	2.42	0.64	3.61	3.30	3.16	6.30	4.48
IXf	1.94	0.49	3.52	3.20	3.68	5.58	4.96
Xf	1.75	0.16	4.35	2.64	3.32	5.66	4.99
XIf	0.96	0.70	3.39	2.59	2.55	5.52	3.82
XIIf	0.57	0.72	4.28	4.19	4.18	4.77	4.88
ADAM SMITH							
Ia	1.72	0.33	4.73	1.57	3.77	6.17	4.66
If	1.04	0.37	5.16	4.18	5.11	6.66	5.37
IIf	1.11	0.29	5.54	2.91	4.30	6.50	6.50
IIIf	1.48	1.32	4.64	3.65	3.41	7.52	5.36
IVf	2.17	0.02	4.34	2.94	3.74	6.36	3.88
Vf	1.67	0.14	4.71	3.73	4.22	6.71	4.77
VIf	1.38	1.01	4.53	4.04	4.09	6.61	5.55
VIIf	1.86	0.11	4.80	3.65	4.54	5.85	5.01
VIIIf	2.15	0.33	5.55	4.87	4.56	7.85	4.45
IXf	1.60	0.15	5.38	5.65	4.97	6.27	5.72
Xf	1.98	0.53	4.31	3.32	3.58	8.19	5.35
XIf	1.55	0.01	4.69	2.90	4.74	6.31	5.10
XIIf	0.99	0.60	4.35	5.86	3.81	7.87	5.06

Table 53

COMPARISON OF EXPERIMENTAL SITUATIONS--Critical Ratios of Mean Scores
Grant Study Subjects (normal reading) vs. High School Subjects (microfilm reading)

	Blinking Number	Fixations Number	Fixations per Line	Fixation Sigma Sc.	Lines Read Number	Regressions Number	Regressions per Line
LORNA DOONE							
Ia	2.00	0.40	3.65	5.13	2.51	8.01	5.46
If	2.67	2.02	3.67	4.09	1.87	7.25	5.80
IIf	2.51	1.20	4.00	4.64	2.75	7.32	5.44
IIIf	3.29	1.53	3.55	5.00	2.05	7.38	5.41
IVf	3.15	1.39	3.74	2.20	2.45	6.50	4.63
Vf	2.64	0.65	4.98	6.00	3.64	8.23	5.55
VIf	2.52	0.88	5.23	6.06	3.32	8.37	6.91
VIIf	2.24	0.05	3.86	5.20	2.86	7.13	4.85
VIIIf	2.91	0.89	3.91	3.40	2.25	8.20	5.36
IXf	2.45	0.04	4.59	3.96	3.56	6.47	6.05
Xf	2.78	0.14	5.02	5.00	3.52	8.48	6.76
XIf	2.33	0.34	4.79	6.05	2.75	8.63	5.55
XIIf	1.93	0.65	5.18	6.94	2.90	9.81	6.24
ADAM SMITH							
Ia	2.97	0.81	5.28	2.65	2.93	9.73	5.83
If	2.56	0.25	6.00	5.83	3.89	9.35	6.46
IIf	2.41	0.64	5.98	4.77	3.57	8.09	7.95
IIIf	2.80	2.09	4.76	4.16	2.24	9.30	6.45
IVf	3.34	0.56	4.11	4.05	2.50	8.94	4.40
Vf	3.09	1.23	5.73	4.86	3.52	8.94	5.63
VIf	2.20	1.69	6.03	4.07	4.09	8.83	7.45
VIIf	2.40	1.29	6.46	8.26	4.44	8.95	6.52
VIIIf	2.78	1.08	6.79	6.68	4.70	9.88	4.92
IXf	2.85	0.55	6.27	10.14	4.76	8.56	6.47
Xf	3.04	1.59	5.90	4.47	3.39	10.17	6.45
XIf	2.23	0.89	6.20	4.80	3.88	9.10	6.38
XIIf	1.96	0.14	6.73	6.81	4.35	10.53	6.17

Table 54

COMPARISON OF EXPERIMENTAL SITUATIONS--Critical Ratios of Mean Scores

Grant Study Subjects (microfilm reading) vs. High School Subjects (normal reading)

	Blinking Number	Fixations Number	Fixations per Line	Fixation Sigma Sc.	Lines Read Number	Regressions Number	Regressions per Line
LORNA DOONE							
Ia	0.01	2.73	0.24	0.61	1.68	0.30	0.55
If	0.60	2.30	0.47	0.51	0.16	0.39	0.28
IIf	0.44	0.90	0.96	0.15	0.60	0.17	0.44
IIIf	0.37	0.64	0.87	0.24	0.43	0.35	0.36
IVf	1.16	1.13	0.66	0.55	0.05	0.39	0.02
Vf	0.41	1.28	0.39	0.37	0.08	0.24	0.16
VIf	0.41	0.58	0.91	0.66	0.64	0.33	0.18
VIIf	0.36	2.03	0.76	0.35	0.05	1.21	0.53
VIIIf	0.10	0.84	0.89	0.03	0.39	0.21	0.32
IXf	0.61	0.63	1.64	0.85	1.28	0.49	1.04
Xf	1.13	1.87	1.29	0.25	0.36	0.60	0.48
XIf	1.18	0.66	0.82	0.06	0.63	0.10	0.25
XIIf	1.47	4.63	0.97	0.50	0.06	0.58	0.31
ADAM SMITH							
Ia	0.72	2.04	0.24	0.38	1.35	0.80	0.80
If	0.33	1.22	0.27	0.82	1.17	1.39	1.06
IIf	1.02	0.47	0.62	1.00	0.89	1.81	1.44
IIIf	0.18	0.49	0.15	1.74	0.08	1.72	0.85
IVf	0.12	0.60	0.60	0.96	1.04	1.12	0.85
Vf	0.62	1.44	0.20	1.55	0.99	1.13	1.02
VIf	0.40	0.33	0.51	1.42	0.48	1.23	1.01
VIIf	0.44	1.33	0.06	1.06	0.36	0.98	0.72
VIIIf	0.03	0.72	0.06	2.28	0.38	1.61	1.03
IXf	0.46	1.28	0.10	1.18	0.18	0.85	1.26
Xf	0.08	1.55	0.46	1.38	0.90	1.40	1.29
XIf	0.08	0.90	0.32	0.77	0.66	1.15	0.85
XIIf	0.08	2.42	0.32	1.14	0.14	1.26	0.63

Table 55

COMPARISON OF EXPERIMENTAL SITUATIONS--Critical Ratios of Standard Deviations
Grant Study Subjects (normal reading) vs. Grant Study Subjects (microfilm reading)

	Blinking Number	Fixations Number	Fixations per Line	Fixation Sigma Sc.	Lines Read Number	Regressions Number	Regressions per Line
LORNA DOONE							
Ia	1.20	0.19	1.56	1.69	0.92	1.68	1.57
If	1.37	0.42	1.57	0.95	0.37	1.60	1.70
IIf	1.44	0.51	0.67	1.74	0.39	1.76	1.45
IIIf	1.29	0.88	1.65	1.82	0.37	0.99	2.17
IVf	1.91	1.88	1.56	2.25	1.37	0.95	1.48
Vf	1.64	1.36	1.52	1.54	1.26	0.34	1.24
VIf	1.26	1.03	0.85	2.02	0.27	0.81	1.17
VIIf	1.25	0.80	1.49	2.05	0.44	0.45	1.21
VIIIf	1.42	0.29	1.61	0.48	0.69	0.65	1.26
IXf	1.74	0.15	1.19	0.55	0.23	0.44	0.59
Xf	1.46	0.85	0.87	2.06	0.63	1.12	1.19
XIf	1.42	0.56	1.51	1.69	0.67	1.14	1.65
XIIf	1.68	0.14	1.40	1.52	0.48	2.00	1.12
ADAM SMITH							
Ia	1.01	1.57	0.72	1.42	0.90	1.62	1.95
If	1.06	1.54	1.26	1.70	0.80	2.02	2.36
IIf	1.72	0.71	0.57	2.00	0.68	1.12	1.89
IIIf	1.74	1.26	0.64	0.38	0.49	0.52	1.46
IVf	1.56	1.22	0.46	1.44	0.56	2.18	2.03
Vf	2.21	1.04	1.09	1.06	0.47	1.55	1.70
VIf	1.30	0.91	1.70	0.39	0.18	0.50	1.97
VIIf	0.59	0.92	1.43	2.15	0.01	2.19	2.90
VIIIf	1.17	0.42	1.10	1.39	0.33	1.97	2.78
IXf	1.27	0.64	0.80	1.84	0.26	1.67	2.47
Xf	0.54	1.09	1.90	0.99	0.58	1.36	2.81
XIf	0.83	1.66	1.54	0.98	0.60	2.23	2.44
XIIf	0.66	0.63	0.21	0.06	0.01	2.07	2.62

Table 56

COMPARISON OF EXPERIMENTAL SITUATIONS--Critical Ratios of Standard Deviations

High School Subjects (normal reading) vs. High School Subjects (microfilm reading)

	Blinking Number	Fixations Number	Fixations per Line	Fixation Sigma Sc.	Lines Read Number	Regressions Number	Regressions per Line
LORNA DOONE							
Ia	0.37	0.87	1.00	0.54	0.11	0.70	1.93
If	1.38	0.39	0.45	1.66	2.52	0.31	0.33
IIf	0.58	0.51	0.56	1.10	1.77	0.44	1.68
IIIf	1.06	0.49	1.16	1.26	1.26	0.49	1.72
IVf	2.50	0.09	0.41	0.26	0.96	0.04	1.55
Vf	2.40	0.60	0.20	1.56	2.30	0.41	1.80
VIf	1.48	1.15	0.13	1.10	2.08	0.13	1.09
VIIf	0.22	0.51	0.86	1.86	1.85	0.44	2.10
VIIIf	2.05	0.34	0.93	0.63	1.48	0.15	1.90
IXf	1.78	0.66	0.72	0.92	2.30	0.36	1.73
Xf	0.10	0.34	0.27	1.68	1.93	0.20	0.87
XIf	1.74	0.96	0.33	1.85	1.62	0.80	1.36
XIIf	0.03	0.08	0.25	2.24	1.80	0.76	1.56
ADAM SMITH							
Ia	2.56	0.72	0.11	0.27	0.78	0.82	1.92
If	0.76	0.56	1.00	0.30	0.11	0.56	2.11
IIf	0.74	1.23	0.52	0.00	0.37	0.02	1.24
IIf	0.44	1.40	0.67	0.80	0.46	0.75	1.48
IVf	2.34	0.14	0.01	1.18	0.41	0.57	2.30
Vf	2.15	1.00	1.08	0.95	0.00	0.08	2.51
VIf	1.15	0.43	0.14	1.77	1.69	0.11	1.08
VIIf	0.68	1.30	0.20	1.90	1.45	0.83	1.94
VIIIf	2.47	0.06	1.43	0.07	1.07	0.10	3.36
IXf	1.52	0.03	1.28	2.67	2.04	1.01	2.91
Xf	2.04	0.74	0.10	1.52	1.39	0.01	1.69
XIf	0.68	0.06	0.06	0.82	1.90	0.00	2.06
XIIf	1.05	0.45	0.12	2.62	2.06	0.38	2.28

Table 57

COMPARISON OF EXPERIMENTAL SITUATIONS--Critical Ratios of Standard Deviations

Grant Study Subjects (normal reading) vs. High School Subjects (normal reading)

	Blinking Number	Fixations Number	Fixations per Line	Fixation Sigma Sc.	Lines Read Number	Regressions Number	Regressions per Line
LORNA DOONE							
Ia	3.15	0.03	0.65	0.46	0.88	1.16	0.03
If	2.23	0.34	1.34	0.78	1.12	1.50	1.23
IIf	2.74	0.36	0.44	1.40	1.00	1.66	0.48
IIIf	2.33	0.21	0.30	1.18	0.26	0.68	0.41
IVf	1.74	1.00	1.18	1.90	0.33	0.91	0.76
Vf	1.74	0.61	1.18	1.88	1.67	0.65	0.73
VIf	2.02	1.78	0.99	1.24	0.35	0.75	0.97
VIIf	2.25	0.82	1.01	2.45	1.52	0.24	0.22
VIIIf	1.88	1.66	1.03	0.58	0.61	0.23	0.21
IXf	2.56	0.46	0.29	0.32	0.72	0.25	0.64
Xf	2.64	0.49	1.03	1.42	0.73	0.26	0.52
XIf	0.79	0.24	1.40	1.80	0.62	0.52	0.69
XIIf	1.76	0.44	0.93	1.83	0.22	1.40	0.15
ADAM SMITH							
Ia	2.17	0.97	2.48	0.57	1.80	1.71	1.50
If	3.06	0.07	0.65	1.50	1.64	2.72	2.01
IIf	2.19	0.12	0.54	1.39	0.78	2.15	1.90
IIIf	2.66	1.24	0.26	1.02	0.83	1.84	1.07
IVf	1.50	0.46	0.91	1.06	0.80	2.81	1.78
Vf	2.34	0.01	0.80	1.62	0.91	1.39	1.48
VIf	1.68	1.71	2.05	2.04	0.88	1.14	2.03
VIIf	2.75	0.19	1.51	1.96	0.81	2.27	2.78
VIIIf	0.56	1.36	0.50	0.39	0.88	2.68	2.10
IXf	1.27	0.29	0.68	1.76	1.31	1.64	2.42
Xf	0.64	0.51	1.90	2.45	1.34	2.50	2.96
XIf	1.27	0.09	1.38	0.55	0.12	2.64	2.03
XIIf	1.06	0.89	1.64	1.32	0.56	2.35	2.13

Table 58

COMPARISON OF EXPERIMENTAL SITUATIONS--Critical Ratios of Standard Deviations

Grant Study Subjects (microfilm reading) vs. High School Subjects (microfilm reading)

	Blinking Number	Fixations Number	Fixations per Line	Fixation Sigma Sc.	Lines Read Number	Regressions Number	Regressions per Line
LORNA DOONE							
Ia	2.24	0.72	0.03	1.75	1.62	1.26	0.41
If	2.24	0.47	0.71	1.81	1.98	0.43	0.22
IIf	2.15	0.36	0.33	1.45	1.23	0.56	0.75
IIIf	2.16	0.61	0.26	1.90	1.36	0.81	0.17
IVf	2.36	0.90	0.03	0.72	1.91	0.08	0.84
Vf	2.48	0.19	0.17	1.22	1.96	0.10	1.34
VIf	2.20	1.67	0.02	0.18	2.01	0.06	0.89
VIIf	1.40	0.50	0.34	1.37	0.83	0.25	1.26
VIIIf	2.44	2.15	0.29	0.53	1.55	0.72	0.55
IXf	2.59	0.35	0.20	0.07	1.55	0.56	0.60
Xf	1.60	0.70	0.10	2.29	1.86	0.69	0.18
XIf	1.15	1.26	0.44	1.75	0.42	1.40	0.35
XIIf	0.07	0.50	0.27	1.97	1.19	1.44	0.64
ADAM SMITH							
Ia	3.25	1.34	0.31	1.16	0.22	0.72	1.46
If	1.91	1.95	0.38	0.53	1.02	0.50	1.72
IIf	1.31	1.94	0.48	0.73	0.47	1.19	1.24
IIIf	0.84	1.42	0.29	0.16	0.80	0.70	1.10
IVf	2.29	1.74	0.48	1.55	0.65	0.42	2.06
Vf	2.27	1.92	0.80	0.34	0.45	0.97	2.34
VIf	1.54	2.10	0.31	0.62	0.73	0.55	1.16
VIIf	2.79	1.93	0.29	2.09	0.70	0.65	1.76
VIIIf	2.02	1.68	0.85	0.96	0.54	0.94	2.90
IXf	1.52	0.89	1.18	2.75	0.61	0.99	2.86
Xf	2.11	2.14	0.10	0.22	0.64	1.44	1.91
XIf	1.13	1.53	0.12	1.29	1.50	0.64	1.59
XIIf	1.42	0.18	0.44	1.68	1.58	0.01	1.73

Table 59

COMPARISON OF EXPERIMENTAL SITUATIONS--Critical Ratios of Standard Deviations
Grant Study Subjects (normal reading) vs. High School Subjects (microfilm reading)

	Blinking Number	Fixations Number	Fixations per Line	Fixation Sigma Sc.	Lines Read Number	Regressions Number	Regressions per Line
LORNA DOONE							
Ia	2.98	0.90	1.59	0.07	0.78	0.35	1.91
If	3.06	0.05	0.93	0.95	1.69	0.97	1.52
IIf	3.05	0.86	0.99	0.34	0.86	0.98	2.06
IIIf	2.97	0.28	1.43	0.07	1.02	0.16	2.04
IVf	3.40	1.09	1.54	1.69	0.65	0.77	2.16
Vf	3.35	1.18	1.36	0.37	0.83	0.23	2.34
VIf	2.98	0.72	0.87	2.17	1.80	0.78	1.94
VIIf	2.40	0.31	1.77	0.80	0.39	0.19	2.26
VIIIf	3.22	1.94	1.85	0.06	0.92	0.07	1.74
IXf	3.45	0.20	1.00	0.62	1.75	0.12	1.17
Xf	2.69	0.15	0.77	0.31	1.31	0.37	1.35
XIf	2.34	0.73	1.11	0.07	1.07	0.23	1.94
XIIf	1.74	0.36	1.16	0.54	1.61	0.46	1.69
ADAM SMITH							
Ia	3.61	0.26	0.51	0.30	1.11	0.75	2.92
If	2.65	0.50	1.58	1.23	1.73	1.96	3.32
IIf	2.68	1.34	1.04	1.40	1.13	1.96	2.76
IIIf	2.38	0.18	0.92	0.22	1.26	1.12	2.33
IVf	3.19	0.60	0.93	0.12	1.19	2.00	3.30
Vf	3.50	1.00	1.79	0.74	0.91	1.39	3.30
VIf	2.54	1.34	1.94	0.34	0.90	0.98	2.76
VIIf	3.09	1.13	1.68	0.08	0.69	2.17	3.63
VIIIf	2.81	1.31	1.85	0.46	0.21	2.25	3.96
IXf	2.50	0.26	1.87	1.30	0.87	2.12	3.85
Xf	2.48	1.22	1.97	1.19	0.06	2.29	3.64
XIf	1.85	0.16	1.44	0.29	1.99	2.19	3.30
XIIf	1.97	0.45	1.73	1.62	1.57	1.64	3.46

Table 60

COMPARISON OF EXPERIMENTAL SITUATIONS--Critical Ratios of Standard Deviations

Grant Study Subjects (microfilm reading) vs. High School Subjects (normal reading)

	Blinking Number	Fixations Number	Fixations per Line	Fixation Sigma Sc.	Lines Read Number	Regressions Number	Regressions per Line
LORNA DOONE							
Ia	2.48	0.16	0.97	1.29	1.71	0.59	1.60
If	1.06	0.08	0.26	0.18	0.77	0.12	0.54
IIf	1.70	0.15	0.24	0.38	0.63	0.13	1.01
IIIf	1.27	1.08	1.39	0.75	0.11	0.34	1.86
IVf	0.22	0.99	0.44	0.47	1.07	0.04	0.77
Vf	0.11	0.79	0.38	0.40	0.47	0.32	0.53
VIf	0.90	2.53	0.15	0.94	0.08	0.06	0.21
VIIf	1.20	0.01	0.53	0.58	1.12	0.68	1.01
VIIIf	0.55	1.90	0.65	0.10	0.08	0.87	1.44
IXf	1.12	0.32	0.92	0.86	0.94	0.20	1.21
Xf	1.52	0.36	0.17	0.76	0.10	0.88	0.69
XIf	0.68	0.33	0.12	0.12	1.25	0.64	1.04
XIIf	0.10	0.58	0.52	0.38	0.70	0.73	0.98
ADAM SMITH							
Ia	1.33	0.66	0.32	0.89	0.99	0.10	0.55
If	2.46	1.49	0.64	0.23	0.91	1.05	0.50
IIf	0.61	0.83	0.04	0.73	0.10	1.20	0.00
IIIf	1.26	0.02	0.38	0.65	0.35	1.40	0.43
IVf	0.07	1.63	0.47	0.43	0.24	0.98	0.33
Vf	0.18	1.04	0.30	0.62	0.45	0.90	0.26
VIf	0.43	2.40	0.45	2.24	1.04	0.66	0.08
VIIf	2.38	0.74	0.09	0.25	0.80	0.11	0.24
VIIIf	0.64	1.72	0.63	1.04	0.56	1.04	1.02
IXf	0.00	0.92	0.11	0.09	1.54	0.03	0.09
Xf	0.11	1.55	0.00	1.71	0.80	1.43	0.27
XIf	0.47	1.58	0.18	0.43	0.48	0.64	0.59
XIIf	0.41	0.26	0.56	1.28	0.55	0.59	0.73

Table 61

SUMMARY CHART OF EYE-MOVEMENT MEASURES
SHOWING DIFFERENTIAL EFFECTS OF THE
EXPERIMENTAL SITUATIONS ON MEAN PERFORMANCE

	Lorna Doone	Adam Smith
G.S. vs. G.S.M. Table 49		
H.S. vs. H.S.M. Table 50	Fixations per Line Fixation Sigma Score Lines Read Number Regressions Number Regressions per Line	Fixations per Line Lines Read Number Regressions Number Regressions per Line
G.S. vs. H.S. Table 51	Fixations per Line	Fixations per Line
G.S.M. vs. H.S.M. Table 52	Fixations per Line Lines Read Number Regressions Number Regressions per Line	Fixations per Line Lines Read Number Regressions Number Regressions per Line
G.S. vs. H.S.M. Table 53	Fixations per Line Fixation Sigma Score Regressions Number Regressions per Line	Fixations per Line Fixation Sigma Score Lines Read Number Regressions Number Regressions per Line
G.S.M. vs. H.S. Table 54		

Table 62

FREQUENCY OF RESPONSE TO ITEM #19
OF THE QUESTIONNAIRE

After reading Lorna Doone

Part	a)	b)	c)	d)	e)
G.S.	7	2	1		
H.S.	7	1	1	1	
G.S.M.	5	3	2		
H.S.M.	3	3	4		
Total	22	9	8	1	0

After reading Adam Smith

Part	a)	b)	c)	d)	e)
G.S.	4	3	2	1	
H.S.	4	4	1	1	
G.S.M.	3	5	1	1	
H.S.M.	3	3	1	3	
Total	14	15	5	6	0

Table 63

COMPREHENSION SCORES

Grant Study Subjects (Normal Reading)

Lorna Doone

Exerc. #	1	2	3	4	5	6	7	8	9	10	11	12	Final
# of Q's	28	32	21	20	22	27	25	25	22	28	20	23	
G.S. 1	21	27	17	14	17	24	22						19/22
G.S. 2	27	27	16	16	17	25	20						22/25
G.S. 3	27	29	17	19									14/14
G.S. 4	27	25	19	18	21	24	25						19/24
G.S. 5	20	23	20	14	15								15/19
G.S. 6	22	27	18	17	19	25	21	23	19	25			25/30
G.S. 7	26	28	19	14	20	21							19/19
G.S. 8	23	27	18	17	18	25	22						17/20
G.S. 9	18	21	15	12	18	21	23	18	15				24/28
G.S. 10	25	23	17	15	19	26							16/19

Table 64

COMPREHENSION SCORES

Grant Study Subjects (Normal Reading)

Adam Smith

Exerc. #	1	2	3	4	5	6	7	8	9	10	11	12	Final
# of Q's	22	20	20	25	25	25	19	25	17	20	26	25	
G.S. 1	12	13	10	15	16	16	16						22/28
G.S. 2	16	14	14	15	14	16	11	19	14				34/41
G.S. 3	14	16	17	21									23/26
G.S. 4	18	15	16	18	22								23/28
G.S. 5	15	13	14	16									20/26
G.S. 6	16	13	13	20	20	20	15	15					31/36
G.S. 7	17	16	13	16	22	18	15	21					25/32
G.S. 8	17	15	15	16	21								24/27
G.S. 9	8	9	6	7	6	9	6	8	10	7			25/41
G.S. 10	14	16	10	18	17								21/26

Table 65

COMPREHENSION SCORES

High School Subjects (Normal Reading)

Lorna Doone

Exerc. #	1	2	3	4	5	6	7	8	9	10	11	12	Final
# of Q's	28	32	21	20	22	27	25	25	22	28	20	23	
H.S. 1	20	23	17	14	11	22	19	19	16	18	13	10	36/43
H.S. 2	25	25	16	17	16	19	17	19	16	22	18	16	38/45
H.S. 3	19	23	17	13	19	17							12/18
H.S. 4	24	26	17	16	16	23	21	19					23/25
H.S. 5	21	26	17	14	17	22							18/22
H.S. 6	20	24	18	12	10	20							13/19
H.S. 7	12	24	17	13	15	20	16	21	19				25/28
H.S. 8	26	30	17	17	20	24	23	20	19				26/32
H.S. 9	23	27	19	16	18	24	22						21/24
H.S.10	24	26	19	11	17	26	22						18/20

Table 66

COMPREHENSION SCORES

High School Subjects (Normal Reading)

Adam Smith

Exerc. #	1	2	3	4	5	6	7	8	9	10	11	12	Final
# of Q's	22	20	20	25	25	25	19	25	17	20	26	25	
H.S. 1	7	7	6	6	9	18	12	10	14	9	11		29/42
H.S. 2	14	13	11	17	19	20	17	15	12	10	18		35/42
H.S. 3	5	5	6	8	9								11/24
H.S. 4	16	18	17	18	20	15	18	14					23/26
H.S. 5	7	11	14	12									20/25
H.S. 6	8	2	6	8	5								13/27
H.S. 7	8	6	7	10	8	8	13	8	10				23/41
H.S. 8	15	13	13	19	21	20	13	17					24/32
H.S. 9	15	15	13	15	19	20							19/27
H.S. 10	9	13	10	11	16								15/19

Table 67

COMPREHENSION SCORES

Grant Study Subjects (Microfilm)

Lorna Doone

Exerc. #	1	2	3	4	5	6	7	8	9	10	11	12	Final
# of Q's	28	32	21	20	22	27	25	25	22	28	20	23	
G.S.M. 1	28	27	18	19	20								17/19
G.S.M. 2	21	23	18	17	19	25	19	19	14	22	12		29/33
G.S.M. 3	23	30	19	18	20	25	21	24	19				23/26
G.S.M. 4	22	25	19	17	16	23	21	16	15				22/26
G.S.M. 5	24	29	19	18	20	26	24	22					23/25
G.S.M. 6	25	28	18	15									15/15
G.S.M. 7				15	20	25	23	24	19	24	19	23	28/31
G.S.M. 8	24	26	19	17	21	25	22	20					23/25
G.S.M. 9	25	27	17	15	18	25	21	22					23/24
G.S.M. 10	26	28	19	17	19								16/17

Table 68

COMPREHENSION SCORES

Grant Study Subjects (Microfilm)

Adam Smith

Exerc. #	1	2	3	4	5	6	7	8	9	10	11	12	Final
# of Q's	22	20	20	25	25	25	19	25	17	20	26	25	
G.S.M. 1	18	19	18	21									20/23
G.S.M. 2	16	13	15	12	10	15	15						22/28
G.S.M. 3	14	16	14	18	19	20	17	19					28/35
G.S.M. 4	14	10	11	20	16	16	10						20/28
G.S.M. 5	14	14	16	18	21	20	15						29/31
G.S.M. 6	16	13	21	19									24/27
G.S.M. 7	17	16	15	17	22	23	18						27/30
G.S.M. 8	16	17	14	20	20	24	18	16	16				34/40
G.S.M. 9	14	16	11	16	19	18	13						26/34
G.S.M. 10	13	18	12	12									23/27

Table 69

COMPREHENSION SCORES

High School Subjects (Microfilm)

Lorna Doone

Exerc. #	1	2	3	4	5	6	7	8	9	10	11	12	Final
# of Q's	28	32	21	20	22	27	25	25	22	28	20	23	
H.S.M. 1	18	18	19	13									15/20
H.S.M. 2	10	23	8	11	9	18	11	15	15				24/31
H.S.M. 3	17	18	14	4	14	15	13	15	16				13/25
H.S.M. 4	22	24	17	16	17	24	23						19/22
H.S.M. 5	7	8	10	5									15/28
H.S.M. 6	13	21	16	11	12								10/16
H.S.M. 7	4	7	5	4	12	12							16/33
H.S.M. 8	21	21	18	9	13	19							21/22
H.S.M. 9	18	24	12	17	14	21	20	21	16	23	12	17	29/37
H.S.M. 10	25	28	16	15	15	24							19/19

Table 70

COMPREHENSION SCORES

High School Subjects (Microfilm)

Adam Smith

Exerc. #	1	2	3	4	5	6	7	8	9	10	11	12	Final
# of Q's	22	20	20	25	25	25	19	25	17	20	26	25	
H.S.M. 1	7	6	11	10									19/41
H.S.M. 2	5	16	10	1	12	3	4	9					17/36
H.S.M. 3	11	4	7	8	9	11	7	10	9	7			26/45
H.S.M. 4	7	13	13	9	11	15							19/28
H.S.M. 5	15	21	15	17									9/14
H.S.M. 6	23	26	15	12	17	24							17/20
H.S.M. 7	14	10	9	15	12	16							22/27
H.S.M. 8	8	5	9	7									14/27
H.S.M. 9	17	13	15	12	16	13	13	11	12	13	13		37/45
H.S.M. 10	15	12	14	15	19								20/23

Table 71

INTERSPERSED COMPREHENSION SCORES

Average Percent Correct

	G.S.			H.S.	
Subj.	D	S	Subj.	D	S
1	79.1	65.0	1	68.6	47.9
2	82.3	69.2	2	77.2	67.9
3	92.5	80.2	3	72.5	31.9
4	77.9	79.8	4	80.7	76.3
5	75.9	68.8	5	77.6	52.4
6	86.1	74.1	6	68.6	30.6
7	87.0	67.6	7	71.1	41.0
8	85.5	77.3	8	87.8	71.8
9	73.9	39.6	9	85.1	70.7
10	80.4	69.0	10	82.0	57.1
Average	82.1	60.7	Average	77.1	54.8

	G.S.M.			H.S.M.	
Subj.	D	S	Subj.	D	S
1	90.9	87.5	1	70.1	40.6
2	71.8	54.9	2	55.8	27.2
3	80.3	76.3	3	58.7	39.9
4	79.1	62.5	4	80.3	52.8
5	91.0	77.5	5	67.9	37.4
6	87.4	77.3	6	60.0	34.0
7	90.4	83.1	7	77.9	58.8
8	87.8	82.1	8	70.8	37.2
9	85.7	69.4	9	73.3	63.4
10	89.3	68.4	10	83.5	70.1
Average	85.4	73.9	Average	69.8	46.1

Table 72

FINAL COMPREHENSION SCORES

Percent Correct

	G.S.			H.S.	
Subj.	D	S	Subj.	D	S
1	86.3	78.6	1	83.7	69.0
2	88.0	82.9	2	84.4	83.3
3	100.0	88.5	3	66.6	45.8
4	79.1	82.1	4	92.0	88.4
5	78.9	76.9	5	81.8	80.0
6	83.3	86.1	6	68.4	48.1
7	100.0	78.1	7	89.3	56.0
8	85.0	88.8	8	81.2	75.0
9	85.7	60.9	9	87.5	70.3
10	84.2	80.7	10	90.0	78.9
Average	87.0	80.4	Average	82.5	69.5

	G.S.M.			H.S.M.	
Subj.	D	S	Subj.	D	S
1	89.5	86.9	1	75.0	46.3
2	87.8	78.5	2	77.4	47.2
3	88.4	80.0	3	52.0	57.7
4	84.6	71.4	4	86.3	67.8
5	92.0	93.5	5	53.5	64.2
6	100.0	88.8	6	62.5	85.0
7	90.4	90.0	7	48.4	81.4
8	92.0	85.0	8	95.4	51.8
9	95.8	76.4	9	78.3	82.2
10	94.1	85.1	10	100.0	86.9
Average	91.5	83.6	Average	72.9	67.0

Table 73

ALPHA CYCLES IN AN ENCEPHALOGRAM

Experimental condition	Number of cycles	Length of record	Rate Cycles/sec.
Reading	26	95.8 mm.	8.14
	6	23.0	7.82
	8	29.3	8.19
Total	40	148.1	8.10
Eyes closed			
in a dark room	14	42.0	10.00
	13	40.0	9.74
	16	50.0	9.60
	14	43.5	9.65
	17	52.0	9.80
Total	74	227.5	9.75
in a lighted room	16	51.0	9.41
	12	38.0	9.45
	17	53.7	9.47
	13	40.0	9.74
	19	57.2	9.94
	9	28.5	9.47
	7	21.7	9.66
Total	93	290.1	9.61

Table 74

ANALYSIS OF THE DIFFERENCES AMONG MEAN SCORES ON THE KEYSTONE STEREOGRAMS

Tests	Means	t-ratios	P-value	N
#1 vs. #2	M_1=10.19 M_2=11.69	2.05 *	5%-2%	36
#1 vs. #3	M_1=10.44 M_3=13.97	3.29 *	<1%	32
#1 vs. #4	M_1=10.44 M_4=14.22	3.23 *	<1%	32
#3 vs. #4	M_3=14.13 M_4=14.32	0.19	90%-80%	31

* Significant at the 5% level of confidence

Table 75

ANALYSIS OF THE DIFFERENCES AMONG MEAN SCORES ON THE ZEISS STEREOGRAMS

Tests	Means	t-ratios	P-value	N
#1 vs. #2	M_1=4.37 M_2=4.45	0.29	80%-70%	38
#1 vs. #3	M_1=4.50 M_3=5.06	1.44	20%-10%	34
#1 vs. #4	M_1=4.50 M_4=5.03	1.47	20%-10%	34
#3 vs. #4	M_3=5.06 M_4=5.03	0.13	90%-80%	34

Bibliography

1. Abernethy, E. M., "Photographic records of eye-movements in studying spelling," *J. Educ. Psychol.,* 1929, **20,** 695-701.

2. Ahrens, A., *Untersuchungen über die Bewegung der Augen beim Schreiben,* Rostock, 1891.

3. American Optical Company, Scientific Instruments Division, *Rhythm reading—the Ophthalm-o-graph,* American Optical Co., 1937.

4. Ames, A., W. F. Dearborn, and W. O. Fenn, *Eye fatigue in the reading of microfilm,* Report of the Advisory Committee of the Committee on Scientific Aids to Learning, 1938.

5. Anderson, I. H., "Studies in the eye-movements of good and poor readers," *Psychol. Monogr.,* 1937, **48,** 1-35.

6. Anderson, I. H., "The effect of letter-position on range of apprehension scores with special reference to reading disability," *School of Education Bulletin* (University of Michigan, Ann Arbor, 1946), 18, no. 3, 37-40.

6a. Anon. (Editorial), "How many foot candles?" *Amer. J. Publ. Hlth.,* 1946, **36,** 1040-1041.

7. Arai, T., "Mental fatigue," Columbia Univ., Contributions to Education, Teachers College Series, 1912, no. 54.

8. Arnold, D. C., and M. A. Tinker, "The fixational pause of the eyes," *J. Exp. Psychol.,* 1939, **25,** 271-280.

9. Arrigo, A., "Grafica dei Movimenti dell'Occhio durante la Lettura," *An. Oftal. e. Clin. Ocul.,* 1929, **57,** 1-4.

10. Ash, I. E., "Fatigue and its effects upon control," *Arch. Psychol.,* 1914, **4,** no. 31.

11. Atkins, E. W., "The efficiency of the eye under different intensities of illumination," *J. Comp. Psychol.,* 1927, **7,** 1-37.

12. Bárány, R., "Apparat zur Messung der Rollbewegungen des Auges," *Zeitschr. f. Sinnesphysiol.,* 1910, **45,** 59.

13. Barmack, J. E., "Boredom and other factors in the physiology of mental effort," *Arch. Psychol.,* 1937, no. 218.

14. Barnes, B., "Eye-movements," *Amer. J. Psychol.,* 1905, **16**, 199-207.

15. Bartlett, F. C., "Fatigue following highly skilled work," *Nature,* 1941, **47**, 717-718.

16. Bartley, S. H., "A factor in visual fatigue," *Psychosomatic Med.,* 1942, **4**, 369-375.

17. Bartley, S. H., and G. H. Bishop, "Factors determining the form of the electrical response from the optic cortex of the rabbit," *Amer. J. Physiol.,* 1933, **103**, 173-184.

18. Bartley, S. H., and E. Chute, "A preliminary clarification of the concept of fatigue," *Psychol. Rev.,* 1945, **52**, 169-174.

19. Bass, F., "Experiment in schoolroom ventilation with reduced air supply through individual ducts," *Trans. Amer. Soc. Heat. and Vent. Engrs.,* 1913, **19**, 328-360.

20. Bass, F., "The recirculating of air in a schoolroom in Minneapolis," *Trans. Amer. Soc. Heat. and Vent. Engrs.,* 1915, **21**, 109-125.

21. Bayle, E., "The nature and causes of regressive movements in reading," *J. Exp. Educ.,* 1942, **11**, 16-36.

22. Beacher, L. L., "Possibilities of glare reducing visual acuity," *Amer. J. Optom.,* 1932, **9**, 338-340.

23. Bell, C., "On the motions of the eye, in illustration of the uses of the muscles and nerves of the orbit," *Phil. Trans.,* 1823, pt. 1, 166-186.

24. Benedict, F. G., W. R. Miles, P. Roth, and H. M. Smith, "Human vitality and efficiency under prolonged restricted diet," Carnegie Institution of Washington, 1919, no. 280.

25. Bentley, M., "Leading and legibility," *Psychol. Monogr.,* 1921, **30**, 48-61.

26. Berg, F., "Bemerkungen zur Theorie der ophthalmometrischen Messungen von Fläckenkrümmungen," *Acta Ophthal.,* 1929, **7**, 225-243.

27. Betts, E. A., "A study of paper as a factor in type visibility," *Optom. Wkly.,* 1942, **33**, 229-233.

28. Bills, A. G., "The influence of muscular tension on the efficiency of mental work," *Amer. J. Psychol.,* 1927, **38**, 227-251.

29. Bills, A. G., "Inhibition and facilitation," *Psychol. Bull.,* 1927, **24**, 473-487.

30. Bills, A. G., "Mental work," *Psychol. Bull.,* 1929, **26**, 499-526.

31. Bills, A. G., "Blocking: a new principle of mental fatigue," *Amer J. Psychol.,* 1931, **43**, 230-245.

32. Bills, A. G., "A comparative study of mental fatigue and anoxemia," *Psychol. Bull.,* 1936, **33**, 814.

33. Bills, A. G., "Blocking in mental fatigue and anoxemia compared," *J. Exp. Psychol.,* 1937, **20**, 437-452.

34. Bills, A. G., "Facilitation and inhibition in mental work," *Psychol. Bull.,* 1937, **34**, 286-309.

35. Bills, A. G., "Fatigue in mental work," *Physiol. Rev.,* 1937, **17**, 436-453.

36. Bills, A. G., *The psychology of efficiency: a discussion of the hygiene of mental work,* New York: Harper, 1943.

37. Bitterman, M. E., "Fatigue defined as reduced efficiency," *Amer. J. Psychol.,* 1944, **57**, 569-573.

38. Bitterman, M. E., "Electromyographic recording of eyelid movements," *Amer. J. Psychol.,* 1945, **58**, 112-113.

39. Bitterman, M. E., "Heart rate and frequency of blinking as indices of visual efficiency," *J. Exp. Psychol.,* 1945, **35**, 279-292.

40. Bitterman, M. E., and E. Soloway, "The relation between frequency of blinking and effort expended in mental work," *J. Exp. Psychol.,* 1946, **36**, 134-136.

40a. Blackhurst, J. H., "Size of type as related to readability in the first four grades," *Sch. and Soc.,* 1922, **16**, 697-700.

40b. Blackhurst, J. H., "Leading as related to readability in the first four grades," *Sch. and Soc.,* 1923, **17**, 363-364.

40c. Blackhurst, J. H., "Length of line as related to readability in the first four grades," *Sch. and Soc.,* 1923, **18**, 328-330.

41. Blount, W. P., "Studies of the movements of the eyelids of animals: blinking," *Quart. J. Exp. Physiol.,* 1927, **18**, 111-125.

42. Bose, J. C. (See Nuttall, 261.)

43. Brandt, H. F., "A bidimensional eye-movement camera," *Amer. J. Psychol.,* 1937, **49**, 666-669.

44. Brandt, H. F., *The psychology of seeing,* New York: Philosophical Library, 1945.

45. Breland, K., and M. K. Breland, "Legibility of newspaper headlines printed in capitals and in lower case," *J. Appl. Psychol.,* 1944, **28**, 117-120.

46. Broom, M. E., "The reliability of the reading graph yielded by the ophthalmograph," *Sch. and Soc.,* 1940, **52**, 205-208.

47. Brozek, J. M., "Psychologic factors in relation to performance and fatigue," *Fed. Proc. Amer. Soc. Exp. Biol.,* 1943, **2**, 134-144.

48. Brückner, A., "Ueber die Anfangsgeschwindigkeit der Augenbewegungen," *Pflüger's Arch.,* 1902, **90**, 73-93.

49. Bryan, A. I., "Legibility of Library of Congress cards and their reproductions," *College and Research Libraries,* 1945, **6**, 447-464.

50. Buckingham, B. R., "New data on the typography of textbooks," *Yearb. Nat. Soc. Stud. Educ.,* 1931, **30**, (II), 93-125.

51. Burtt, H. E., and C. Basch, "Legibility of Bodoni, Baskerville Roman, and Cheltenham type faces," *J. Appl. Psychol.*, 1923, **7**, 237-245.

52. Buswell, G. T., "An experimental study of the eye-voice span in reading," *Suppl. Educ. Monogr.*, 1920, no. 17.

53. Buswell, G. T., "Fundamental reading habits: a study of their development," *Suppl. Educ. Monogr.*, 1922, no. 21.

54. Buswell, G. T., "Diagnostic studies in arithmetic," *Suppl. Educ. Monogr.*, 1926, no. 30.

55. Buys, E., "Uber die Nystagmographie beim Menschen," *Internat. Zentralbl. f. Ohrenhk.*, 1910-11, **9**, 57-65.

56. Carmichael, L., "Sir Charles Bell: a contribution to the history of physiological psychology," *Psychol. Rev.*, 1926, **33**, 188-217.

57. Cason, H., "The organic nature of fatigue," *Amer. J. Psychol.*, 1935, **47**, 337-342.

58. Celle, J., and E. de Cooman. (See 69a.)

59. Chase, A. M., "Photosensitive pigments from the retina of the frog," *Science*, 1938, **87**, 238.

60. Clark, B., "A camera for simultaneous record of horizontal and vertical movements of both eyes," *Amer. J. Psychol.*, 1934, **46**, 325-326.

61. Clark, B., and N. Warren, "The effect of loss of sleep on visual tests," *Amer. J. Optom.*, 1939, **16**, 80-95.

62. Clark, B., and N. Warren, "A photographic study of reading during a sixty-five-hour vigil," *J. Educ. Psychol.*, 1940, **31**, 383-390.

63. Cobb, P. W., "The effect on foveal vision of bright surroundings—II," *Psychol. Rev.*, 1914, **21**, 23-32.

64. Cobb, P. W., "Eye fatigue," *Trans. Illum. Eng. Soc.*, 1927, **22**, 426-429.

65. Cobb, P. W., and F. K. Moss, "Eye fatigue and its relation to light and work," *J. Franklin Inst.*, 1925, **200**, 239-247.

66. Cobb, P. W., and F. K. Moss, "The fixational pause of the eyes," *J. Exp. Psychol.*, 1926, **9**, 359-367.

67. Cobb, S., and A. Forbes, "Electromyographic studies of muscular fatigue in man," *J. Nerv. and Ment. Dis.*, 1923, **58**, 273-274.

68. Coburn, E. B., "The ophthalmo-kinetograph, an apparatus to record ocular movements," *Arch. Ophthal.*, 1905, **34**, 1-5.

69. Cogan, D. G., "Medical progress: popular misconceptions pertaining to ophthalmology," *New England J. Med.*, 1941, **224**, 462-466.

69a. Colle, J., and E. de Cooman, "Recherches sur l'électrorétinogramme," *Compt. rend. Soc. biol.*, 1931, **108**, 273-276.

70. Cords, R., "Über Hebelnystagmographie," *Graefe's Arch. f. Ophthal.*, 1927, **118**, 771-784.

71. Couch, F. H., and J. C. Fox, "Photographic study of ocular movements in mental disease," *Arch. Neur. Psychiat.*, 1934, **31**, 556-578.

72. Courts, F. A., "The influence of muscular tension on the eyelid reflex," *J. Exp. Psychol.,* 1940, **27,** 678-689.

73. Courts, F. A., "Relations between muscular tension and performance," *Psychol. Bull.,* 1942, **39,** 347-367.

74. Crosland, H. R., and G. Johnson, "The range of apprehension as affected by inter-letter hair-spacing and by the characteristics of individual letters," *J. Appl. Psychol.,* 1928, 12, 82-124.

75. Darrow, C. W., "Some physiological conditions of efficiency," *Psychol. Bull.,* 1927, 24, 488-505.

76. Davis, R. C., "The relation of muscle action potentials to difficulty and frustration," *J. Exp. Psychol.,* 1938, **23,** 141-158.

77. Davis, R. C., "Patterns of muscular activity during 'mental work' and their constancy," *J. Exp. Psychol.,* 1939, 24, 451-465.

78. Dearborn, W. F., "The psychology of reading," *Arch. Phil. Psychol. Sci. Methods,* 1906, no. 4.

79. Dearborn, W. F., and I. H. Anderson, "Aniseikonia as related to disability in reading," *J. Exp. Psychol.,* 1938, **23,** 559-577.

80. Dearborn, W. F., and H. M. Leverett, "Visual defects and reading," *J. Exp. Educ.,* 1945, **13,** 111-124.

81. Delabarre, E. B., "A method of recording eye-movements," *Amer. J. Psychol.,* 1898, **9,** 572-574.

82. Diefendorf, A. R., and R. Dodge, "An experimental study of the ocular reactions of the insane from photographic records," *Brain,* 1908-09, 31, 451-489.

83. Dodge, R., "Five types of eye movement in the horizontal meridian plane of the field of regard," *Amer. J. Physiol.,* 1903, 8, 307-329.

84. Dodge, R., "The illusion of clear vision during eye movement," *Psychol. Bull.,* 1905, **2,** 193-199.

85. Dodge, R., "An experimental study of visual fixation," *Psychol. Monogr.,* 1907, **8,** 1-95.

86. Dodge, R., "The laws of relative fatigue," *Psychol. Rev.,* 1917, 24, 89-113.

87. Dodge, R., "A mirror-recorder for photographing the compensatory movements of closed eyes," *J. Exp. Psychol.,* 1921, 4, 165-174.

88. Dodge, R., "The latent time of compensatory eye-movements," *J. Exp. Psychol.,* 1921, **4,** 247-269.

89. Dodge, R., and F. G. Benedict, "Psychological effects of alcohol," Carnegie Institution of Washington, 1915, no. 232.

90. Dodge, R., and T. S. Cline, "The angle velocity of eye movements," *Psychol. Rev.,* 1901, **8,** 145-157.

91. Dodge, R., and W. R. Miles, "A floating mirror technique for recording eye-movements," *Amer. J. Psychol.,* 1931, **43,** 124-126.

92. Dohlman, G., "Towards a method for quantitative measurement of the functional capacity of the vestibular apparatus," *Acta Oto-laryng.,* 1935, **23,** 50-62.

93. Dolley, D. H., "The morphology of functional depression in nerve cells and its significance for the normal and abnormal physiology of the cell," *J. Med. Res.,* 1913-14, **24,** 65-129.

94. Dolley, D. H., "Fatigue of excitation and fatigue of depression," *Internat. Monatsschr. f. Anat. u. Physiol.,* 1915, **31,** 35-62.

95. Duke-Elder, W. S., *Text-book of ophthalmology,* St. Louis: Mosby, 1934.

96. Engelking, E., "Der Schwellenwert der Pupillenreaktion und seine Beziehungen zum Problem der pupillomotorischen Aufnahmeorgane," *Zeitschr. f. Sinnesphysiol.,* 1919, **50,** 319-337.

97. Erdmann, B., and R. Dodge, *Psychologische Untersuchungen über das Lesen auf experimenteller Grundlage,* Niemeyer, 1898.

98. Eurich, A. C., "The reliability and validity of photographic eye-movement records," *J. Educ. Psychol.,* 1933, **24,** 118-122.

99. Fairbanks, G., "The relation between eye-movements and voice in the oral reading of good and poor silent readers," *Psychol. Monogr.,* 1937, **48,** 78-107.

100. Fenn, W. O., and J. B. Hursh, "Movements of the eyes when the lids are closed," *Amer. J. Physiol.,* 1937, **118,** 8-14.

101. Ferree, C. E., and G. Rand, "The effect of variations in intensity of illumination on functions of importance to the working eye," *Trans. Illum. Eng. Soc.,* 1920, **15,** 769-792.

102. Ferree, C. E., and G. Rand, "The effect of intensity of illumination on the acuity of the normal eye and eyes slightly defective as to refraction," *Amer. J. Psychol.,* 1923, **34,** 244-249.

103. Ferree, C. E., and G. Rand, "Better lighting for workers," *Pers. J.,* 1936, **15,** 207-213.

104. Ferree, C. E., and G. Rand, "Prescribing light. An important factor in the care and treatment of the eye," *Brit. J. Ophthal.,* 1938, 22, 641-669.

105. Ferree, C. E., and G. Rand, "Optimum working conditions for the eye," *Sight Sav. Rev.,* 1940, **10,** 3-12.

106. Ferree, C. E., and G. Rand, "Work and its illumination," *Pers. J.,* 1940, **19,** pt. I, 55-64, pt. II, 93-98.

107. Foltz, E. E., F. T. Jung, and L. E. Cisler, "The effect of some internal factors on human work output and recovery," *Amer. J. Physiol.,* 1944, **141,** 641-646.

108. Fox, J. C., and R. Dodge, "Optic nystagmus. II. Variations in nystagmographic records of eye movement," *Arch. Neur. Psychiat.,* 1929, **22,** 55-74.

109. Freeman, F. N., *Experimental education,* Boston: Houghton Mifflin, 1916.

110. Freeman, G. L., *Introduction to physiological psychology,* New York: Ronald, 1934.

111. Futch, O., "A study of eye-movements in the reading of Latin," *J. Gen. Psychol.,* 1935, 13, 434-463.

112. Galley, L., "Ein neuer Nystagmograph (Mikrokinetograph)," *Zeitschr. f. Psychol.,* 1926, 101, 182-189.

113. Garrett, H. E., *Statistics in psychology and education,* (2d ed.), New York: Longmans, Green, 1937.

114. Gates, A. I., "Diurnal variations in memory and association," Univ. of California Publications in Psychology, 1916, 1, 323-344.

115. Gates, A. I., "Variations in efficiency during the day, together with practice effects, sex differences, and correlations," Univ. of California Publications in Psychology, 1916, 2, 1-156.

116. George, E. J., J. A. Toren, and J. W. Lowell, "Study of the ocular movements in the horizontal plane," *Amer. J. Ophthal.,* 1923, 6, 833-838.

117. Gertz, H., "Uber die kompensatorische Gegenwendung der Augen bei spontan bewegtem Kopfe," *Zeitschr. f. Sinnesphysiol.,* 1913, 47, 420-431.

118. Gilbert, L. C., "A projector-stand to facilitate plotting," *Amer. J. Psychol.,* 1940, 53, 441-442.

119. Gilbert, L. C.; and D. W. Gilbert, "Reading before the eye-movement camera versus reading away from it," *Elem. Sch. J.,* 1942, 42, 443-447.

120. Gilliland, A. R., "The effect on reading of changes in the size of type," *Elem. Sch. J.,* 1923, 24, 138-146.

121. Glaze, J. A., "The effects of practice on fatigue," *Amer. J. Psychol.,* 1930, 42, 628-630.

122. Goorley, J. T., "Chemical factors of fatigue," *Res. Quart. Amer. Assoc. Hlth. Phys. Educ. Rec.,* 1939, 10, 89-102.

123. Gray, C. T., "Types of reading ability as exhibited through tests and laboratory experiments," *Suppl. Educ. Monogr.,* 1917, no. 5.

124. Griffing, H., and S. I. Franz, "On the conditions of fatigue in reading," *Psychol. Rev.,* 1896, 3, 513-530.

125. Grossart, F., "Das tachistoskopische Verlesen unter besonderer Berücksichtigung des Einflusses von Gefühlen und der Frage des objektiven und subjektiven Typus," *Arch f. d. Gesamt. Psychol.,* 1921, 41, 121-200.

126. Grünberg, G. I.,"Uber eine neue einfache Methods der Nystagmographie," *Zeitschr. f. Hals-, Nasen-, u. Ohrenheilk.,* 1923-24, 7, 382-389.

127. Guilford, J. P., "'Fluctuations of attention' with weak visual stimuli," *Amer. J. Psychol.,* 1927, 38, 534-583.

128. Guilford, J. P., and K. M. Dallenbach, "A study of the autokinetic sensation," *Amer. J. Psychol.,* 1928, 40, 83-91.

129. Guilford, J. P., and J. Helson, "Eye-movements and the phi-phenomenon," *Amer. J. Psychol.,* 1929, 41, 595-606.

130. Guillery, G., "Ueber die Schnelligkeit der Augenbewegungen," *Pflüger's Arch.,* 1898, 73, 87-116.

131. Hadley, J. M., "Some relationships between electrical signs of central and peripheral activity. II. During 'mental work,'" *J. Exp. Psychol.,* 1941, 28, 53-62.

132. Halstead, W. C., "A method for the quantitative recording of eye movements," *J. Psychol.,* 1938, 6, 177-180.

133. Halverson, H. M., and S. M. Newhall, "Correlations between movements of the eyeball and the eyelid," *Psychol. Bull.,* 1934, 31, 708.

134. Hamilton, F. M., "A quantitative study of the psychological processes involved in word perception," *Arch. Psychol.,* 1907, 1, no. 9.

135. Harbinson, M. R., and F. C. Bartlett, "An investigation of the relation between discomfort and disability resulting from glaring light," *Brit. J. Psychol.,* 1934, 24, 313-319.

136. Hartridge, H., "Physiological eye-strain," Proc. Physiol. Soc., *J. Physiol.,* 1919-20, 53, i-ii.

137. Hecht, S., "The nature of the photoreceptor process," in *A handbook of general experimental psychology,* C. Murchison (ed.), Worcester: Clark Univ. Press, 1934, 704-828.

138. Heck, W. H., *The efficiency of grammar grade pupils in reasoning tests in arithmetic at different periods of the school day,* Lynchburg, Va.: Bell, 1913.

139. Heller, R., *Untersuchungen über 'Gesamtform' und ihre Bedeutung fur das tachistoskopische Lesen im indirekten Sehen,* Dissertation, University of Zurich, 1911.

140. Herrick, C. J., *Brains of rats and men,* Chicago: Univ. of Chicago Press, 1926.

141. Hoffman, A. C., *The effect of prolonged reading on the oculomotor system,* Dissertation, University of Rochester, 1941.

142. Hoffman, A. C., "Eye-movements during prolonged reading," *J. Exp. Psychol.,* 1946, 36, 95-118.

143. Hoffman, A. C., B. Wellman, and L. Carmichael, "A quantitative comparison of the electrical and photographic techniques of eye-movement recording," *J. Exp. Psychol.,* 1939, 24, 40-53.

144. Hollingworth, H. L., "Variations in efficiency during the working day," *Psychol. Rev.,* 1914, 21, 473-491.

145. Holt, E. B., "Eye-movement and central anaesthesia. I. The problem of anaesthesia during eye-movement," *Psychol. Monogr.,* 1903, 4, 3-45.

146. Holt, E. B., "Vision during dizziness," *Psychol. Bull.,* 1906, 3, 68-70.

147. Hovde, H. T., "The relative effects of size of type, leading and context," *J. Appl. Psychol.,* 1929, **13,** 600-629.

148. Hovde, H. T., "The relative effects of size of type, leading and context," *J. Appl. Psychol.,* 1930, **14,** 63-73.

149. Huey, E. B., "Preliminary experiments in the physiology and psychology of reading," *Amer. J. Psychol.,* 1898, **9,** 575-586.

150. Huey, E. B., "On the psychology and physiology of reading. I," *Amer. J. Psychol.,* 1900, 11, 283-302.

151. Illuminating Engineering Society, "American recommended practice of industrial lighting," *Trans. Illum. Eng.,* 1942, **37,** 275-321.

152. Imus, H. A., J. W. M. Rothney, and R. M. Bear, "An evaluation of visual factors in reading," Dartmouth College Publications, 1938.

153. Ipsen, G., "Zur Theorie des Erkennens," *Neue Psychol. Studien,* 1926, **1,** 279-471.

154. Israel, H. E., "Accommodation and convergence under low illumination," *J. Exp. Psychol.,* 1923, **6,** 223-233.

155. Jackson, E., "Visual fatigue," *Amer. J. Ophthal.,* 1921, **4,** 119-122.

156. Jacobson, E., "Electrical measurements of neuromuscular states during mental activities. I. Imagination of movement involving skeletal muscles," *Amer. J. Physiol.,* 1930, **91,** 567-608.

157. Jacobson, E., "Electrical measurements of neuromuscular states during mental activities. III. Visual imagination and recollection," *Amer. J. Physiol.,* 1930, **95,** 694-702.

158. Jacobson, E., and F. L. Kraft, "Contraction potentials (right quadriceps femoris) in man during reading," *Amer. J. Physiol.,* 1942, **137,** 1-5.

159. Jasper, H. H., "Cortical excitatory state and synchronism in the control of bioelectric autonomous rhythms," *Cold Spring Harbor Symp. Quant. Biol.,* 1936, **4,** 320-328.

160. Jasper, H. H., "Electrical signs of cortical activity," *Psychol. Bull.,* 1937, **34,** 411-481.

161. Jasper, H. H., and R. Y. Walker, "The Iowa eye-movement camera," *Science,* 1931, **74,** 291-294.

162. Jastak, J., "Interferences in reading," *Psychol. Bull.,* 1934, **31,** 244-272.

163. Javal, L. E., "Essai sur la Physiologie de la Lecture," *Annales d'Oculistique,* 1879, **82,** 242-253.

164. Johnson, H. M., "The real meaning of fatigue," *Harper's Mag.,* 1929, **158,** 187-193.

165. Judd, C. H., "Photographic records of convergence and divergence," *Psychol. Monogr.,* 1907, **8,** 370-423.

166. Judd, C. H., and G. T. Buswell, "Silent reading: a study of the various types," *Suppl. Educ. Monogr.,* 1922, no. 23.

167. Judd, C. H., C. N. McAllister, and W. M. Steele, "General introduction to a series of studies of eye movements by means of kinetoscopic photographs," *Psychol. Monogr.*, 1905, 7, 1-16.

168. Jung, R., "Eine elektrische Methode zur mehrfachen Registrierung von Augenbewegungen und Nystagmus," *Klin. Wschr.*, 1939, **18**, 21-24.

169. Karslake, J. S., "The Purdue eye-camera: a practical apparatus for studying the attention value of advertisements," *J. Appl. Psychol.*, 1940, 24, 417-440.

170. Karslake, J. S., and J. Tiffin, "Supplementary equipment useful in research on eye movement," *Amer. J. Psychol.*, 1939, 52, 625-629.

171. Klein, T., *De l'Influence de l'Éclairage sur l'Acuité visuelle*, Paris, 1873.

172. Koch, E., "Über die Geschwindigkeit der Augenbewegungen," *Arch. f. d. Gesamt. Psychol.*, 1908, 13, 196-253.

173. König, A., *Die Abhangigkeit der Sehschärfe von der Beleuchtungsintensität*, Berlin: Sitzbr. Akad. Wiss., 1897.

174. Kohlrausch, A., "Elektrische Phänomena der Augen," *Hdb. d. Nörmalen u. Patholog. Physiol.*, 1931, 12, 1393-1496.

175. Korte, W., "Uber die Gestaltauffassung im indirekten Sehen," *Zeitschr. f. Psychol.*, 1923, 93, 17-82.

176. Künzler, W., *Methodologische Beiträge zur experimentellen Untersuchung der Lesevorgänge bei kurzen Expositionszeiten*, Dissertation, University of Zurich, 1913.

177. Kurtz, J. I., "Physiological and psychological causes of ocular fatigue," *J. Gen. Psychol.*, 1932, 7, 211-214.

178. Kurtz, J. I., "General and ocular fatigue problems," *Amer. J. Optom.*, 1937, 14, pt. I, 273-280, pt. II, 308-317.

179. Kurtz, J. I., "An experimental study of ocular fatigue," *Amer. J. Optom.*, 1938, 15, 86-117.

180. Kutzner, O., "Kritische und experimentelle Beiträge zur Psychologie des Lesens mit besonderer Berücksichtigung des Problems der Gestaltqualität," *Arch. f. d. Gesamt. Psychol.*, 1916, 35, 157-251.

181. LaGrone, C. W., "An experimental study of the relationship of peripheral perception to factors in reading," *J. Exp. Educ.*, 1942, 11, 37-49.

182. Laird, D. A., "Relative performance of college students as conditioned by time of day and day of week," *J. Exp. Psychol.*, 1925, 8, 50-63.

183. Lamansky, S., "Bestimmung der Winkelgeschwindigkeit der Blickbewegung, respective Augenbewegung," *Pflüger's Arch.*, 1869, 2, 418-422.

184. Lamare, A., "Des Mouvements des Yeux dans la Lecture," *Bull. Mém. Soc. Franc. d'Ophtal.*, 1892, 10, 354-364.

185. Lancaster, W. B., "Ocular symptoms of faulty illumination," *Amer. J. Ophthal.*, 1932, 15, 783-788.

186. Landolt, A., "Nouvelles Recherches sur la Physiologie des Mouvements des Yeux," *Arch. d'Optalmo.*, 1891, **11**, 385-395.

187. Lebensohn, J. E., "The eye and sleep," *Arch. Ophthal.*, 1941, **25**, 401-411.

188. Lee, F. S., and B. Aronovitch, "On Weichardt's supposed 'fatigue toxin,'" *Amer. J. Physiol.*, 1924, **69**, 92-100.

189. Lindquist, E. F., *A first course in statistics,* Boston: Houghton Mifflin, 1938.

190. Lindquist, E. F., *Statistical analysis in educational research,* Boston: Houghton Mifflin, 1940.

191. Lindsley, D. B., and W. S. Hunter, "A note on polarity potentials from the human eye," *Proc. Nat. Acad. Sci.*, 1939, **25**, 180-183.

192. Löwenstein, O., and E. D. Friedman, "Pupillographic studies. I. Present state of pupillography; its method and diagnostic significance," *Arch. Ophthal.*, 1942, 27, 969-993.

193. Logan, H. L., "The anatomy of visual efficiency," *Trans. Illum. Eng.*, 1941, **36**, 1057-1108.

194. Loomis, A. L., E. N. Harvey, and G. Hobart, "Electrical potentials of the human brain," *J. Exp. Psychol.*, 1936, **19**, 249-279.

195. Lord, E. E., L. Carmichael, and W. F. Dearborn, "Special disabilities in learning to read and write," *Harvard Stud. Educ. Psychol.*, 1925.

196. Loring, M. W., "An investigation of the law of eye-movements," *Psychol. Rev.*, 1915, 22, 354-370.

197. Luckiesh, M., and F. K. Moss, "A correlation between illumination intensity and nervous muscular tension resulting from visual effort," *J. Exp. Psychol.*, 1933, **16**, 540-555.

198. Luckiesh, M., and F. K. Moss, "Muscular tension resulting from glare," *J. Gen. Psychol.*, 1933, 8, 455-460.

199. Luckiesh, M., and F. K. Moss, "The effect of visual effort upon the heart-rate," *J. Gen. Psychol.*, 1935, **13**, 131-138.

200. Luckiesh, M., and F. K. Moss, "Fatigue of the extrinsic ocular muscles while reading under sodium and tungsten light," *J. Opt. Soc. Amer.*, 1935, 25, 216-217.

201. Luckiesh, M., and F. K. Moss, "Relative visibility of print in terms of illumination intensity," *Sight Sav. Rev.*, 1935, 5, 272-280.

202. Luckiesh, M., and F. K. Moss, "The eyelid reflex as a criterion of ocular fatigue," *J. Exp. Psychol.*, 1937, **20**, 589-596.

203. Luckiesh, M., and F. K. Moss, *The science of seeing,* New York: Van Nostrand, 1937.

204. Luckiesh, M., and F. K. Moss, "Effects of leading on readability," *J. Appl. Psychol.*, 1938, 22, 140-160.

205. Luckiesh, M., and F. K. Moss, "Visibility and readability of print on white and tinted papers," *Sight Sav. Rev.*, 1938, 8, 123-134.

206. Luckiesh, M., and F. K. Moss, "Brightness-contrasts in seeing," *Trans. Illum. Eng. Soc.*, 1939, 34, 571-597.

207. Luckiesh, M., and F. K. Moss, "Frequency of blinking as a clinical criterion of ease of seeing," *Amer. J. Ophthal.*, 1939, 22, 616-621.

208. Luckiesh, M., and F. K. Moss, "Boldness as a factor in type-design and typography," *J. Appl. Psychol.*, 1940, 24, 170-183.

209. Luckiesh, M., and F. K. Moss, "Criteria of readability," *J. Exp. Psychol.*, 1940, 27, 256-270.

210. Luckiesh, M., and F. K. Moss, "A summary of researches involving blink-rate as a criterion of ease of seeing," *Trans. Illum. Eng.*, 1940, 35, 19-32.

211. Luckiesh, M., and F. K. Moss, "The extent of the perceptual span in reading," *J. Gen. Psychol.*, 1941, 25, 267-272.

212. Luckiesh, M., and F. K. Moss, "Visibility and seeing," *J. Franklin Inst.*, 1941, 231, 323-343.

213. Luckiesh, M., and F. K. Moss, "Illumination and visual efficiency," *Amer. J. Optom.*, 1942, 19, 5-15.

214. Luckiesh, M., and F. K. Moss, "Intrinsic brightness as a factor in discomfort from glare," *J. Opt. Soc. Amer.*, 1942, 32, 6-7.

215. Luckiesh, M., and F. K. Moss, "The task of reading," *Elem. Sch. J.*, 1942, 42, 510-514.

216. Luckiesh, M., A. H. Taylor, and R. H. Sinden, "Bearing of illumination intensity upon efficiency of visual operations," *Electrical World*, 1921, 78, 668-670.

217. MacPherson, S. J., "The effectiveness of lighting—its numerical assessment by methods based on blinking rates," *Trans. Illum. Eng.*, 1943, 38, 520-522.

218. Mailloux, N. M., and M. Newburger, "The work curves of psychotic individuals," *J. Abnorm. Soc. Psychol.*, 1941, 36, 110-114.

218a. Maity, H. P., "Diurnal course of efficiency," *Indian J. Psychol.*, 1929, 4, 127-133.

219. Marsh, H. D., "The diurnal course of efficiency," *Arch. Phil. Psychol. Sci. Methods,* 1906, no. 7.

220. Martin, G. W., "The evidence of mental fatigue during school hours," *J. Exp. Ped. Tng.*, 1911, 1, 39-45, 137-147.

221. Marx, E., "Untersuchungen über Fixation unter verschiedenen Bedingungen," *Zeitschr. f. Sinnesphysiol.*, 1913, 47, 79-96.

222. Marx, E., and W. Trendelenburg, "Uber die Genauigkeit der Einstellung des Auges beim Fixieren," *Zeitschr. f. Sinnesphysiol.*, 1911, 45, 87-102.

223. Maxfield, K. E., *The blind child and his reading,* New York: American Foundation for the Blind, 1928.

224. McAllister, C. N., "The fixation of points in the visual field," *Psychol. Monogr.,* 1905, 7, 17-53.

225. McFarland, R. A., "The psycho-physiological effects of reduced oxygen pressure," *Res. Publ. Assoc. Nerv. Ment. Dis.,* 1939, **19**, 112-143.

226. McFarland, R. A., J. N. Evans, and M. H. Halperin, "Ophthalmic aspects of acute oxygen deficiency," *Arch. Ophthal.,* 1941, **26**, 886-913.

227. McFarland, R. A., A. H. Holway, and L. M. Hurvich, *Studies of visual fatigue,* Boston: Harvard Grad. Sch. of Bus. Admin., 1942.

228. McFarland, R. A., C. A. Knehr, and C. Berens, "The effects of oxygen deprivation on eye movements in reading," *J. Exp. Psychol.,* 1937, **21**, 1-25.

229. McFarland, R. A., C. A. Knehr, and C. Berens, "The effects of anoxemia on ocular movements while reading," *Amer. J. Ophthal.,* 1937, **20**, 1204-1219.

230. McFarland, R. A., C. A. Knehr, and C. Berens, "Metabolism and pulse rate as related to reading under high and low levels of illumination," *J. Exp. Psychol.,* 1939, **25**, 65-75.

231. McNally, J. H., "The readability of certain type sizes and forms in sight-saving classes," Columbia Univ. Contributions to Education, Teachers College Series, 1943, no. 883.

232. Mead, L. C., "The influence of size of test stimuli, interpupillary distance, and age on stereoscopic depth perception," *J. Exp. Psychol.,* 1943, **33**, 148-158.

233. Melian, A., "La Fatiga ocular: sus Factores y Características," *Psicotécnia* 1940, **1**, 81-101.

234. Meyers, I. L., "Electronystagmography: a graphic study of the action currents in nystagmus," *Arch. Neur. Psychiat.,* 1929, **21**, 901-918.

235. Miles, W. R., "Alcohol and human efficiency," Carnegie Institution of Washington, 1924, no. 333.

236. Miles, W. R., "The peep-hole method for observing eye movements in reading," *J. Gen. Psychol.,* 1928, **1**, 373-374.

237. Miles, W. R., "Horizontal eye movements at the onset of sleep," *Psychol. Rev.,* 1929, **36**, 122-141.

238. Miles, W. R., "Elevation of the eye-balls on winking," *J. Exp. Psychol.,* 1931, **14**, 311-332.

239. Miles, W. R., "An early eye-movement photograph," *Psychol. Monogr.,* 1936, **47**, xxxi-xxxvi.

240. Miles, W. R., "Einthoven string galvanometer used with a vacuum tube microvoltmeter," *Rev. Sci. Instrum.,* 1939, **10**, 134-136.

241. Miles, W. R., "Experimental modification of the polarity potential of the human eye," *Science,* 1939, **90**, 404.

242. Miles, W. R., "Experimental modification of the polarity potential of the human eye," *Yale J. Biol. Med.*, 1939-40, 12, 161-183.

243. Miles, W. R., "Influence of pressure and other factors on the polarity potential of the human eye," *Psychol. Bull.*, 1939, 36, 536.

244. Miles, W. R., "Performance of the Einthoven galvanometer with input through a vacuum tube microvoltmeter," *J. Exp. Psychol.*, 1939, 25, 76-90.

245. Miles, W. R., "The steady polarity potential of the human eye," *Proc. Nat. Acad. Sci.*, 1939, 25, 25-36.

246. Miles, W. R., "Reliability of measurements of the steady polarity potential of the eye," *Proc. Nat. Acad. Sci.*, 1939, 25, 128-137.

247. Miles, W. R., "The steady potential of the human eye in subjects with unilateral enucleation," *Proc. Nat. Acad. Sci.*, 1939, 25, 349-358.

248. Miles, W. R., "Modification of the human-eye potential by dark and light adaptation," *Science,* 1940, 91, 456.

249. Miles, W. R., and H. R. Laslett, "Eye movement and visual fixation during profound sleepiness," *Psychol. Rev.*, 1931, 38, 1-13.

250. Miles, W. R., and E. Shen, "Photographic recording of eye movements in the reading of Chinese in vertical and horizontal axes: method and preliminary results," *J. Exp. Psychol.*, 1925, 8, 344-362.

251. Mosso, A., *Fatigue* (Trans. by M. Drummond and W. B. Drummond), New York: Putnam, 1904.

252. Mowrer, O. H., T. C. Ruch, and N. E. Miller, "The corneo-retinal potential difference as the basis of the galvanometric method of recording eye movements," *Amer. J. Physiol.*, 1936, 114, 423-428.

253. Murray, E., "Dysintegration of breathing and eye-movements in stutterers during silent reading and reasoning," *Psychol. Monogr.*, 1932, 43, 218-275.

254. Murroughs, T. R., and L. Manas, "Fatigue in the central nervous system," *Optom. Wkly.*, 1944, 35, 1189-1190.

255. Muscio, B., "Is a fatigue test possible?" *Brit. J. Psychol.*, 1921, 12, 31-46.

256. Muscio, B., "Feeling-tone in industry," *Brit. J. Psychol.*, 1921, 12, 150-162.

257. Myers, C. S., "Conceptions of fatigue and adaptation," *Psychol. Rev.*, 1925, 32, 1-16.

258. Myers, C. S., "Conceptions of mental fatigue," *Amer. J. Psychol.*, 1937, 50, 296-306.

259. Newburger, M., "The relative importance of homogeneity and difficulty in the development of mental fatigue at two different levels of intelligence," *J. Appl. Psychol.*, 1942, 26, 81-93.

260. Newhall, S. M., "Instrument for observing ocular movements," *Amer. J. Psychol.*, 1928, 40, 628-629.

261. Nuttall, G. C., "Fatigue and its problems," *Contemp. Rev.*, 1922, 122, 212-218.

262. Öhrwall, H., "Die Bewegungen des Auges während des Fixierens," *Skand. Arch. f. Physiol.*, 1912, 27, 65-86.

263. Ohm, J., "Zur graphischen Registrierung des Augenzitterns der Bergleute und der Lidbewegungen," *Zeitschr. f. Augenheilk.*, 1914, 32, 4-8.

264. Ohm, J., "Eine Registriervorrichtung für wagerechte Augen- und Lidbewegungen," *Zeitschr. f. Augenheilk.*, 1916-17, 36, 198-202.

265. Ohm, J., "Die Hebelnystagmographie. Ihre Geschichte, Fehler, Leistungen and Vervollkommnung," *Graefe's Arch. f. Ophthal.*, 1928, 120, 235-252.

266. Orchansky, J., "Eine Methode die Augenbewegungen direct zu untersuchen (Ophthalmographie)," *Centralbl. f. Physiol.*, 1899, 12, 785-790.

267. Orton, S. T., "The neurologic basis of elementary education," *Arch. Neur. Psychiat.*, 1929, 21, 641-647.

268. Ôsumi, M., and T. Honda, "Yakan tokusho shôdo (Illumination in reading at night)," *Ganka Rinshô Ihô,* 1939, 34, 945.

269. Parent, H., *Atlas d'Ophtalmoscopie,* Paris: Giroux (ed.), 1900.

270. Park, G. E., and R. S. Park, "Further evidence of change in position of the eyeball during fixation," *Arch. Ophthal.*, 1940, 23, 1216-1230.

271. (Parsons, J. H.), Review of: "Report of the committee appointed to select the best faces of types and modes of display for government printing" and "A note on the legibility of printed matter" (by L. A. Legros), *Brit. J. Ophthal.*, 1922, 6, 475-479.

272. Paterson, D. G., and M. A. Tinker, "Studies of typographical factors influencing speed of reading. II. Size of type," *J. Appl. Psychol.*, 1929, 13, 120-130.

273. Paterson, D. G., and M. A. Tinker, "Studies of typographical factors influencing speed of reading. IV. Effect of practice on equivalence of test forms," *J. Appl. Psychol.*, 1930, 14, 211-217.

274. Paterson, D. G., and M. A. Tinker, "Studies of typographical factors influencing speed of reading. VI. Black type versus white type," *J. Appl. Psychol.*, 1931, 15, 241-247.

275. Paterson, D. G., and M. A. Tinker, "Studies of typographical factors influencing speed of reading. VIII. Space between lines or leading." *J. Appl. Psychol.*, 1932, 16, 388-397.

276. Paterson, D. G., and M. A. Tinker, "Studies of typographical factors influencing speed of reading. X. Style of type face," *J. Appl. Psychol.*, 1932, 16, 605-613.

277. Paterson, D. G., and M. A. Tinker, "Studies of typographical factors influencing speed of reading. XII. Printing surface," *J. Appl. Psychol.,* 1936, 20, 128-131.

278. Paterson, D. G., and M. A. Tinker, *How to make type readable,* New York: Harper, 1940.

279. Paterson, D. G., and M. A. Tinker, "Influence of line width on eye movements," *J. Exp. Psychol.,* 1940, 27, 572-577.

280. Paterson, D. G., and M. A. Tinker, "Influence of size of type on eye movements," *J. Appl. Psychol.,* 1942, 26, 227-230.

281. Paterson, D. G., and M. A. Tinker, "Eye movements in reading type sizes in optimal line widths," *J. Educ. Psychol.,* 1943, 34, 547-551.

282. Paterson, D. G., and M. A. Tinker, "Eye movements in reading optimal and non-optimal typography," *J. Exp. Psychol.,* 1944, 34, 80-83.

283. Paterson, D. G., and M. A. Tinker, "Readability of newspaper headlines printed in capitals and in lower case," *J. Appl. Psychol.,* 1946, 30, 161-168.

(See also Tinker, M. A., and D. G. Paterson.)

284. Peak, H., "Modification of the lid-reflex by voluntarily induced sets," *Psychol. Monogr.,* 1931, 42, 1-68.

285. Peak, H., "Dr. Courts on the influence of muscular tension on the lid reflex," *J. Exp. Psychol.,* 1942, 30, 515-517.

286. Peppard, H. M., *Sight without glasses,* New York: Blue Ribbon Books, 1936.

287. Peterson, J., and L. W. Allison, "Controls of the eye-wink mechanism," *J. Exp. Psychol.,* 1931, 14, 144-154.

288. Pillsbury, W. B., "A study in apperception," *Amer. J. Psychol.,* 1897, 8, 315-393.

289. Piltz, J., "Ein neuer Apparat zum Photographieren der Pupillenbewegungen," *Neurol. Centralbl.,* 1904, 23, 801-811.

290. Poffenberger, A. T., "The effects of continuous work upon output and feelings," *J. Appl. Psychol.,* 1928, 12, 459-467.

291. Poffenberger, A. T., *Principles of applied psychology* (rev. ed.), New York: D. Appleton-Century, 1942.

292. Ponder, E., and W. P. Kennedy, "On the act of blinking," *Quart. J. Exp. Physiol.,* 1927, 18, 89-110.

293. Preston, K., H. P. Schwankl, and M. A. Tinker, "The effect of variations in color of print and background on legibility," *J. Gen. Psychol.,* 1932, 6, 459-461.

294. Ranson, S. W., *The anatomy of the nervous system from the standpoint of development and function* (7th ed.), Philadelphia: Saunders, 1943.

295. Reeves, P., "The response of the average pupil to various intensities of light," *J. Opt. Soc. Amer.,* 1920, 4, 35-44.

296. Reid, C., "The mechanism of voluntary muscular fatigue," *Quart. J. Exp. Physiol.,* 1928-29, **19**, 17-42.

297. Riley, H. A., "The central nervous system control of the ocular movements and the disturbances of this mechanism," *Arch. Ophthal.,* 1930, **4**, 640-661, 885-910.

298. Robinson, E. S., "Mental work," *Psychol. Bull.,* 1921, **18**, 456-482.

299. Robinson, E. S., "Work of the integrated organism," in *A handbook of general experimental psychology,* C. Murchison (ed.), Worcester: Clark Univ. Press, 1934, 571-650.

300. Robinson, E. S., and A. G. Bills, "Two factors in the work decrement," *J. Exp. Psychol.,* 1926, **9**, 415-443.

301. Robinson, E. S., and F. R. Robinson, "Practice and the work decrement," *Amer. J. Psychol.,* 1932, **44**, 547-551.

302. Robinson, L. A., "Mental fatigue and school efficiency," *Bull. Winthrop Normal and Industrial Coll. of S.C.,* 1912, **5**, no. 2.

303. Rodin, F. H., and R. R. Newell, "Movements of eyes under cover," *Arch. Ophthal.,* 1934, **12**, 525-535.

304. Roethlein, B. E., "The relative legibility of different faces of printing types," *Amer. J. Psychol.,* 1912, **23**, 1-36.

305. Romano, J., G. L. Engel, E. B. Ferris, H. W. Ryder, J. P. Webb, and M. A. Blankenhorn, "Problems of fatigue as illustrated by experiences in the decompression chamber," *War Med.,* 1944, **6**, 102-105.

306. Ruediger, W. C., "The field of distinct vision," *Arch. Psychol.,* 1907, **1**, no. 5.

307. Ryan, T. A., "Varieties of fatigue," *Amer. J. Psychol.,* 1944, **57**, 565-569.

308. Salzmann, M., *The anatomy and histology of the human eyeball,* (Trans. by Dr. E. V. L. Brown), Chicago, 1912.

309. Sayers, R. R., and D. Harrington, "Physiological effect of high temperatures and humidities with and without air motion," U.S. Bureau of Mines, Reports of Investigations, serial no. 2464.

310. Schackwitz, A., "Apparat zur Aufzeichnung der Augenbewegungen beim zusammenhägenden Lesen (Nystagmograph)," *Zeitschr. f. Psychol. u. Physiol. d. Sinnesorg.,* 1912, **63**, 442-453.

311. Schmidt, W. A., "An experimental study in the psychology of reading," *Suppl. Educ. Monogr.,* 1917, **1**, no. 2.

312. Schott, E., "Über die Registrierung des Nystagmus und anderer Augenbewegungen vermittels des Saitengalvanometers," *Deutsch. Arch. f. klin. Med.,* 1922, **140**, 79-90.

313. Schumann, F., "Anhang. Das Erkennungsurteil," *Zeitschr. Psychol.,* 1921-22, **88**, 205-224.

314. Scofield, C. F., "The effects of mild doses of alcohol and caffeine on optic nystagmus," *Psychol. Monogr.,* 1936, 47, 217-241.

315. Sharp, L. H., "Effects of residual tension on output and energy expenditure in muscular work," *J. Exp. Psychol.,* 1941, 29, 1-22.

316. Shaw, E. R., *School hygiene,* New York: Macmillan, 1901.

317. Simpson, R. G., "Does the amount of free reading influence the student's control of his eye movements in reading ordinary printed matter?" *J. Educ. Psychol.,* 1943, 34, 313-315.

318. Smith, D. E., "An example of continuous work without work decrement," *Bull. Canad. Psychol. Assn.,* 1941, 1, 45-46.

319. Smith, K. R., "Fatigue," *Psychol. Bull.,* 1941, 38, 364-369.

320. Snell, P. A., "An introduction to the experimental study of visual fatigue," *J. Soc. Motion Picture Eng.,* 1933, 20, 367-390.

321. Sorenson, H., *Statistics for students of psychology and education,* New York: McGraw-Hill, 1936.

322. Spaeth, R. A., "The problem of fatigue," *J. Industr. Hygiene,* 1919-20, 1, 22-53.

323. Specht, H., "Fatigue and hours of service of interstate truck drivers. V. Eye-movements and related phenomena," *U.S. Publ. Hlth. Bull.,* 1941, 265, 209-225.

324. Spencer, L. T., "The curve of continuous work and related phenomena," *Psychol. Bull.,* 1927, 24, 467-472.

325. Stanton, F. N., and H. E. Burtt, "The influence of surface and tint of paper on the speed of reading," *J. Appl. Psychol.,* 1935, 19, 683-693.

326. Stecher, L. I., "The effect of humidity on nervousness and on general efficiency," *Arch. Psychol.,* 1916, 5, no. 38.

327. Stetson, R. H., and J. A. McDill, "Mechanism of the different types of movement," *Psychol. Monogr.,* 1923, 32, 18-40.

328. Stoy, E. G., "A preliminary study of ocular attitudes in thinking of spatial relations," *J. Gen. Psychol.,* 1930, 4, 379-385.

329. Stratton, G. M., "Eye-movements and the aesthetics of visual form," *Phil. Stud.,* 1902, 20, 336-359.

330. Stratton, G. M., "Symmetry, linear illusions, and the movements of the eye," *Psychol. Rev.,* 1906, 13, 82-96.

331. Stromberg, E. L., "The reliability of monocular photography in the investigation of reading," *J. Educ. Psychol.,* 1942, 33, 118-127.

332. Struycken, H. J. L., "Die Registrierung des Nystagmus," *Ned. Tijdschr. v. Gen.,* 1918, 1, 621.

333. Sturrock, W., "Let's evaluate present day seeing requirements—footcandles," *Trans. Illum. Eng.,* 1942, 37, 347-357.

334. Sundberg, C. G., "Über die Blickbewegung und die Bedeutung des

indirekten Sehens für das Blicken," *Skand. Arch. f. Physiol.,* 1917-18, 35, 1-50.

335. Taylor, E. A., *Controlled reading,* Chicago: Univ. Chicago Press, 1937.

336. Telford, C. W., and N. Thompson, "Some factors influencing voluntary and reflex eyelid responses," *J. Exp. Psychol.,* 1933, **16,** 524-539.

337. Thorndike, E. L. (See 339a).

338. Thorndike, E. L., "The curve of work and the curve of satisfyingness," *J. Appl. Psychol.,* 1917, **1,** 265-267.

339. Thorndike, E. L., *Educational psychology,* vol. iii, *Mental work and fatigue and individual differences and their causes,* New York: Columbia Univ., Teachers College, 1921.

339a. Thorndike, E. L., W. A. McCall, and J. C. Chapman, "Ventilation in relation to mental work," Columbia Univ., Contributions to Education, Teachers College Series, 1916, no. 78.

340. Thorndike, E. L., G. J. Ruger, and W. A. McCall, "The effects of outside air and recirculated air upon the intellectual achievement and improvement of school pupils," *Sch. and Soc.,* 1916, **3,** 679-684.

341. Tinker, M. A., "Legibility and eye movement in reading," *Psychol. Bull.,* 1927, **24,** 621-639.

342. Tinker, M. A., "The relative legibility of the letters, the digits, and of certain mathematical signs," *J. Gen. Psychol.,* 1928, **1,** 472-496.

343. Tinker, M. A., "The relative legibility of modern and old style numerals," *J. Exp. Psychol.,* 1930, **13,** 453-461.

344. Tinker, M. A., "Apparatus for recording eye-movements," *Amer. J. Psychol.,* 1931, **43,** 115-118.

345. Tinker, M. A., "The influence of form of type on the perception of words," *J. Appl. Psychol.,* 1932, **16,** 167-174.

346. Tinker, M. A., "Studies in scientific typography," *Psychol. Bull.,* 1932, **29,** 670-671.

347. Tinker, M. A., "Use and limitations of eye-movement measures of reading," *Psychol. Bull.,* 1933, **30,** 583.

348. Tinker, M. A., "Illumination and the hygiene of reading," *J. Educ. Psychol.,* 1934, **25,** 669-680.

349. Tinker, M. A., "The reliability and validity of eye-movement measures of reading," *Psychol. Bull.,* 1934, **31,** 741.

350. Tinker, M. A., "Hygienic lighting intensities," *J. Industr. Hygiene,* 1935, **17,** 258-262.

351. Tinker, M. A., "Illumination intensities for reading," *Amer. J. Ophthal.,* 1935, **18,** 1036-1039.

352. Tinker, M. A., "Eye movement, perception, and legibility in reading," *Psychol. Bull.,* 1936, **33,** 275-290.

353. Tinker, M. A., "Reliability and validity of eye-movement measures of reading," *J. Exp. Psychol.,* 1936, **19**, 732-746.

354. Tinker, M. A., "Time taken by eye-movements in reading," *J. Genet. Psychol.,* 1936, **48**, 468-471.

355. Tinker, M. A., "Facts concerning hygienic illumination intensities," *Sch. and Soc.,* 1938, 47, 120-121.

356. Tinker, M. A., "Speed *versus* comprehension in reading as affected by level of difficulty," *J. Educ. Psychol.,* 1939, **30**, 81-94.

357. Tinker, M. A., "The effect of illumination intensities upon speed of perception and upon fatigue in reading," *J. Educ. Psychol.,* 1939, **30**, 561-571.

358. Tinker, M. A., "Illumination standards for effective and comfortable vision," *J. Consult. Psychol.,* 1939, **3**, 11-20.

359. Tinker, M. A., "Effect of visual adaptation upon intensity of light preferred for reading," *Psychol. Bull.,* 1940, **37**, 575.

360. Tinker, M. A., "The effect of adaptation upon visual efficiency in illumination studies," *Amer. J. Optom.,* 1942, **19**, 143-151.

361. Tinker, M. A., "Illumination intensities preferred for reading with direct lighting," *Amer. J. Optom.,* 1944, **21**, 213-219.

362. Tinker, M. A., "Reliability of blinking frequency employed as a measure of readability," *J. Exp. Psychol.,* 1945, **35**, 418-424.

362a. Tinker, M. A., "Illumination standards," *Amer. J. Publ. Hlth.,* 1946, **36**, 963-973.

363. Tinker, M. A., "The study of eye movements in reading," *Psychol. Bull.,* 1946, **43**, 93-120.

363a. Tinker, M. A., "Validity of frequency of blinking as a criterion of readability," *J. Exp. Psychol.,* 1946, **36**, 453-460.

364. Tinker, M. A., and D. G. Paterson, "Influence of type form on speed of reading," *J. Appl. Psychol.,* 1928, **12**, 359-368.

365. Tinker, M. A., and D. G. Paterson, "Studies of typographical factors influencing speed of reading. III. Length of line," *J. Appl. Psychol.,* 1929, **13**, 205-219.

366. Tinker, M. A., and D. G. Paterson, "Studies of typographical factors influencing speed of reading. V. Simultaneous variation of type size and line length," *J. Appl. Psychol.,* 1931, **15**, 72-78.

367. Tinker, M. A., and D. G. Paterson, "Studies of typographical factors influencing speed of reading. VII. Variations in color of print and background," *J. Appl. Psychol.,* 1931, **15**, 471-479.

368. Tinker, M. A., and D. G. Paterson, "Studies of typographical factors influencing speed of reading. IX. Reductions in size of newspaper print," *J. Appl. Psychol.,* 1932, **16**, 525-531.

369. Tinker, M. A., and D. G. Paterson, "Studies of typographical factors influencing speed of reading. XI. Rôle of set in typographical studies," *J. Appl. Psychol.*, 1935, **19**, 647-651.

370. Tinker, M. A., and D. G. Paterson, "Studies of typographical factors influencing speed of reading. XIII. Methodological considerations," *J. Appl. Psychol.*, 1936, **20**, 132-145.

371. Tinker, M. A., and D. G. Paterson, "Legibility of newsprint," *Psychol. Bull.*, 1939, **36**, 634.

372. Tinker, M. A., and D. G. Paterson, "Eye-movements in reading black print on white background and red print on dark green background," *Amer. J. Psychol.*, 1944, **57**, 93-94.

372a. Tinker, M. A., and D. G. Paterson, "Effect of line width and leading on readability of newspaper type," *Journalism Quart.*, 1946, **23**, 307-309.

(See also Paterson, D. G., and M. A. Tinker.)

373. Totten, E., "Eye-spots for photographic records of eye-movements," *J. Comp. Psychol.*, 1926, **6**, 287-289.

374. Travis, R. C., "Experimental studies in ocular behavior: I. The Dodge mirror-recorder for photographing eye-movements," *J. Gen. Psychol.*, 1932, **7**, 311-327.

375. Travis, R. C., "The latency and velocity of the eye in saccadic movements," *Psychol. Monogr.*, 1936, **47**, 242-249.

376. Troland, L. T., "An analysis of the literature concerning the dependency of visual functions upon illumination intensity," *Trans. Illum. Eng. Soc.*, 1931, **26**, 107-196.

377. Updike, D. B., *Printing types,* Cambridge: Harvard Univ. Press, 1922.

378. Veasey, C. A., "Summary of criteria for adequate artificial lighting," *Dis. Eye, Ear, Nose, Throat,* 1941, **1**, 238-240.

379. Vernon, M. D., "Methods of recording eye movements," *Brit. J. Ophthal.*, 1928, **12**, 113-130.

380. Vernon, M. D., "The movements of the eyes in reading," *Brit. J. Ophthal.*, 1928, **12**, 130-139.

381. Vernon, M. D., "An apparatus for the photographic recording of eye movements," *Brit. J. Psychol.*, 1930, **21**, 64-67.

382. Verworn, M., *General physiology,* London: Macmillan, 1899.

383. Wagner, J., "Experimentelle Beiträge zur Psychologie des Lesens," *Zeitschr. f. Psychol.*, 1918, **80**, 1-75.

384. Wald, G., "Photo-labile pigments of the chicken retina," *Nature,* 1937, **140**, 545-546.

385. Walker, R. Y., "The eye-movements of good readers," *Psychol. Monogr.*, 1933, **44**, 95-117.

386. Walton, A., "Some minor improvements in eye-movement camera technique," *Psychol. Bull.*, 1933, **30**, 593.

387. Warren, N., and B. Clark, "Blocking in mental and motor tasks during a 65-hour vigil," *J. Exp. Psychol.,* 1937, **21,** 97-105.

388. Watson, J. B., *Psychology from the standpoint of a behaviorist,* Philadelphia: Lippincott, 1919.

389. Weaver, H. E., "Photographing eye movements during music reading," *Psychol. Bull.,* 1931, **28,** 211-212.

390. Webster, H. A., and M. A. Tinker, "The influence of type face on the legibility of print," *J. Appl. Psychol.,* 1935, **19,** 43-52.

391. Webster, H. A., and M. A. Tinker, "The influence of paper surface on the perceptibility of print," *J. Appl. Psychol.,* 1935, **19,** 145-147.

392. Weiskotten, T. F., and J. E. Ferguson, "A further study of the effects of loss of sleep," *J. Exp. Psychol.,* 1930, **13,** 247-266.

393. Weiss, O., "Die zeitlicke Dauer des Lidschlages," *Zeitschr. f. Sinnesphysiol.,* 1911, **45,** 307-312.

394. Wendt, G. R., and R. Dodge, "Practical directions for stimulating and for photographically recording eye-movements of animals," *J. Comp. Psychol.,* 1938, **25,** 9-49.

395. White, L. R., R. H. Britten, J. E. Ives, and L. R. Thompson, "Studies in illumination. II. Relationship of ocular efficiency and ocular fatigue among the letter separators in the Chicago post-office," *U.S. Publ. Hlth. Bull.,* 1929, **181,** 1-58.

396. Whiting, H. F., and H. B. English, "Fatigue tests and incentives," *J. Exp. Psychol.,* 1925, **8,** 33-49.

397. Wichodzew, A., "Zur Kenntnis des Einflusses der Kopfneigung zur Schulter auf die Augenbewegungen," *Zeitschr. f. Sinnesphysiol.,* 1912, **46,** 394-431.

398. Wilkins, M. C., *A tachistoscope experiment in reading,* Master's thesis, Columbia University, 1917.

399. Winch, W. H., "Mental fatigue in day school children, as measured by arithmetical reasoning," *Brit. J. Psychol.,* 1911, **4,** 315-341.

400. Winch, W. H., "Mental fatigue in day school children as measured by immediate memory," *J. Educ. Psychol.,* 1912, **3,** pt. I, 18-28, pt. II, 75-82.

401. Winch, W. H., "Mental adaptation during the school day as measured by arithmetical reasoning," *J. Educ. Psychol.,* 1913, **4,** pt. I, 17-28, pt. II, 71-84.

402. Winkler, H., "Die Monotonie der Arbeit," *Zeitschr. f. Angew. Psychol.,* 1922, **20,** 46-88.

403. Winkler, K., "Prüfung der Eignung für anstrengende Seharbeit," *Psychotechn. Zeitschr.,* 1933, **8,** 69-79.

404. Witmer, J., "Über Nystagmographie," *Graefe's Arch. f. Ophthal.,* 1917, **93,** 226-236.

405. Woodworth, R. S., *Experimental psychology,* New York: Holt, 1938.

406. Wyatt, S., F. A. Fraser, and F. G. Stock, "Fan ventilation in a humid weaving shed," Industr. Fat. Res. Bd. Report (London), 1926, no. 37.

407. Yaglou, C. P., "To gauge workroom temperatures," *Industr. Psychol.,* 1927, 2, 3-7.

408. Yochelson, S., *Effects of rest-pauses on work decrement,* Dissertation, Yale University, 1930.

409. Zeitler, J., "Tachistoskopische Versuche über das Lesen," *Phil. Stud.,* 1900, 16, 380-463.

Index of Names

Index of Subjects